A.D.A.M. Student
Atlas of Anatomy

A.D.A.M. Student Atlas of Anatomy

Todd R. Olson, Ph.D.
Associate Professor
Department of Anatomy & Structural Biology
Albert Einstein College of Medicine
Bronx, New York

Illustrative Art
A.D.A.M.® Software, Inc.
Atlanta, Georgia

Cadaver Photographs
The Bassett Collection
Stanford University
School of Medicine
Stanford, California

with the assistance of
Wojciech Pawlina, M.D.
Assistant Professor
Department of
Anatomy & Cell Biology
University of Florida
College of Medicine
Gainesville, Florida

Williams & Wilkins
A WAVERLY COMPANY

BALTIMORE • PHILADELPHIA • LONDON • PARIS • BANGKOK
BUENOS AIRES • HONG KONG • MUNICH • SYDNEY • TOKYO • WROCLAW

Editor: Timothy S. Satterfield
Managing Editor: Crystal Taylor
Production Manager: Paula Huber
Project Editor: Janet M. Krejci
Illustration Planners: Mario Fernández, Wayne Hubbel, Raymond Lowman, Donna Smith, Lorraine Wrzoseck
Typesetter: The Image Foundry, Ltd., Baltimore, MD
Printer: Metropole Litho, Montreal, Canada

Copyright © 1996 Williams & Wilkins
Imagery © 1996 A.D.A.M. Software, Inc.

351 West Camden Street
Baltimore, Maryland 21201-2436 USA

Rose Tree Corporate Center
1400 North Providence Road
Building II, Suite 5025
Media, Pennsylvania 19063-2043 USA

Printed in Canada

Library of Congress Cataloging-in-Publication Data

Olson, Todd R.
   A.D.A.M. student atlas of anatomy with the assistance of Wojciech Pawlina; illustrative art by
A.D.A.M. Software, Inc.; cadaver photographs from the Bassett collection.
      p.   cm.
   Includes index.
   ISBN 0-683-00042-X
   1. Human anatomy—Atlases. I. Pawlina, Wojciech. II. Title. III. Title: Student atlas of anatomy.
   [DNLM: 1. Anatomy—atlases. QS 17 052a 1996]
QM25.047 1996
611'.0022'2—dc20
DNLM/DLC
for Library of Congress   95-11593
                                                                              CIP

To purchase additional copies of this book, call our customer service department at (800) 638-0672 or fax orders to (800) 447-8438. For other book services, including chapter reprints and large quantity sales, ask for the Special Sales department.

Canadian customers should call (800) 268-4178, or fax (905) 470-6780. For all other calls originating outside the United States, please call (410) 528-4223 or fax us at (410) 528-8550.

Visit Williams & Wilkins on the Internet http://www.wwilkins.com or contact our customer service department at custserv@wwilkins.com. Williams & Wilkins customer service representatives are available from 8:30am to 6:00pm, EST, Monday through Friday, for either telephone or Internet access.

For more information about A.D.A.M. Software, Inc. and their complete line of educational multimedia software products, visit their web site at www.adam.com or call (800) 755-2326

96 97 98 99 00
2 3 4 5 6 7 8 9 10

A.D.A.M.® is a registered trademark of A.D.A.M. Software, Inc.

Dedication

To my family, especially my parents and my wife, Sarah, for the support and encouragement that have constantly been a part of their love; to my friends for the many pleasures and insights that I have experienced in our camaraderie; and to my teachers, colleagues, and students for having made education an exciting and rewarding lifelong endeavor.

Foreword

During the course of my training in medical illustration, I relied heavily upon the most important tool a student can have in the study of gross anatomy: the anatomy atlas. The extent of my atlas collection reflected this importance; no one atlas provided the ultimate reference, so I felt I had to have them all. However, my extensive collection could not provide an adequate picture of the three-dimensional relationships within the body. In particular, superficial-to-deep relationships were a struggle to comprehend within the two-dimensional world of an anatomy atlas. Although I could discover the three-dimensional anatomical relationships in the dissection lab, standing over a cadaver all day was not a viable option. So, like most students, I relied upon the atlas as my primary tool for learning and turned to dissection for reinforcement and the three-dimensional visualization I ultimately required. The gap between the representations of the atlas and the reality of the human body eventually led me to envision and help create a computerized, multimedia version of a dissectable human body: *A.D.A.M.,* or *Animated Dissection of Anatomy for Medicine.* The first version of *A.D.A.M.* has now evolved into a family of related products: the *A.D.A.M. Scholar Series.*

In developing that first *A.D.A.M.* product, my team of medical illustrators and anatomists assembled the most comprehensive set of medical images ever created. Presenting these images through a computer allowed a user to peel away each structure of the anatomy, one layer at a time, from the skin to the bones, and from four views. This major achievement overcame many of the limitations of the anatomy atlas, allowing students to navigate through a virtual body to any depth they chose.

At about the same time A.D.A.M. Software completed the first *A.D.A.M.* product, I met Dr. Todd Olson. From the first time he saw *A.D.A.M.,* Todd appreciated its value to anatomy education. He quickly became an advocate for the product and began to experiment with ways he could use it in his courses at Albert Einstein College of Medicine. Todd recognized early on, however, that widespread student access to the rich image database would be limited by the slow pace of computerization in medical education. In response to this recognition, A.D.A.M. Software began discussions with Williams & Wilkins about the creation of a printed student atlas modeled on the strategy of the multimedia *A.D.A.M.* product: to give students the ability to explore superficial-to-deep relationships while maintaining a clear sense of orientation within the body. Further discussions led to the idea to include cadaver photographs from the world-renowned collection of David L. Bassett, M.D. As the manuscript evolved, I sensed a product with a real competitive advantage over other atlases. Some provided good illustrations but no photos; others had photos but few illustrations. I remembered my days in gross anatomy flipping from one type of atlas to the other. This product would have it all!

Todd's clear vision of what he wanted to achieve as a teacher of anatomy and the passion, talent, and commitment of A.D.A.M. medical illustrators Eric Grafman and Ed Stewart resulted in a work which, in my opinion, is one of the most impressive anatomy atlases on the market today. This atlas embodies many of the same qualities that have made the electronic *A.D.A.M.* products so valuable. From page to page, the images are arranged to give the viewer a sense of moving ever deeper into the body. Within many illustrations, a technique called "ghosting" reveals the anatomic relationships between semitransparent superficial structures and underlying structures. Additionally, *A.D.A.M. Student Atlas of Anatomy* allows side-by-side comparison of the A.D.A.M. images and the Bassett cadaver photographs. The resulting work represents a milestone in the presentation of anatomic information.

I like to think that this atlas represents human accomplishment at its best. The talent, dedication, and professionalism of those who created it can be seen on every page. It is my hope that as *A.D.A.M. Student Atlas of Anatomy* helps students more fully visualize the complexity of the human body, it can also contribute to a better understanding of ourselves as human beings, enabling us to open doors to a better educated and healthier society.

Gregory M. Swayne
President
A.D.A.M. Software, Inc.

Preface

Our knowledge of human gross anatomy has changed relatively little in the past 100 years; however, the time devoted to the study of anatomy by medical students has decreased greatly. Gross anatomy was the principal course taught in the first year of medical school for the first half of this century. Today, the spectacular development of bioscience technology has resulted in first-year medical students devoting two to three times as much study to cellular, subcellular, molecular, and biochemical processes than to gross anatomy.

Anatomists have successfully responded to this new curricular challenge in two ways. Most significantly, the amount of information covered in our courses has been distilled to those aspects of anatomy that are clinically relevant and, therefore, of greatest potential value to a student's future medical practice. Second, anatomic details pertinent to specialty study are now taught in postgraduate programs and are not part of the anatomic essentials taught during the basic medical education.

Although a new generation of introductory textbooks has been written that reduce gross anatomy to essential concepts and present it within a practical, clinical context, for some time I have thought it remarkable that no one had attempted to incorporate these new perspectives into an anatomy atlas for beginning students. Then, in the winter of 1994, at the request of Williams & Wilkins, I prepared a proposal for just such a new human anatomy atlas using the electronic images in the A.D.A.M. database and the exquisite collection of dissection photographs in Dr. David Bassett's *Stereoscopic Atlas of Human Anatomy,* which is housed in the Division of Human Anatomy at Stanford University School of Medicine.

A.D.A.M. Student Atlas of Anatomy is foremost a visual guide and interactive learning resource to be used in conjunction with a clinical anatomy textbook. In the structure and content of the atlas, I have emphasized those structures that are fundamental to the clinical education of every medical student. It has not been my intention to create a comprehensive atlas nor an atlas to accompany laboratory dissection. I have included more images of fewer structures; particularly, more images of those parts of the body that present the beginning student with the greatest difficulty to comprehend and appreciate three-dimensionally. It is important that those who use this atlas understand both its distinctive emphasis and limited scope, and appreciate the necessity of a more comprehensive atlas as their knowledge of human anatomy matures.

Nowhere in *A.D.A.M. Student Atlas of Anatomy* is the emphasis on essential and difficult material more evident than in Chapter 4, which covers the pelvic contents and perineum. These topics are treated in a substantially expanded format than is normally found in traditional atlases for two reasons. First, the major clerkship of obstetrics and gynecology, and to a lesser extent the field of urology, dictate the necessity of knowing the basic anatomy of the pelvis and perineum. Second, experience indicates that this region is possibly the most difficult for first-time students to understand. The pelvis and perineum present unique problems of spatial and surface relationships, compounded by the fact that dissection of the pelvis only partially reveals its contents in situ and is difficult and time-consuming, even for an experienced prosector working on an ideal specimen.

It is ultimately the objective in teaching patient-oriented anatomy to provide the student with an understanding of the composite anatomy of all or selected regions of the body; however, experience has convinced me that many students find it easier initially to have information organized by systems. The extensive systemic sections in *A.D.A.M. Student Atlas of Anatomy* should not only make it more useful for first-year medical students, but also make it a valuable resource for allied health students who learn anatomy systemically but have never had a regional atlas that emphasized this approach. I have included lengthy systemic sections at the beginning of the chapters on the trunk (Chapter 1), pelvis and perineum (Chapter 4), limbs (Chapters 5 and 6), and head and neck (Chapter 7). Systemic descriptions were not included in the chapters on the thoracic and abdominal contents (Chapters 2 and 3) because the systemic anatomy of the body walls of these regions is covered extensively in Chapter 1 and because the distribution and pattern of deeper neurovascular structures can be clearly appreciated in the sequence of dissection images in each of these two chapters.

In organizing the atlas, I have arranged cadaveric photographs to provide beginning students with an overview of some of the more important dissections that are seen in the laboratory. In most cases, photographs are numerically labeled to facilitate their use in practical examination review. Their placement adjacent to corresponding A.D.A.M. images, which serve as the keys to the numbered structures in the photographs, offers the student a detailed artistic image (instead of a highly simplified schematic drawing) that enhances what is most important in the view. In addition, the student needs to apply anatomic knowledge in the identification of the numerically labeled structures.

The student who is using *A.D.A.M. Student Atlas of Anatomy* to the fullest advantage must identify anatomic landmarks, find these landmarks on a second figure (the key image), and then identify the structure by locating it relative to the landmarks. This is precisely the observation and orientation process that anatomists are trying to teach in the laboratory.

An appreciation of both cross-sectional and radiographic anatomy is important in many areas of basic clinical work. However, given the circumscribed scope of this atlas, it was impossible to incorporate more than a limited number of cross-sectional and radiographic images into each chapter. Those that are included either best display the distribution of a prominent structure (e.g., the peritoneum) or provide another means of visualizing the relationships within a region.

Acknowledgments

A.D.A.M. Student Atlas of Anatomy is the result of a major collective effort, and I extend my appreciation to all of the individuals who contributed to this project, in particular, Paula Huber and Tim Satterfield of Williams & Wilkins, Gregory Swayne of A.D.A.M. Software, Dr. Robert Chase of Stanford University School of Medicine, and Dr. Arthur F. Dalley II of Creighton University School of Medicine.

Dr. Wojciech Pawlina, of University of Florida College of Medicine, worked tirelessly on this project from almost its inception, and his critical advice contributed significantly to the quality of this book and, indeed, made its completion possible.

I acknowledge the talent, dedication, and professionalism of all those at A.D.A.M. Software who are responsible for the artwork in this atlas and in the original *A.D.A.M. Comprehensive.* Their efforts and commitment are clearly visible on every page of this book. I thank Ed Stewart, Eric Grafman, Lynda Leigh Levy, Lelayne Weiss, Virginia Sue Mabry, Dee Mustafa-Bowne, Bill Blakesley, Barry Golivesky, Cordero Jenkins, Cindy Quamme, Suzanne Swayne, Audra Brand, Stephanie Calabrese, Ron Collins, Mary Beth Clough, Dan Johnson, Kyle McNeir, Meredith Nienkamp, Lisa Quattrini, and Laura Petrides. In addition, I would like to extend my appreciation to Tim Brammer and Roger Jackson for their technical assistance and support.

The following individuals at Williams & Wilkins brought their expertise, enthusiasm, and commitment to quality to this project: Crystal Taylor, Mary Finch, Anne Stewart Seitz, and Janet Krejci.

I wish to thank Dottie Mims of the Image Foundry, Ltd.

My gratitude is extended to Dr. Keith Moore for use of tables from his book *Clinically Oriented Anatomy,* Third Edition, published in 1992 by Williams & Wilkins. I am grateful to Dr. Lothar Wicke for use of several radiographic images from his *Atlas of Radiographic Anatomy,* Fifth Edition, published in 1994 by Lea & Febiger.

Gregory Smith of St. Mary's College of California, Dr. Sharon Sawitzke, and Dr. Burton Dornfest provided invaluable insight and suggestions while reviewing the atlas during its production. The input of Dr. Thomas Gest into an earlier version of the project was also very helpful. Dr. Olga Malakhova of University of Florida College of Medicine deserves a special acknowledgment for the help and consultation she provided Dr. Pawlina to further his labors on the *Atlas.*

Many individuals contributed to my education as an anatomist and, thus, to this endeavor, and I extend my sincere appreciation and indebtedness to Dr. Ralph Ger, Dr. Peter Satir, Dr. Ilya Glezer, Dr. Herbert Srebnik, Professor Michael Day, and my dear friend the late Dr. Warren Kinzey.

Colleagues in the American Association of Clinical Anatomists are too numerous to name here, although I wish to acknowledge them as well as my fellow course directors here in New York: Drs. Ernest April, N. Barry Berg, Bruce Bogart, Ray Dannenhoffer, Daria Dykyj, Fakhry Girgis, Mahmood Khan, Jeffrey Laitman, Martin Levine, Leon Martino, Anthony Mercurio, Nikos Solounias, and Eugene Wenk, for the conversations that we have had about the teaching of clinical anatomy and its role in medical education.

Although all of my former and current anatomy students have contributed to my experience and insights that I developed into the concept and organization of this book, six students at Albert Einstein College of Medicine deserve recognition for their work on and support of this project: Debbie Chirnomas, Benjamin Cilento, Sharon Goldstein, Soleyman Rokhsar, Kimberly Valenti, and Christine Yuen.

Finally, I would like to thank the many students in Albert Einstein College of Medicine's Class of 1999 for their helpful comments on many of the chapters in this book.

A.D.A.M. Student Atlas of Anatomy Team

Anatomic Illustration

Eric D. Grafman, *Project Director and Medical Illustrator*

Ed M. Stewart, *Production Manager and Medical Illustrator*

Lynda Leigh Levy, *Medical Illustrator*

Lelayne Weiss, *Illustrator*

Virginia Sue Mabry, *Illustrator*

Dee Mustafa-Bowne, *Illustrator*

Photo Retouch

Bill Blakesley, *Medical Illustrator*

Barry Golivesky, *Graphic Designer*

Cordero D. Jenkins, *Illustrator*

Cindy Quamme, *Graphic Designer*

Post Production

Suzanne Swayne

Lelayne Weiss

Audra Brand

Product Manager

Stephanie Calabrese

A.D.A.M. Software Comprehensive Team

Gregory M. Swayne, *Executive Producer and Medical Illustrator*

Ron Collins, *Project Director and Medical Illustrator*

Mary Beth Clough, *Medical Illustrator*

Dan Johnson, *Medical Illustrator*

Kyle McNeir, *Medical Illustrator*

Meredith Nienkamp, *Medical Illustrator*

Lisa Quattrini, *Medical Illustrator*

Lelayne Weiss, *Illustrator*

Virginia Sue Mabry, *Illustrator*

Dee Mustafa-Bowne, *Illustrator*

Cindy Quamme, *Graphic Designer*

Contents

Credits

Many of the tables and all of the radiographs appearing in this atlas are used with permission from the following:

Moore, KL, Clinically Oriented Anatomy, 3rd ed. Baltimore: Williams & Wilkins, 1992.
Tables 1.1, 1.2, 1.3, 1.4, 4.1, 4.2, 5.1, 5.2, 5.3, 5.6, 6.1, 6.2, 6.3, 6.4, 6.5, 6.6, 7.1, 7.2, 7.3, 7.4, 7.5, 7.6, 7.7, 7.8, 7.9, 8.1, and 8.2.

Wicke L, Röntgen-Anatomie Normalbefund, 4th German ed. München-Wein-Baltimore: Urban & Schwarzenberg, 1992.
Radiographs in Plates 2.20, 2.36, 3.12, 3.22, 3.26, 3.28, 3.36, 5.42, 5.52, 5.58, 6.36, 6.46, 6.62, 7.1, 7.6, and 7.8.

The Publishers have made every effort to trace the copyright holders for borrowed material. If they have inadvertently overlooked any, they will be pleased to make the necessary arrangements at the first opportunity.

User's Guide

A.D.A.M. Student Atlas of Anatomy was designed to be an interactive pictorial guide for the beginning student to master both basic human anatomic methodology and terminology as well as the three-dimensional relationships of the body's constituent parts. The next few pages explain how to use the illustrations and special features of the atlas to their fullest advantage.

Three-Dimensional Anatomy

Among the problems faced by the beginning anatomy student, none is more universally perplexing than acquiring an appreciation of the three-dimensional relationships within the human body. Recent anatomy books have addressed this problem largely through the inclusion of cross sections and computed tomographic (CT) and magnetic resonance imaging (MRI) scans. Typically, anatomy atlases and textbooks illustrate a region from only one of the four traditional vertical perspectives (i.e., anterior, posterior, medial, lateral), and students are left to extrapolate the anatomy of the third dimension from a two-dimensional picture.

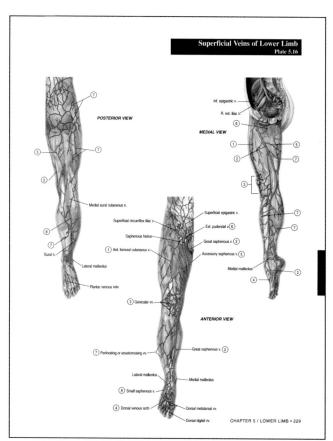

One of the most effective ways to overcome this problem is to illustrate the region in question from an orientation that is at right angles to the original perspective. Using the distinctive ability of *A.D.A.M.* illustrations to view the body from any one of the four vertical perspectives, included are at least two, sometimes more, orientations in many of the plates. For example, the medial, anterior, and posterior views of the leg in Plate 5.16 make visualizing the location, distribution, and relationships of the superficial veins, especially the clinically important saphenous vein, and cutaneous nerves of the lower limb much easier. The extensive use of these multiple views is one of the most striking and valuable characteristics of *A.D.A.M. Student Atlas of Anatomy.*

Labels and Key and Test Images

The two figures here from Plate 1.48 demonstrate the **three ways that structures are labeled in the atlas** and the rationale for the labeling.

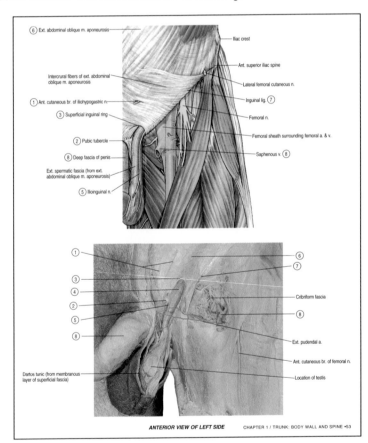

First, the ***iliac crest*** in the *top* figure and the ***cribriform fascia*** in the *lower* are **identified simply by** name because both of these structures are not present in both figures.

Second, the **superficial inguinal ring** and **deep fascia of penis** are identified by name in the *top* figure and are associated with a *circled number.* The presence of **circled numbers next to structure names** indicates that the figure is a **key image.** A key image should be used in identifying structures **labeled only by a circled number on a test image,** which is the third type of labeling used in the atlas.

Third, a **test image** is typically located on the plate to the *right* of a key image; however, sometimes a test image is placed on the *same* plate as a key image, as occurs in Plate 1.48, the example used here.

Circled numbers are placed randomly on test images to emphasize the importance of associating structural landmarks on corresponding key images and test images. The correlation of a particular number with a particular structure is valid only within a plate or within adjacent plates. For example, the **ilioinguinal n.** is labeled ⑬ in the key image on Plate 1.48, but it is labeled ④ on Plate 1.50. The only exception to this pattern is the series of plates on the perineum (Plates 4.39–4.50) where a number is consistently assigned to a structure throughout the series.

Anatomical Nomenclature

The anglicized and classical terminology used in *A.D.A.M. Student Atlas of Anatomy* follows the sixth edition of *Nomina Anatomica.* In some cases, the use of brackets [ ] and parentheses ( ) has formal meaning in the internationally recognized code of anatomical nomenclature.

Brackets signify:
1. An officially recognized alternative name or synonym.
    Fibularis [Peroneus] longus m.
    L. vagus n. [CN X], where CN refers to a cranial nerve
    L. gastro-omental [gastroepiploic] v.
2. An equivalent anatomical name.
    Subcostal n. [T12], where T12 = 12th thoracic spinal n.
    C1 [Atlas]

Parentheses identify:
1. An official name of inconsistent structures.
    (Accessory parotid gland)
    (Frontal suture)

2. Eponyms and alternative names that are not officially recognized as appropriate in contemporary usage.
    L. colic (splenic) flexure
    Costoaxillary (ext. mammary) v.
    Hepatopancreatic ampulla (of Vater)

3. Additional components of a name that are usually omitted but have been added for clarification or that are supplemental to the name.
    Greater tuberosity (of humerus)
    Acromion (process of scapula)
    Posterior basal bronchopulmonary segment (S10)

4.   Motor and sensory segmental and spinal nerve levels of a peripheral nerve.
         Femoral n. (L2–L4)
         Lat. femoral cutaneous n. (L2, L3)
         Middle cluneal nn. (dorsal rami of S1–S3)

         Two adjacent spinal nn., are separated by a comma; however, when more than two spinal nn. are involved, only the cranial and caudal-most are listed, separated by a dash.

5.   Conditions specific or unique to the image or dissection.
         L. rectus abdominis m. (reflected medially)
         R. primary bronchus (pulled to L.)

6.   In some names, long dashes replace or are used in conjunction with parentheses.
         Biceps femoris m.—long head tendon
         Vestibular bulb of vagina—corpus spongiosum
         Superficial perineal fascia—membranous layer (Colles')
         Urinary bladder—empty

Abbreviations

The following abbreviations are used in this atlas. **Bold** entries are abbreviated everywhere they appear, other entries are sometimes abbreviated in order to save space.

&	**= and**	inf.	= inferior	nn.	= nerves
a.	**= artery**	int.	= internal	pt.	= part
aa.	**= arteries**	**L.**	**= Left**	port.	= portion
ant.	= anterior	lat.	= lateral	post.	= posterior
asc.	= ascending	**lig.**	**= ligament**	proc.	= process
br.	**= branch**	**ligg.**	**= ligaments**	**R.**	**= Right**
brr.	**= branches**	**m.**	**= muscle**	sup.	= superior
comm.	**= communicating**	**mm.**	**= muscles**	trib.	= tributary
desc.	= descending	med.	= medial	**v.**	**= vein**
ext.	= external	**n.**	**= nerve**	**vv.**	**= veins**

Another system of abbreviation is used when labels for segmental structures (i.e., vertebrae, spinal or intercostal nerves, ribs) are superimposed on or immediately adjacent to the structure. Thus, **C6** on or next to a vertebra identifies the sixth cervical vertebra; the "C" distinguishes the vertebral type and the number its segmental location. Abbreviations used this way are:

         C = Cervical
         Cc = Coccygeal
         L = Lumbar
         R = Rib
         S = Sacral
         T = Thoracic

Trunk:
Body Wall and Spine

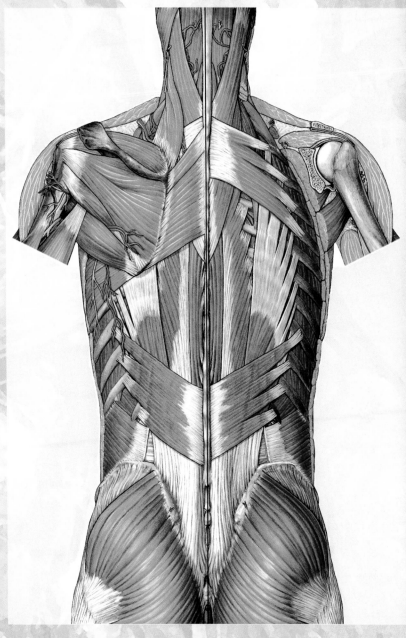

Chapter **1**

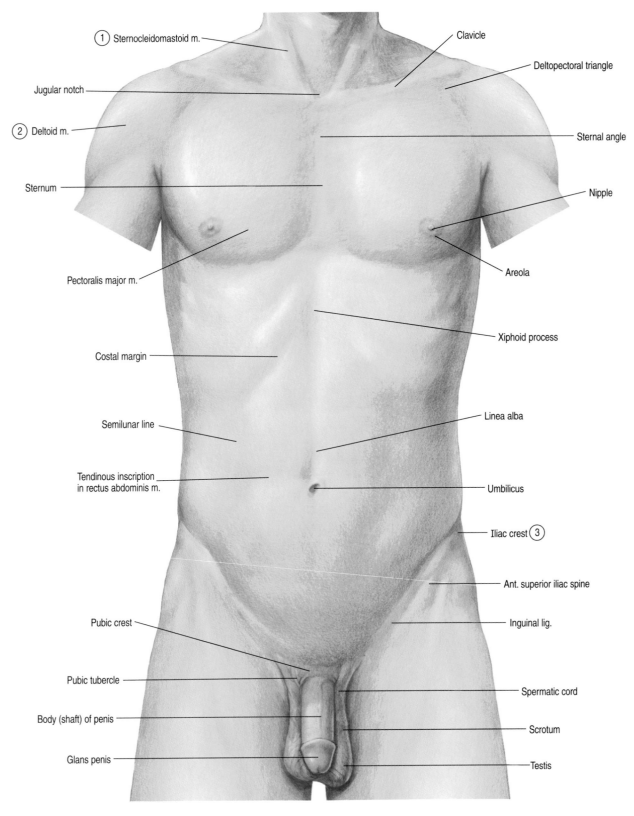

① Sternocleidomastoid m.

Clavicle

Jugular notch

Deltopectoral triangle

② Deltoid m.

Sternal angle

Sternum

Nipple

Areola

Pectoralis major m.

Xiphoid process

Costal margin

Linea alba

Semilunar line

Tendinous inscription in rectus abdominis m.

Umbilicus

Iliac crest ③

Ant. superior iliac spine

Pubic crest

Inguinal lig.

Pubic tubercle

Spermatic cord

Body (shaft) of penis

Scrotum

Glans penis

Testis

ANTERIOR VIEW

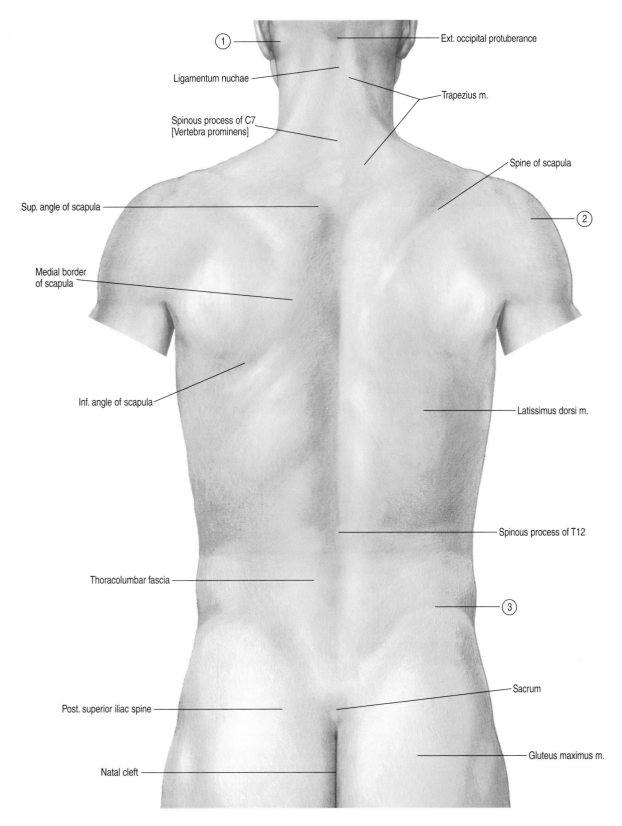

①   Ext. occipital protuberance

Ligamentum nuchae

Trapezius m.

Spinous process of C7
[Vertebra prominens]

Spine of scapula

Sup. angle of scapula

②

Medial border
of scapula

Inf. angle of scapula

Latissimus dorsi m.

Spinous process of T12

Thoracolumbar fascia

③

Sacrum

Post. superior iliac spine

Gluteus maximus m.

Natal cleft

POSTERIOR VIEW

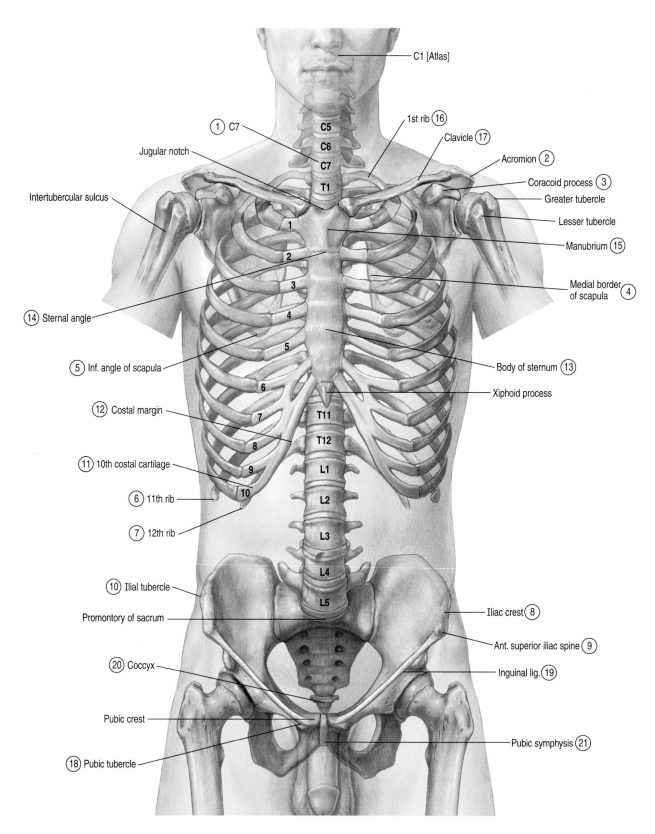

C1 [Atlas]

1st rib (16)

Clavicle (17)

① C7

C5

C6

C7

T1

Jugular notch

Acromion ②

Coracoid process ③

Greater tubercle

Lesser tubercle

Intertubercular sulcus

1

Manubrium (15)

2

3

Medial border of scapula ④

4

(14) Sternal angle

5

⑤ Inf. angle of scapula

6

Body of sternum (13)

Xiphoid process

(12) Costal margin

7

T11

8

T12

(11) 10th costal cartilage

9

L1

⑥ 11th rib

10

L2

⑦ 12th rib

L3

L4

(10) Ilial tubercle

L5

Iliac crest ⑧

Promontory of sacrum

Ant. superior iliac spine ⑨

(20) Coccyx

Inguinal lig. (19)

Pubic crest

Pubic symphysis (21)

(18) Pubic tubercle

ANTERIOR VIEW

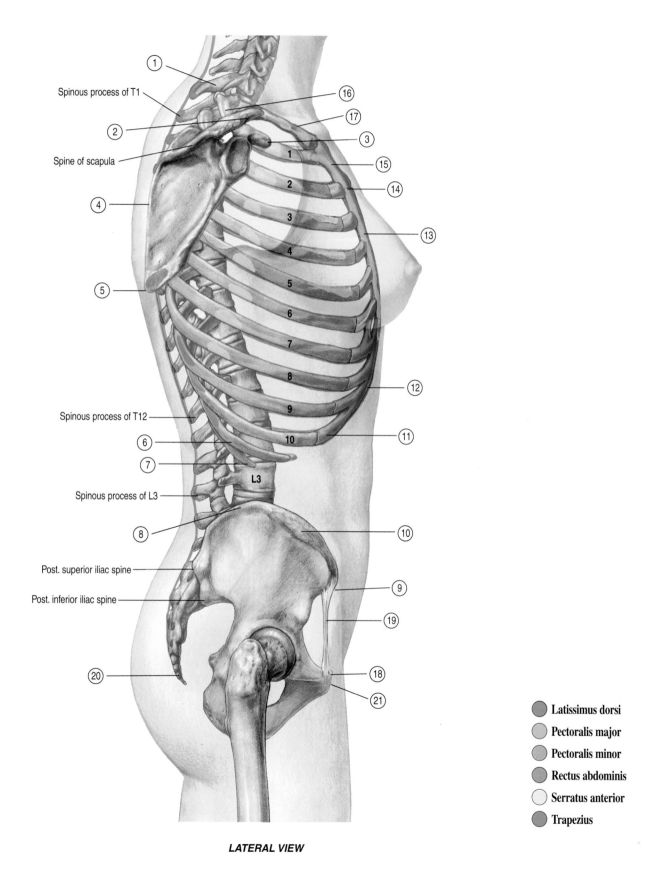

①

Spinous process of T1

②

Spine of scapula

④

⑤

Spinous process of T12

⑥

⑦

Spinous process of L3

⑧

Post. superior iliac spine

Post. inferior iliac spine

⑳

⑯

⑰

③

1

2

3

4

5

6

7

8

9

10

L3

⑮

⑭

⑬

⑫

⑪

⑩

⑨

⑲

⑱

㉑

LATERAL VIEW

🔴 **Latissimus dorsi**

🟡 **Pectoralis major**

🟢 **Pectoralis minor**

🔵 **Rectus abdominis**

⚪ **Serratus anterior**

🔴 **Trapezius**

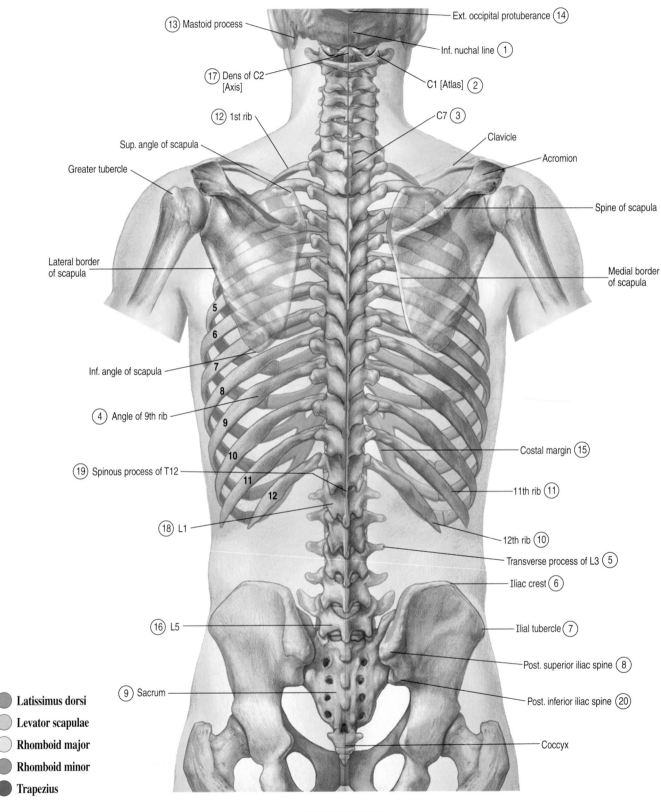

13 Mastoid process

Ext. occipital protuberance 14

Inf. nuchal line 1

17 Dens of C2 [Axis]

C1 [Atlas] 2

12 1st rib

C7 3

Sup. angle of scapula

Clavicle

Greater tubercle

Acromion

Spine of scapula

Lateral border of scapula

Medial border of scapula

5

6

Inf. angle of scapula

7

4 Angle of 9th rib

8

9

Costal margin 15

10

19 Spinous process of T12

11

11th rib 11

12

18 L1

12th rib 10

Transverse process of L3 5

Iliac crest 6

16 L5

Ilial tubercle 7

Post. superior iliac spine 8

9 Sacrum

Post. inferior iliac spine 20

Coccyx

● Latissimus dorsi
● Levator scapulae
○ Rhomboid major
● Rhomboid minor
● Trapezius

POSTERIOR VIEW

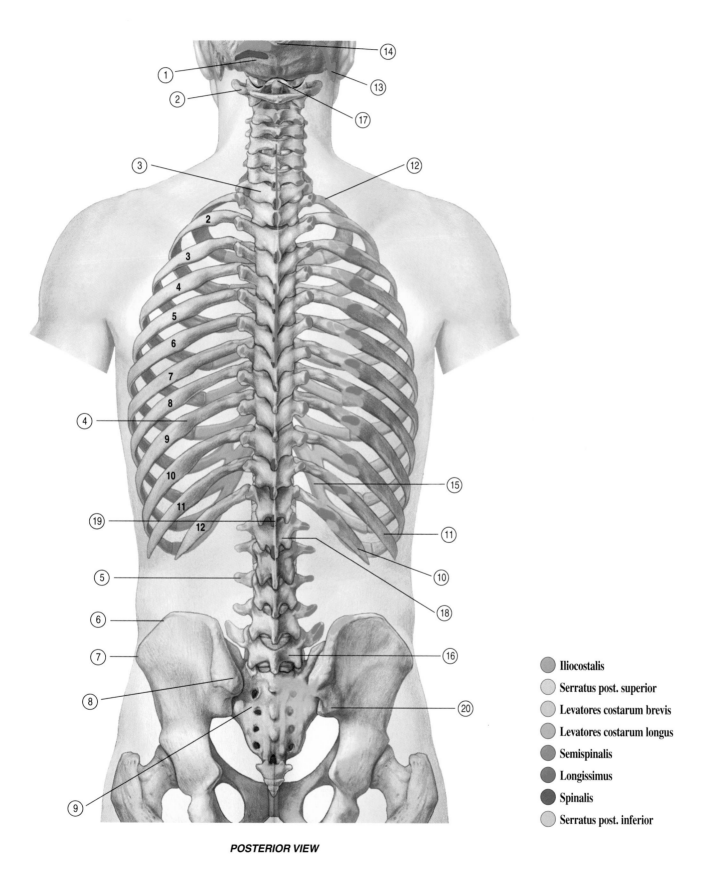

POSTERIOR VIEW

Iliocostalis

Serratus post. superior

Levatores costarum brevis

Levatores costarum longus

Semispinalis

Longissimus

Spinalis

Serratus post. inferior

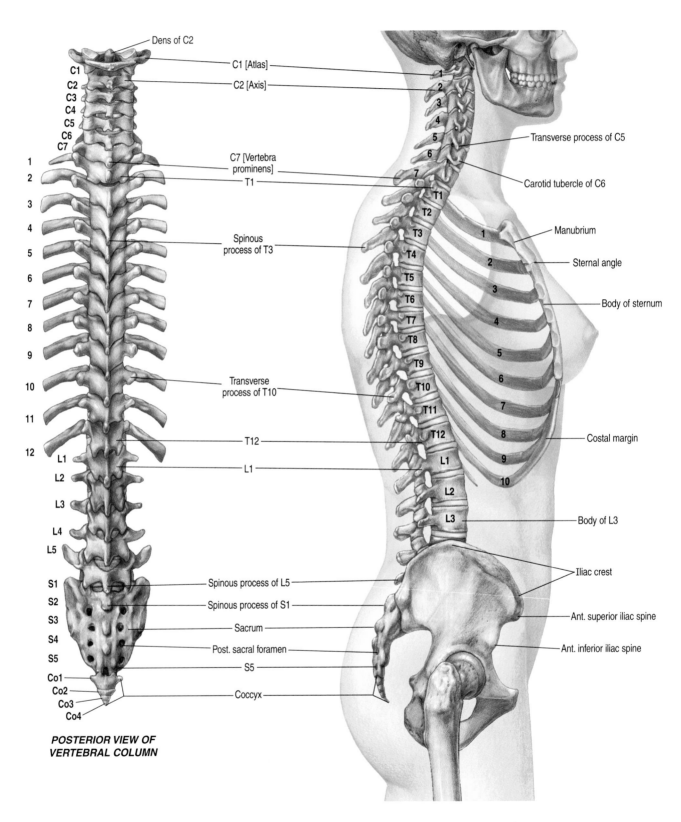

Dens of C2

C1 [Atlas]

C2 [Axis]

C1
C2
C3
C4
C5
C6
C7

C7 [Vertebra prominens]

T1

Spinous process of T3

Transverse process of T10

T12

L1

Spinous process of L5

Spinous process of S1

Sacrum

Post. sacral foramen

S5

Coccyx

Transverse process of C5

Carotid tubercle of C6

Manubrium

Sternal angle

Body of sternum

Costal margin

Body of L3

Iliac crest

Ant. superior iliac spine

Ant. inferior iliac spine

**POSTERIOR VIEW OF
VERTEBRAL COLUMN**

**LATERAL VIEW OF RIGHT
HALF OF SKELETON**

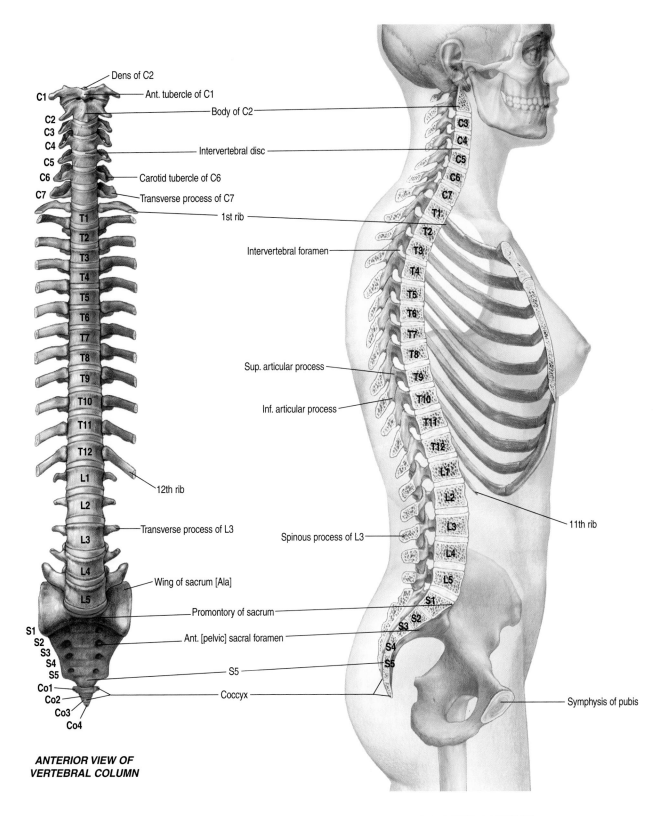

Dens of C2

Ant. tubercle of C1

Body of C2

Intervertebral disc

Carotid tubercle of C6

Transverse process of C7

1st rib

Intervertebral foramen

Sup. articular process

Inf. articular process

12th rib

Transverse process of L3

Wing of sacrum [Ala]

Promontory of sacrum

Ant. [pelvic] sacral foramen

S5

Coccyx

Spinous process of L3

11th rib

Symphysis of pubis

**ANTERIOR VIEW OF
VERTEBRAL COLUMN**

**RIGHT LATERAL VIEW OF
MEDIAN SECTIONED SKELETON**

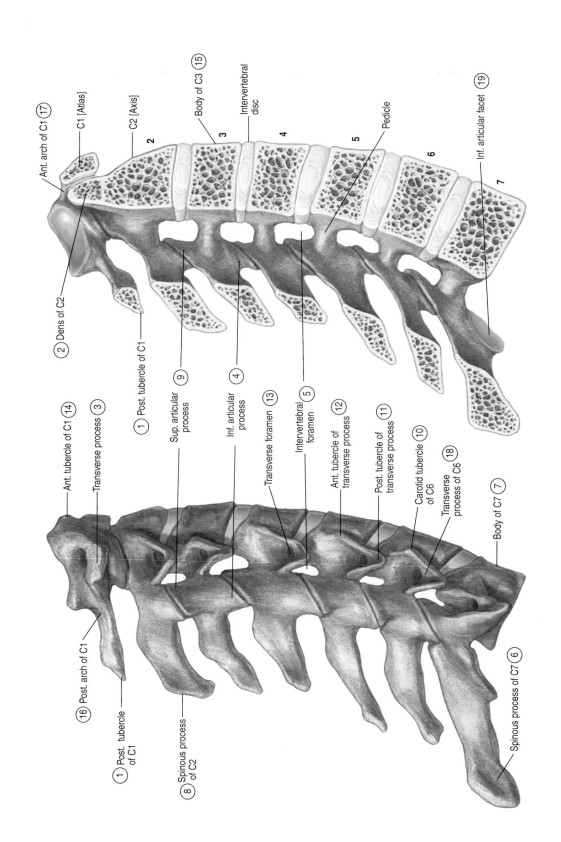

MEDIAN SECTION OF CERVICAL VERTEBRAE

LATERAL VIEW OF CERVICAL VERTEBRAE

Ant. arch of C1 (17)
C1 [Atlas]
C2 [Axis]
Body of C3 (15)
Intervertebral disc
Pedicle
Inf. articular facet (19)

(2) Dens of C2
(1) Post. tubercle of C1
(9) Sup. articular process
(4) Inf. articular process
(13) Transverse foramen
(5) Intervertebral foramen
(12) Ant. tubercle of transverse process
(11) Post. tubercle of transverse process
(10) Caroid tubercle of C6
(18) Transverse process of C6
(7) Body of C7

Ant. tubercle of C1 (14)
Transverse process (3)

(16) Post. arch of C1
(1) Post. tubercle of C1
(8) Spinous process of C2
(6) Spinous process of C7

POSTEROLATERAL VIEW OF CERVICAL VERTEBRAE

Bifurcated spinous process

ANTEROLATERAL VIEW OF CERVICAL VERTEBRAE

Thoracic Vertebrae
Plate 1.11

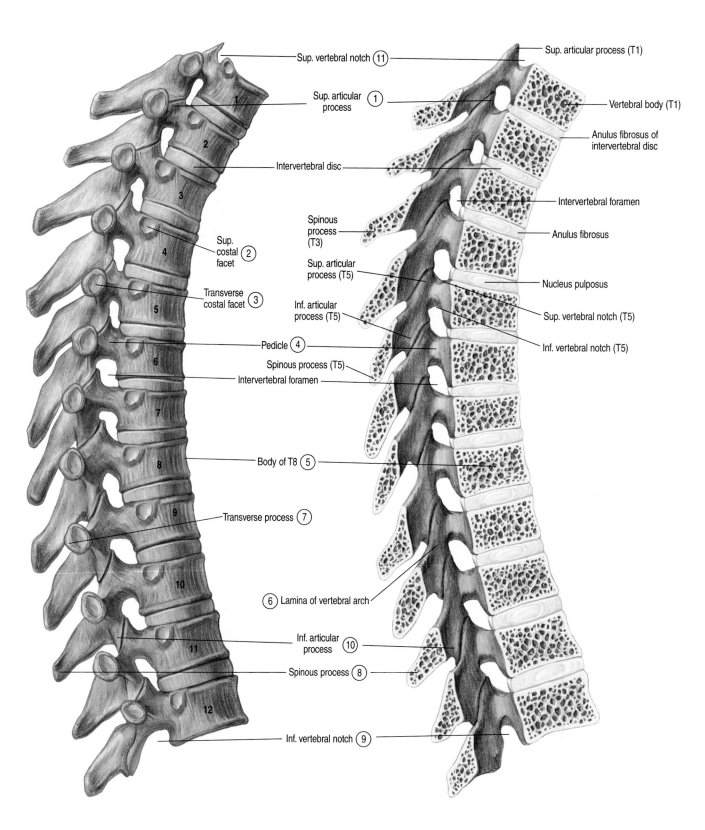

Sup. vertebral notch ⑪

Sup. articular process ①

Intervertebral disc

Sup. costal facet ②

Transverse costal facet ③

Spinous process (T3)

Sup. articular process (T5)

Inf. articular process (T5)

Pedicle ④

Spinous process (T5)

Intervertebral foramen

Body of T8 ⑤

Transverse process ⑦

⑥ Lamina of vertebral arch

Inf. articular process ⑩

Spinous process ⑧

Inf. vertebral notch ⑨

Sup. articular process (T1)

Vertebral body (T1)

Anulus fibrosus of intervertebral disc

Intervertebral foramen

Anulus fibrosus

Nucleus pulposus

Sup. vertebral notch (T5)

Inf. vertebral notch (T5)

LATERAL VIEW OF THORACIC VERTEBRAE

MIDSAGITTAL SECTION OF THORACIC VERTEBRAE

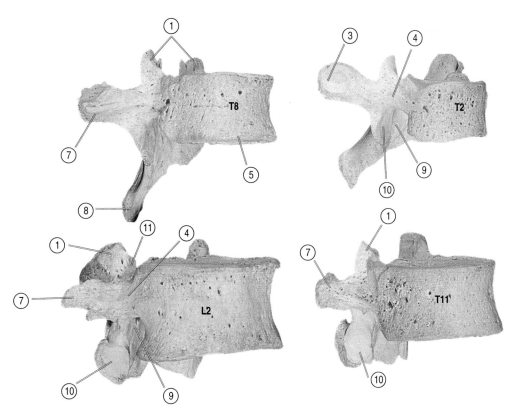

ANTEROLATERAL VIEW OF T8, T2, L2 & T11

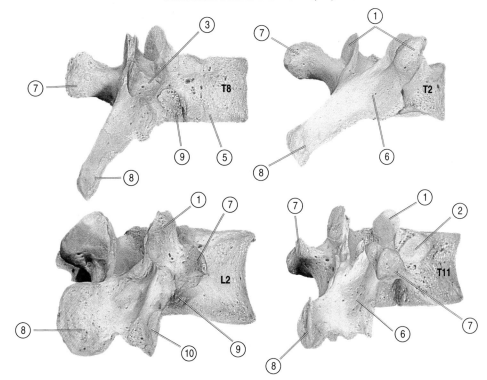

POSTEROLATERAL VIEW OF T8, T2, L2 & T11

Lumbar Vertebrae
Plate 1.13

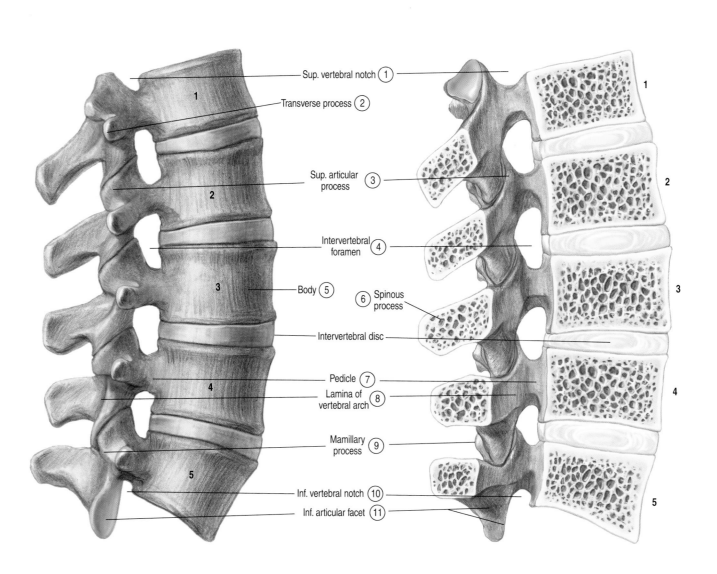

Sup. vertebral notch ①

Transverse process ②

Sup. articular process ③

Intervertebral foramen ④

Body ⑤

⑥ Spinous process

Intervertebral disc

Pedicle ⑦

Lamina of vertebral arch ⑧

Mamillary process ⑨

Inf. vertebral notch ⑩

Inf. articular facet ⑪

**LATERAL VIEW OF
LUMBAR VERTEBRAE**

**MEDIAN SECTION
OF LUMBAR VERTEBRAE**

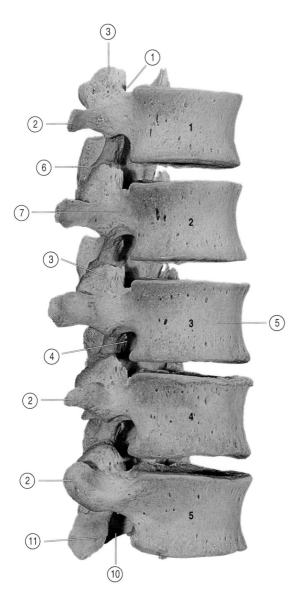

**ANTEROLATERAL VIEW
OF LUMBAR VERTEBRAE**

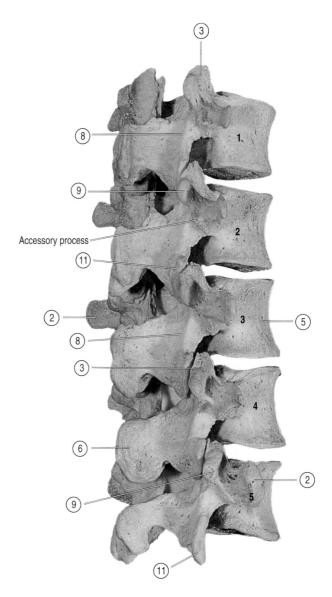

Accessory process

**POSTEROLATERAL VIEW
OF LUMBAR VERTEBRAE**

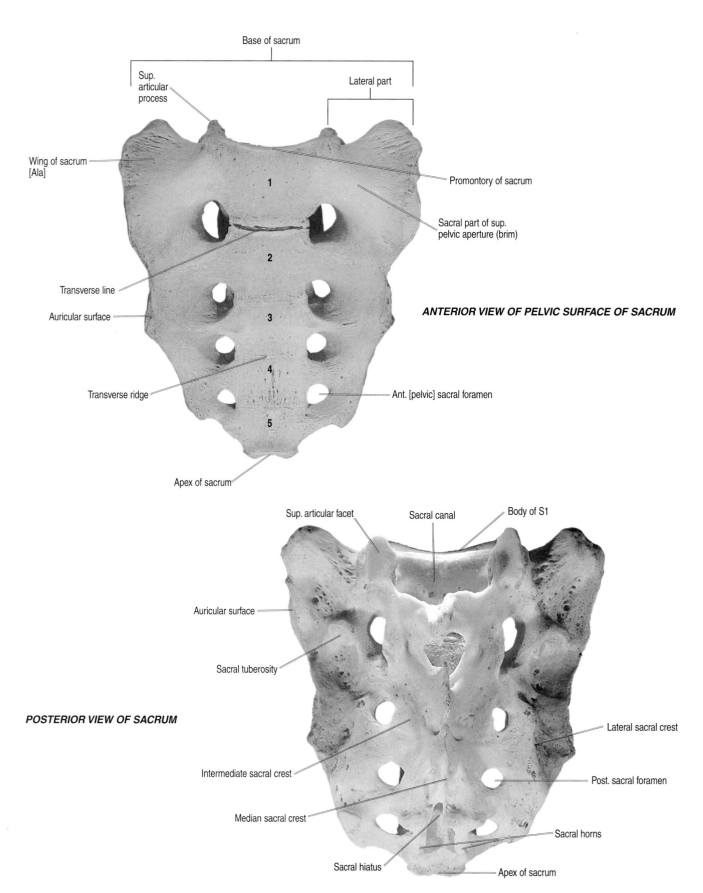

Base of sacrum

Sup. articular process

Lateral part

Wing of sacrum [Ala]

Promontory of sacrum

1

Sacral part of sup. pelvic aperture (brim)

2

Transverse line

ANTERIOR VIEW OF PELVIC SURFACE OF SACRUM

Auricular surface

3

Transverse ridge

4

Ant. [pelvic] sacral foramen

5

Apex of sacrum

Sup. articular facet

Sacral canal

Body of S1

Auricular surface

Sacral tuberosity

POSTERIOR VIEW OF SACRUM

Lateral sacral crest

Intermediate sacral crest

Post. sacral foramen

Median sacral crest

Sacral horns

Sacral hiatus

Apex of sacrum

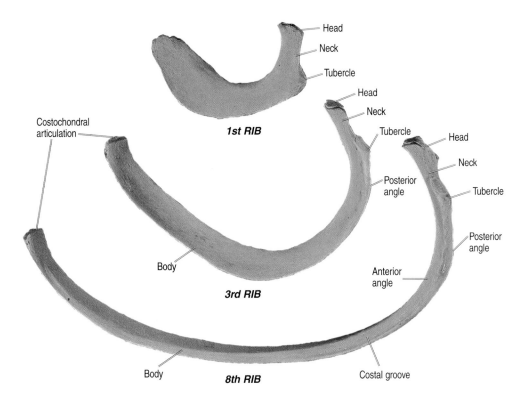

Head
Neck
Tubercle

1st RIB

Costochondral articulation

Head
Neck
Tubercle

Head
Neck

Posterior angle

Tubercle

Body

Posterior angle

Anterior angle

3rd RIB

Body

8th RIB

Costal groove

INFERIOR VIEW OF RIBS 1, 3 & 8 (RIGHT SIDE)

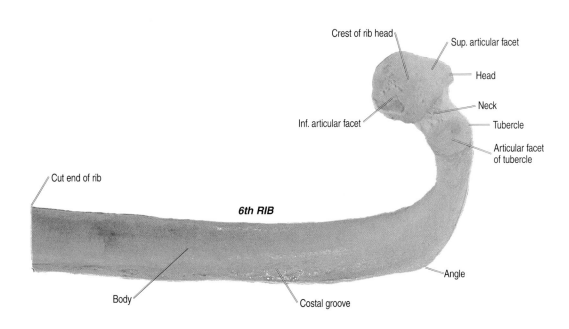

Crest of rib head

Sup. articular facet

Head

Neck

Inf. articular facet

Tubercle

Articular facet of tubercle

Cut end of rib

6th RIB

Angle

Body

Costal groove

MEDIAL VIEW OF PROXIMAL END OF RIGHT 6TH RIB

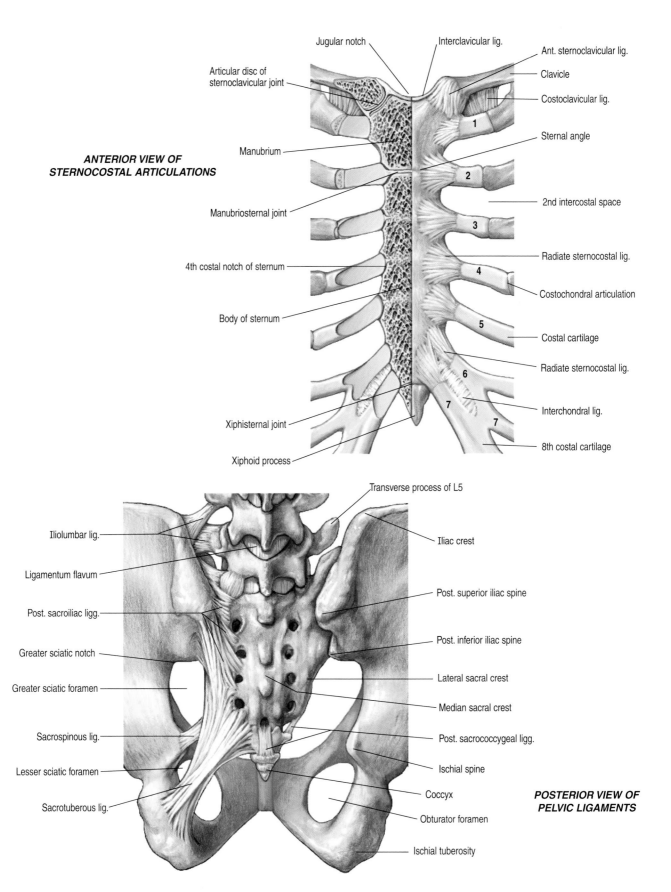

ANTERIOR VIEW OF STERNOCOSTAL ARTICULATIONS

Jugular notch

Interclavicular lig.

Ant. sternoclavicular lig.

Clavicle

Costoclavicular lig.

Articular disc of sternoclavicular joint

Sternal angle

Manubrium

2nd intercostal space

Manubriosternal joint

Radiate sternocostal lig.

4th costal notch of sternum

Costochondral articulation

Body of sternum

Costal cartilage

Radiate sternocostal lig.

Interchondral lig.

Xiphisternal joint

8th costal cartilage

Xiphoid process

Transverse process of L5

Iliolumbar lig.

Iliac crest

Ligamentum flavum

Post. superior iliac spine

Post. sacroiliac ligg.

Post. inferior iliac spine

Greater sciatic notch

Lateral sacral crest

Greater sciatic foramen

Median sacral crest

Sacrospinous lig.

Post. sacrococcygeal ligg.

Lesser sciatic foramen

Ischial spine

Coccyx

Sacrotuberous lig.

Obturator foramen

Ischial tuberosity

POSTERIOR VIEW OF PELVIC LIGAMENTS

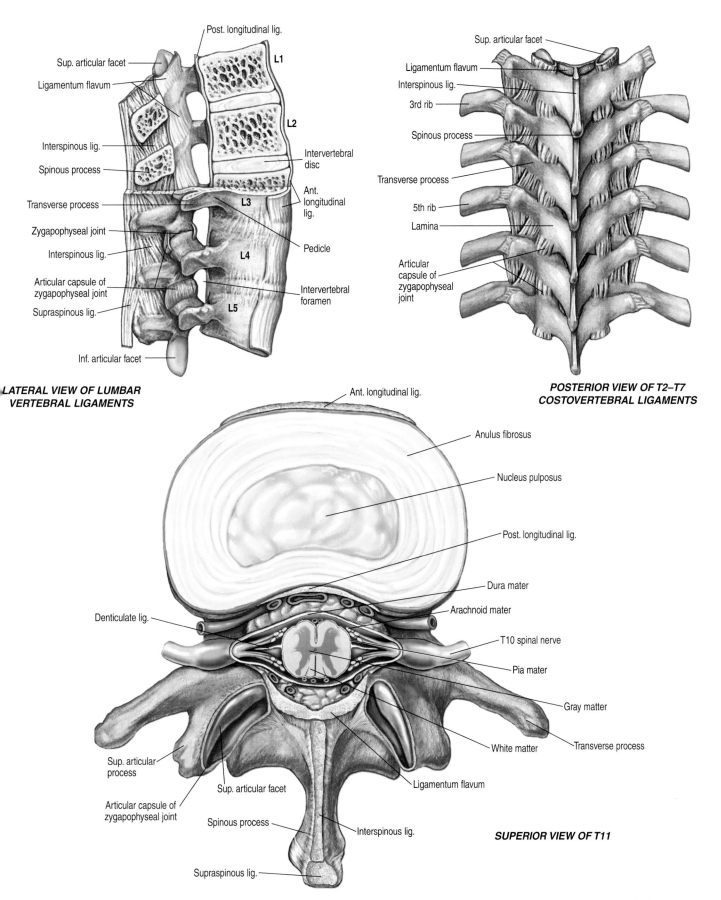

Lateral View of Lumbar Vertebral Ligaments

Post. longitudinal lig.

Sup. articular facet

Ligamentum flavum

Interspinous lig.

Spinous process

Transverse process

Zygapophyseal joint

Interspinous lig.

Articular capsule of zygapophyseal joint

Supraspinous lig.

Inf. articular facet

L1

L2

Intervertebral disc

Ant. longitudinal lig.

L3

Pedicle

L4

Intervertebral foramen

L5

**LATERAL VIEW OF LUMBAR
VERTEBRAL LIGAMENTS**

Sup. articular facet

Ligamentum flavum

Interspinous lig.

3rd rib

Spinous process

Transverse process

5th rib

Lamina

Articular capsule of zygapophyseal joint

**POSTERIOR VIEW OF T2–T7
COSTOVERTEBRAL LIGAMENTS**

Ant. longitudinal lig.

Anulus fibrosus

Nucleus pulposus

Post. longitudinal lig.

Dura mater

Arachnoid mater

T10 spinal nerve

Pia mater

Gray matter

Transverse process

White matter

Denticulate lig.

Ligamentum flavum

Sup. articular process

Articular capsule of zygapophyseal joint

Sup. articular facet

Spinous process

Interspinous lig.

SUPERIOR VIEW OF T11

Supraspinous lig.

Muscles—Thoracic Wall
Table 1.1

Muscle	Superior or Medial Attachment	Inferior or Lateral Attachment	Innervation	Action(s)
External intercostal		Sup. border of rib bounding intercostal space caudally, muscular from costal tubercle to end of rib with membranous connection to sternum		Elevate ribs in inspiration
Internal intercostal	Inf. border of rib that bounds intercostal space cranially	Sup. border of rib bounding intercostal space caudally, muscular from angle to sternum	1st to 11th intercostal nn. & subcostal n.	
Innermost intercostal		Separated from int. intercostal mm. only by neurovascular bundle		
Subcostal	Inf. border lateral to angle of rib that bounds intercostal space cranially	Int. surface near angle of rib that bounds intercostal space caudally, best developed between ribs 6 & 12, may cross 2 intercostal spaces		Depress ribs in expiration
Transversus thoracis	Int. surface of body & xiphoid of sternum	Inf. border of 2nd to 6th costal cartilages	1st to 11th intercostal nn.	Depress costal cartilages in expiration
Levatores costarum L. c. brevis m. L. c. longus m.	Transverse processes of C7 to T11	Between tubercle & angle on ext. surface of rib caudal to vertebral attachment	Dorsal primary rami of C8 & T1 to T11 spinal nn.	Elevate ribs in inspiration; laterally flex spine
Serratus posterior superior	Inf. part of ligamentum nuchae & spinous process from C7 to T2/T3	Sup. border of 2nd to 5th ribs just lateral to angles	2nd to 5th intercostal nn.	Elevate ribs in inspiration
Serratus posterior inferior	Spinous processes & thoracolumbar fascia from T11/T12 to L3	Inf. border of 9th/10th to 12th ribs just lateral to angles	9th to 11th intercostal nn. & subcostal n.	Depress ribs in expiration

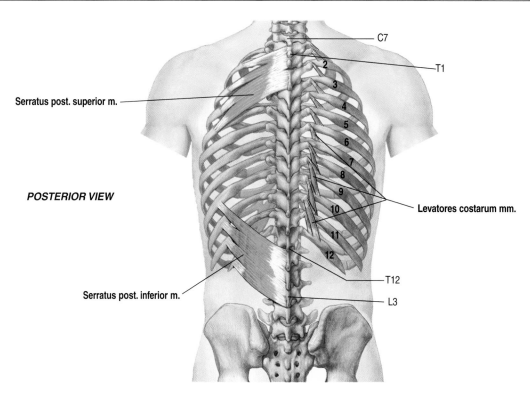

POSTERIOR VIEW

Serratus post. superior m.

Serratus post. inferior m.

Levatores costarum mm.

C7
T1
2
3
4
5
6
7
8
9
10
11
12
T12
L3

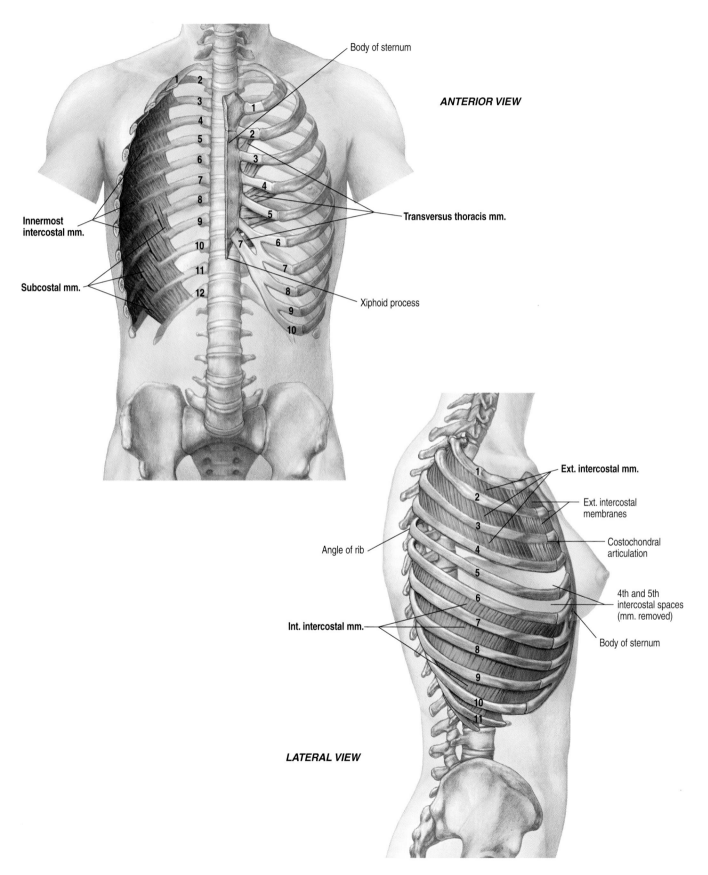

Body of sternum

ANTERIOR VIEW

Transversus thoracis mm.

**Innermost
intercostal mm.**

Subcostal mm.

Xiphoid process

Ext. intercostal mm.

Ext. intercostal
membranes

Costochondral
articulation

4th and 5th
intercostal spaces
(mm. removed)

Body of sternum

Angle of rib

Int. intercostal mm.

LATERAL VIEW

Muscles—Abdominal Wall
Table 1.2

Muscle	Lateral or Superior Attachment	Medial or Inferior Attachment	Innervation	Action(s)
External oblique	Ext. surfaces of 5th to 12th ribs	Linea alba, pubic tubercle & ant. half of iliac crest	Inf. six thoracic nn. & subcostal n.	Compress & support abdominal viscera; flex & rotate trunk
Internal oblique	Thoracolumbar fascia, ant. two-thirds of iliac crest & lateral half of inguinal lig.	Inf. borders of 10th to 12th ribs, linea alba & pubis via the conjoint tendon	Ventral rami of inf. six thoracic & first lumbar nn.	
Transversus abdominis	Int. surfaces of 7th to 12th costal cartilages, thoracolumbar fascia, iliac crest & lateral third of inguinal lig.	Linea alba with aponeurosis of int. oblique, pubic crest & pecten pubis via conjoint tendon		Compress & support abdominal viscera
Rectus abdominis	Xiphoid process & 5th to 7th costal cartilages	Pubic symphysis & pubic crest	Ventral rami of inf. six thoracic nn.	Flex trunk & compress abdominal viscera
Quadratus lumborum	Medial half of inf. border of 12th rib & tips of lumbar transverse processes	Iliolumbar lig. & int. lip of iliac crest	Ventral rami of T12 & L1 to L4	Extend & laterally fixes the vertebral column; flex 12th rib during inspiration
Cremaster	Inf. edge of int. abdominal oblique, inguinal lig., pubic tubercle & pubic crest	Invest spermatic cord and testis	Genital br. of genitofemoral n. (L1 & L2)	Retract testis

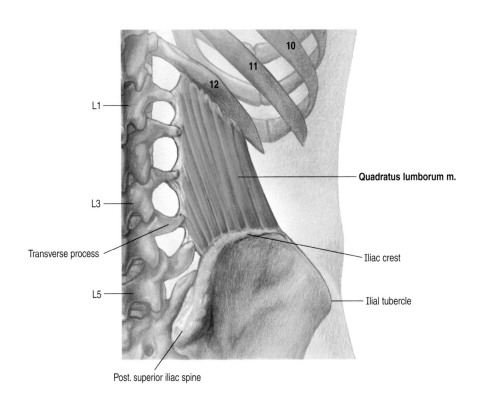

POSTERIOR VIEW

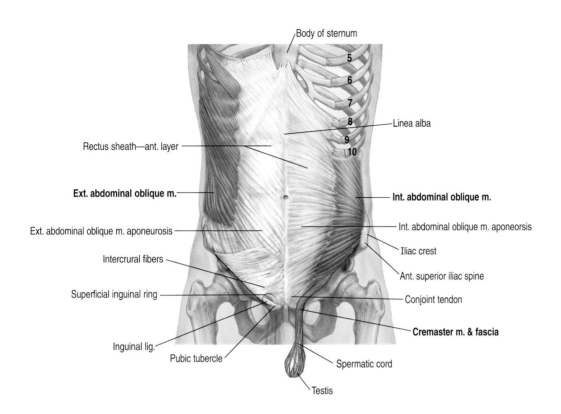

Body of sternum

5
6
7
8 — Linea alba
9
10

Rectus sheath—ant. layer

Ext. abdominal oblique m.

Ext. abdominal oblique m. aponeurosis

Intercrural fibers

Superficial inguinal ring

Inguinal lig.

Pubic tubercle

Int. abdominal oblique m.

Int. abdominal oblique m. aponeorsis

Iliac crest

Ant. superior iliac spine

Conjoint tendon

Cremaster m. & fascia

Spermatic cord

Testis

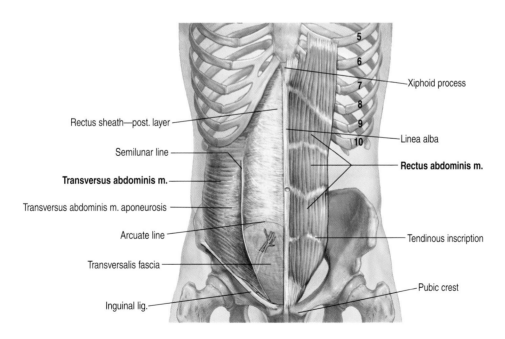

5
6
7 — Xiphoid process
8
9
10 — Linea alba

Rectus sheath—post. layer

Semilunar line

Transversus abdominis m.

Transversus abdominis m. aponeurosis

Arcuate line

Transversalis fascia

Inguinal lig.

Rectus abdominis m.

Tendinous inscription

Pubic crest

ANTERIOR VIEWS

Intrinsic Muscles of the Back
Table 1.3

Intrinsic Muscles of the Back[a]

Muscle	Inferior or Medial Attachment	Superior or Lateral Attachment	Innervation	Action(s)
SUPERFICIAL—SPINOTRANSVERSE GROUP				
Splenius capitis	Inf. half of ligamentum nuchae, spinous processes of C7 to T3/T4	Mastoid process, lateral third of the sup. nuchal line	Dorsal primary rami of middle cervical spinal nn.	Unilaterally, rotate & laterally flex neck to same side; bilaterally, extend the neck & head
Splenius cervicis	Spinous processes of T3/T4 to T6	Post. tubercles of transverse processes of C1 to C3	Dorsal primary rami of lower cervical spinal nn.	
INTERMEDIATE LAYER—ERECTOR SPINAE GROUP				
Iliocostalis m. *l. cervicis* *l. thoracis* *l. lumborum*	Sacrum, medial part of iliac crest, 12th to 3rd ribs	Angles of all ribs, transverse processes of C7 to C4	Dorsal primary rami of all cervical, thoracic & lumbar spinal nn.	Unilaterally, flex vertebral column to same side; bilaterally, extend vertebral column; important in maintaining erect posture while standing or walking
Longissimus m. *L. capitis* *L. cervicis* *L. thoracis*	Sacrum, transverse processes of all vertebrae from L5 to C7, transverse & articular processes of C6 to C4	Transverse processes of all vertebrae from T12 to C2; angles of all ribs, mastoid process		
Spinalis m. *S. capitis* *S. cervicis* *S. thoracis*	Spinous processes of L2/L3 to T11, ligamentum nuchae & spinous processes of T2 to C7, transverse processes of C7/C6 to C2, articular processes of C6 to C4	Spinous processes from T9/T8 to C7/C6, spinous processes of C3/C4 & C2, occipital bone between sup. & inf. nuchal lines with semispinalis m.		
DEEP LAYER—TRANSVERSOSPINAL GROUP				
Semispinalis m. *S. capitis* *S. cervicis* *S. thoracis*	Transverse processes of all vertebrae from T10 to C3, articular processes of C6 to C4	Spinous processes from T4 to C2, occipital bone between sup. & inf. nuchal lines; usually includes spinalis capitis m.	Dorsal primary rami of T6 to T1, all cervical spinal nn.	Unilaterally, lateral flex and/or rotate vertebral column & head to opposite side; bilaterally, extend vertebral column & head
Multifidus	All lamina from S4 to C2, transverse processes L5 to T1, articular processes C7 to C3	Spinous process of all vertebrae; spans 1 to 3 vertebrae	Dorsal primary rami of T6 to C1 spinal nn.	Unilaterally, lateral flex and/or rotate vertebral column to opposite side; bilaterally, extend or stabilize vertebral column
Rotatores	Transverse processes of all vertebrae L5 to T2	Lamina & roots of spinous process of next vertebra superiorly; best developed in thoracic region	Dorsal primary rami of L4 to T1 spinal nn.	

[a]The most superficial layer also includes the trapezius, latissimus dorsi, levator scapulae & rhomboid muscles which move the upper limb. The intermediate layer is formed by the serratus posterior muscles. The muscles of both of these layers are considered extrinsic to the back. The intrinsic muscles of the back form the deepest three back muscle layers.

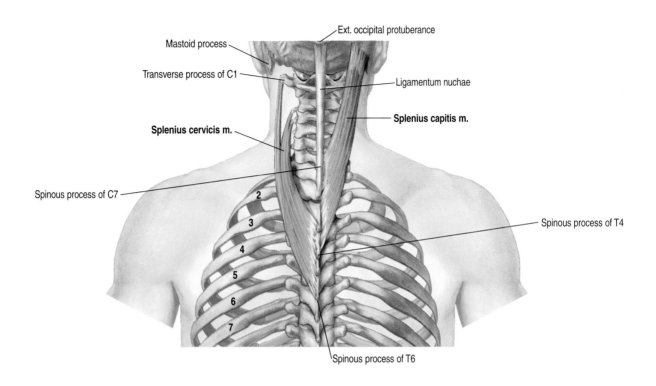

Ext. occipital protuberance

Mastoid process

Transverse process of C1

Splenius cervicis m.

Ligamentum nuchae

Splenius capitis m.

Spinous process of C7

Spinous process of T4

Spinous process of T6

POSTERIOR VIEWS

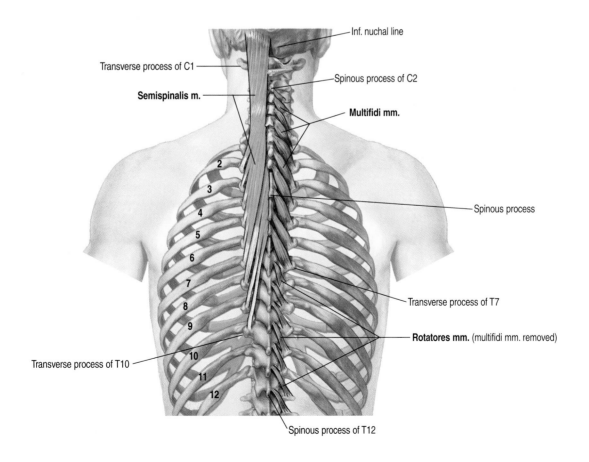

Inf. nuchal line

Transverse process of C1

Spinous process of C2

Semispinalis m.

Multifidi mm.

Spinous process

Transverse process of T7

Rotatores mm. (multifidi mm. removed)

Transverse process of T10

Spinous process of T12

Muscles—Erector Spinae
Plate 1.22

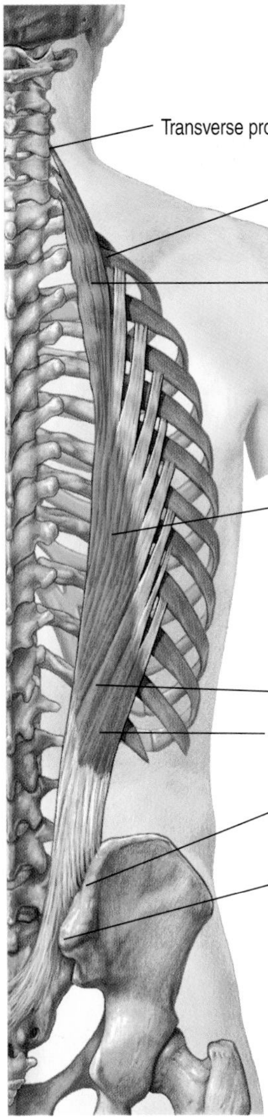
Transverse process of C4
Angle of 2nd rib
Iliocostalis cervicis m.
Iliocostalis thoracis m.
Iliocostalis lumborum m.
Iliocostalis m.
Iliac crest
Post. superior iliac spine

POSTERIOR VIEWS

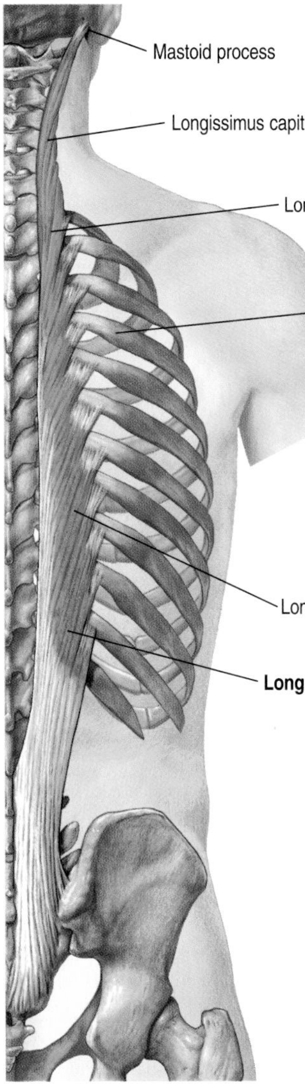
Mastoid process
Longissimus capitis m.
Longissimus cervicis m.
Angle of rib
Longissimus thoracis m.
Longissimus m.

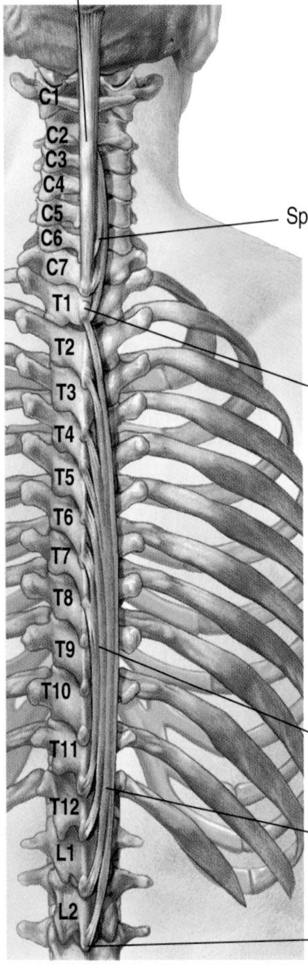
Ligamentum nuchae
C1
C2
C3
C4
C5
C6
C7
T1
T2
T3
T4
T5
T6
T7
T8
T9
T10
T11
T12
L1
L2
Spinous cervicis m.
Spinous process of T1
Spinalis thoracis m.
Spinalis m.
Spinous process of L2

Muscle	Inferior or Medial Attachment	Superior or Lateral Attachment	Innervation	Action(s)
DEEP LAYER—SUBOCCIPITAL GROUP				
Rectus capitis posterior major	Spinous process of C2	Lateral part of inf. nuchal line	Dorsal primary ramus of C1 [suboccipital] n.	Unilaterally, rotate head to same side; bilaterally, extend head at atlanto-occipital joint
Rectus capitis posterior minor	Post. tubercle of C1	Medial part of inf. nuchal line		
Obliquus capitis superior	Transverse process of C1	Sup. to inf. nuchal line		Unilaterally, rotate C1 & head to same side around odontoid process; bilaterally, extend head at atlanto-axial joint
Obliquus capitis inferior	Spinous process of C2	Transverse process of C1		

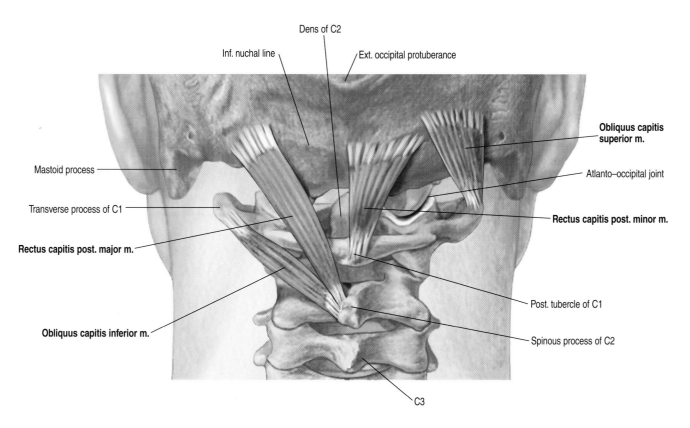

POSTERIOR VIEW

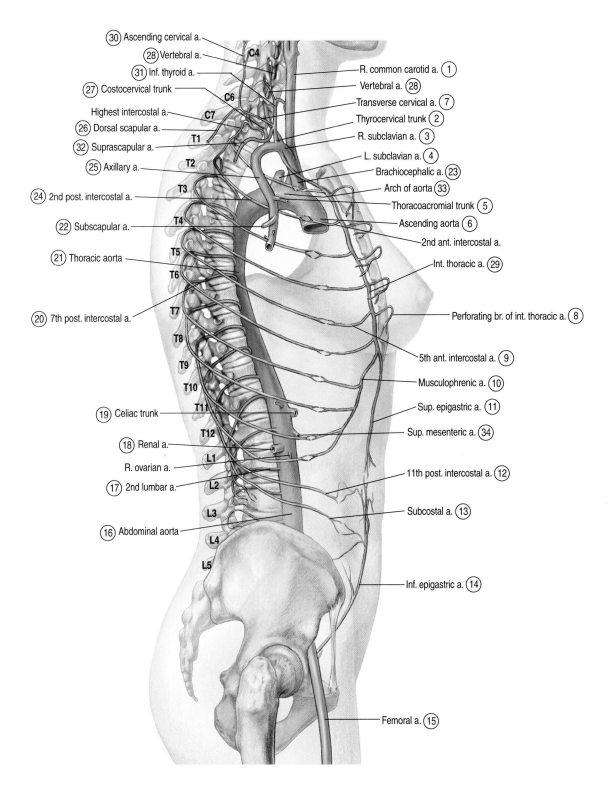

30 Ascending cervical a.
28 Vertebral a.
31 Inf. thyroid a.
27 Costocervical trunk
Highest intercostal a.
26 Dorsal scapular a.
32 Suprascapular a.
25 Axillary a.
24 2nd post. intercostal a.
22 Subscapular a.
21 Thoracic aorta
20 7th post. intercostal a.
19 Celiac trunk
18 Renal a.
R. ovarian a.
17 2nd lumbar a.
16 Abdominal aorta

C4
C6
C7
T1
T2
T3
T4
T5
T6
T7
T8
T9
T10
T11
T12
L1
L2
L3
L4
L5

R. common carotid a. 1
Vertebral a. 28
Transverse cervical a. 7
Thyrocervical trunk 2
R. subclavian a. 3
L. subclavian a. 4
Brachiocephalic a. 23
Arch of aorta 33
Thoracoacromial trunk 5
Ascending aorta 6
2nd ant. intercostal a.
Int. thoracic a. 29
Perforating br. of int. thoracic a. 8
5th ant. intercostal a. 9
Musculophrenic a. 10
Sup. epigastric a. 11
Sup. mesenteric a. 34
11th post. intercostal a. 12
Subcostal a. 13
Inf. epigastric a. 14
Femoral a. 15

RIGHT LATERAL VIEW

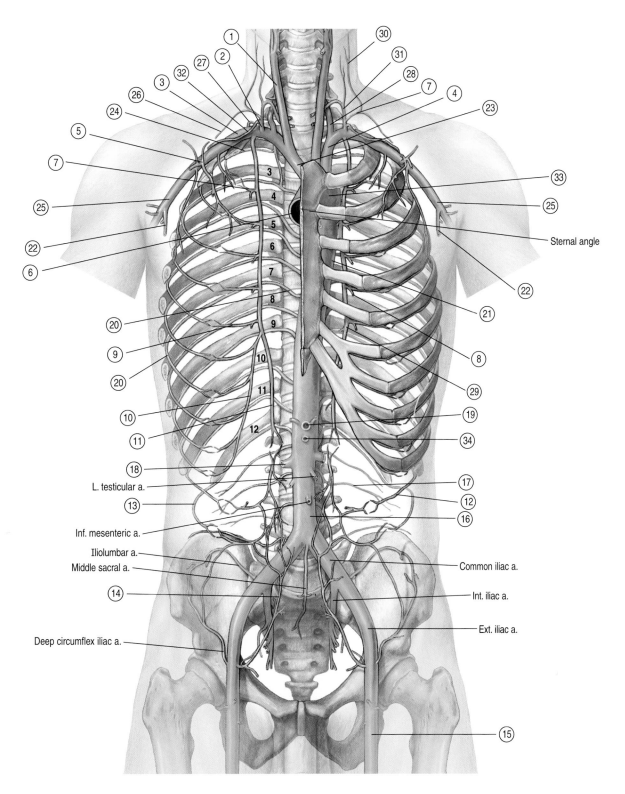

L. testicular a.

Inf. mesenteric a.

Iliolumbar a.

Middle sacral a.

Deep circumflex iliac a.

Sternal angle

Common iliac a.

Int. iliac a.

Ext. iliac a.

ANTERIOR VIEW

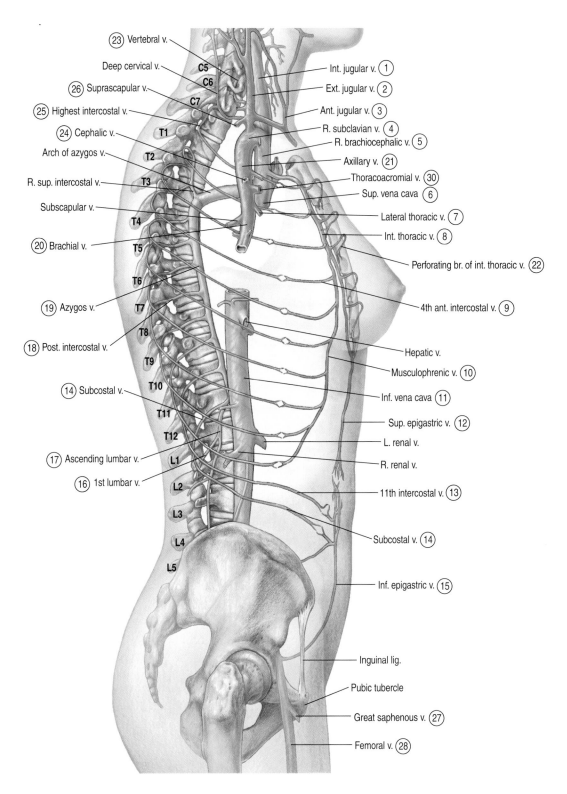

23 Vertebral v.

Deep cervical v.

C5
C6

26 Suprascapular v.

C7

25 Highest intercostal v.

T1

24 Cephalic v.

T2

Arch of azygos v.

T3

R. sup. intercostal v.

Subscapular v.

T4

20 Brachial v.

T5

T6

19 Azygos v.

T7

T8

18 Post. intercostal v.

T9

T10

14 Subcostal v.

T11

T12

17 Ascending lumbar v.

L1

16 1st lumbar v.

L2

L3

L4

L5

Int. jugular v. 1

Ext. jugular v. 2

Ant. jugular v. 3

R. subclavian v. 4

R. brachiocephalic v. 5

Axillary v. 21

Thoracoacromial v. 30

Sup. vena cava 6

Lateral thoracic v. 7

Int. thoracic v. 8

Perforating br. of int. thoracic v. 22

4th ant. intercostal v. 9

Hepatic v.

Musculophrenic v. 10

Inf. vena cava 11

Sup. epigastric v. 12

L. renal v.

R. renal v.

11th intercostal v. 13

Subcostal v. 14

Inf. epigastric v. 15

Inguinal lig.

Pubic tubercle

Great saphenous v. 27

Femoral v. 28

RIGHT LATERAL VIEW

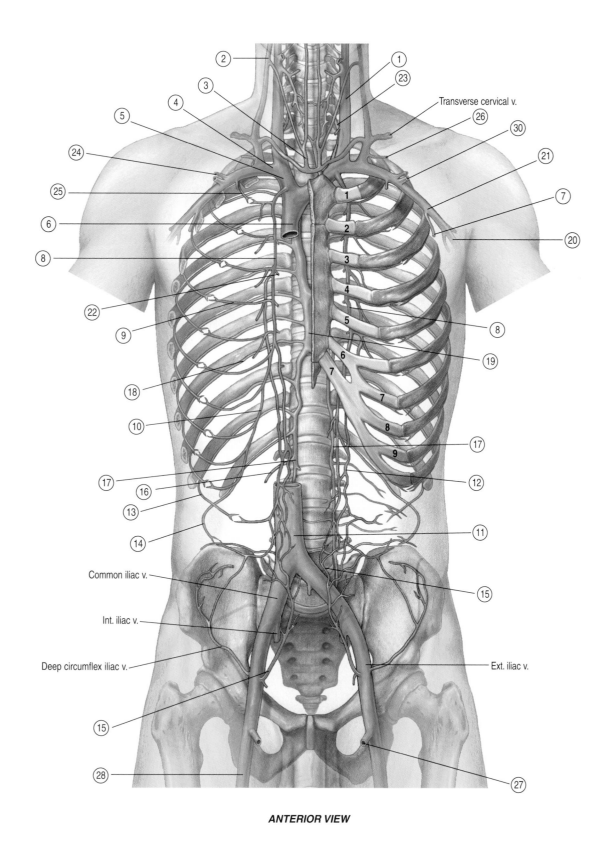

Transverse cervical v.

Common iliac v.

Int. iliac v.

Deep circumflex iliac v.

Ext. iliac v.

ANTERIOR VIEW

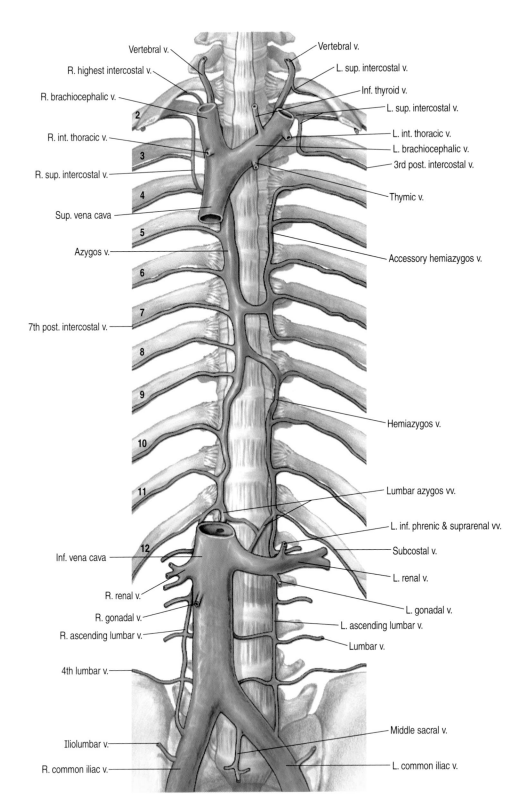

Vertebral v.

Vertebral v.

R. highest intercostal v.

L. sup. intercostal v.

R. brachiocephalic v.

Inf. thyroid v.

L. sup. intercostal v.

R. int. thoracic v.

L. int. thoracic v.

L. brachiocephalic v.

R. sup. intercostal v.

3rd post. intercostal v.

Thymic v.

Sup. vena cava

Azygos v.

Accessory hemiazygos v.

7th post. intercostal v.

Hemiazygos v.

Lumbar azygos vv.

L. inf. phrenic & suprarenal vv.

Subcostal v.

Inf. vena cava

L. renal v.

R. renal v.

R. gonadal v.

L. gonadal v.

L. ascending lumbar v.

R. ascending lumbar v.

Lumbar v.

4th lumbar v.

Middle sacral v.

Iliolumbar v.

L. common iliac v.

R. common iliac v.

2 3 4 5 6 7 8 9 10 11 12

ANTERIOR VIEW

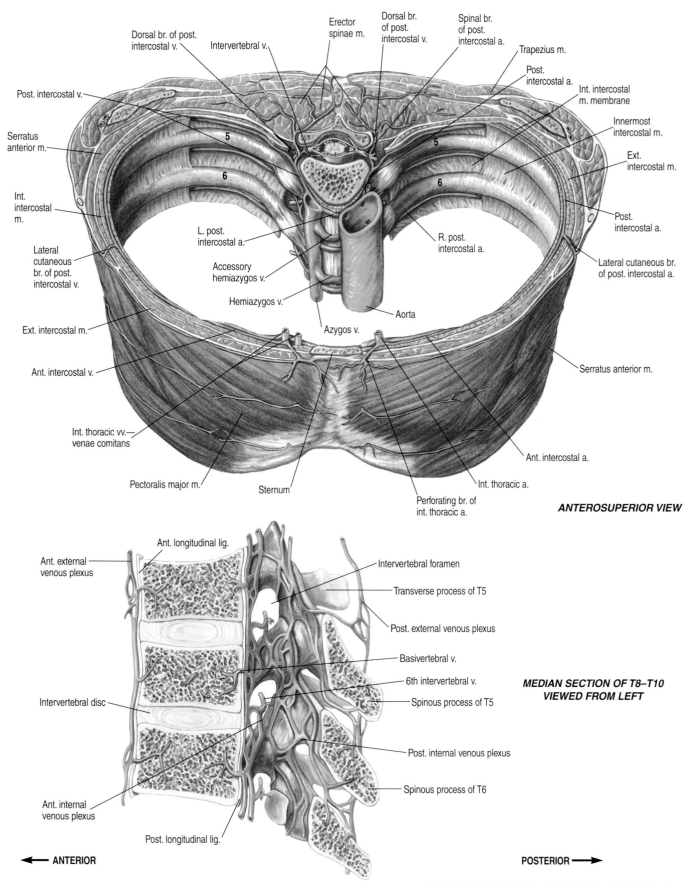

Erector spinae m.

Dorsal br. of post. intercostal v.

Dorsal br. of post. intercostal v.

Intervertebral v.

Spinal br. of post. intercostal a.

Dorsal br. of post. intercostal v.

Trapezius m.

Post. intercostal a.

Post. intercostal v.

Serratus anterior m.

Int. intercostal m. membrane

Innermost intercostal m.

Ext. intercostal m.

5

5

6

6

Int. intercostal m.

Post. intercostal a.

Lateral cutaneous br. of post. intercostal v.

L. post. intercostal a.

Accessory hemiazygos v.

R. post. intercostal a.

Lateral cutaneous br. of post. intercostal a.

Ext. intercostal m.

Hemiazygos v.

Aorta

Ant. intercostal v.

Azygos v.

Serratus anterior m.

Int. thoracic vv.— venae comitans

Ant. intercostal a.

Pectoralis major m.

Sternum

Int. thoracic a.

Perforating br. of int. thoracic a.

ANTEROSUPERIOR VIEW

Ant. longitudinal lig.

Ant. external venous plexus

Intervertebral foramen

Transverse process of T5

Post. external venous plexus

Basivertebral v.

6th intervertebral v.

***MEDIAN SECTION OF T8–T10
VIEWED FROM LEFT***

Intervertebral disc

Spinous process of T5

Post. internal venous plexus

Ant. internal venous plexus

Spinous process of T6

Post. longitudinal lig.

⬅ **ANTERIOR**

POSTERIOR ➡

Spinal Cord Vasculature
Plate 1.29

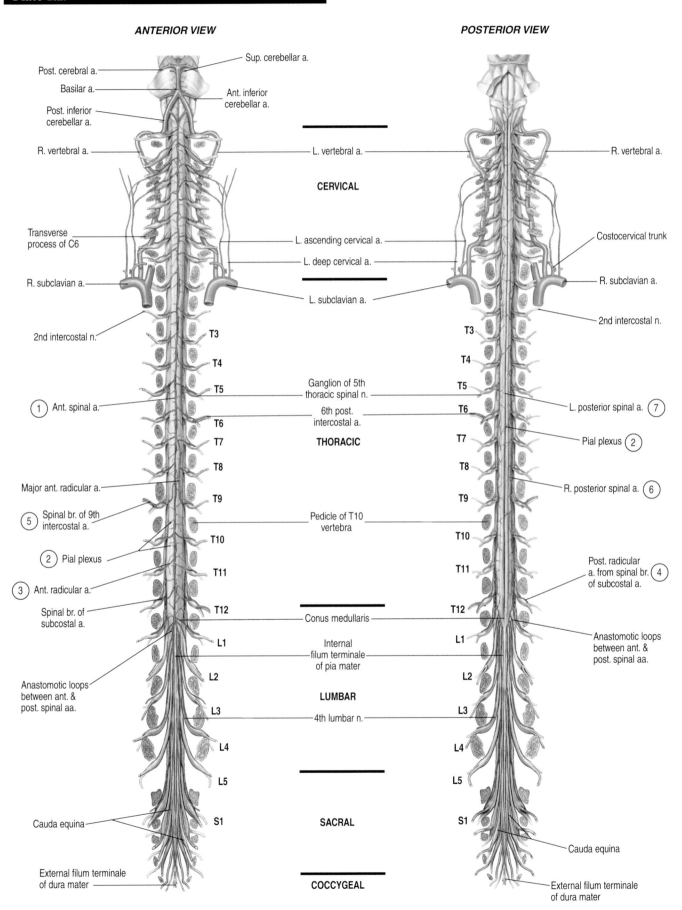

ANTERIOR VIEW

Post. cerebral a.

Sup. cerebellar a.

Basilar a.

Ant. inferior cerebellar a.

Post. inferior cerebellar a.

R. vertebral a.

L. vertebral a.

CERVICAL

Transverse process of C6

L. ascending cervical a.

L. deep cervical a.

R. subclavian a.

L. subclavian a.

2nd intercostal n.

T3

T4

T5

Ganglion of 5th thoracic spinal n.

① Ant. spinal a.

T6

6th post. intercostal a.

T7

THORACIC

T8

Major ant. radicular a.

T9

⑤ Spinal br. of 9th intercostal a.

Pedicle of T10 vertebra

T10

② Pial plexus

T11

③ Ant. radicular a.

T12

Spinal br. of subcostal a.

Conus medullaris

L1

Internal filum terminale of pia mater

L2

Anastomotic loops between ant. & post. spinal aa.

LUMBAR

L3

4th lumbar n.

L4

L5

Cauda equina

S1

SACRAL

External filum terminale of dura mater

COCCYGEAL

POSTERIOR VIEW

R. vertebral a.

Costocervical trunk

R. subclavian a.

2nd intercostal n.

T3

T4

T5

L. posterior spinal a. ⑦

T6

Pial plexus ②

T7

T8

R. posterior spinal a. ⑥

T9

T10

T11

Post. radicular a. from spinal br. ④ of subcostal a.

T12

L1

Anastomotic loops between ant. & post. spinal aa.

L2

L3

L4

L5

S1

Cauda equina

External filum terminale of dura mater

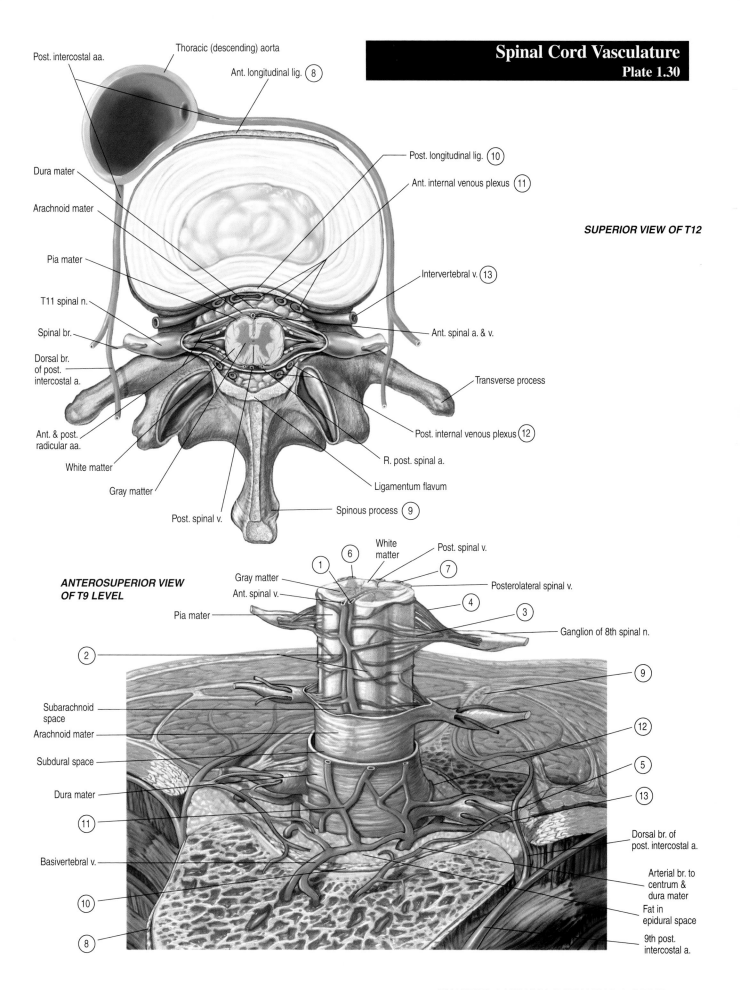

Post. intercostal aa.

Thoracic (descending) aorta

Ant. longitudinal lig. (8)

Dura mater

Arachnoid mater

Pia mater

T11 spinal n.

Spinal br.

Dorsal br.
of post.
intercostal a.

Ant. & post.
radicular aa.

White matter

Gray matter

Post. spinal v.

Post. longitudinal lig. (10)

Ant. internal venous plexus (11)

SUPERIOR VIEW OF T12

Intervertebral v. (13)

Ant. spinal a. & v.

Transverse process

Post. internal venous plexus (12)

R. post. spinal a.

Ligamentum flavum

Spinous process (9)

*ANTEROSUPERIOR VIEW
OF T9 LEVEL*

White
matter

Gray matter

Ant. spinal v.

Pia mater

Post. spinal v.

Posterolateral spinal v.

Ganglion of 8th spinal n.

Subarachnoid
space

Arachnoid mater

Subdural space

Dura mater

Basivertebral v.

Dorsal br. of
post. intercostal a.

Arterial br. to
centrum &
dura mater

Fat in
epidural space

9th post.
intercostal a.

Dermatomes & Cutaneous Innervation
Plate 1.31

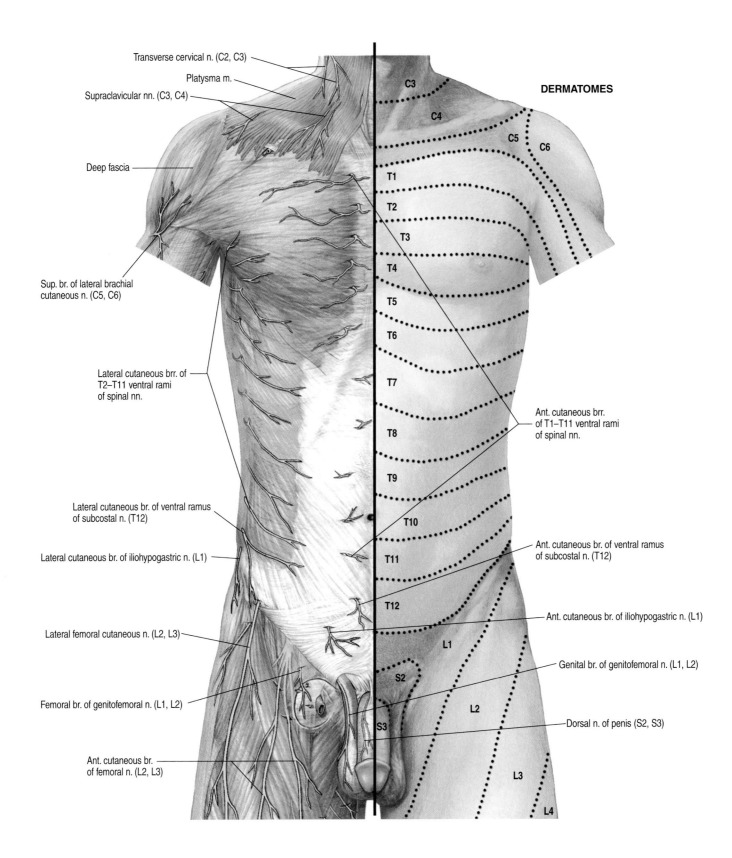

Transverse cervical n. (C2, C3)

Platysma m.

Supraclavicular nn. (C3, C4)

Deep fascia

Sup. br. of lateral brachial cutaneous n. (C5, C6)

Lateral cutaneous brr. of T2–T11 ventral rami of spinal nn.

Lateral cutaneous br. of ventral ramus of subcostal n. (T12)

Lateral cutaneous br. of iliohypogastric n. (L1)

Lateral femoral cutaneous n. (L2, L3)

Femoral br. of genitofemoral n. (L1, L2)

Ant. cutaneous br. of femoral n. (L2, L3)

DERMATOMES

C3
C4
C5
C6
T1
T2
T3
T4
T5
T6
T7
T8
T9
T10
T11
T12
L1
S2
S3
L2
L3
L4

Ant. cutaneous brr. of T1–T11 ventral rami of spinal nn.

Ant. cutaneous br. of ventral ramus of subcostal n. (T12)

Ant. cutaneous br. of iliohypogastric n. (L1)

Genital br. of genitofemoral n. (L1, L2)

Dorsal n. of penis (S2, S3)

ANTERIOR VIEW

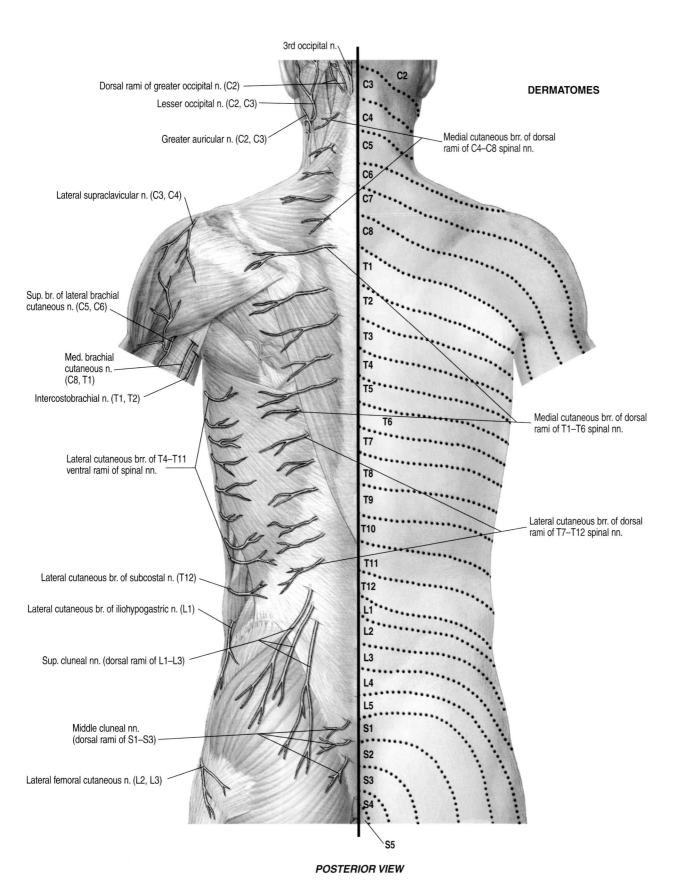

DERMATOMES

3rd occipital n.

Dorsal rami of greater occipital n. (C2)

Lesser occipital n. (C2, C3)

Greater auricular n. (C2, C3)

Lateral supraclavicular n. (C3, C4)

Sup. br. of lateral brachial cutaneous n. (C5, C6)

Med. brachial cutaneous n. (C8, T1)

Intercostobrachial n. (T1, T2)

Lateral cutaneous brr. of T4–T11 ventral rami of spinal nn.

Lateral cutaneous br. of subcostal n. (T12)

Lateral cutaneous br. of iliohypogastric n. (L1)

Sup. cluneal nn. (dorsal rami of L1–L3)

Middle cluneal nn. (dorsal rami of S1–S3)

Lateral femoral cutaneous n. (L2, L3)

Medial cutaneous brr. of dorsal rami of C4–C8 spinal nn.

Medial cutaneous brr. of dorsal rami of T1–T6 spinal nn.

Lateral cutaneous brr. of dorsal rami of T7–T12 spinal nn.

C2
C3
C4
C5
C6
C7
C8
T1
T2
T3
T4
T5
T6
T7
T8
T9
T10
T11
T12
L1
L2
L3
L4
L5
S1
S2
S3
S4
S5

POSTERIOR VIEW

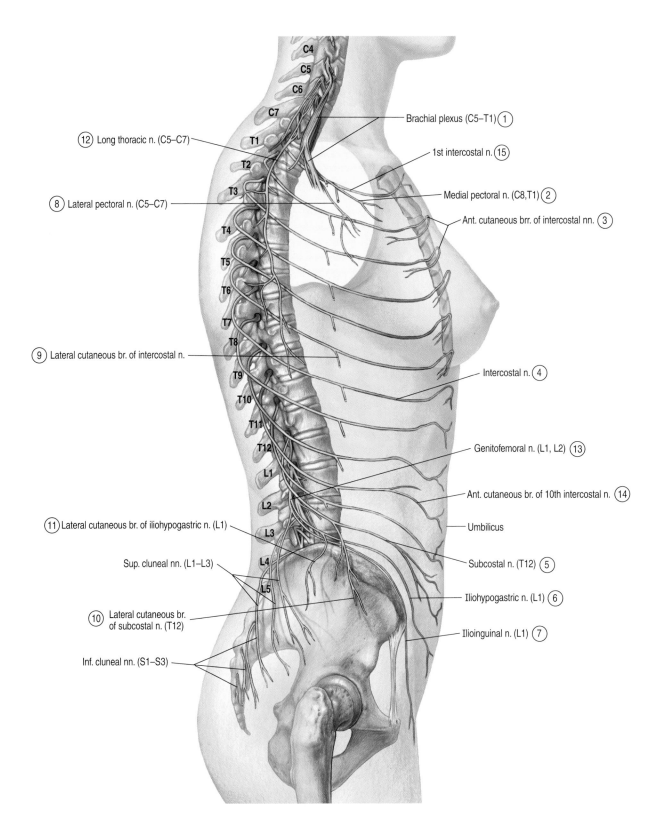

C4
C5
C6
C7
T1
T2
T3
T4
T5
T6
T7
T8
T9
T10
T11
T12
L1
L2
L3
L4
L5

(12) Long thoracic n. (C5–C7)

(8) Lateral pectoral n. (C5–C7)

(9) Lateral cutaneous br. of intercostal n.

(11) Lateral cutaneous br. of iliohypogastric n. (L1)

Sup. cluneal nn. (L1–L3)

(10) Lateral cutaneous br. of subcostal n. (T12)

Inf. cluneal nn. (S1–S3)

Brachial plexus (C5–T1) (1)

1st intercostal n. (15)

Medial pectoral n. (C8,T1) (2)

Ant. cutaneous brr. of intercostal nn. (3)

Intercostal n. (4)

Genitofemoral n. (L1, L2) (13)

Ant. cutaneous br. of 10th intercostal n. (14)

Umbilicus

Subcostal n. (T12) (5)

Iliohypogastric n. (L1) (6)

Ilioinguinal n. (L1) (7)

RIGHT LATERAL VIEW

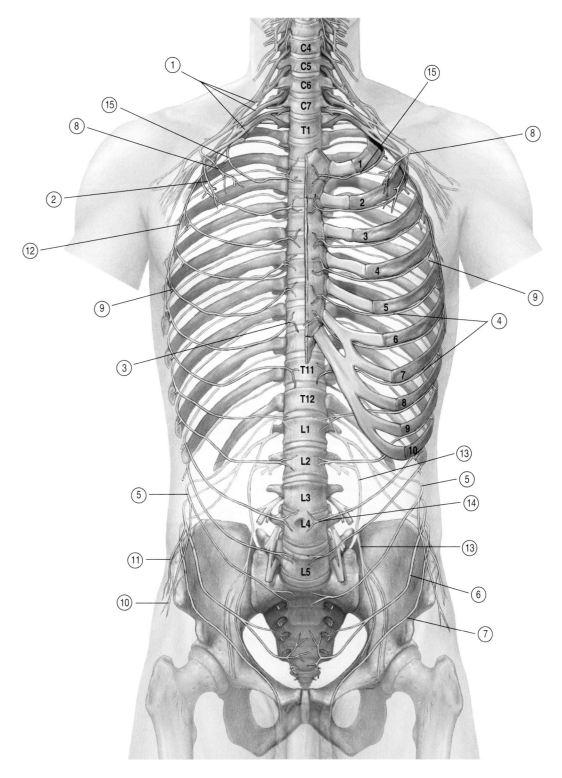

ANTERIOR VIEW

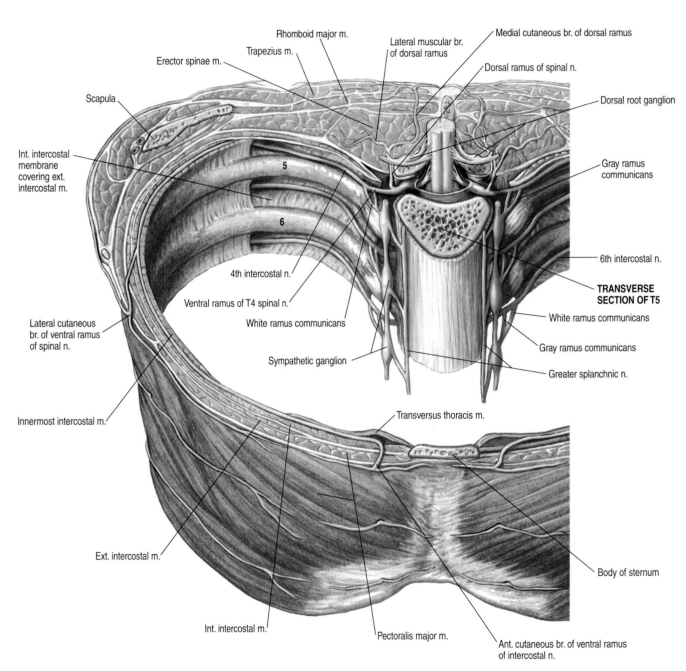

Rhomboid major m.

Trapezius m.

Lateral muscular br. of dorsal ramus

Medial cutaneous br. of dorsal ramus

Erector spinae m.

Dorsal ramus of spinal n.

Scapula

Dorsal root ganglion

Int. intercostal membrane covering ext. intercostal m.

Gray ramus communicans

5

6

6th intercostal n.

4th intercostal n.

TRANSVERSE SECTION OF T5

Ventral ramus of T4 spinal n.

White ramus communicans

White ramus communicans

Lateral cutaneous br. of ventral ramus of spinal n.

Gray ramus communicans

Sympathetic ganglion

Greater splanchnic n.

Innermost intercostal m.

Transversus thoracis m.

Ext. intercostal m.

Body of sternum

Int. intercostal m.

Pectoralis major m.

Ant. cutaneous br. of ventral ramus of intercostal n.

ANTEROSUPERIOR

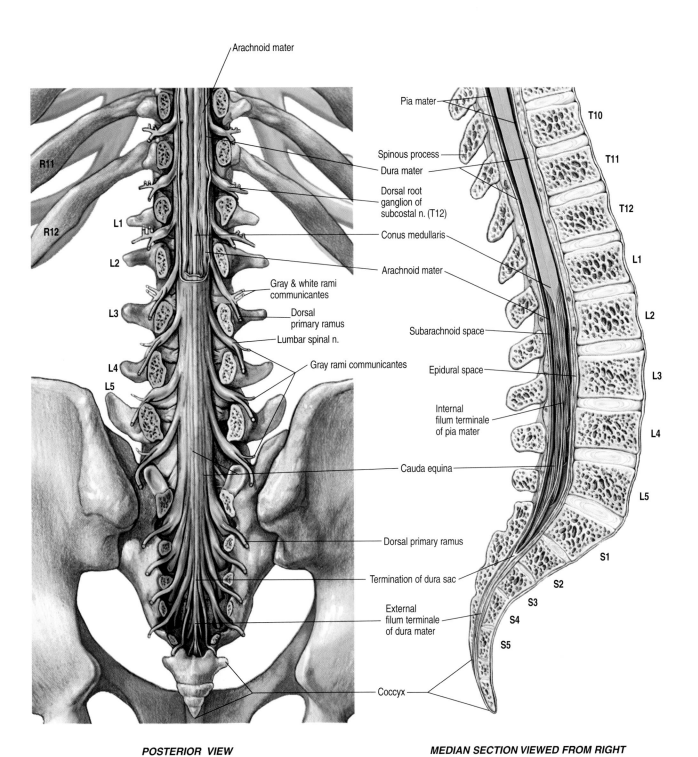

Arachnoid mater

R11

R12

L1

L2

L3

L4

L5

Gray & white rami communicantes

Dorsal primary ramus

Lumbar spinal n.

Gray rami communicantes

Pia mater

Spinous process

Dura mater

Dorsal root ganglion of subcostal n. (T12)

Conus medullaris

Arachnoid mater

Subarachnoid space

Epidural space

Internal filum terminale of pia mater

Cauda equina

Dorsal primary ramus

Termination of dura sac

External filum terminale of dura mater

Coccyx

T10

T11

T12

L1

L2

L3

L4

L5

S1

S2

S3

S4

S5

POSTERIOR VIEW

MEDIAN SECTION VIEWED FROM RIGHT

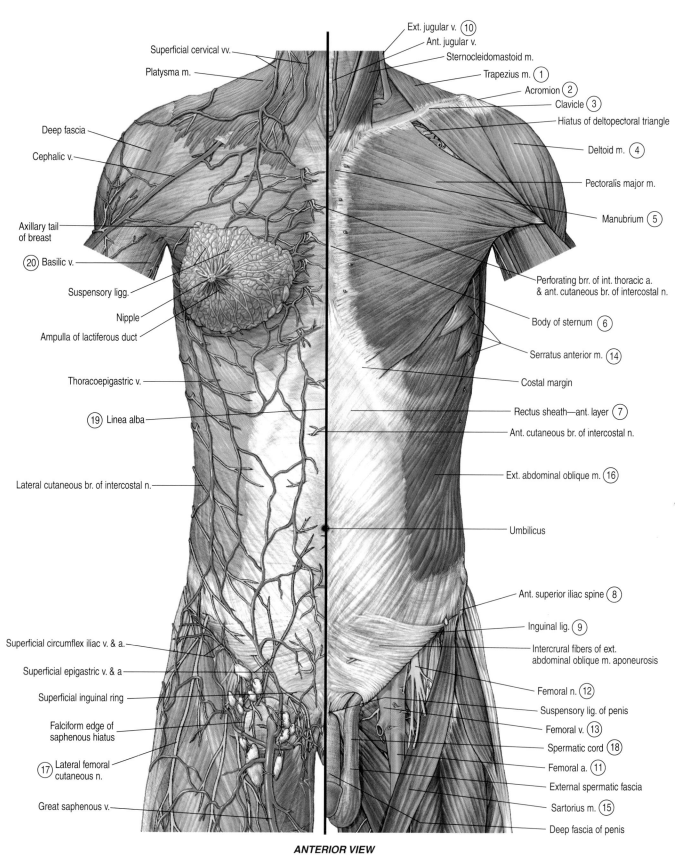

Ext. jugular v. ⑩
Ant. jugular v.
Sternocleidomastoid m.
Trapezius m. ①
Acromion ②
Clavicle ③
Hiatus of deltopectoral triangle
Deltoid m. ④
Pectoralis major m.
Manubrium ⑤
Perforating brr. of int. thoracic a. & ant. cutaneous br. of intercostal n.
Body of sternum ⑥
Serratus anterior m. ⑭
Costal margin
Rectus sheath—ant. layer ⑦
Ant. cutaneous br. of intercostal n.
Ext. abdominal oblique m. ⑯
Umbilicus
Ant. superior iliac spine ⑧
Inguinal lig. ⑨
Intercrural fibers of ext. abdominal oblique m. aponeurosis
Femoral n. ⑫
Suspensory lig. of penis
Femoral v. ⑬
Spermatic cord ⑱
Femoral a. ⑪
External spermatic fascia
Sartorius m. ⑮
Deep fascia of penis

Superficial cervical vv.
Platysma m.
Deep fascia
Cephalic v.
Axillary tail of breast
⑳ Basilic v.
Suspensory ligg.
Nipple
Ampulla of lactiferous duct
Thoracoepigastric v.
⑲ Linea alba
Lateral cutaneous br. of intercostal n.
Superficial circumflex iliac v. & a.
Superficial epigastric v. & a.
Superficial inguinal ring
Falciform edge of saphenous hiatus
⑰ Lateral femoral cutaneous n.
Great saphenous v.

ANTERIOR VIEW

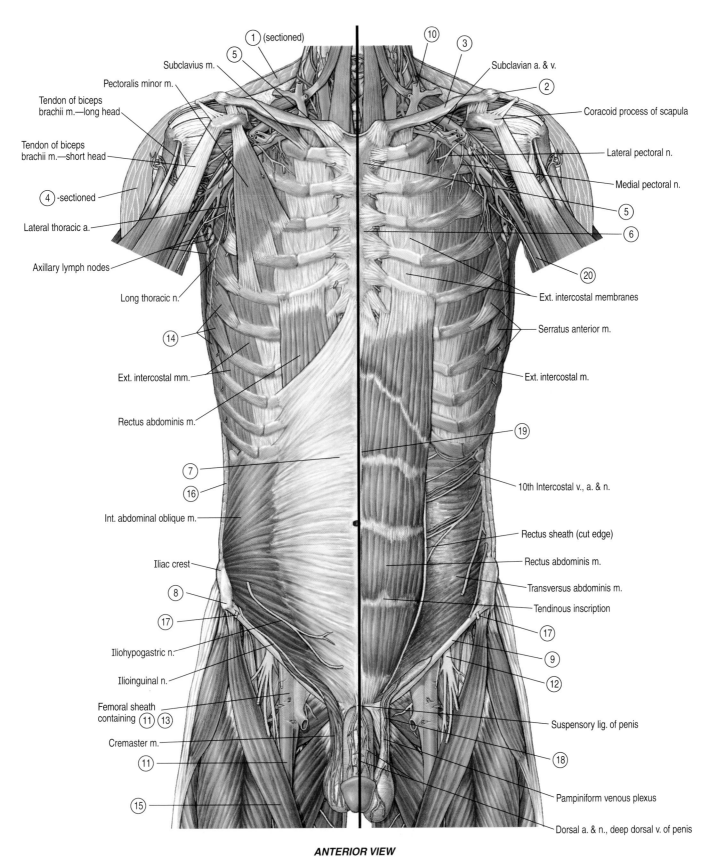

① (sectioned)

⑤

Subclavius m.

Pectoralis minor m.

Tendon of biceps
brachii m.—long head

Tendon of biceps
brachii m.—short head

④ -sectioned

Lateral thoracic a.

Axillary lymph nodes

Long thoracic n.

⑭

Ext. intercostal mm.

Rectus abdominis m.

⑦

⑯

Int. abdominal oblique m.

Iliac crest

⑧

⑰

Iliohypogastric n.

Ilioinguinal n.

Femoral sheath
containing ⑪ ⑬

Cremaster m.

⑪

⑮

⑩ ③

Subclavian a. & v.

②

Coracoid process of scapula

Lateral pectoral n.

Medial pectoral n.

⑤

⑥

⑳

Ext. intercostal membranes

Serratus anterior m.

Ext. intercostal m.

⑲

10th Intercostal v., a. & n.

Rectus sheath (cut edge)

Rectus abdominis m.

Transversus abdominis m.

Tendinous inscription

⑰

⑨

⑫

Suspensory lig. of penis

⑱

Pampiniform venous plexus

Dorsal a. & n., deep dorsal v. of penis

ANTERIOR VIEW

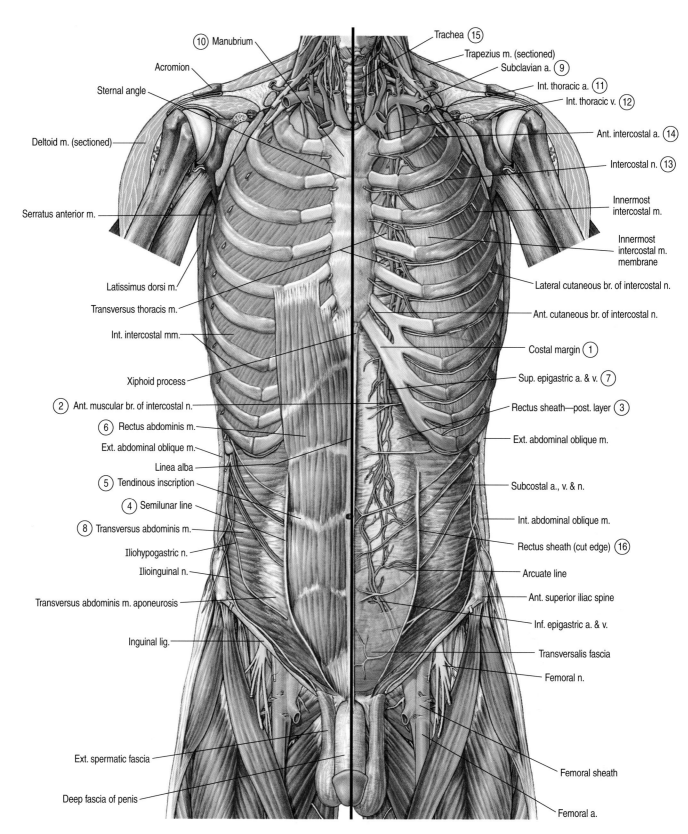

10 Manubrium

Acromion

Sternal angle

Deltoid m. (sectioned)

Serratus anterior m.

Latissimus dorsi m.

Transversus thoracis m.

Int. intercostal mm.

Xiphoid process

2 Ant. muscular br. of intercostal n.

6 Rectus abdominis m.

Ext. abdominal oblique m.

Linea alba

5 Tendinous inscription

4 Semilunar line

8 Transversus abdominis m.

Iliohypogastric n.

Ilioinguinal n.

Transversus abdominis m. aponeurosis

Inguinal lig.

Ext. spermatic fascia

Deep fascia of penis

Trachea 15

Trapezius m. (sectioned)

Subclavian a. 9

Int. thoracic a. 11

Int. thoracic v. 12

Ant. intercostal a. 14

Intercostal n. 13

Innermost intercostal m.

Innermost intercostal m. membrane

Lateral cutaneous br. of intercostal n.

Ant. cutaneous br. of intercostal n.

Costal margin 1

Sup. epigastric a. & v. 7

Rectus sheath—post. layer 3

Ext. abdominal oblique m.

Subcostal a., v. & n.

Int. abdominal oblique m.

Rectus sheath (cut edge) 16

Arcuate line

Ant. superior iliac spine

Inf. epigastric a. & v.

Transversalis fascia

Femoral n.

Femoral sheath

Femoral a.

ANTERIOR VIEW

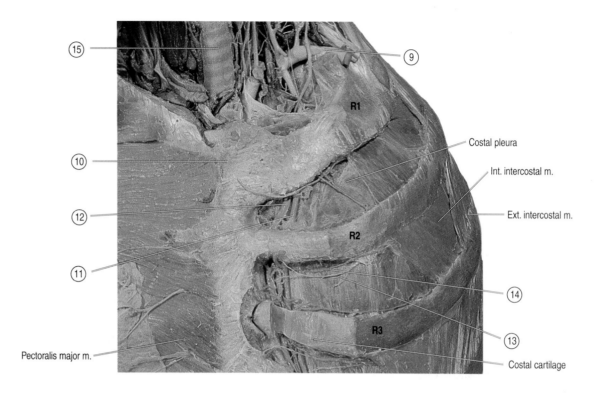

Costal pleura

Int. intercostal m.

Ext. intercostal m.

R1

R2

R3

Pectoralis major m.

Costal cartilage

ANTERIOR VIEW OF LEFT SUPERIOR PORTION OF THORACIC WALL

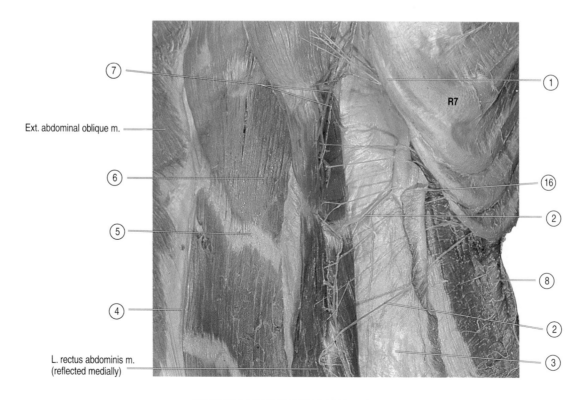

R7

Ext. abdominal oblique m.

L. rectus abdominis m.
(reflected medially)

ANTERIOR VIEW OF SUBCOSTAL PORTION OF ABDOMINAL WALL

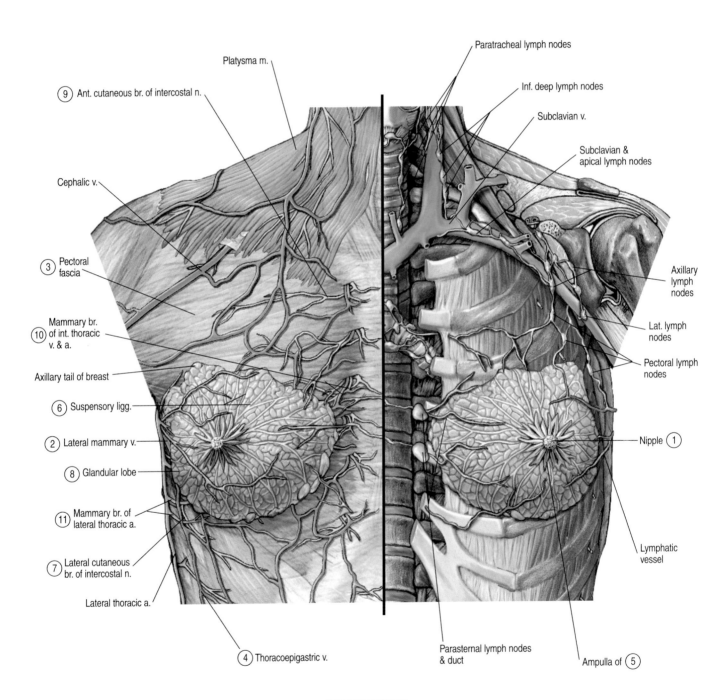

Platysma m.

Paratracheal lymph nodes

⑨ Ant. cutaneous br. of intercostal n.

Inf. deep lymph nodes

Subclavian v.

Subclavian & apical lymph nodes

Cephalic v.

③ Pectoral fascia

Axillary lymph nodes

Mammary br.
⑩ of int. thoracic v. & a.

Lat. lymph nodes

Axillary tail of breast

Pectoral lymph nodes

⑥ Suspensory ligg.

② Lateral mammary v.

Nipple ①

⑧ Glandular lobe

⑪ Mammary br. of lateral thoracic a.

⑦ Lateral cutaneous br. of intercostal n.

Lymphatic vessel

Lateral thoracic a.

④ Thoracoepigastric v.

Parasternal lymph nodes & duct

Ampulla of ⑤

ANTERIOR VIEW

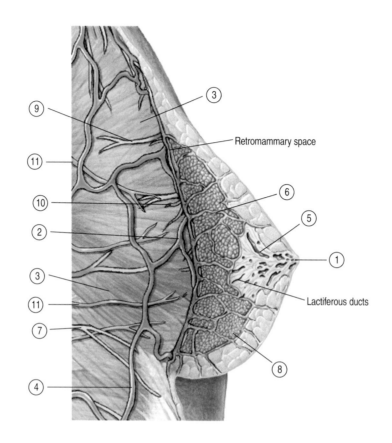

Retromammary space

Lactiferous ducts

RIGHT LATERAL VIEW OF MEDIAN SECTIONED BREAST

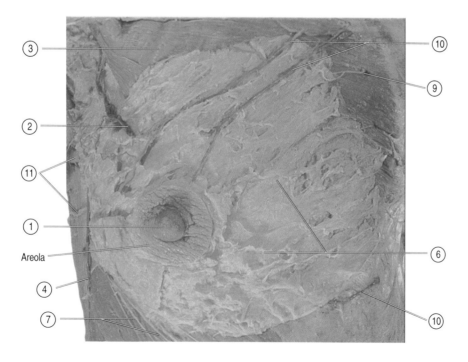

Areola

ANTERIOR VIEW OF RIGHT BREAST

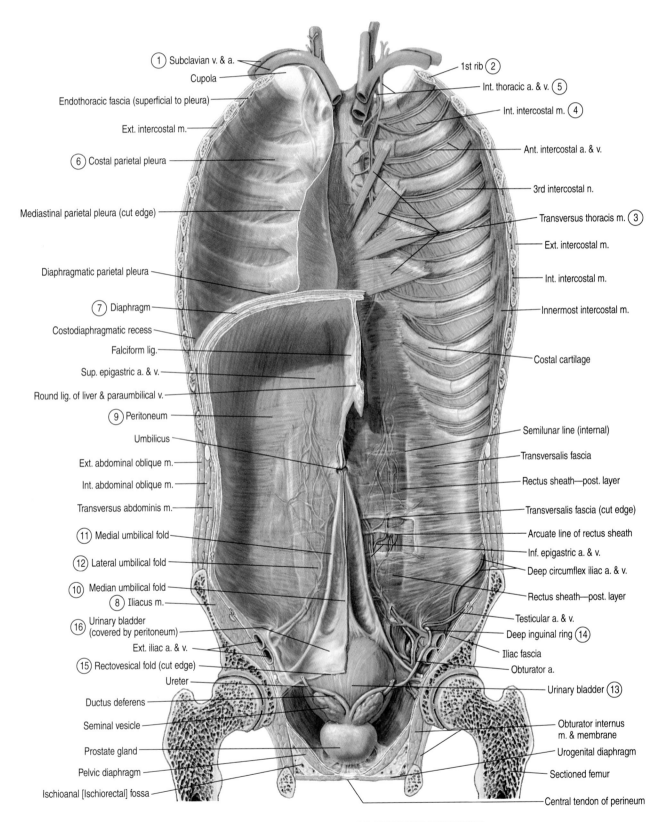

① Subclavian v. & a.

Cupola

Endothoracic fascia (superficial to pleura)

Ext. intercostal m.

⑥ Costal parietal pleura

Mediastinal parietal pleura (cut edge)

Diaphragmatic parietal pleura

⑦ Diaphragm

Costodiaphragmatic recess

Falciform lig.

Sup. epigastric a. & v.

Round lig. of liver & paraumbilical v.

⑨ Peritoneum

Umbilicus

Ext. abdominal oblique m.

Int. abdominal oblique m.

Transversus abdominis m.

⑪ Medial umbilical fold

⑫ Lateral umbilical fold

⑩ Median umbilical fold

⑧ Iliacus m.

⑯ Urinary bladder (covered by peritoneum)

Ext. iliac a. & v.

⑮ Rectovesical fold (cut edge)

Ureter

Ductus deferens

Seminal vesicle

Prostate gland

Pelvic diaphragm

Ischioanal [Ischiorectal] fossa

1st rib ②

Int. thoracic a. & v. ⑤

Int. intercostal m. ④

Ant. intercostal a. & v.

3rd intercostal n.

Transversus thoracis m. ③

Ext. intercostal m.

Int. intercostal m.

Innermost intercostal m.

Costal cartilage

Semilunar line (internal)

Transversalis fascia

Rectus sheath—post. layer

Transversalis fascia (cut edge)

Arcuate line of rectus sheath

Inf. epigastric a. & v.

Deep circumflex iliac a. & v.

Rectus sheath—post. layer

Testicular a. & v.

Deep inguinal ring ⑭

Iliac fascia

Obturator a.

Urinary bladder ⑬

Obturator internus m. & membrane

Urogenital diaphragm

Sectioned femur

Central tendon of perineum

POSTERIOR (INTERNAL) VIEW OF ANTERIOR BODY WALL

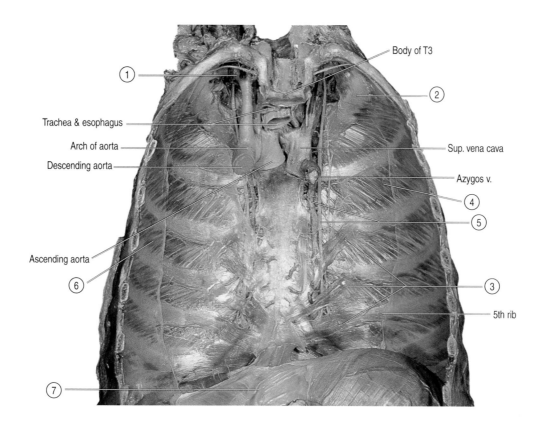

Body of T3

① ②

Trachea & esophagus

Arch of aorta

Descending aorta

Sup. vena cava

Azygos v.

④

⑤

Ascending aorta

⑥ ③

5th rib

⑦

POSTERIOR (INTERNAL) VIEW OF ANTERIOR THORACIC WALL

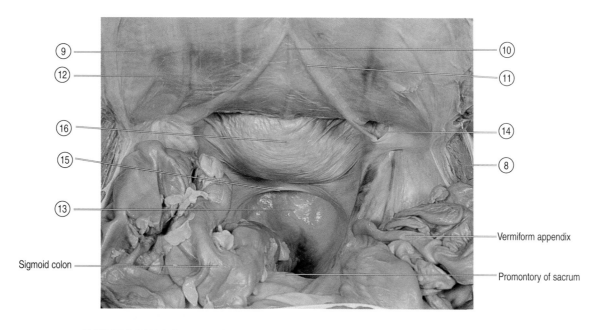

⑨ ⑩

⑫ ⑪

⑯ ⑭

⑮ ⑧

⑬

Vermiform appendix

Sigmoid colon

Promontory of sacrum

POSTEROSUPERIOR VIEW OF ANTERIOR ABDOMINAL WALL & PELVIC CONTENTS

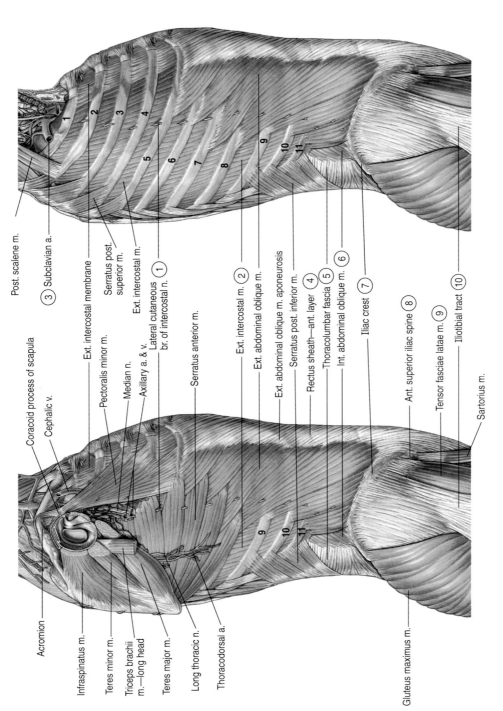

Post. scalene m.

③ Subclavian a.

Ext. intercostal membrane

Serratus post. superior m.

Ext. intercostal m.

① Lateral cutaneous br. of intercostal n.

② Ext. intercostal m.

Ext. abdominal oblique m.

Ext. abdominal oblique m. aponeurosis

Serratus post. inferior m.

④ Rectus sheath—ant. layer

⑤ Thoracolumbar fascia

⑥ Int. abdominal oblique m.

⑦ Iliac crest

⑧ Ant. superior iliac spine

⑨ Tensor fasciae latae m.

⑩ Iliotibial tract

Sartorius m.

Coracoid process of scapula

Cephalic v.

Pectoralis minor m.

Median n.

Axillary a. & v.

Serratus anterior m.

Acromion

Infraspinatus m.

Teres minor m.

Triceps brachii m.—long head

Teres major m.

Long thoracic n.

Thoracodorsal a.

Gluteus maximus m.

RIGHT LATERAL VIEWS

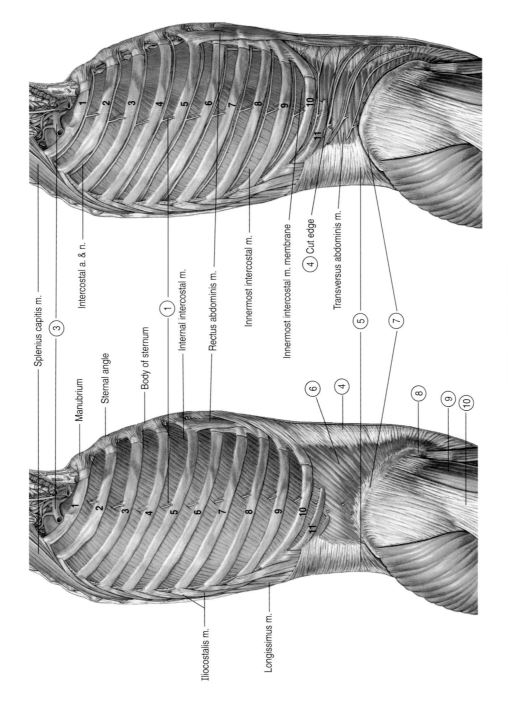

Splenius capitis m.

③

Intercostal a. & n.

Manubrium

Sternal angle

Body of sternum

①

Internal intercostal m.

Rectus abdominis m.

Innermost intercostal m.

Innermost intercostal m. membrane

④ Cut edge

Transversus abdominis m.

⑥

④

⑤

⑦

⑧

⑨

⑩

Iliocostalis m.

Longissimus m.

RIGHT LATERAL VIEWS

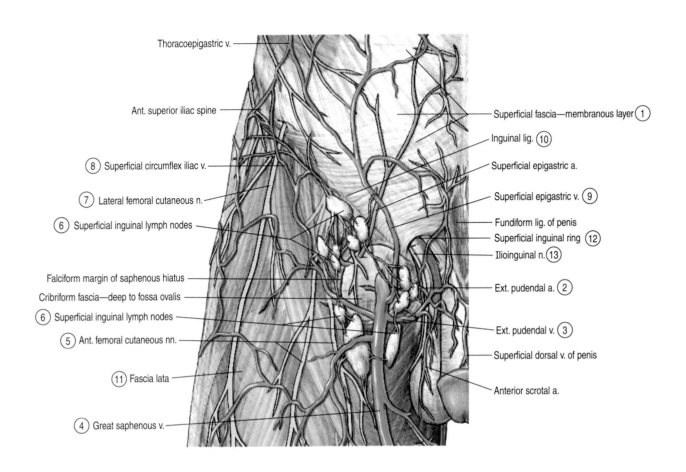

Thoracoepigastric v.

Ant. superior iliac spine

(8) Superficial circumflex iliac v.

(7) Lateral femoral cutaneous n.

(6) Superficial inguinal lymph nodes

Falciform margin of saphenous hiatus

Cribriform fascia—deep to fossa ovalis

(6) Superficial inguinal lymph nodes

(5) Ant. femoral cutaneous nn.

(11) Fascia lata

(4) Great saphenous v.

Superficial fascia—membranous layer (1)

Inguinal lig. (10)

Superficial epigastric a.

Superficial epigastric v. (9)

Fundiform lig. of penis

Superficial inguinal ring (12)

Ilioinguinal n. (13)

Ext. pudendal a. (2)

Ext. pudendal v. (3)

Superficial dorsal v. of penis

Anterior scrotal a.

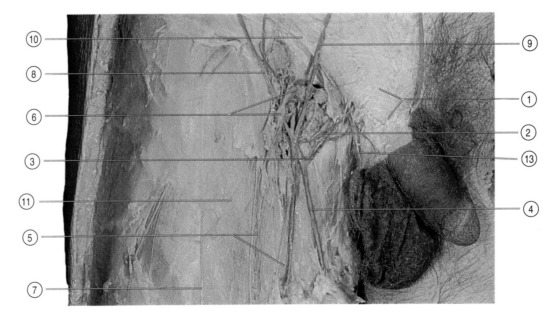

ANTERIOR VIEWS OF RIGHT SIDE

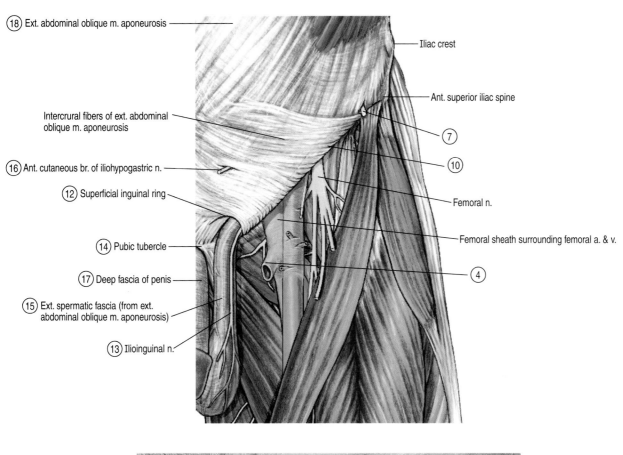

(18) Ext. abdominal oblique m. aponeurosis

Iliac crest

Ant. superior iliac spine

Intercrural fibers of ext. abdominal oblique m. aponeurosis

(7)

(10)

(16) Ant. cutaneous br. of iliohypogastric n.

Femoral n.

(12) Superficial inguinal ring

Femoral sheath surrounding femoral a. & v.

(14) Pubic tubercle

(17) Deep fascia of penis

(4)

(15) Ext. spermatic fascia (from ext. abdominal oblique m. aponeurosis)

(13) Ilioinguinal n.

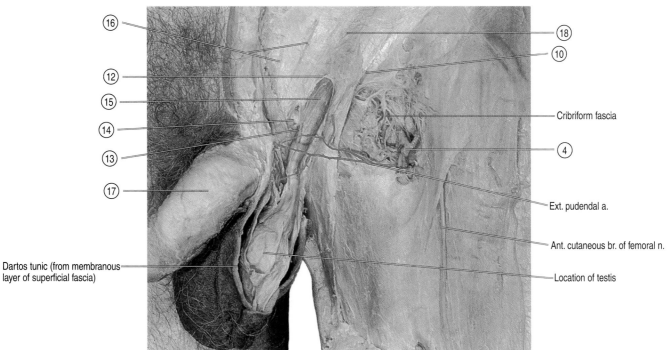

(16)

(18)

(10)

(12)

(15)

Cribriform fascia

(14)

(13)

(4)

(17)

Ext. pudendal a.

Ant. cutaneous br. of femoral n.

Dartos tunic (from membranous layer of superficial fascia)

Location of testis

ANTERIOR VIEWS OF LEFT SIDE

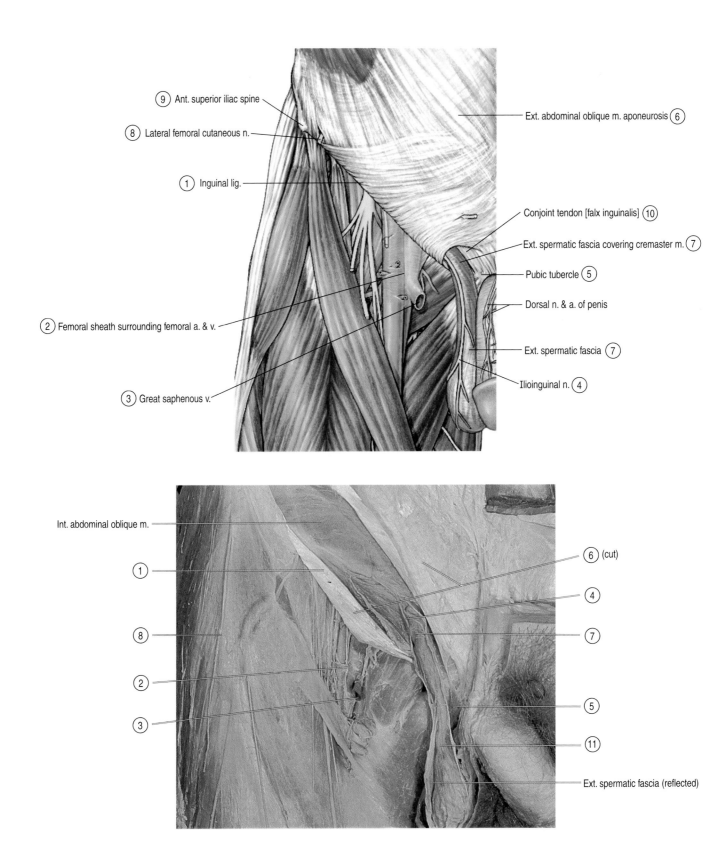

9 Ant. superior iliac spine

8 Lateral femoral cutaneous n.

1 Inguinal lig.

2 Femoral sheath surrounding femoral a. & v.

3 Great saphenous v.

Ext. abdominal oblique m. aponeurosis 6

Conjoint tendon [falx inguinalis] 10

Ext. spermatic fascia covering cremaster m. 7

Pubic tubercle 5

Dorsal n. & a. of penis

Ext. spermatic fascia 7

Ilioinguinal n. 4

Int. abdominal oblique m.

1

8

2

3

6 (cut)

4

7

5

11

Ext. spermatic fascia (reflected)

ANTERIOR VIEWS OF RIGHT SIDE

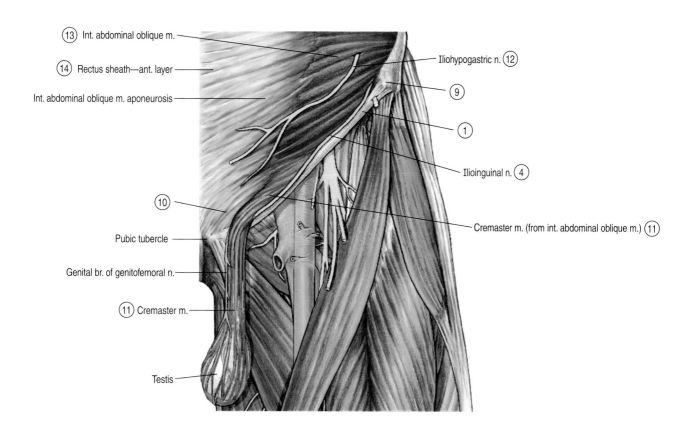

(13) Int. abdominal oblique m.

(14) Rectus sheath—ant. layer

Int. abdominal oblique m. aponeurosis

Iliohypogastric n. (12)

(9)

(1)

Ilioinguinal n. (4)

(10)

Cremaster m. (from int. abdominal oblique m.) (11)

Pubic tubercle

Genital br. of genitofemoral n.

(11) Cremaster m.

Testis

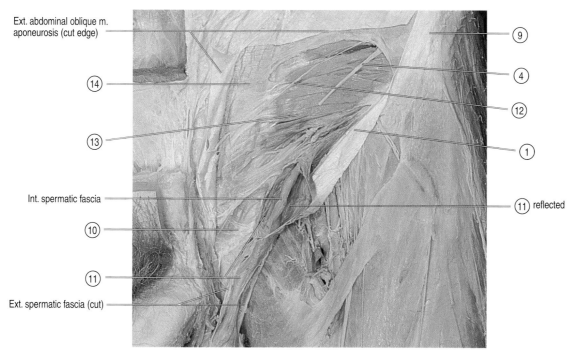

Ext. abdominal oblique m. aponeurosis (cut edge)

(9)

(4)

(14)

(12)

(13)

(1)

Int. spermatic fascia

(11) reflected

(10)

(11)

Ext. spermatic fascia (cut)

ANTERIOR VIEWS OF LEFT SIDE

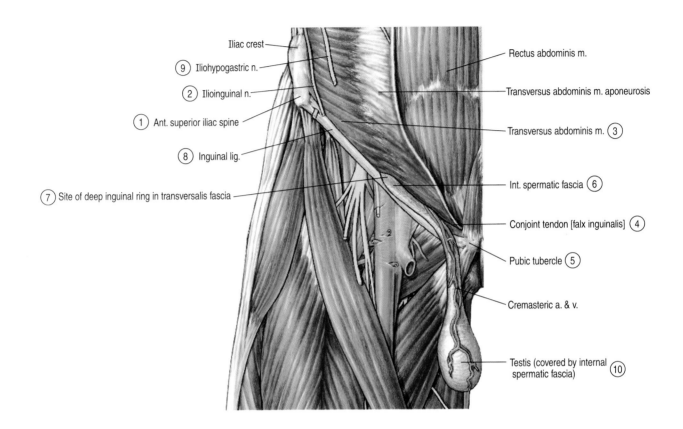

Iliac crest

(9) Iliohypogastric n.

(2) Ilioinguinal n.

(1) Ant. superior iliac spine

(8) Inguinal lig.

(7) Site of deep inguinal ring in transversalis fascia

Rectus abdominis m.

Transversus abdominis m. aponeurosis

Transversus abdominis m. (3)

Int. spermatic fascia (6)

Conjoint tendon [falx inguinalis] (4)

Pubic tubercle (5)

Cremasteric a. & v.

Testis (covered by internal spermatic fascia) (10)

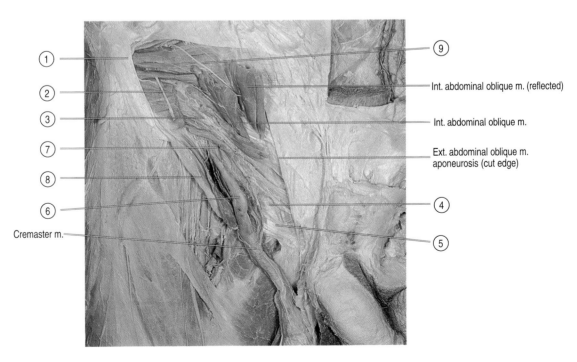

(1)

(2)

(3)

(7)

(8)

(6)

Cremaster m.

(9)

Int. abdominal oblique m. (reflected)

Int. abdominal oblique m.

Ext. abdominal oblique m. aponeurosis (cut edge)

(4)

(5)

ANTERIOR VIEWS

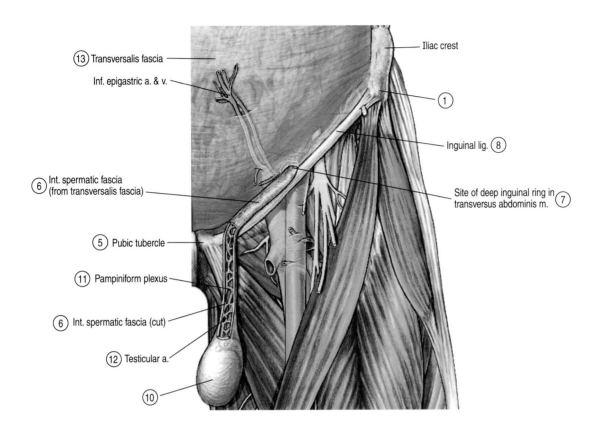

Transversalis fascia (13)

Inf. epigastric a. & v.

Iliac crest

(1)

Inguinal lig. (8)

Int. spermatic fascia (6) (from transversalis fascia)

Site of deep inguinal ring in transversus abdominis m. (7)

(5) Pubic tubercle

(11) Pampiniform plexus

(6) Int. spermatic fascia (cut)

(12) Testicular a.

(10)

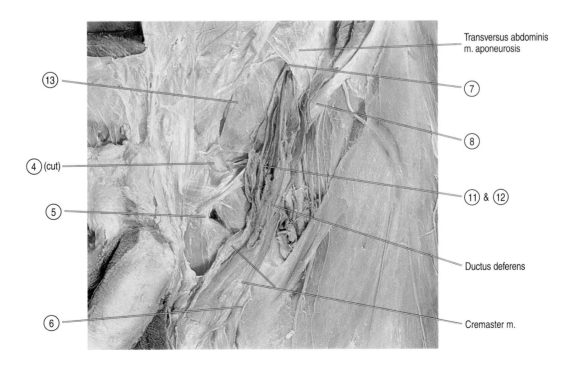

(13)

Transversus abdominis m. aponeurosis

(7)

(8)

(4) (cut)

(5)

(11) & (12)

Ductus deferens

(6)

Cremaster m.

ANTERIOR VIEWS

Superficial Back
Plate 1.53

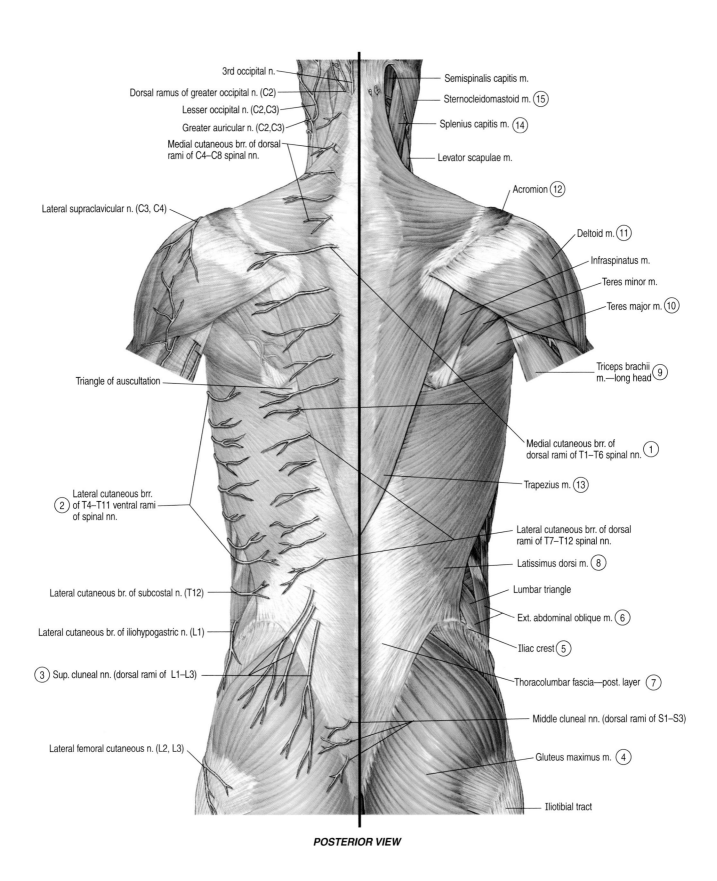

3rd occipital n.

Dorsal ramus of greater occipital n. (C2)

Lesser occipital n. (C2,C3)

Greater auricular n. (C2,C3)

Medial cutaneous brr. of dorsal rami of C4–C8 spinal nn.

Lateral supraclavicular n. (C3, C4)

Triangle of auscultation

Lateral cutaneous brr. (2) of T4–T11 ventral rami of spinal nn.

Lateral cutaneous br. of subcostal n. (T12)

Lateral cutaneous br. of iliohypogastric n. (L1)

(3) Sup. cluneal nn. (dorsal rami of L1–L3)

Lateral femoral cutaneous n. (L2, L3)

Semispinalis capitis m.

Sternocleidomastoid m. (15)

Splenius capitis m. (14)

Levator scapulae m.

Acromion (12)

Deltoid m. (11)

Infraspinatus m.

Teres minor m.

Teres major m. (10)

Triceps brachii m.—long head (9)

Medial cutaneous brr. of dorsal rami of T1–T6 spinal nn. (1)

Trapezius m. (13)

Lateral cutaneous brr. of dorsal rami of T7–T12 spinal nn.

Latissimus dorsi m. (8)

Lumbar triangle

Ext. abdominal oblique m. (6)

Iliac crest (5)

Thoracolumbar fascia—post. layer (7)

Middle cluneal nn. (dorsal rami of S1–S3)

Gluteus maximus m. (4)

Iliotibial tract

POSTERIOR VIEW

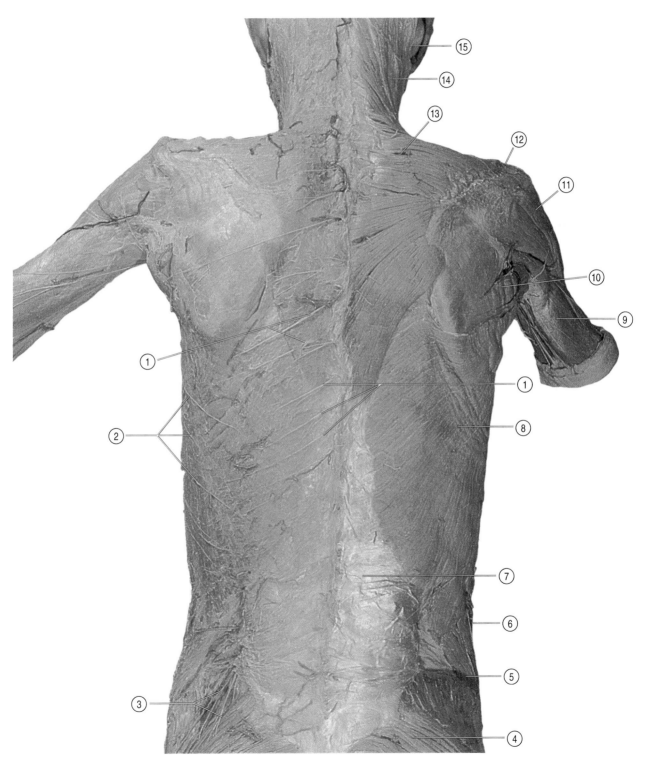

POSTERIOR VIEW

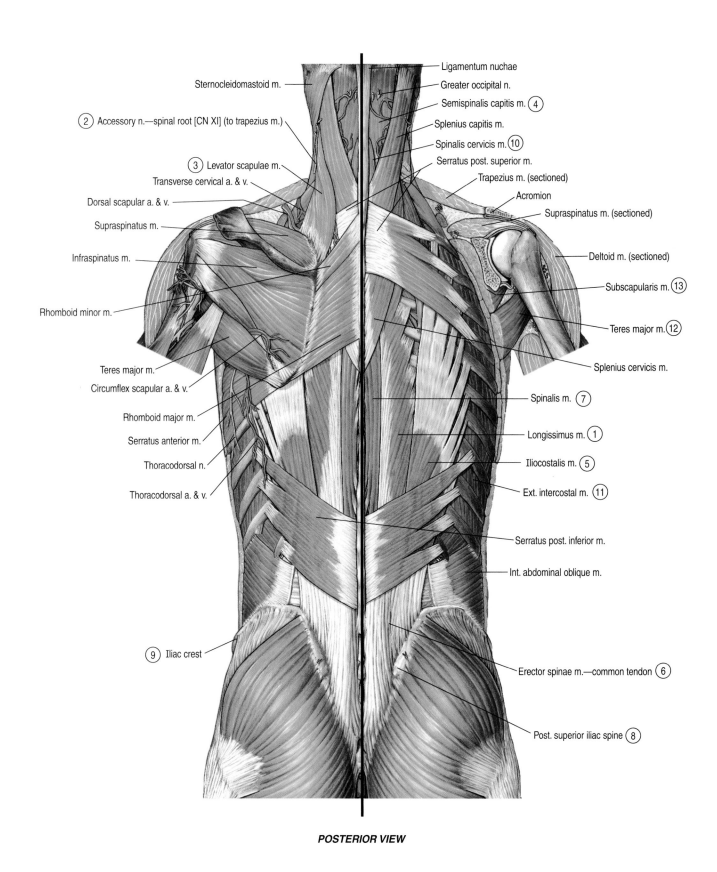

Ligamentum nuchae

Sternocleidomastoid m.

Greater occipital n.

Semispinalis capitis m. (4)

(2) Accessory n.—spinal root [CN XI] (to trapezius m.)

Splenius capitis m.

Spinalis cervicis m. (10)

(3) Levator scapulae m.

Serratus post. superior m.

Transverse cervical a. & v.

Trapezius m. (sectioned)

Acromion

Dorsal scapular a. & v.

Supraspinatus m. (sectioned)

Supraspinatus m.

Deltoid m. (sectioned)

Infraspinatus m.

Subscapularis m. (13)

Rhomboid minor m.

Teres major m. (12)

Splenius cervicis m.

Teres major m.

Circumflex scapular a. & v.

Spinalis m. (7)

Rhomboid major m.

Longissimus m. (1)

Serratus anterior m.

Iliocostalis m. (5)

Thoracodorsal n.

Ext. intercostal m. (11)

Thoracodorsal a. & v.

Serratus post. inferior m.

Int. abdominal oblique m.

(9) Iliac crest

Erector spinae m.—common tendon (6)

Post. superior iliac spine (8)

POSTERIOR VIEW

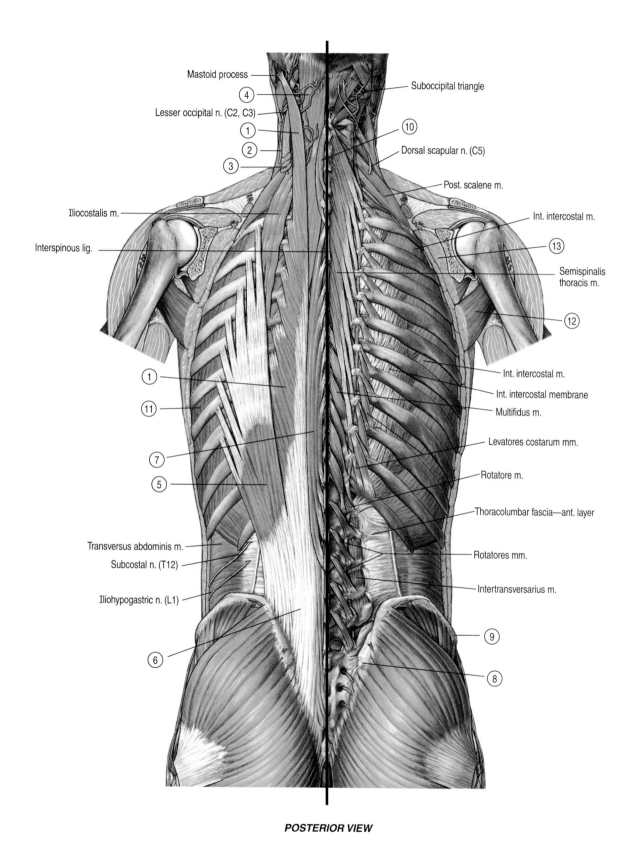

Mastoid process

④

Lesser occipital n. (C2, C3)

①

②

③

Iliocostalis m.

Interspinous lig.

①

⑪

⑦

⑤

Transversus abdominis m.

Subcostal n. (T12)

Iliohypogastric n. (L1)

⑥

Suboccipital triangle

⑩

Dorsal scapular n. (C5)

Post. scalene m.

Int. intercostal m.

⑬

Semispinalis
thoracis m.

⑫

Int. intercostal m.

Int. intercostal membrane

Multifidus m.

Levatores costarum mm.

Rotatore m.

Thoracolumbar fascia—ant. layer

Rotatores mm.

Intertransversarius m.

⑨

⑧

POSTERIOR VIEW

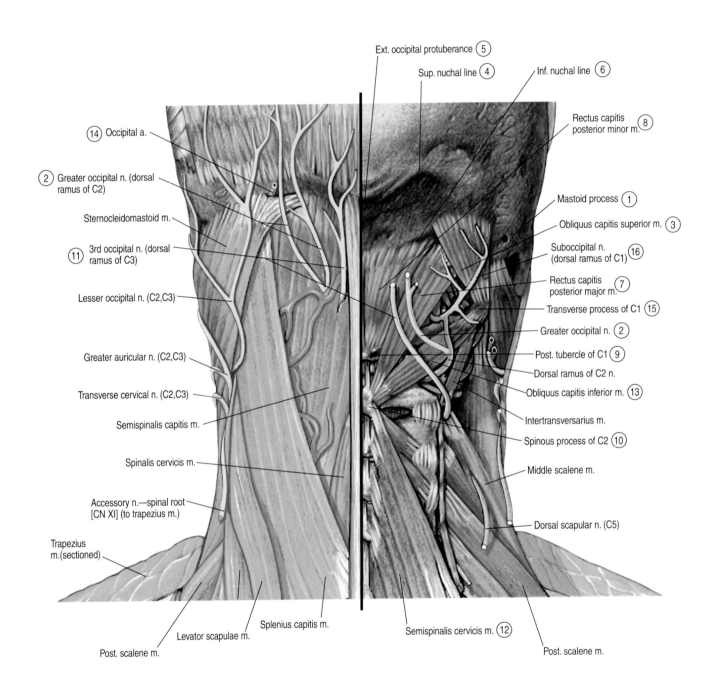

Ext. occipital protuberance ⑤

Sup. nuchal line ④

Inf. nuchal line ⑥

⑭ Occipital a.

② Greater occipital n. (dorsal ramus of C2)

Sternocleidomastoid m.

⑪ 3rd occipital n. (dorsal ramus of C3)

Lesser occipital n. (C2,C3)

Greater auricular n. (C2,C3)

Transverse cervical n. (C2,C3)

Semispinalis capitis m.

Spinalis cervicis m.

Accessory n.—spinal root [CN XI] (to trapezius m.)

Trapezius m.(sectioned)

Post. scalene m.

Levator scapulae m.

Splenius capitis m.

Rectus capitis posterior minor m. ⑧

Mastoid process ①

Obliquus capitis superior m. ③

Suboccipital n. (dorsal ramus of C1) ⑯

Rectus capitis posterior major m. ⑦

Transverse process of C1 ⑮

Greater occipital n. ②

Post. tubercle of C1 ⑨

Dorsal ramus of C2 n.

Obliquus capitis inferior m. ⑬

Intertransversarius m.

Spinous process of C2 ⑩

Middle scalene m.

Dorsal scapular n. (C5)

Semispinalis cervicis m. ⑫

Post. scalene m.

POSTERIOR VIEW

POSTERIOR VIEW OF CRANIAL BASE & UPPER CERVICAL REGION

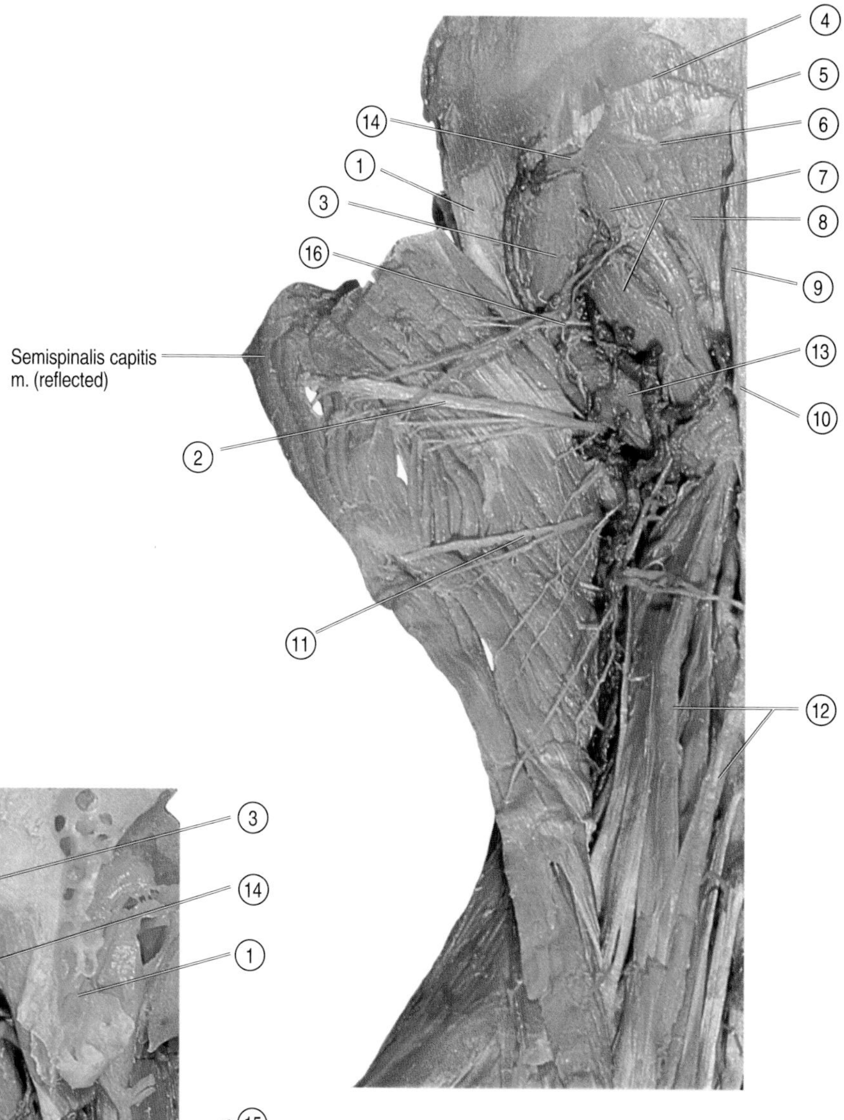

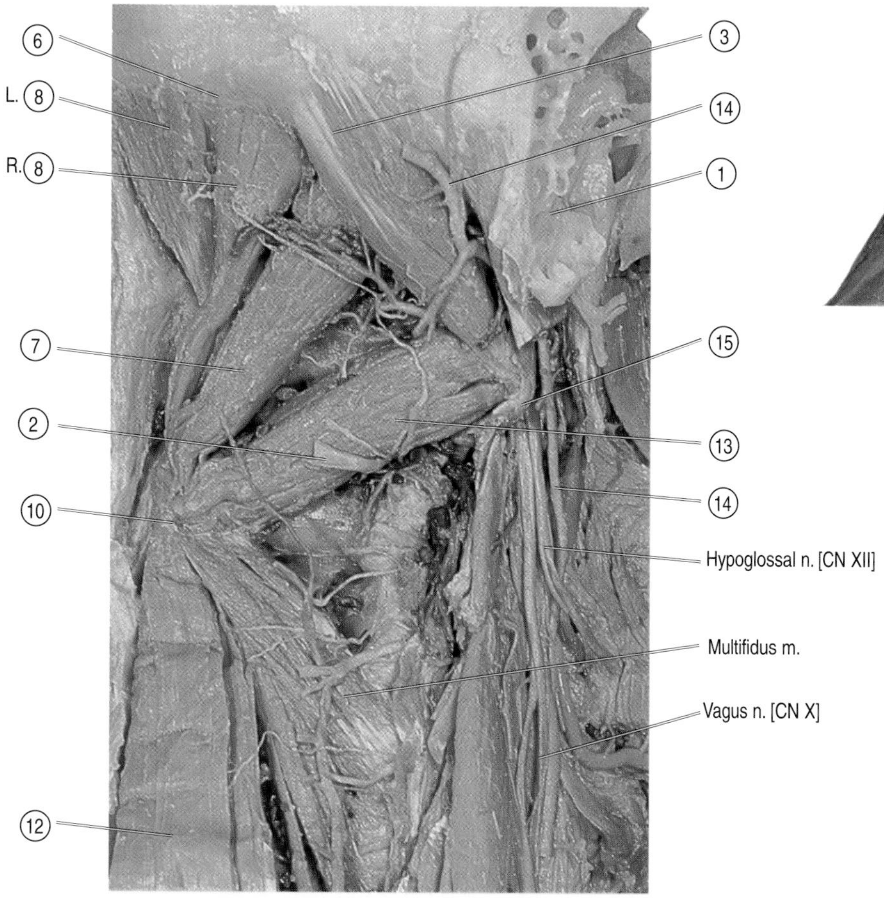

4
5
14
6
1
7
3
8
16
9
Semispinalis capitis m. (reflected)
13
10
2
11
12

6
3
L. 8
14
R. 8
1
7
15
2
13
10
14
Hypoglossal n. [CN XII]
Multifidus m.
Vagus n. [CN X]
12

POSTERIOR VIEW OF RIGHT SUBOCCIPITAL TRIANGLE

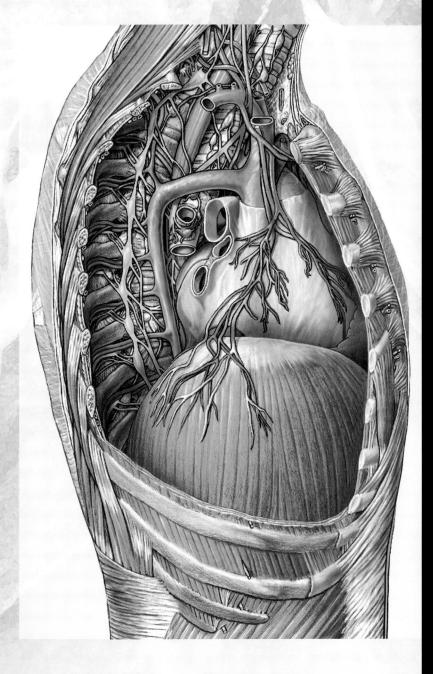

Thorax

Chapter 2

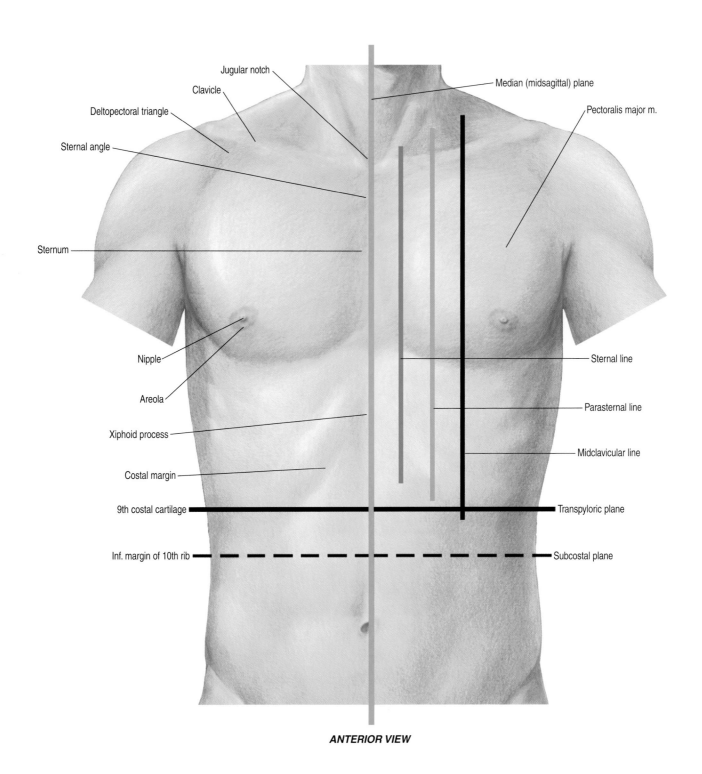

Jugular notch

Clavicle

Deltopectoral triangle

Sternal angle

Sternum

Nipple

Areola

Xiphoid process

Costal margin

9th costal cartilage

Inf. margin of 10th rib

Median (midsagittal) plane

Pectoralis major m.

Sternal line

Parasternal line

Midclavicular line

Transpyloric plane

Subcostal plane

ANTERIOR VIEW

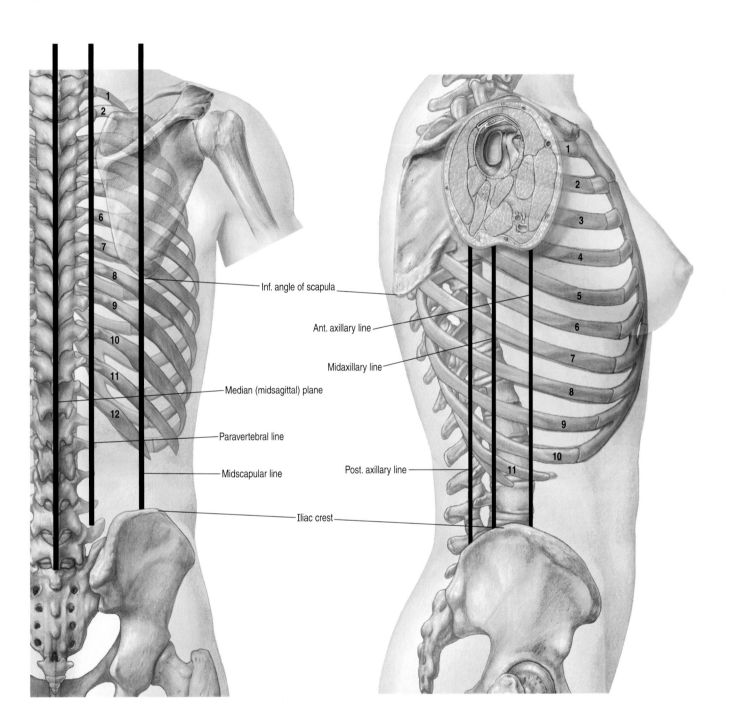

1
2

6

7

8

9

10

11

12

Inf. angle of scapula

Ant. axillary line

Midaxillary line

Median (midsagittal) plane

Paravertebral line

Midscapular line

Post. axillary line

Iliac crest

1

2

3

4

5

6

7

8

9

10

11

POSTERIOR VIEW

RIGHT LATERAL VIEW

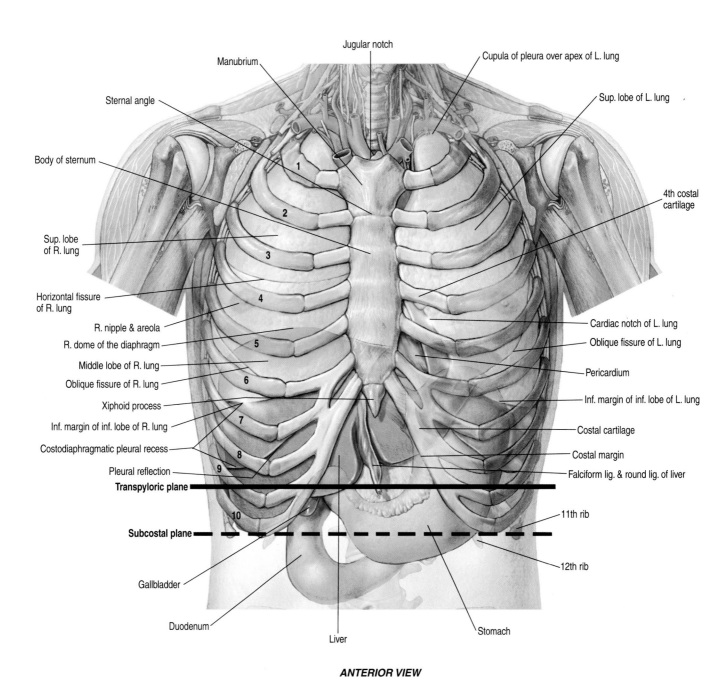

Jugular notch

Manubrium

Cupula of pleura over apex of L. lung

Sternal angle

Sup. lobe of L. lung

Body of sternum

1

4th costal cartilage

2

Sup. lobe of R. lung

3

Horizontal fissure of R. lung

4

Cardiac notch of L. lung

R. nipple & areola

5

Oblique fissure of L. lung

R. dome of the diaphragm

Pericardium

Middle lobe of R. lung

6

Oblique fissure of R. lung

Inf. margin of inf. lobe of L. lung

Xiphoid process

7

Inf. margin of inf. lobe of R. lung

Costal cartilage

Costodiaphragmatic pleural recess

8

Costal margin

9

Pleural reflection

Falciform lig. & round lig. of liver

Transpyloric plane

10

11th rib

Subcostal plane

12th rib

Gallbladder

Duodenum

Liver

Stomach

ANTERIOR VIEW

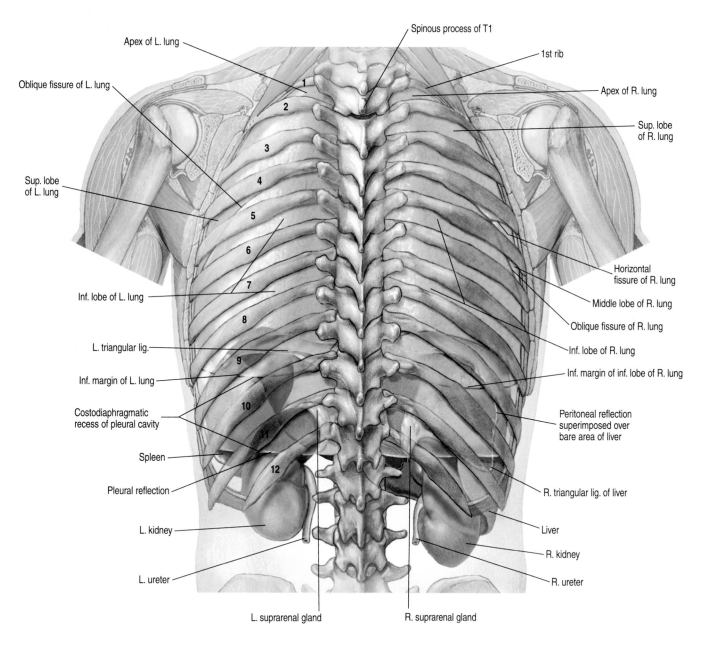

Spinous process of T1

1st rib

Apex of L. lung

Oblique fissure of L. lung

Apex of R. lung

Sup. lobe of R. lung

Sup. lobe of L. lung

Horizontal fissure of R. lung

Middle lobe of R. lung

Inf. lobe of L. lung

Oblique fissure of R. lung

Inf. lobe of R. lung

L. triangular lig.

Inf. margin of inf. lobe of R. lung

Inf. margin of L. lung

Costodiaphragmatic recess of pleural cavity

Peritoneal reflection superimposed over bare area of liver

Spleen

R. triangular lig. of liver

Pleural reflection

Liver

L. kidney

R. kidney

L. ureter

R. ureter

L. suprarenal gland

R. suprarenal gland

1
2
3
4
5
6
7
8
9
10
11
12

POSTERIOR VIEW

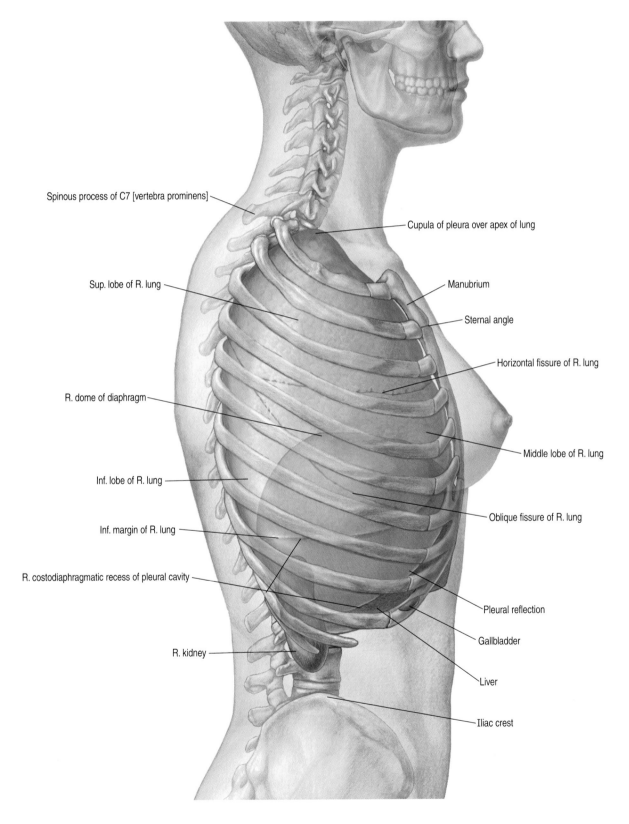

Spinous process of C7 [vertebra prominens]

Sup. lobe of R. lung

R. dome of diaphragm

Inf. lobe of R. lung

Inf. margin of R. lung

R. costodiaphragmatic recess of pleural cavity

R. kidney

Cupula of pleura over apex of lung

Manubrium

Sternal angle

Horizontal fissure of R. lung

Middle lobe of R. lung

Oblique fissure of R. lung

Pleural reflection

Gallbladder

Liver

Iliac crest

RIGHT LATERAL VIEW

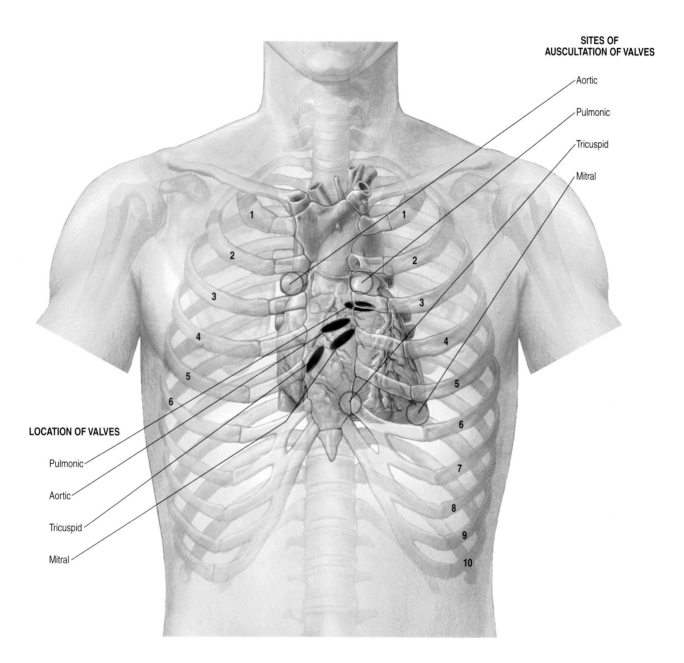

SITES OF
AUSCULTATION OF VALVES

Aortic

Pulmonic

Tricuspid

Mitral

LOCATION OF VALVES

Pulmonic

Aortic

Tricuspid

Mitral

ANTERIOR VIEW

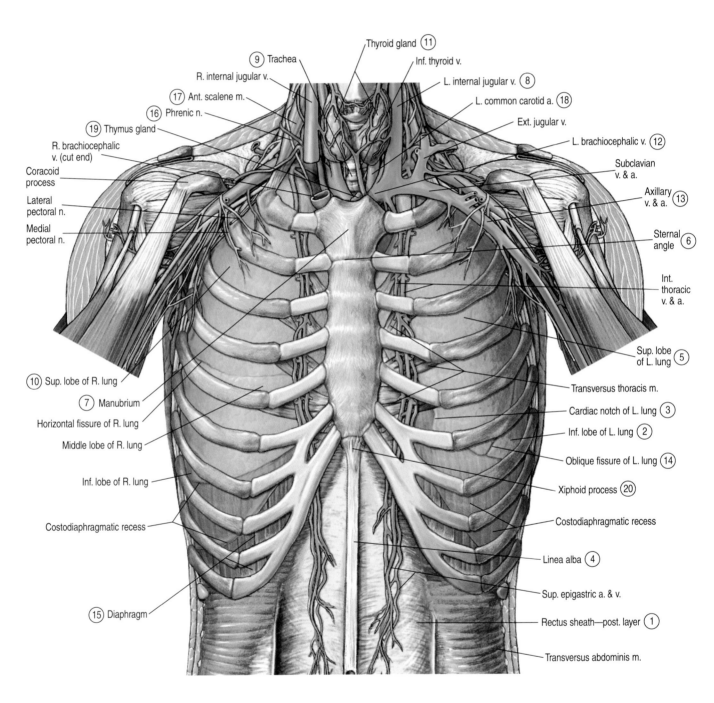

Thyroid gland ⑪

⑨ Trachea

Inf. thyroid v.

R. internal jugular v.

L. internal jugular v. ⑧

⑰ Ant. scalene m.

L. common carotid a. ⑱

⑯ Phrenic n.

Ext. jugular v.

⑲ Thymus gland

L. brachiocephalic v. ⑫

R. brachiocephalic
v. (cut end)

Subclavian
v. & a.

Coracoid
process

Axillary
v. & a. ⑬

Lateral
pectoral n.

Sternal
angle ⑥

Medial
pectoral n.

Int.
thoracic
v. & a.

Sup. lobe
of L. lung ⑤

⑩ Sup. lobe of R. lung

Transversus thoracis m.

⑦ Manubrium

Cardiac notch of L. lung ③

Horizontal fissure of R. lung

Inf. lobe of L. lung ②

Middle lobe of R. lung

Oblique fissure of L. lung ⑭

Inf. lobe of R. lung

Xiphoid process ⑳

Costodiaphragmatic recess

Costodiaphragmatic recess

Linea alba ④

Sup. epigastric a. & v.

⑮ Diaphragm

Rectus sheath—post. layer ①

Transversus abdominis m.

ANTERIOR VIEW

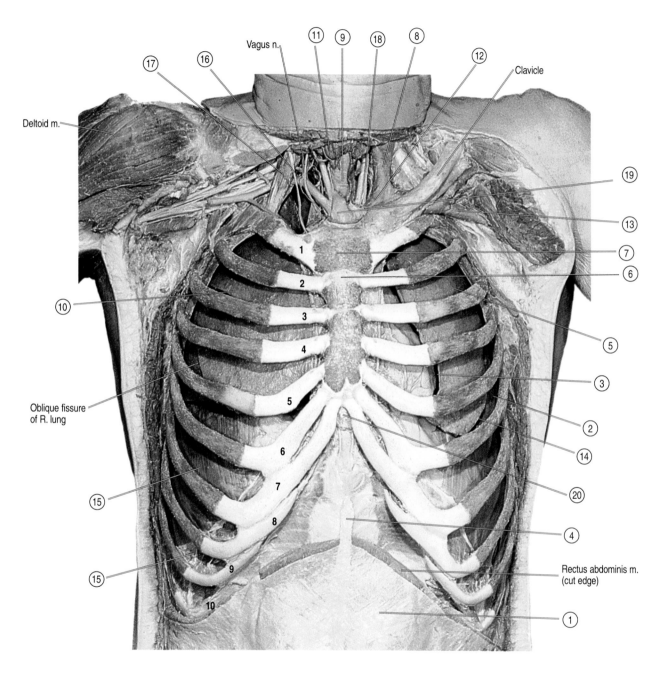

Vagus n.

Clavicle

Deltoid m.

Oblique fissure
of R. lung

Rectus abdominis m.
(cut edge)

ANTERIOR VIEW

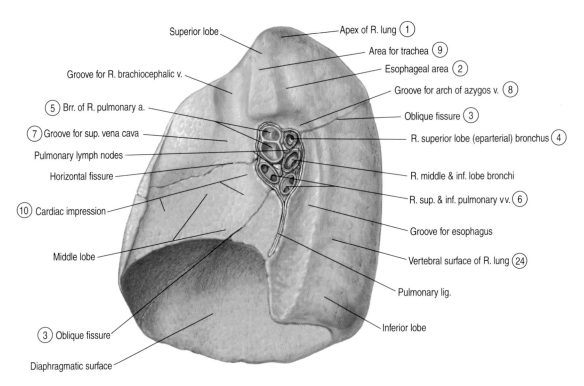

Superior lobe

Apex of R. lung ①

Area for trachea ⑨

Groove for R. brachiocephalic v.

Esophageal area ②

Groove for arch of azygos v. ⑧

⑤ Brr. of R. pulmonary a.

Oblique fissure ③

⑦ Groove for sup. vena cava

R. superior lobe (eparterial) bronchus ④

Pulmonary lymph nodes

R. middle & inf. lobe bronchi

Horizontal fissure

R. sup. & inf. pulmonary vv. ⑥

⑩ Cardiac impression

Groove for esophagus

Middle lobe

Vertebral surface of R. lung ㉔

③ Oblique fissure

Pulmonary lig.

Diaphragmatic surface

Inferior lobe

MEDIAL VIEW OF RIGHT LUNG

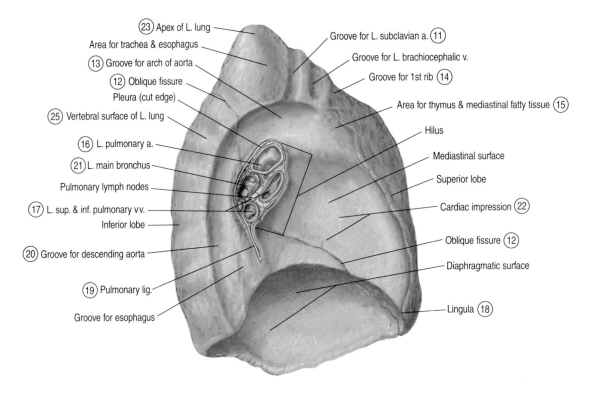

㉓ Apex of L. lung

Groove for L. subclavian a. ⑪

Area for trachea & esophagus

Groove for L. brachiocephalic v.

⑬ Groove for arch of aorta

Groove for 1st rib ⑭

⑫ Oblique fissure

Area for thymus & mediastinal fatty tissue ⑮

Pleura (cut edge)

㉕ Vertebral surface of L. lung

Hilus

⑯ L. pulmonary a.

Mediastinal surface

㉑ L. main bronchus

Superior lobe

Pulmonary lymph nodes

Cardiac impression ㉒

⑰ L. sup. & inf. pulmonary vv.

Inferior lobe

Oblique fissure ⑫

⑳ Groove for descending aorta

Diaphragmatic surface

⑲ Pulmonary lig.

Lingula ⑱

Groove for esophagus

MEDIAL VIEW OF LEFT LUNG

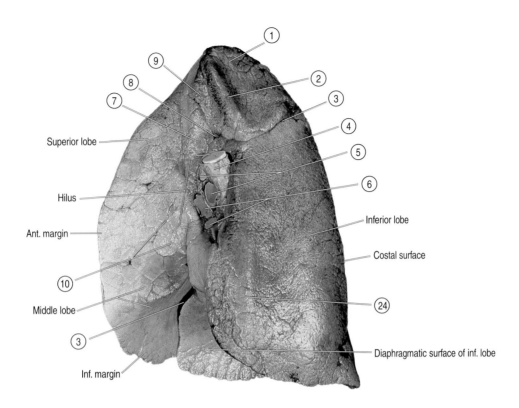

Superior lobe

Hilus

Ant. margin

Middle lobe

Inf. margin

Inferior lobe

Costal surface

Diaphragmatic surface of inf. lobe

POSTEROMEDIAL VIEW OF RIGHT LUNG

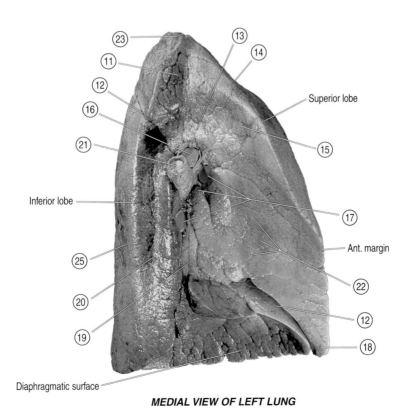

Superior lobe

Inferior lobe

Ant. margin

Diaphragmatic surface

MEDIAL VIEW OF LEFT LUNG

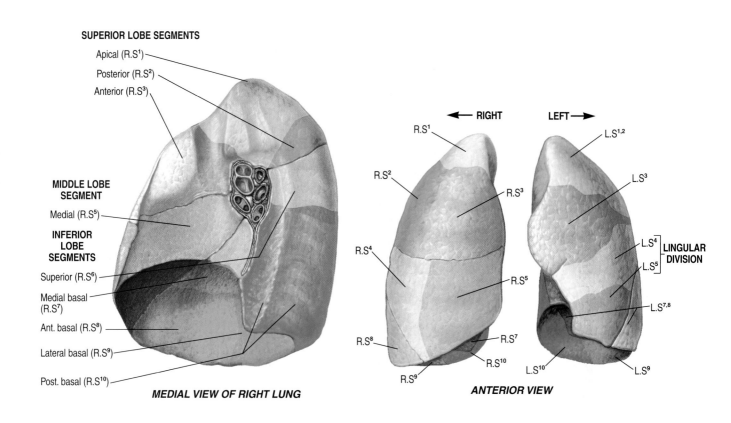

SUPERIOR LOBE SEGMENTS

Apical (R.S^1)

Posterior (R.S^2)

Anterior (R.S^3)

MIDDLE LOBE SEGMENT

Medial (R.S^5)

INFERIOR LOBE SEGMENTS

Superior (R.S^6)

Medial basal (R.S^7)

Ant. basal (R.S^8)

Lateral basal (R.S^9)

Post. basal (R.S^{10})

MEDIAL VIEW OF RIGHT LUNG

◄— RIGHT   LEFT —►

R.S^1

R.S^2

R.S^3

R.S^4

R.S^5

R.S^8

R.S^9

R.S^7

R.S^{10}

L.S^{1,2}

L.S^3

L.S^4 **LINGULAR DIVISION**

L.S^5

L.S^{7,8}

L.S^{10}

L.S^9

ANTERIOR VIEW

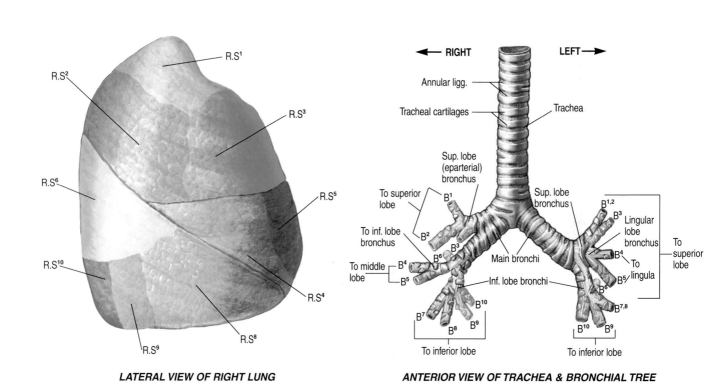

R.S^1

R.S^2

R.S^3

R.S^6

R.S^5

R.S^{10}

R.S^4

R.S^8

R.S^9

LATERAL VIEW OF RIGHT LUNG

◄— RIGHT   LEFT —►

Annular ligg.

Tracheal cartilages

Trachea

Sup. lobe (eparterial) bronchus

Sup. lobe bronchus

To superior lobe

B^1

B^{1,2}

B^3 Lingular lobe bronchus

To inf. lobe bronchus

B^2

B^3

B^6

B^4

To middle lobe

B^4

B^5

Main bronchi

Inf. lobe bronchi

B^5 To lingula

B^6

B^{7,8}

To superior lobe

B^7

B^8 B^9

B^{10}

B^{10} B^9

To inferior lobe

To inferior lobe

ANTERIOR VIEW OF TRACHEA & BRONCHIAL TREE

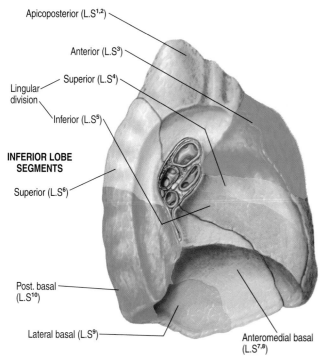

SUPERIOR LOBE SEGMENTS

Apicoposterior (L.S^{1,2})

Anterior (L.S^3)

Superior (L.S^4)

Lingular division

Inferior (L.S^5)

INFERIOR LOBE SEGMENTS

Superior (L.S^6)

Post. basal (L.S^{10})

Lateral basal (L.S^9)

Anteromedial basal (L.S^{7,8})

MEDIAL VIEW OF LEFT LUNG

← LEFT   RIGHT →

L.S^{1,2}

L.S^3

L.S^4

L.S^9

L.S^6

L.S^{10}

R.S^1

R.S^2

R.S^6

R.S^3

R.S^4

R.S^9

R.S^{10}

POSTERIOR VIEW

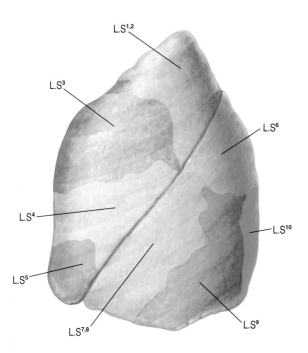

L.S^{1,2}

L.S^3

L.S^6

L.S^4

L.S^{10}

L.S^5

L.S^{7,8}

L.S^9

LATERAL VIEW OF LEFT LUNG

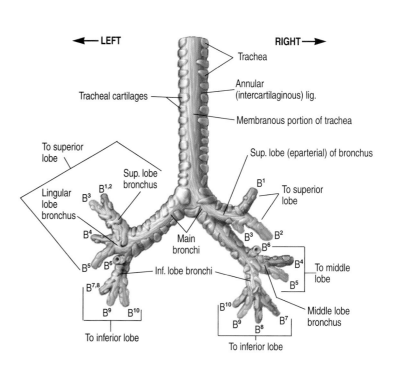

← LEFT   RIGHT →

Trachea

Annular (intercartilaginous) lig.

Tracheal cartilages

Membranous portion of trachea

To superior lobe

Sup. lobe bronchus

Sup. lobe (eparterial) of bronchus

Lingular lobe bronchus

B^3

B^{1,2}

B^1

To superior lobe

B^4

Main bronchi

B^3

B^2

B^5

B^6

B^6

B^4

To middle lobe

Inf. lobe bronchi

B^5

B^{7,8}

Middle lobe bronchus

B^9

B^{10}

B^{10}

B^9

B^8

B^7

To inferior lobe

To inferior lobe

POSTERIOR VIEW OF TRACHEA & BRONCHIAL TREE

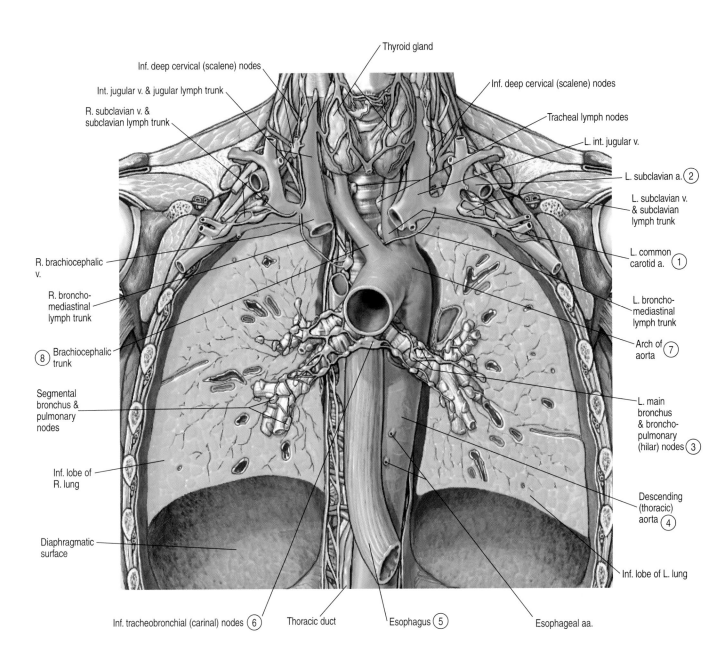

Thyroid gland

Inf. deep cervical (scalene) nodes

Int. jugular v. & jugular lymph trunk

R. subclavian v. & subclavian lymph trunk

Inf. deep cervical (scalene) nodes

Tracheal lymph nodes

L. int. jugular v.

L. subclavian a. ②

L. subclavian v. & subclavian lymph trunk

L. common carotid a. ①

R. brachiocephalic v.

R. broncho-mediastinal lymph trunk

L. broncho-mediastinal lymph trunk

Arch of aorta ⑦

⑧ Brachiocephalic trunk

Segmental bronchus & pulmonary nodes

L. main bronchus & broncho-pulmonary (hilar) nodes ③

Inf. lobe of R. lung

Descending (thoracic) aorta ④

Diaphragmatic surface

Inf. lobe of L. lung

Inf. tracheobronchial (carinal) nodes ⑥

Thoracic duct

Esophagus ⑤

Esophageal aa.

ANTERIOR VIEW WITH CORONALLY SECTIONED LUNGS

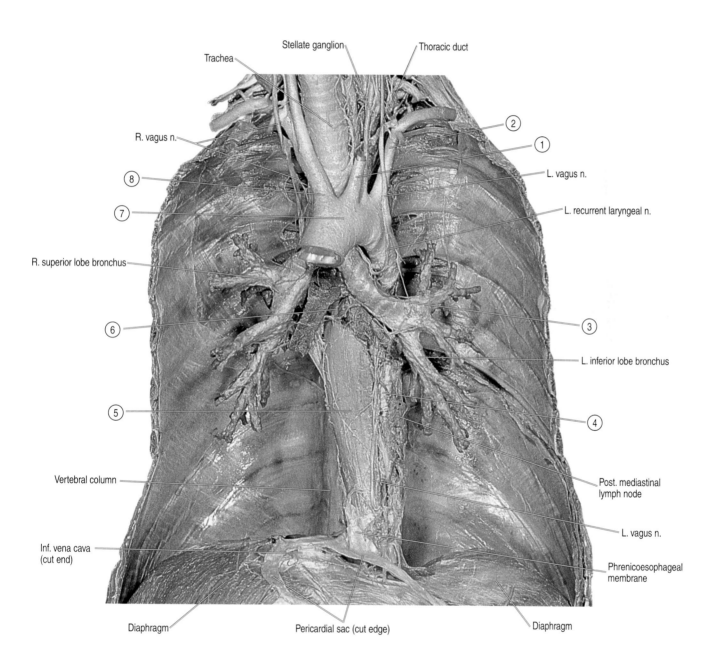

Stellate ganglion

Thoracic duct

Trachea

R. vagus n.

②

①

L. vagus n.

⑧

L. recurrent laryngeal n.

⑦

R. superior lobe bronchus

⑥

③

L. inferior lobe bronchus

⑤

④

Vertebral column

Post. mediastinal lymph node

L. vagus n.

Inf. vena cava (cut end)

Phrenicoesophageal membrane

Diaphragm

Pericardial sac (cut edge)

Diaphragm

ANTERIOR VIEW

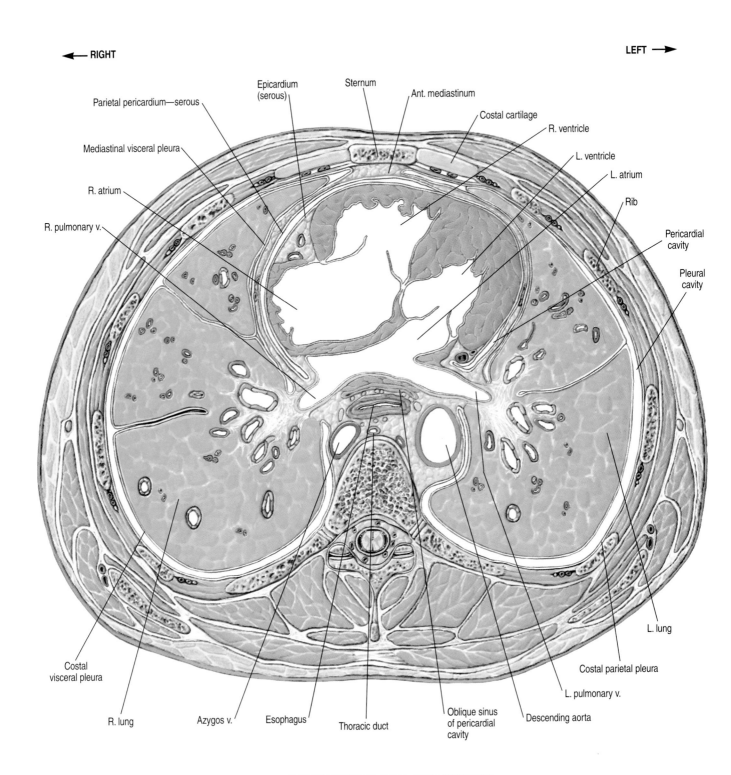

← RIGHT

LEFT →

Epicardium (serous)

Sternum

Ant. mediastinum

Parietal pericardium—serous

Costal cartilage

R. ventricle

Mediastinal visceral pleura

L. ventricle

L. atrium

R. atrium

Rib

R. pulmonary v.

Pericardial cavity

Pleural cavity

Costal visceral pleura

R. lung

Azygos v.

Esophagus

Thoracic duct

Oblique sinus of pericardial cavity

Descending aorta

L. pulmonary v.

Costal parietal pleura

L. lung

TRANSVERSE SECTION AT T8—INFERIOR VIEW

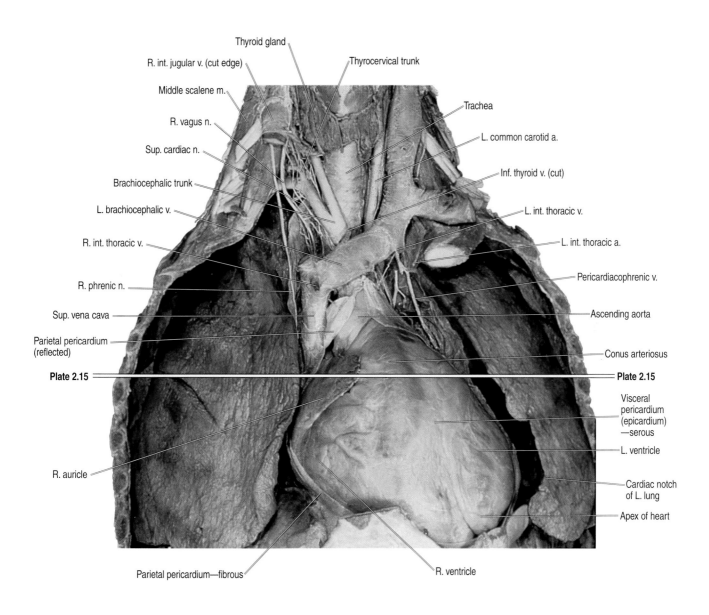

Thyroid gland

R. int. jugular v. (cut edge)

Thyrocervical trunk

Middle scalene m.

Trachea

R. vagus n.

L. common carotid a.

Sup. cardiac n.

Inf. thyroid v. (cut)

Brachiocephalic trunk

L. brachiocephalic v.

L. int. thoracic v.

R. int. thoracic v.

L. int. thoracic a.

R. phrenic n.

Pericardiacophrenic v.

Sup. vena cava

Ascending aorta

Parietal pericardium
(reflected)

Conus arteriosus

Plate 2.15

Plate 2.15

Visceral
pericardium
(epicardium)
—serous

L. ventricle

R. auricle

Cardiac notch
of L. lung

Apex of heart

Parietal pericardium—fibrous

R. ventricle

ANTERIOR VIEW

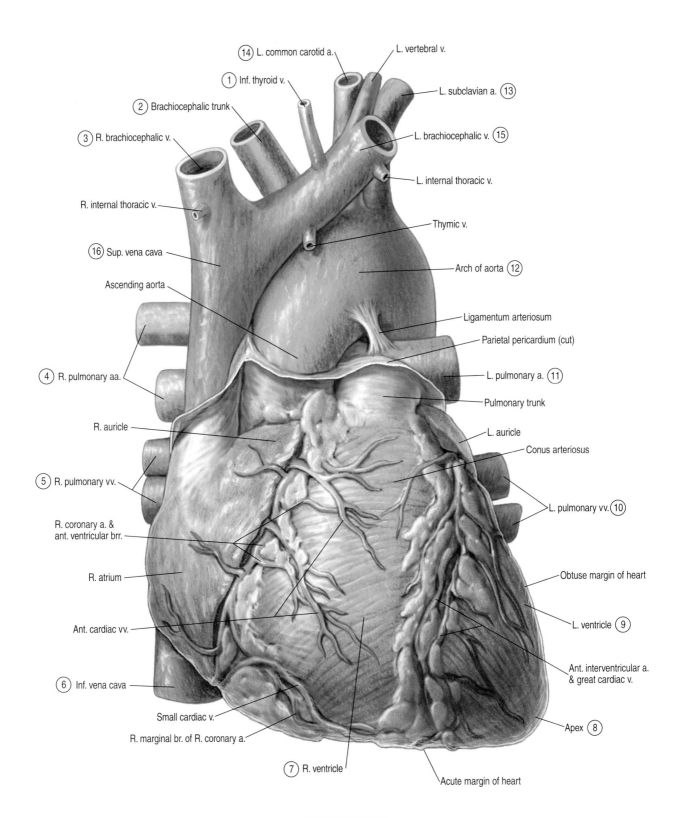

(14) L. common carotid a.
L. vertebral v.
(1) Inf. thyroid v.
L. subclavian a. (13)
(2) Brachiocephalic trunk
(3) R. brachiocephalic v.
L. brachiocephalic v. (15)
L. internal thoracic v.
R. internal thoracic v.
Thymic v.
(16) Sup. vena cava
Arch of aorta (12)
Ascending aorta
Ligamentum arteriosum
Parietal pericardium (cut)
(4) R. pulmonary aa.
L. pulmonary a. (11)
Pulmonary trunk
R. auricle
L. auricle
Conus arteriosus
(5) R. pulmonary vv.
L. pulmonary vv. (10)
R. coronary a. &
ant. ventricular brr.
R. atrium
Obtuse margin of heart
L. ventricle (9)
Ant. cardiac vv.
Ant. interventricular a.
& great cardiac v.
(6) Inf. vena cava
Apex (8)
Small cardiac v.
R. marginal br. of R. coronary a.
(7) R. ventricle
Acute margin of heart

ANTERIOR VIEW

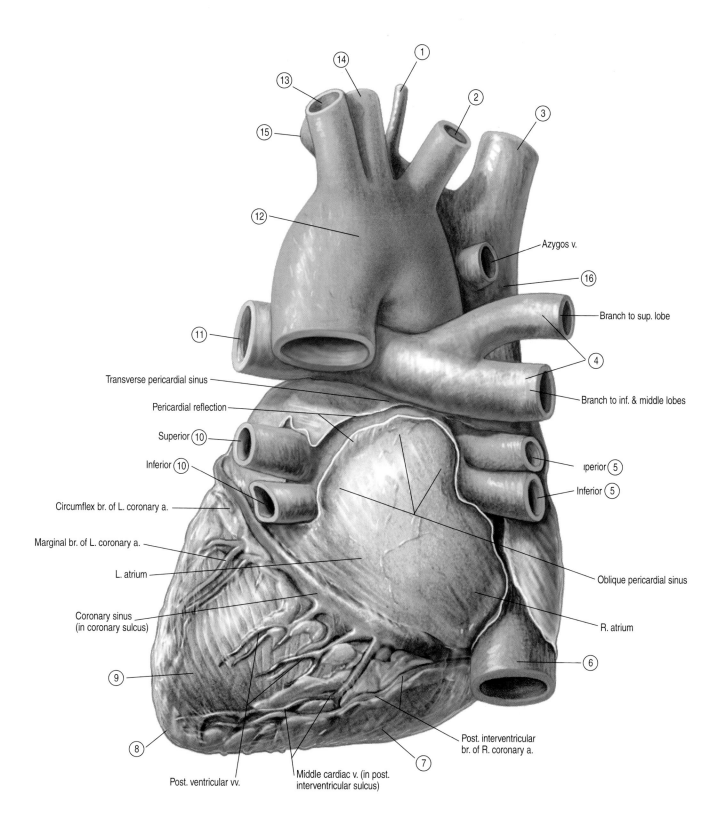

Azygos v.

Branch to sup. lobe

Transverse pericardial sinus

Pericardial reflection

Superior (10)

Inferior (10)

Circumflex br. of L. coronary a.

Marginal br. of L. coronary a.

L. atrium

Coronary sinus
(in coronary sulcus)

Branch to inf. & middle lobes

ıperior (5)

Inferior (5)

Oblique pericardial sinus

R. atrium

Post. interventricular
br. of R. coronary a.

Post. ventricular vv.

Middle cardiac v. (in post.
interventricular sulcus)

POSTERIOR VIEW

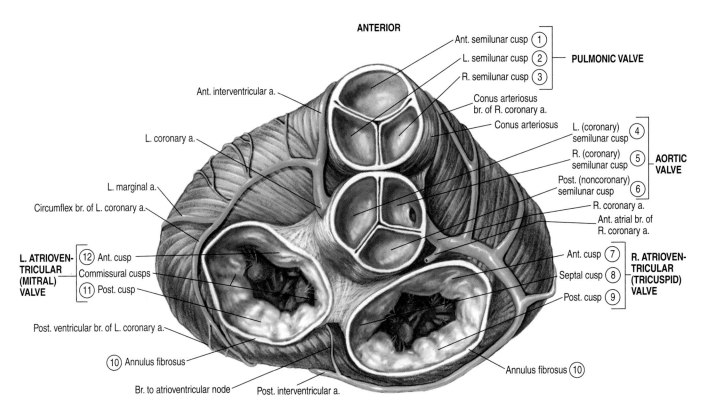

ANTERIOR

Ant. semilunar cusp ① ⎤
L. semilunar cusp ② ⎬ PULMONIC VALVE
R. semilunar cusp ③ ⎦

Ant. interventricular a.

Conus arteriosus
br. of R. coronary a.

Conus arteriosus

L. coronary a.

L. (coronary) ④ ⎤
semilunar cusp

R. (coronary) ⑤ ⎬ AORTIC
semilunar cusp   VALVE

Post. (noncoronary) ⑥ ⎦
semilunar cusp

L. marginal a.

R. coronary a.

Circumflex br. of L. coronary a.

Ant. atrial br. of
R. coronary a.

L. ATRIOVEN-
TRICULAR
(MITRAL)
VALVE

⑫ Ant. cusp
Commissural cusps
⑪ Post. cusp

Ant. cusp ⑦ ⎤
Septal cusp ⑧ ⎬ R. ATRIOVEN-
                  TRICULAR
Post. cusp ⑨ ⎦ (TRICUSPID)
                  VALVE

Post. ventricular br. of L. coronary a.

⑩ Annulus fibrosus

Annulus fibrosus ⑩

Br. to atrioventricular node   Post. interventricular a.

HEART IN DIASTOLE VIEWED FROM BASE WITH ATRIA REMOVED

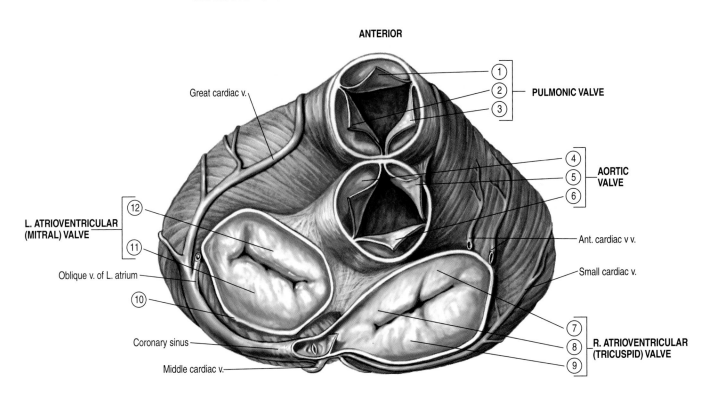

ANTERIOR

① ⎤
② ⎬ PULMONIC VALVE
③ ⎦

Great cardiac v.

④ ⎤
⑤ ⎬ AORTIC
⑥ ⎦ VALVE

L. ATRIOVENTRICULAR
(MITRAL) VALVE

⑫

⑪

Ant. cardiac v v.

Oblique v. of L. atrium

Small cardiac v.

⑩

⑦ ⎤
⑧ ⎬ R. ATRIOVENTRICULAR
⑨ ⎦ (TRICUSPID) VALVE

Coronary sinus

Middle cardiac v.

HEART IN SYSTOLE VIEWED FROM BASE WITH ATRIA REMOVED

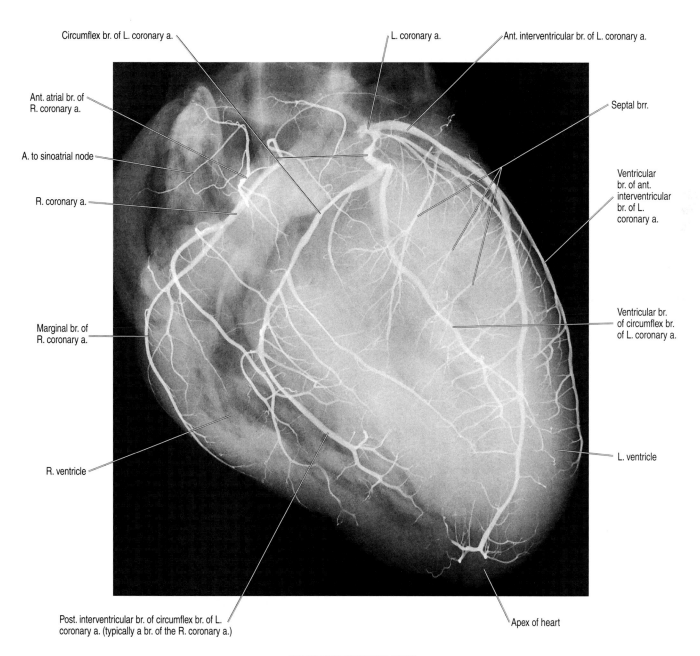

Circumflex br. of L. coronary a.

L. coronary a.

Ant. interventricular br. of L. coronary a.

Ant. atrial br. of R. coronary a.

Septal brr.

A. to sinoatrial node

R. coronary a.

Ventricular br. of ant. interventricular br. of L. coronary a.

Marginal br. of R. coronary a.

Ventricular br. of circumflex br. of L. coronary a.

R. ventricle

L. ventricle

Post. interventricular br. of circumflex br. of L. coronary a. (typically a br. of the R. coronary a.)

Apex of heart

ANTEROPOSTERIOR VIEW

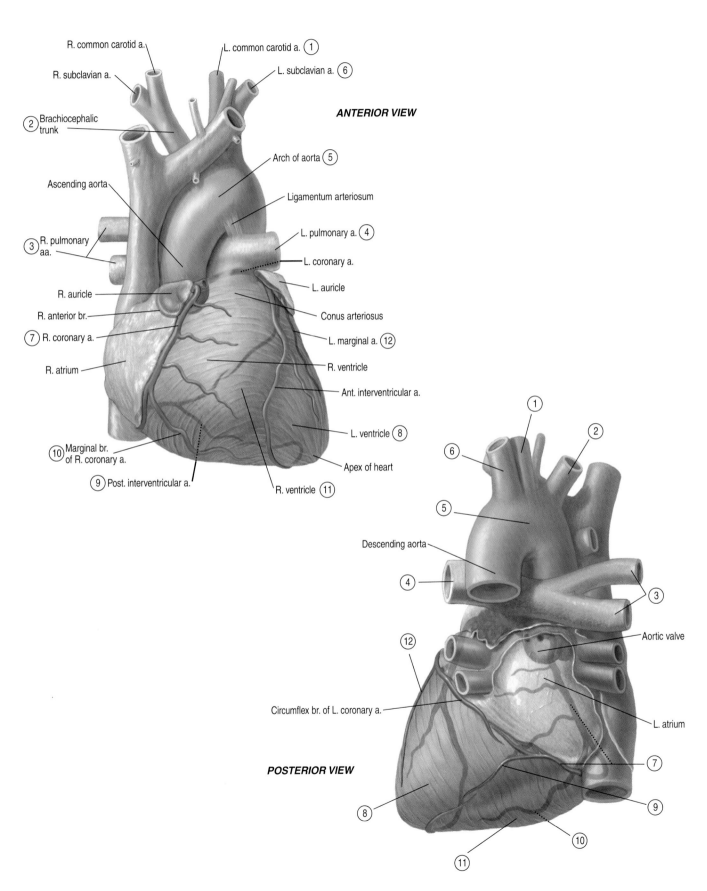

R. common carotid a.

L. common carotid a. (1)

R. subclavian a.

L. subclavian a. (6)

ANTERIOR VIEW

(2) Brachiocephalic trunk

Arch of aorta (5)

Ascending aorta

Ligamentum arteriosum

L. pulmonary a. (4)

(3) R. pulmonary aa.

L. coronary a.

R. auricle

L. auricle

R. anterior br.

Conus arteriosus

(7) R. coronary a.

L. marginal a. (12)

R. atrium

R. ventricle

Ant. interventricular a.

L. ventricle (8)

(10) Marginal br. of R. coronary a.

Apex of heart

(9) Post. interventricular a.

R. ventricle (11)

Descending aorta

Aortic valve

Circumflex br. of L. coronary a.

L. atrium

POSTERIOR VIEW

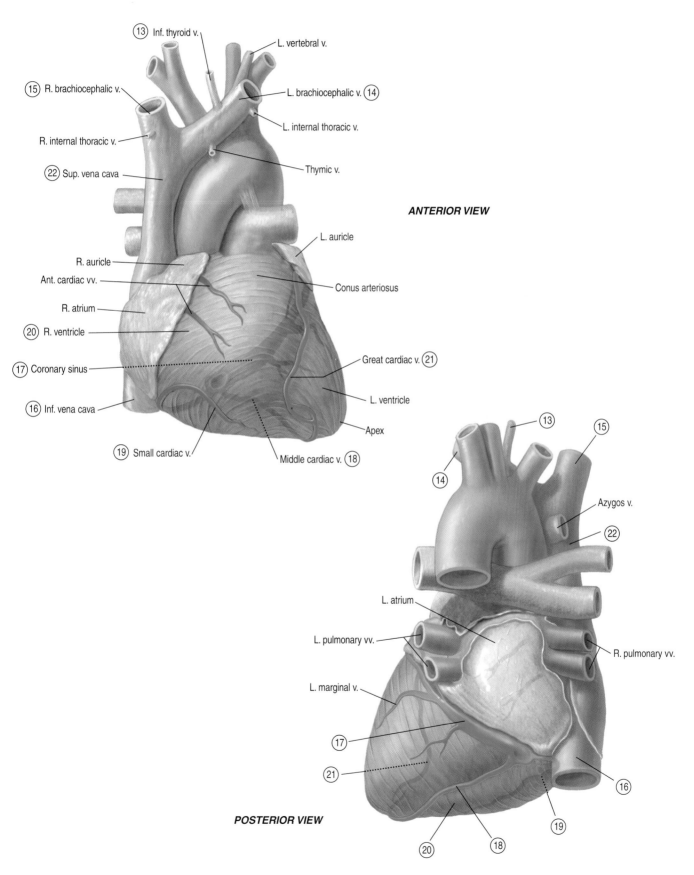

(13) Inf. thyroid v.

L. vertebral v.

(15) R. brachiocephalic v.

L. brachiocephalic v. (14)

L. internal thoracic v.

R. internal thoracic v.

Thymic v.

(22) Sup. vena cava

ANTERIOR VIEW

L. auricle

R. auricle

Ant. cardiac vv.

Conus arteriosus

R. atrium

(20) R. ventricle

(17) Coronary sinus

Great cardiac v. (21)

L. ventricle

(16) Inf. vena cava

Apex

(19) Small cardiac v.

Middle cardiac v. (18)

(13)

(15)

(14)

Azygos v.

(22)

L. atrium

L. pulmonary vv.

R. pulmonary vv.

L. marginal v.

(17)

(21)

(16)

(20)

(18)

(19)

POSTERIOR VIEW

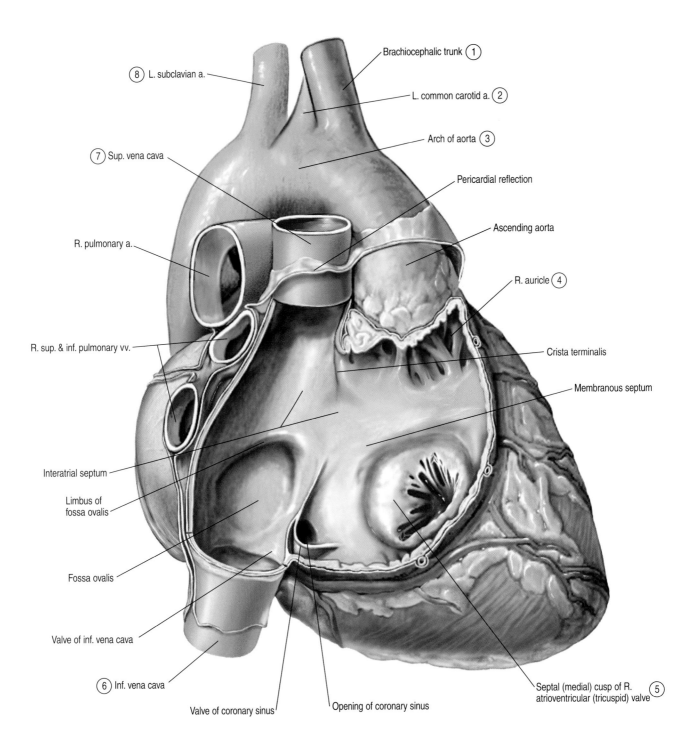

Brachiocephalic trunk ①

⑧ L. subclavian a.

L. common carotid a. ②

Arch of aorta ③

⑦ Sup. vena cava

Pericardial reflection

Ascending aorta

R. pulmonary a.

R. auricle ④

Crista terminalis

R. sup. & inf. pulmonary vv.

Membranous septum

Interatrial septum

Limbus of
fossa ovalis

Fossa ovalis

Valve of inf. vena cava

⑥ Inf. vena cava

Septal (medial) cusp of R.
atrioventricular (tricuspid) valve ⑤

Valve of coronary sinus

Opening of coronary sinus

LATERAL VIEW OF OPENED RIGHT ATRIUM

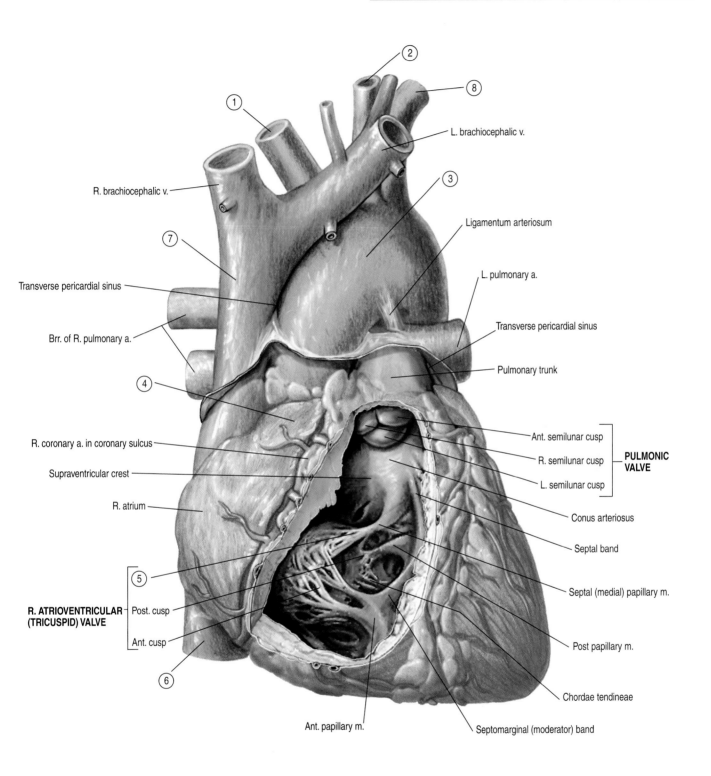

R. brachiocephalic v.

L. brachiocephalic v.

Transverse pericardial sinus

Ligamentum arteriosum

L. pulmonary a.

Brr. of R. pulmonary a.

Transverse pericardial sinus

Pulmonary trunk

R. coronary a. in coronary sulcus

Ant. semilunar cusp

R. semilunar cusp

PULMONIC VALVE

Supraventricular crest

L. semilunar cusp

R. atrium

Conus arteriosus

Septal band

Septal (medial) papillary m.

R. ATRIOVENTRICULAR (TRICUSPID) VALVE

Post. cusp

Ant. cusp

Post papillary m.

Chordae tendineae

Ant. papillary m.

Septomarginal (moderator) band

ANTERIOR VIEW OF OPENED RIGHT VENTRICLE

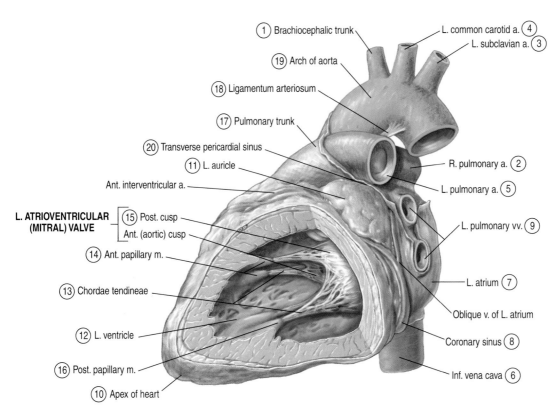

1 Brachiocephalic trunk
L. common carotid a. 4
L. subclavian a. 3
19 Arch of aorta
18 Ligamentum arteriosum
17 Pulmonary trunk
20 Transverse pericardial sinus
11 L. auricle
Ant. interventricular a.
R. pulmonary a. 2
L. pulmonary a. 5
L. ATRIOVENTRICULAR (MITRAL) VALVE 15 Post. cusp
Ant. (aortic) cusp
14 Ant. papillary m.
L. pulmonary vv. 9
13 Chordae tendineae
L. atrium 7
12 L. ventricle
Oblique v. of L. atrium
16 Post. papillary m.
Coronary sinus 8
Inf. vena cava 6
10 Apex of heart

LEFT LATERAL VIEW OF OPENED LEFT VENTRICLE

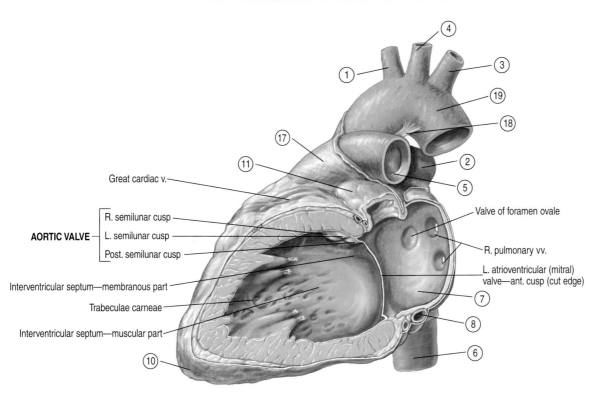

4
1
3
19
18
17
11
2
5
Great cardiac v.
Valve of foramen ovale
AORTIC VALVE R. semilunar cusp
L. semilunar cusp
Post. semilunar cusp
R. pulmonary vv.
L. atrioventricular (mitral) valve—ant. cusp (cut edge)
7
Interventricular septum—membranous part
Trabeculae carneae
8
Interventricular septum—muscular part
6
10

LEFT LATERAL VIEW OF LEFT VENTRICLE & ATRIUM WITH MITRAL VALVE REMOVED

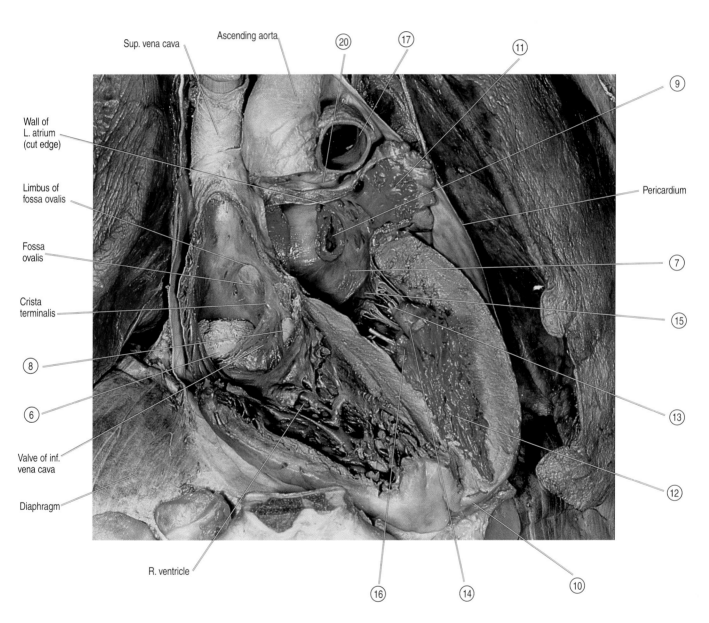

Sup. vena cava

Ascending aorta

20

17

11

9

Wall of
L. atrium
(cut edge)

Limbus of
fossa ovalis

Pericardium

Fossa
ovalis

7

Crista
terminalis

15

8

6

13

Valve of inf.
vena cava

12

Diaphragm

R. ventricle

16

14

10

INTERIOR OF ANTERIOR VIEW OF HEART

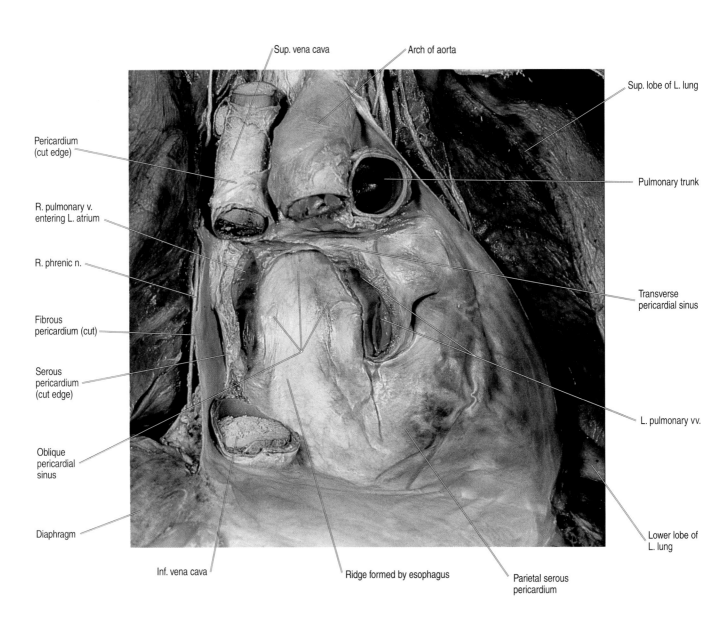

Sup. vena cava

Arch of aorta

Sup. lobe of L. lung

Pericardium (cut edge)

Pulmonary trunk

R. pulmonary v. entering L. atrium

R. phrenic n.

Transverse pericardial sinus

Fibrous pericardium (cut)

Serous pericardium (cut edge)

L. pulmonary vv.

Oblique pericardial sinus

Diaphragm

Lower lobe of L. lung

Inf. vena cava

Ridge formed by esophagus

Parietal serous pericardium

ANTERIOR VIEW OF PERICARDIAL CAVITY WITH HEART REMOVED

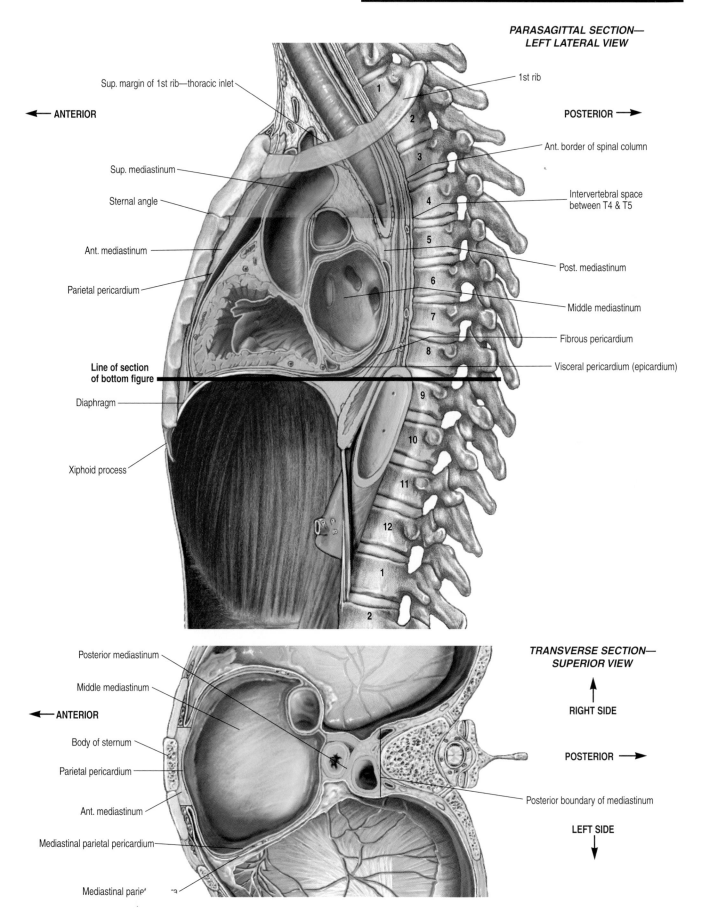

PARASAGITTAL SECTION—LEFT LATERAL VIEW

Sup. margin of 1st rib—thoracic inlet

← ANTERIOR

Sup. mediastinum

Sternal angle

Ant. mediastinum

Parietal pericardium

Line of section of bottom figure

Diaphragm

Xiphoid process

1st rib

POSTERIOR →

Ant. border of spinal column

Intervertebral space between T4 & T5

Post. mediastinum

Middle mediastinum

Fibrous pericardium

Visceral pericardium (epicardium)

TRANSVERSE SECTION—SUPERIOR VIEW

Posterior mediastinum

Middle mediastinum

← ANTERIOR

Body of sternum

Parietal pericardium

Ant. mediastinum

Mediastinal parietal pericardium

Mediastinal parie'

↑ RIGHT SIDE

POSTERIOR →

Posterior boundary of mediastinum

LEFT SIDE ↓

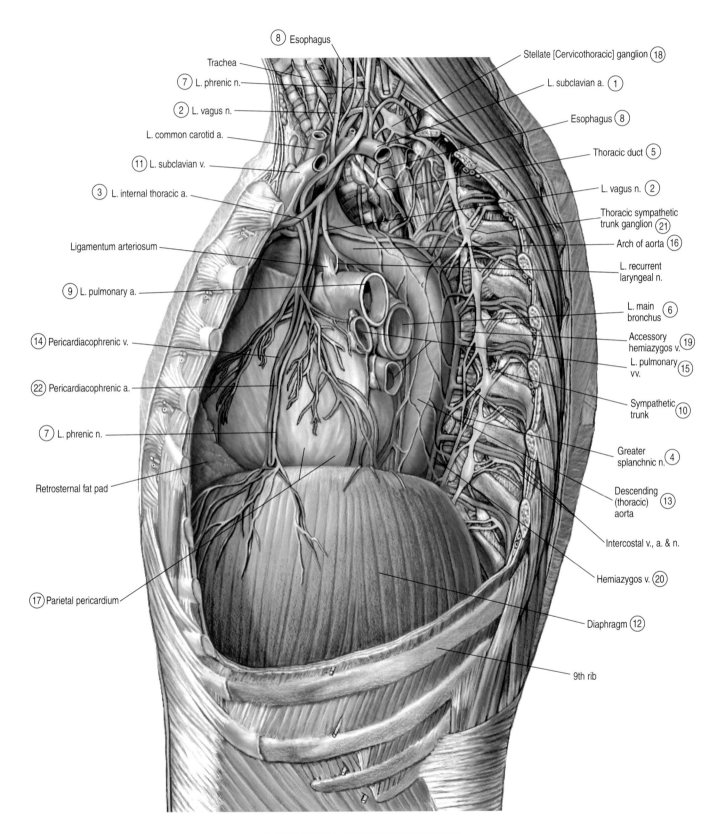

(8) Esophagus

Trachea

(7) L. phrenic n.

(2) L. vagus n.

L. common carotid a.

(11) L. subclavian v.

(3) L. internal thoracic a.

Ligamentum arteriosum

(9) L. pulmonary a.

(14) Pericardiacophrenic v.

(22) Pericardiacophrenic a.

(7) L. phrenic n.

Retrosternal fat pad

(17) Parietal pericardium

Stellate [Cervicothoracic] ganglion (18)

L. subclavian a. (1)

Esophagus (8)

Thoracic duct (5)

L. vagus n. (2)

Thoracic sympathetic trunk ganglion (21)

Arch of aorta (16)

L. recurrent laryngeal n.

L. main bronchus (6)

Accessory hemiazygos v. (19)

L. pulmonary vv. (15)

Sympathetic trunk (10)

Greater splanchnic n. (4)

Descending (thoracic) aorta (13)

Intercostal v., a. & n.

Hemiazygos v. (20)

Diaphragm (12)

9th rib

LEFT LATERAL VIEW OF MEDIASTINUM

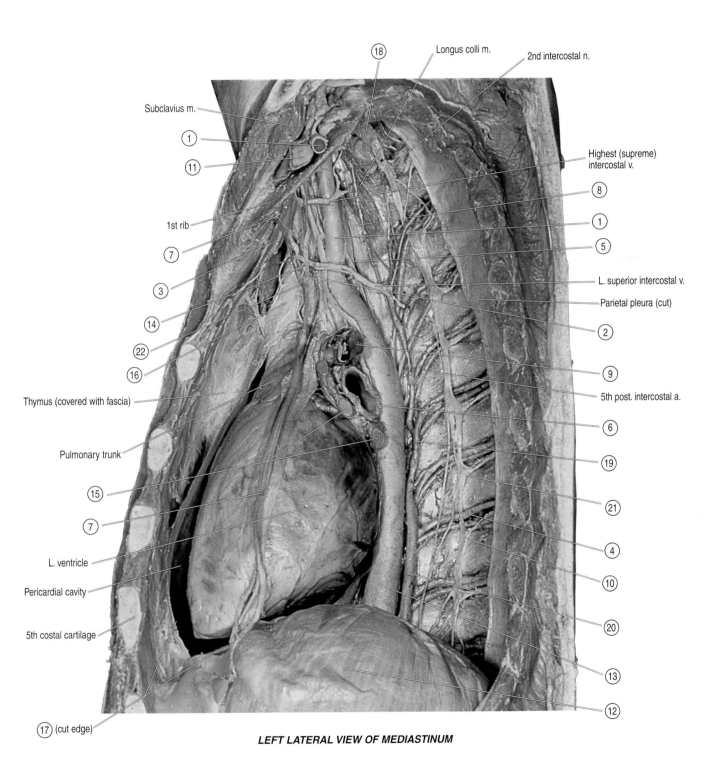

Subclavius m.

① 18 Longus colli m. 2nd intercostal n.

①

⑪

Highest (supreme) intercostal v.

1st rib

⑧

⑦

①

③

⑤

⑭

L. superior intercostal v.

㉒

Parietal pleura (cut)

⑯

②

⑨

Thymus (covered with fascia)

5th post. intercostal a.

⑥

Pulmonary trunk

⑲

⑮

㉑

⑦

④

L. ventricle

⑩

Pericardial cavity

⑳

5th costal cartilage

⑬

⑫

⑰ (cut edge)

LEFT LATERAL VIEW OF MEDIASTINUM

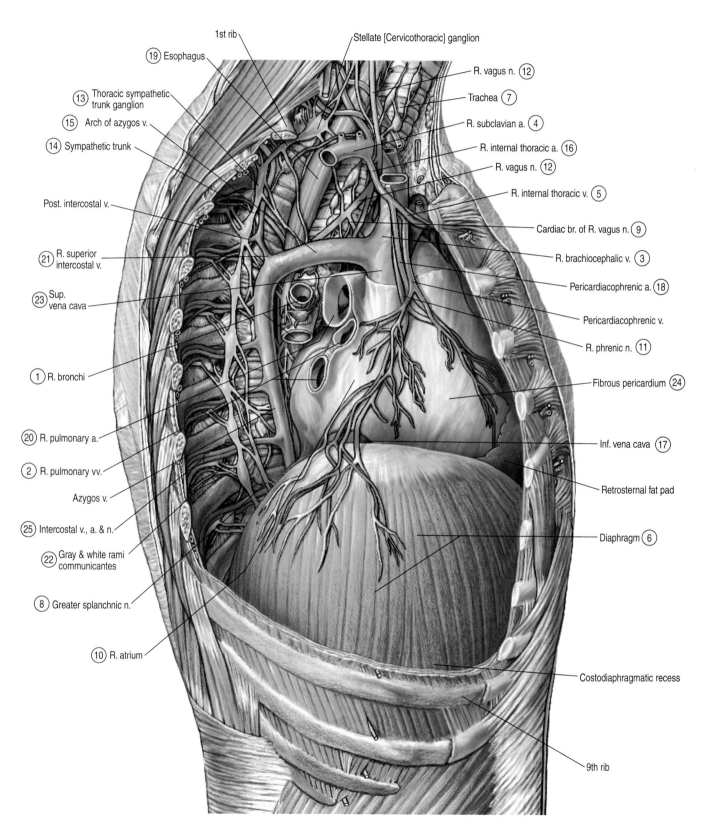

1st rib

Stellate [Cervicothoracic] ganglion

(19) Esophagus

(13) Thoracic sympathetic trunk ganglion

(15) Arch of azygos v.

(14) Sympathetic trunk

Post. intercostal v.

(21) R. superior intercostal v.

(23) Sup. vena cava

(1) R. bronchi

(20) R. pulmonary a.

(2) R. pulmonary vv.

Azygos v.

(25) Intercostal v., a. & n.

(22) Gray & white rami communicantes

(8) Greater splanchnic n.

(10) R. atrium

R. vagus n. (12)

Trachea (7)

R. subclavian a. (4)

R. internal thoracic a. (16)

R. vagus n. (12)

R. internal thoracic v. (5)

Cardiac br. of R. vagus n. (9)

R. brachiocephalic v. (3)

Pericardiacophrenic a. (18)

Pericardiacophrenic v.

R. phrenic n. (11)

Fibrous pericardium (24)

Inf. vena cava (17)

Retrosternal fat pad

Diaphragm (6)

Costodiaphragmatic recess

9th rib

RIGHT LATERAL VIEW OF MEDIASTINUM

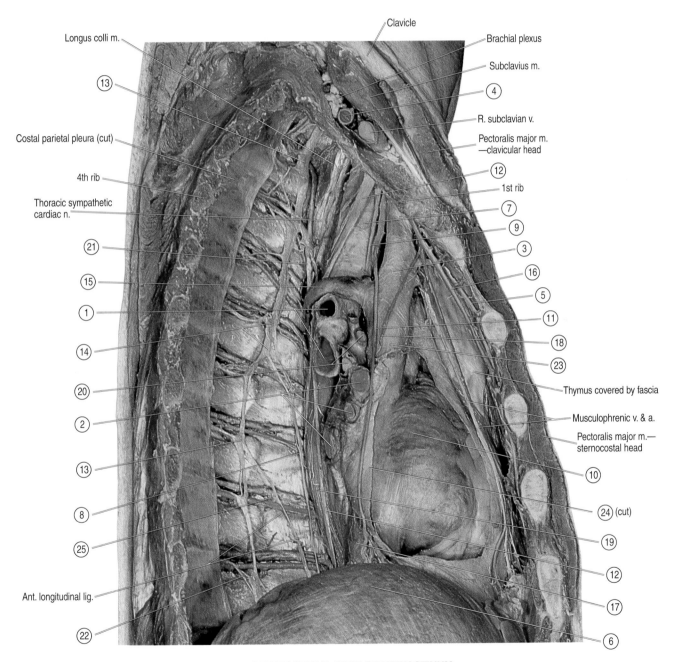

Clavicle

Longus colli m.

Brachial plexus

Subclavius m.

(13)

(4)

R. subclavian v.

Costal parietal pleura (cut)

Pectoralis major m.
—clavicular head

(12)

4th rib

1st rib

Thoracic sympathetic
cardiac n.

(7)

(9)

(21)

(3)

(15)

(16)

(5)

(1)

(11)

(14)

(18)

(23)

(20)

Thymus covered by fascia

(2)

Musculophrenic v. & a.

Pectoralis major m.—
sternocostal head

(13)

(10)

(8)

(24) (cut)

(25)

(19)

(12)

Ant. longitudinal lig.

(17)

(22)

(6)

RIGHT LATERAL VIEW OF MEDIASTINUM

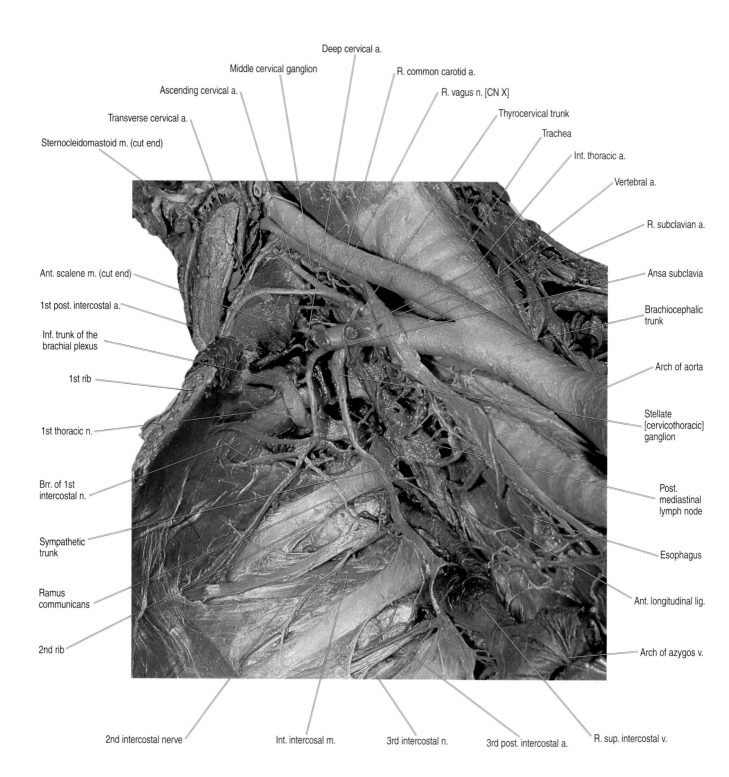

Deep cervical a.

Middle cervical ganglion

R. common carotid a.

Ascending cervical a.

R. vagus n. [CN X]

Transverse cervical a.

Thyrocervical trunk

Trachea

Sternocleidomastoid m. (cut end)

Int. thoracic a.

Vertebral a.

R. subclavian a.

Ant. scalene m. (cut end)

Ansa subclavia

1st post. intercostal a.

Brachiocephalic trunk

Inf. trunk of the brachial plexus

Arch of aorta

1st rib

1st thoracic n.

Stellate [cervicothoracic] ganglion

Brr. of 1st intercostal n.

Post. mediastinal lymph node

Sympathetic trunk

Esophagus

Ramus communicans

Ant. longitudinal lig.

2nd rib

Arch of azygos v.

2nd intercostal nerve

Int. intercosal m.

3rd intercostal n.

3rd post. intercostal a.

R. sup. intercostal v.

RIGHT ANTEROLATERAL INFERIOR OBLIQUE VIEW

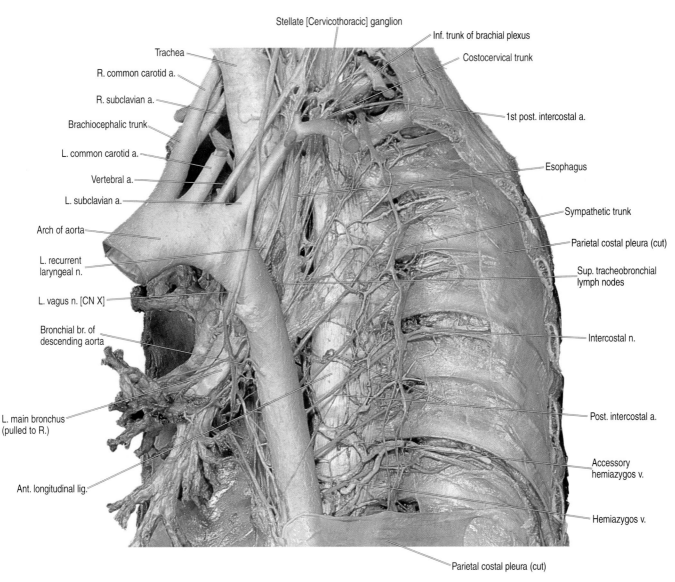

Stellate [Cervicothoracic] ganglion

Inf. trunk of brachial plexus

Trachea

Costocervical trunk

R. common carotid a.

R. subclavian a.

1st post. intercostal a.

Brachiocephalic trunk

L. common carotid a.

Esophagus

Vertebral a.

L. subclavian a.

Sympathetic trunk

Arch of aorta

Parietal costal pleura (cut)

L. recurrent
laryngeal n.

Sup. tracheobronchial
lymph nodes

L. vagus n. [CN X]

Bronchial br. of
descending aorta

Intercostal n.

L. main bronchus
(pulled to R.)

Post. intercostal a.

Accessory
hemiazygos v.

Ant. longitudinal lig.

Hemiazygos v.

Parietal costal pleura (cut)

LEFT ANTEROLATERAL VIEW

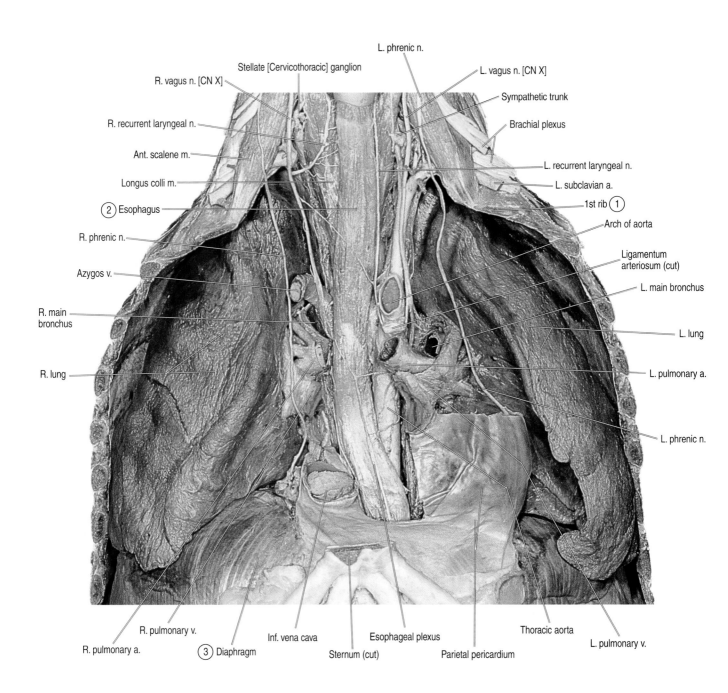

L. phrenic n.

Stellate [Cervicothoracic] ganglion

L. vagus n. [CN X]

R. vagus n. [CN X]

Sympathetic trunk

R. recurrent laryngeal n.

Brachial plexus

Ant. scalene m.

L. recurrent laryngeal n.

Longus colli m.

L. subclavian a.

2 Esophagus

1st rib 1

R. phrenic n.

Arch of aorta

Azygos v.

Ligamentum arteriosum (cut)

L. main bronchus

R. main bronchus

L. lung

R. lung

L. pulmonary a.

L. phrenic n.

R. pulmonary v.

Inf. vena cava

Esophageal plexus

Thoracic aorta

R. pulmonary a.

3 Diaphragm

Sternum (cut)

Parietal pericardium

L. pulmonary v.

ANTERIOR VIEW OF POSTERIOR MEDIASTINAL STRUCTURES

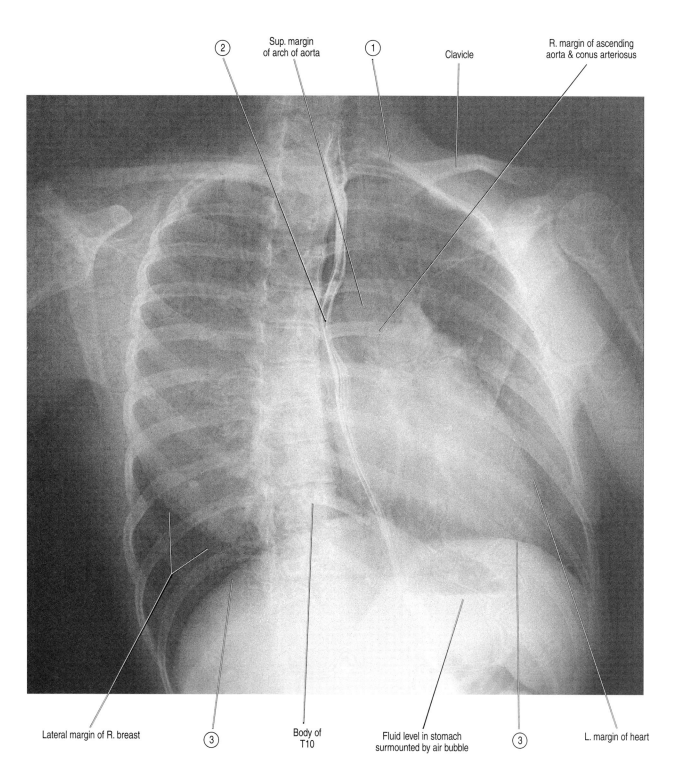

② Sup. margin of arch of aorta ① Clavicle R. margin of ascending aorta & conus arteriosus

Lateral margin of R. breast ③ Body of T10 Fluid level in stomach surmounted by air bubble ③ L. margin of heart

RIGHT ANTERIOR OBLIQUE VIEW OF ESOPHAGUS

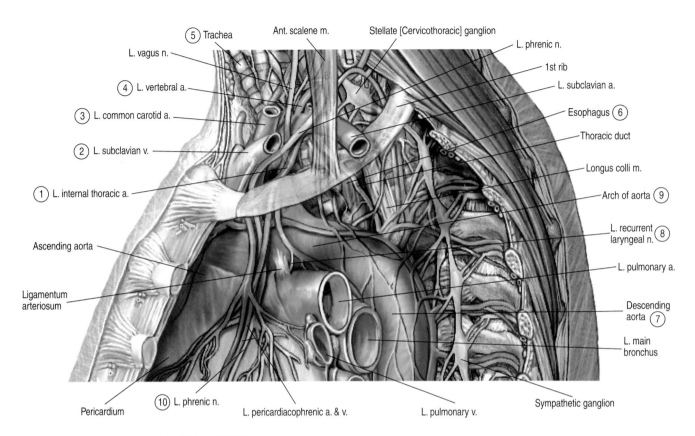

⑤ Trachea   Ant. scalene m.   Stellate [Cervicothoracic] ganglion

L. vagus n.

④ L. vertebral a.

③ L. common carotid a.

② L. subclavian v.

① L. internal thoracic a.

Ascending aorta

Ligamentum arteriosum

L. phrenic n.

1st rib

L. subclavian a.

Esophagus ⑥

Thoracic duct

Longus colli m.

Arch of aorta ⑨

L. recurrent laryngeal n. ⑧

L. pulmonary a.

Descending aorta ⑦

L. main bronchus

Pericardium   ⑩ L. phrenic n.   L. pericardiacophrenic a. & v.   L. pulmonary v.   Sympathetic ganglion

LEFT LATERAL VIEW OF MEDIASTINUM

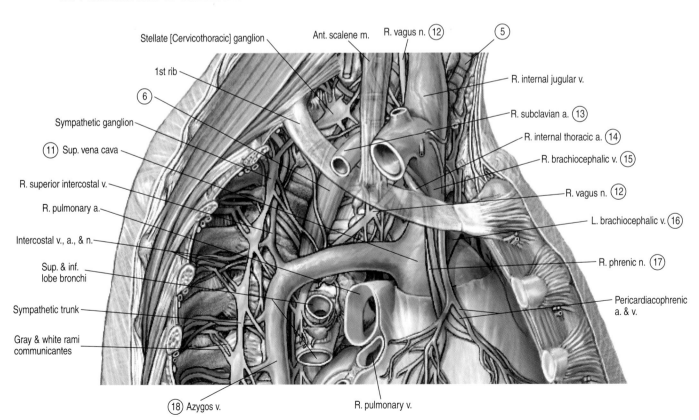

Stellate [Cervicothoracic] ganglion   Ant. scalene m.   R. vagus n. ⑫   ⑤

1st rib

⑥

Sympathetic ganglion

⑪ Sup. vena cava

R. superior intercostal v.

R. pulmonary a.

Intercostal v., a., & n.

Sup. & inf. lobe bronchi

Sympathetic trunk

Gray & white rami communicantes

R. internal jugular v.

R. subclavian a. ⑬

R. internal thoracic a. ⑭

R. brachiocephalic v. ⑮

R. vagus n. ⑫

L. brachiocephalic v. ⑯

R. phrenic n. ⑰

Pericardiacophrenic a. & v.

⑱ Azygos v.   R. pulmonary v.

RIGHT LATERAL VIEW OF MEDIASTINUM

ANTERIOR

◄— RIGHT SIDE

LEFT SIDE —►

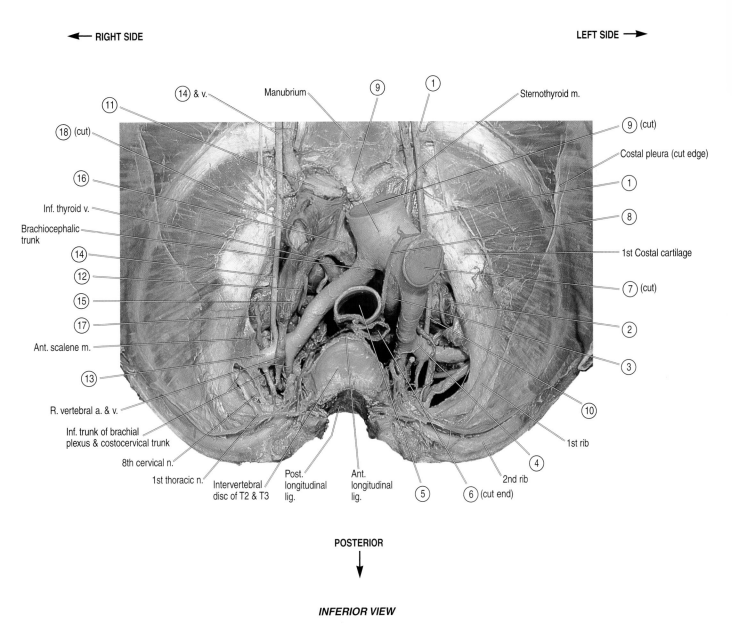

(14) & v.

Manubrium

(9)

(1)

Sternothyroid m.

(11)

(18) (cut)

(9) (cut)

Costal pleura (cut edge)

(16)

(1)

Inf. thyroid v.

(8)

Brachiocephalic trunk

1st Costal cartilage

(14)

(12)

(7) (cut)

(15)

(2)

(17)

Ant. scalene m.

(3)

(13)

(10)

R. vertebral a. & v.

1st rib

Inf. trunk of brachial plexus & costocervical trunk

(4)

8th cervical n.

2nd rib

1st thoracic n.

Intervertebral disc of T2 & T3

Post. longitudinal lig.

Ant. longitudinal lig.

(5)

(6) (cut end)

POSTERIOR

INFERIOR VIEW

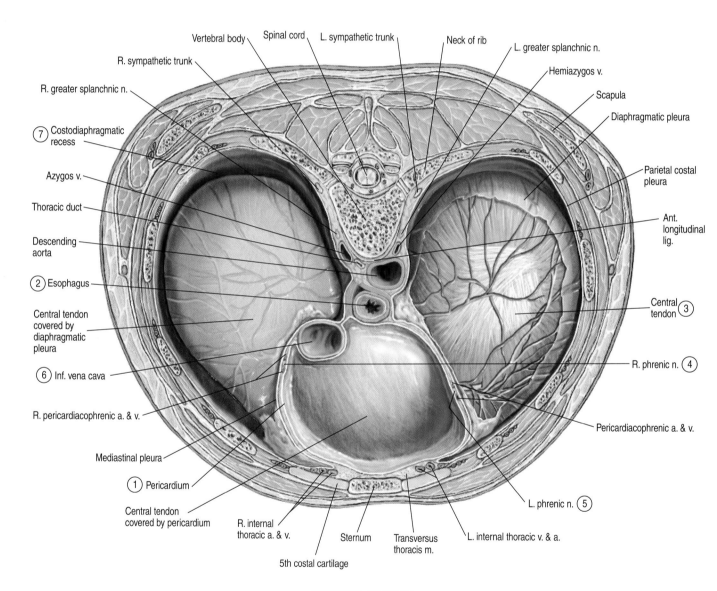

Vertebral body

Spinal cord

L. sympathetic trunk

Neck of rib

L. greater splanchnic n.

R. sympathetic trunk

Hemiazygos v.

R. greater splanchnic n.

Scapula

Diaphragmatic pleura

(7) Costodiaphragmatic recess

Parietal costal pleura

Azygos v.

Thoracic duct

Ant. longitudinal lig.

Descending aorta

(2) Esophagus

Central tendon (3)

Central tendon covered by diaphragmatic pleura

(6) Inf. vena cava

R. phrenic n. (4)

R. pericardiacophrenic a. & v.

Pericardiacophrenic a. & v.

Mediastinal pleura

(1) Pericardium

L. phrenic n. (5)

Central tendon covered by pericardium

R. internal thoracic a. & v.

Sternum

Transversus thoracis m.

L. internal thoracic v. & a.

5th costal cartilage

SUPERIOR SURFACE

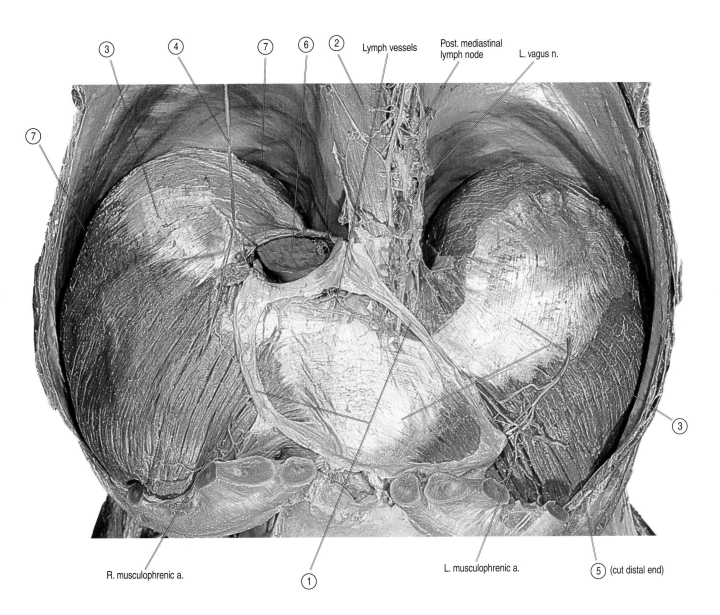

ANTERIOR SUPERIOR OBLIQUE VIEW OF SUPERIOR SURFACE OF DIAPHRAGM

Lymph vessels

Post. mediastinal
lymph node

L. vagus n.

R. musculophrenic a.

L. musculophrenic a.

(cut distal end)

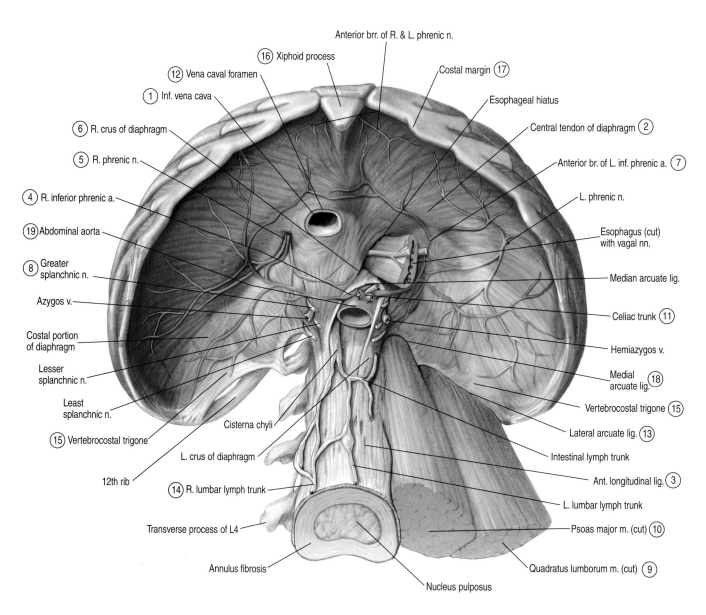

Anterior brr. of R. & L. phrenic n.

(16) Xiphoid process

(12) Vena caval foramen

(1) Inf. vena cava

(6) R. crus of diaphragm

(5) R. phrenic n.

(4) R. inferior phrenic a.

(19) Abdominal aorta

(8) Greater splanchnic n.

Azygos v.

Costal portion of diaphragm

Lesser splanchnic n.

Least splanchnic n.

(15) Vertebrocostal trigone

12th rib

(14) R. lumbar lymph trunk

Transverse process of L4

Annulus fibrosis

Nucleus pulposus

Cisterna chyli

L. crus of diaphragm

Costal margin (17)

Esophageal hiatus

Central tendon of diaphragm (2)

Anterior br. of L. inf. phrenic a. (7)

L. phrenic n.

Esophagus (cut) with vagal nn.

Median arcuate lig.

Celiac trunk (11)

Hemiazygos v.

Medial arcuate lig. (18)

Vertebrocostal trigone (15)

Lateral arcuate lig. (13)

Intestinal lymph trunk

Ant. longitudinal lig. (3)

L. lumbar lymph trunk

Psoas major m. (cut) (10)

Quadratus lumborum m. (cut) (9)

INFERIOR VIEW

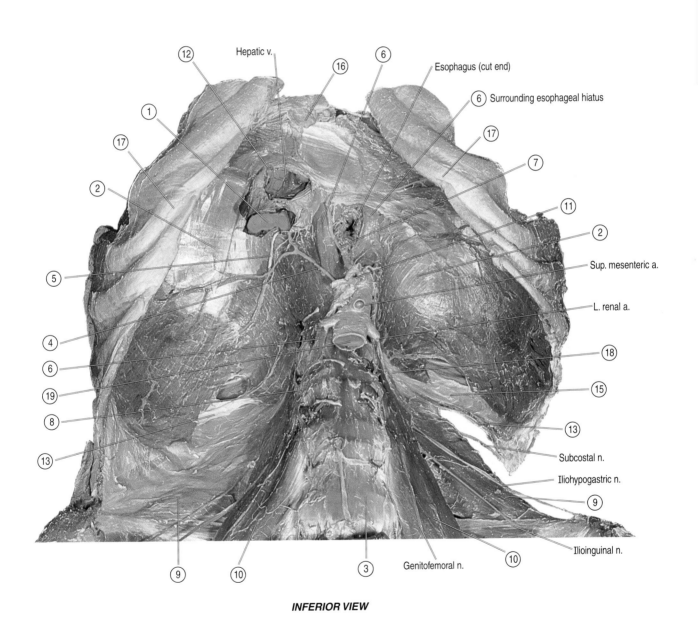

Hepatic v.

Esophagus (cut end)

⑥ Surrounding esophageal hiatus

Sup. mesenteric a.

L. renal a.

Subcostal n.

Iliohypogastric n.

Ilioinguinal n.

Genitofemoral n.

INFERIOR VIEW

Abdomen

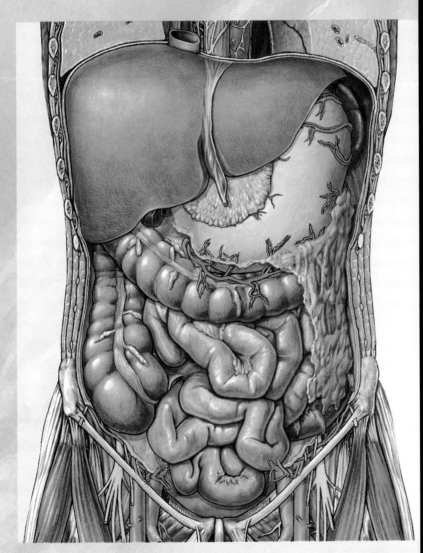

Chapter 3

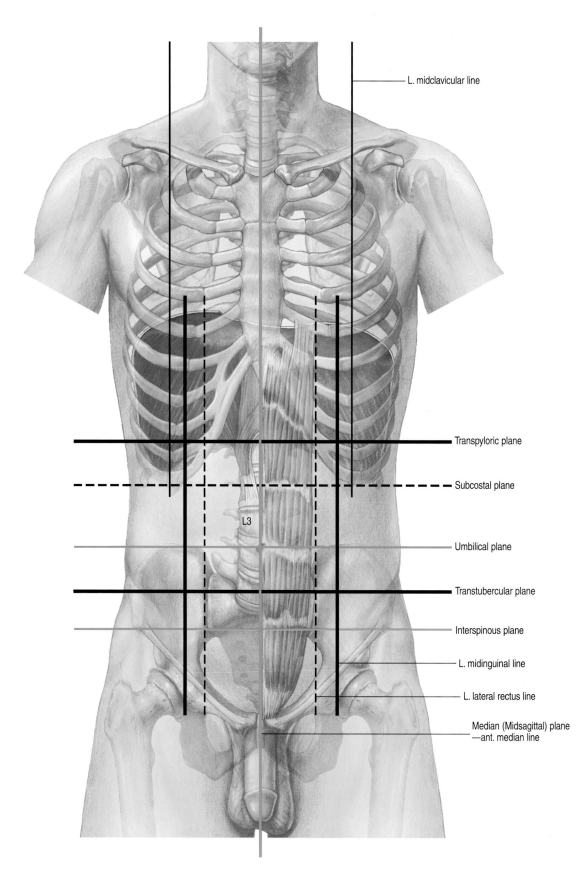

L. midclavicular line

Transpyloric plane

Subcostal plane

L3

Umbilical plane

Transtubercular plane

Interspinous plane

L. midinguinal line

L. lateral rectus line

Median (Midsagittal) plane
—ant. median line

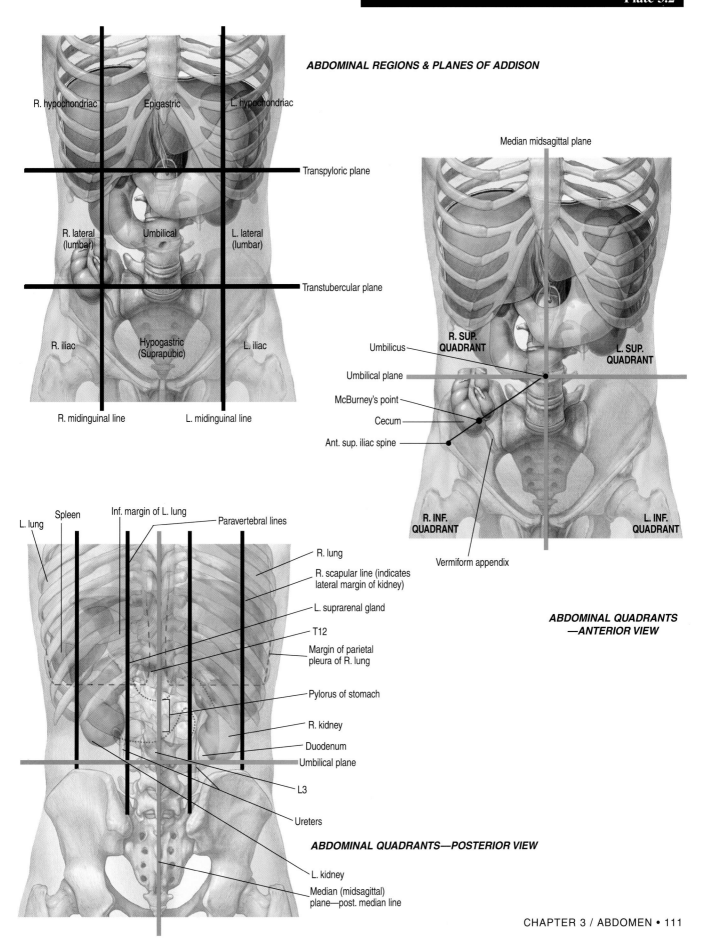

ABDOMINAL REGIONS & PLANES OF ADDISON

R. hypochondriac

Epigastric

L. hypochondriac

Transpyloric plane

R. lateral (lumbar)

Umbilical

L. lateral (lumbar)

Transtubercular plane

R. iliac

Hypogastric (Suprapubic)

L. iliac

R. midinguinal line

L. midinguinal line

Median midsagittal plane

R. SUP. QUADRANT

L. SUP. QUADRANT

Umbilicus

Umbilical plane

McBurney's point

Cecum

Ant. sup. iliac spine

R. INF. QUADRANT

L. INF. QUADRANT

Vermiform appendix

ABDOMINAL QUADRANTS —ANTERIOR VIEW

L. lung

Spleen

Inf. margin of L. lung

Paravertebral lines

R. lung

R. scapular line (indicates lateral margin of kidney)

L. suprarenal gland

T12

Margin of parietal pleura of R. lung

Pylorus of stomach

R. kidney

Duodenum

Umbilical plane

L3

Ureters

ABDOMINAL QUADRANTS—POSTERIOR VIEW

L. kidney

Median (midsagittal) plane—post. median line

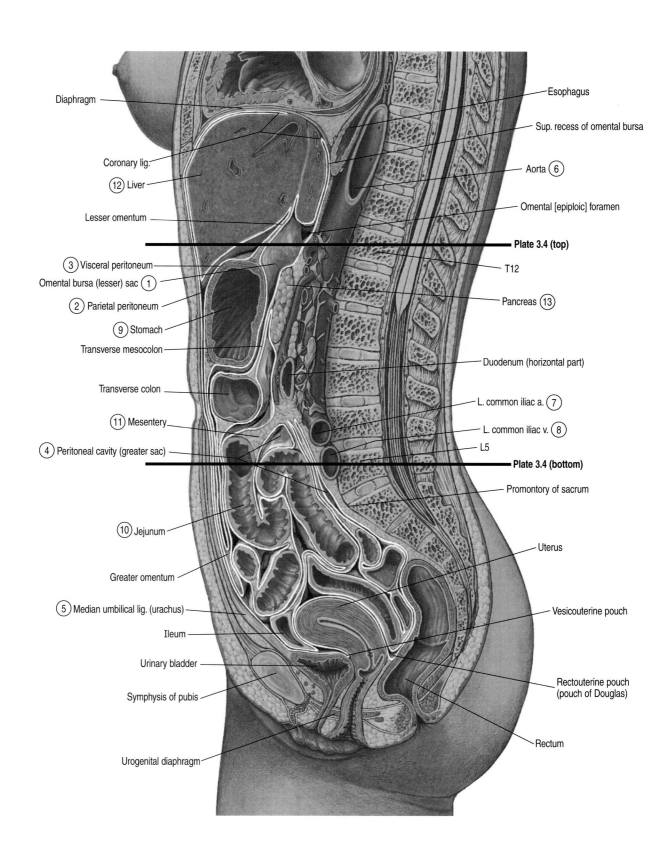

Diaphragm

Coronary lig.

12 Liver

Lesser omentum

3 Visceral peritoneum

Omental bursa (lesser) sac 1

2 Parietal peritoneum

9 Stomach

Transverse mesocolon

Transverse colon

11 Mesentery

4 Peritoneal cavity (greater sac)

10 Jejunum

Greater omentum

5 Median umbilical lig. (urachus)

Ileum

Urinary bladder

Symphysis of pubis

Urogenital diaphragm

Esophagus

Sup. recess of omental bursa

Aorta 6

Omental [epiploic] foramen

Plate 3.4 (top)

T12

Pancreas 13

Duodenum (horizontal part)

L. common iliac a. 7

L. common iliac v. 8

L5

Plate 3.4 (bottom)

Promontory of sacrum

Uterus

Vesicouterine pouch

Rectouterine pouch
(pouch of Douglas)

Rectum

MEDIAN SECTION—LEFT LATERAL VIEW

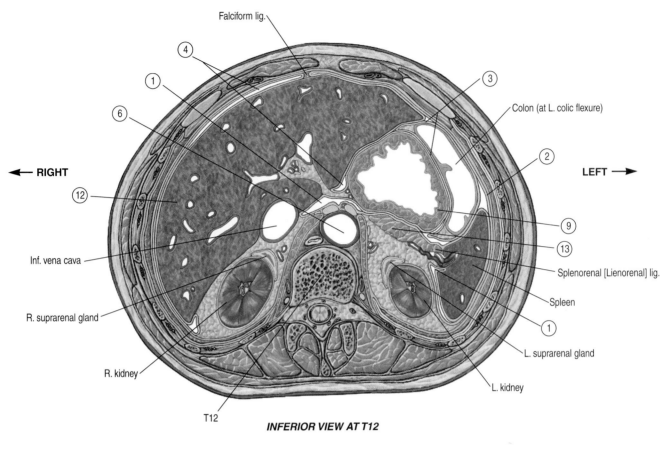

Falciform lig.

④

①

⑥

◀— **RIGHT**

⑫

③

Colon (at L. colic flexure)

②

LEFT —▶

⑨

⑬

Inf. vena cava

Splenorenal [Lienorenal] lig.

Spleen

①

R. suprarenal gland

L. suprarenal gland

R. kidney

L. kidney

T12

INFERIOR VIEW AT T12

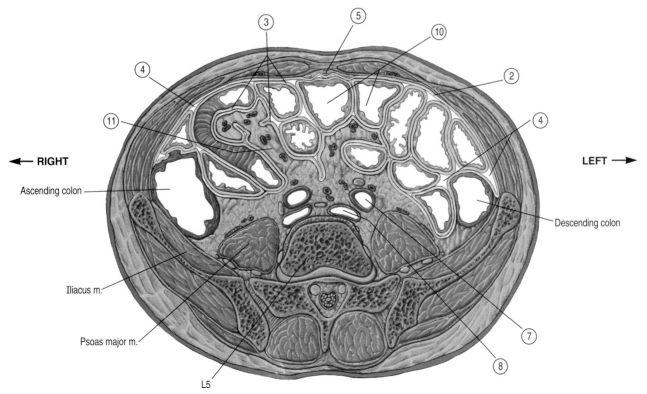

③ ⑤ ⑩

④

②

⑪

④

◀— **RIGHT**

LEFT —▶

Ascending colon

Descending colon

Iliacus m.

Psoas major m.

⑦

⑧

L5

INFERIOR VIEW AT L5

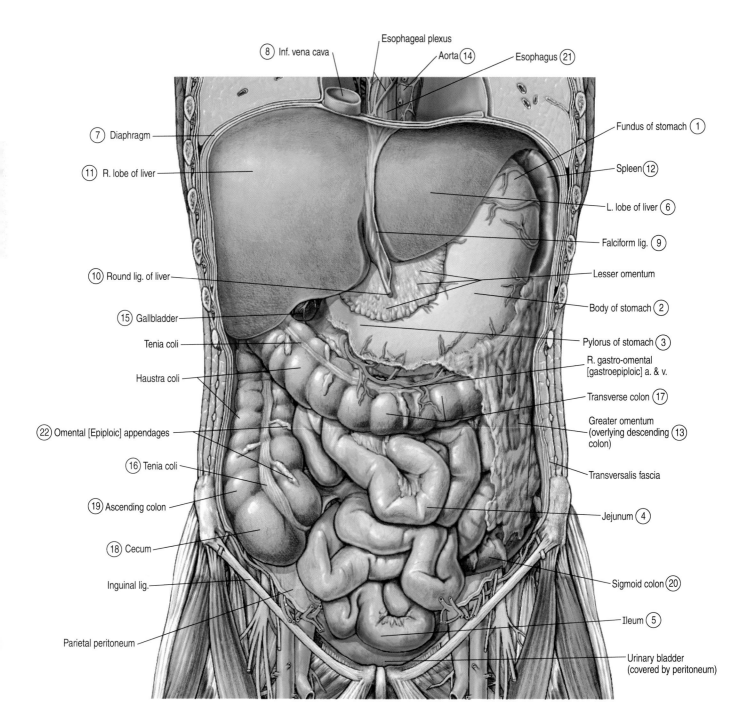

Esophageal plexus

(8) Inf. vena cava

Aorta (14)

Esophagus (21)

(7) Diaphragm

(11) R. lobe of liver

(10) Round lig. of liver

(15) Gallbladder

Tenia coli

Haustra coli

(22) Omental [Epiploic] appendages

(16) Tenia coli

(19) Ascending colon

(18) Cecum

Inguinal lig.

Parietal peritoneum

Fundus of stomach (1)

Spleen (12)

L. lobe of liver (6)

Falciform lig. (9)

Lesser omentum

Body of stomach (2)

Pylorus of stomach (3)

R. gastro-omental
[gastroepiploic] a. & v.

Transverse colon (17)

Greater omentum
(overlying descending (13)
colon)

Transversalis fascia

Jejunum (4)

Sigmoid colon (20)

Ileum (5)

Urinary bladder
(covered by peritoneum)

ANTERIOR VIEW

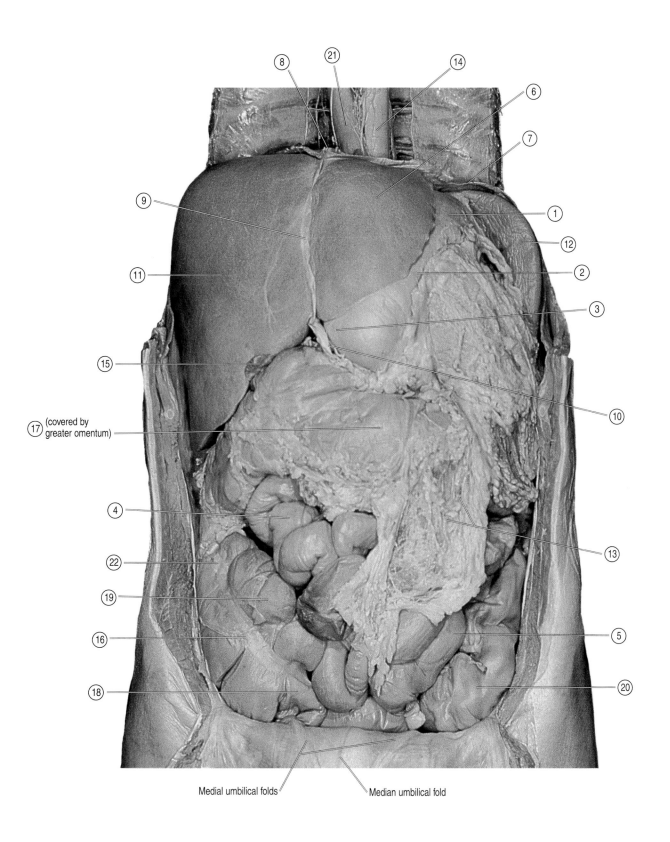

Medial umbilical folds

Median umbilical fold

ANTERIOR VIEW

Root of mesentery   Greater omentum (retracted superiorly)   Tenia coli   Transverse colon   Omental [Epiploic] appendages   Duodenum—horizontal part (retroperitoneal)   Jejunum (retracted to L.)

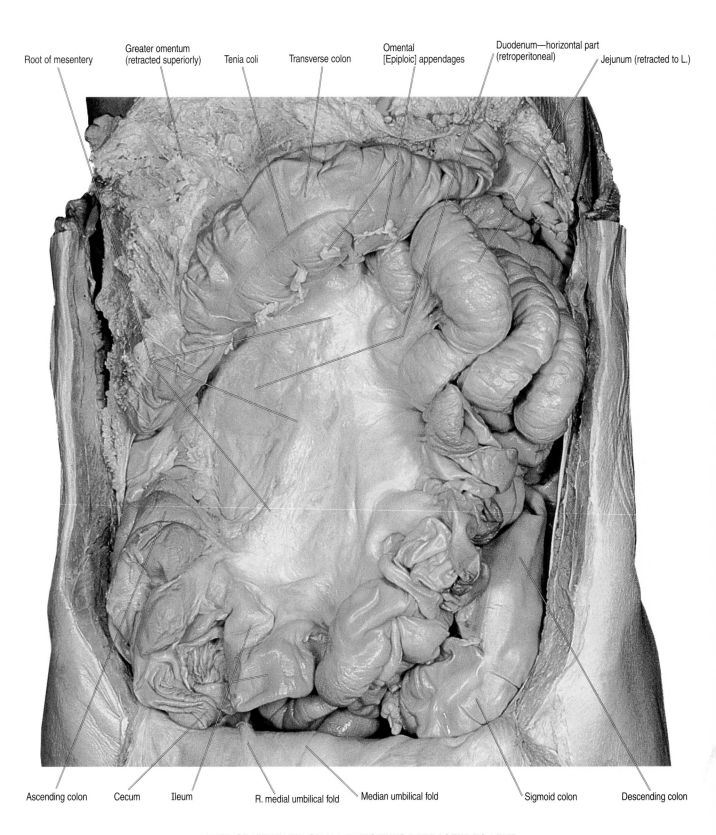

Ascending colon   Cecum   Ileum   R. medial umbilical fold   Median umbilical fold   Sigmoid colon   Descending colon

ANTERIOR VIEW WITH SMALL INTESTINES RETRACTED TO LEFT

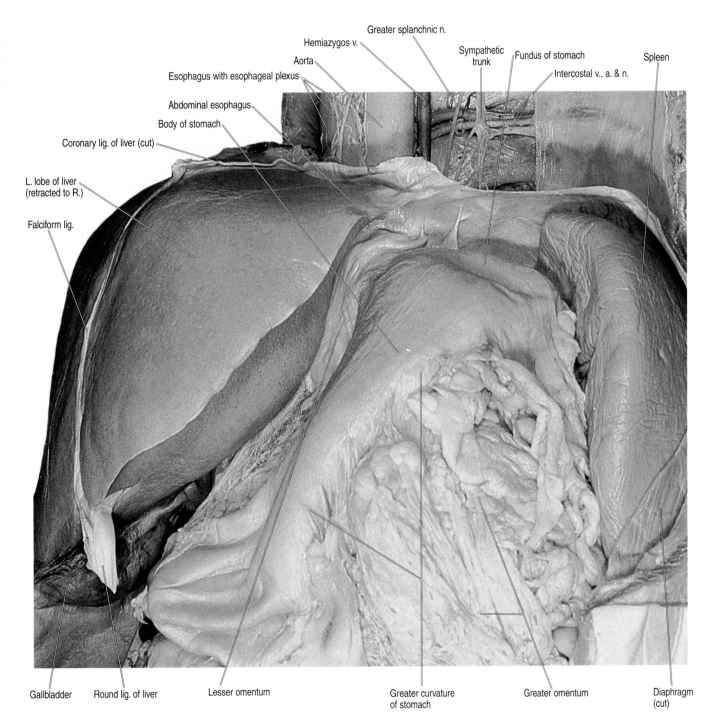

Greater splanchnic n.

Hemiazygos v.

Aorta

Sympathetic
trunk

Fundus of stomach

Spleen

Esophagus with esophageal plexus

Intercostal v., a. & n.

Abdominal esophagus

Body of stomach

Coronary lig. of liver (cut)

L. lobe of liver
(retracted to R.)

Falciform lig.

Gallbladder   Round lig. of liver   Lesser omentum   Greater curvature
of stomach   Greater omentum   Diaphragm
(cut)

LEFT ANTEROLATERAL VIEW

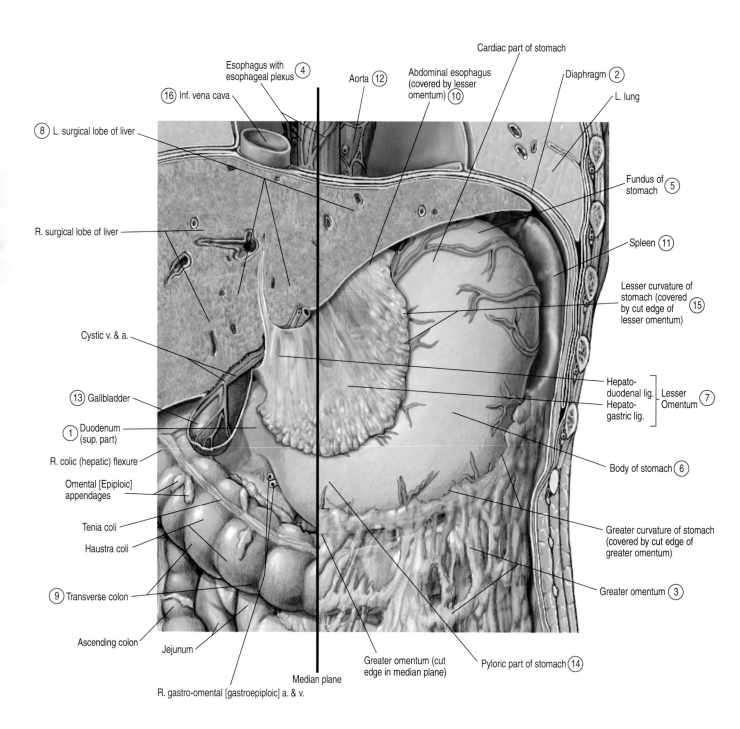

Esophagus with esophageal plexus ④

Aorta ⑫

Cardiac part of stomach

Abdominal esophagus (covered by lesser omentum) ⑩

Diaphragm ②

L. lung

⑯ Inf. vena cava

⑧ L. surgical lobe of liver

Fundus of stomach ⑤

R. surgical lobe of liver

Spleen ⑪

Lesser curvature of stomach (covered by cut edge of lesser omentum) ⑮

Cystic v. & a.

Hepato-duodenal lig. | Lesser
Hepato-gastric lig. | Omentum ⑦

⑬ Gallbladder

① Duodenum (sup. part)

Body of stomach ⑥

R. colic (hepatic) flexure

Omental [Epiploic] appendages

Tenia coli

Haustra coli

Greater curvature of stomach (covered by cut edge of greater omentum)

⑨ Transverse colon

Greater omentum ③

Ascending colon

Jejunum

Greater omentum (cut edge in median plane)

Pyloric part of stomach ⑭

Median plane

R. gastro-omental [gastroepiploic] a. & v.

ANTERIOR VIEW

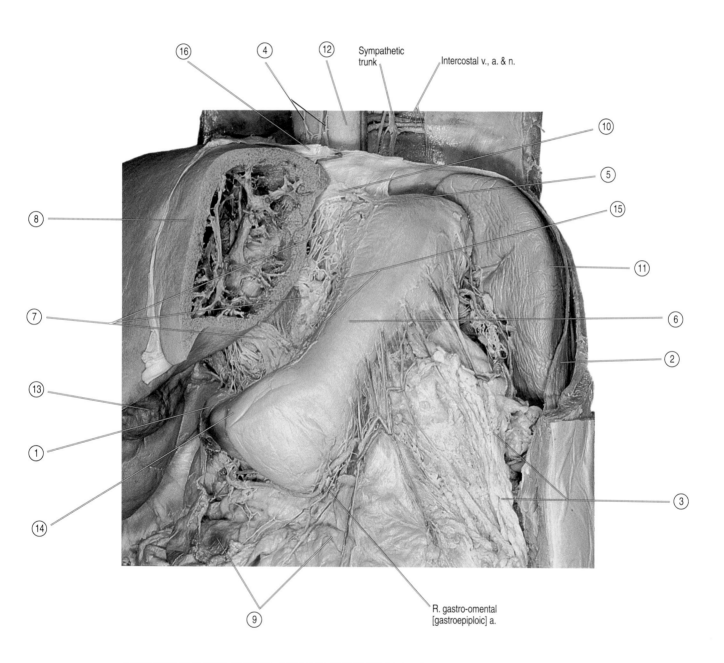

16　4　12　Sympathetic trunk　Intercostal v., a. & n.

10

5

15

11

8

7

6

2

13

1

3

14

9

R. gastro-omental
[gastroepiploic] a.

LEFT ANTEROLATERAL VIEW—LATERAL SEGMENT OF L. LOBE OF LIVER PARTIALLY REMOVED

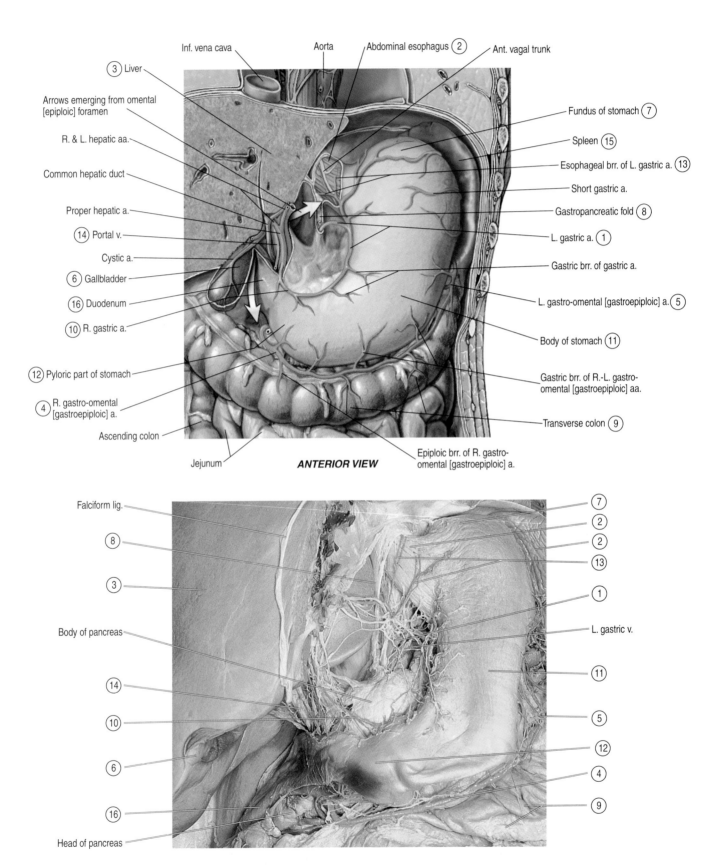

Inf. vena cava

Aorta

Abdominal esophagus ②

Ant. vagal trunk

③ Liver

Arrows emerging from omental [epiploic] foramen

R. & L. hepatic aa.

Common hepatic duct

Proper hepatic a.

⑭ Portal v.

Cystic a.

⑥ Gallbladder

⑯ Duodenum

⑩ R. gastric a.

⑫ Pyloric part of stomach

④ R. gastro-omental [gastroepiploic] a.

Ascending colon

Jejunum

Fundus of stomach ⑦

Spleen ⑮

Esophageal brr. of L. gastric a. ⑬

Short gastric a.

Gastropancreatic fold ⑧

L. gastric a. ①

Gastric brr. of gastric a.

L. gastro-omental [gastroepiploic] a. ⑤

Body of stomach ⑪

Gastric brr. of R.-L. gastro-omental [gastroepiploic] aa.

Transverse colon ⑨

Epiploic brr. of R. gastro-omental [gastroepiploic] a.

ANTERIOR VIEW

Falciform lig.

⑧

③

Body of pancreas

⑭

⑩

⑥

⑯

Head of pancreas

⑦

②

②

⑬

①

L. gastric v.

⑪

⑤

⑫

④

⑨

ANTERIOR VIEW—LIVER LEFT OF FALCIFORM LIG. REMOVED

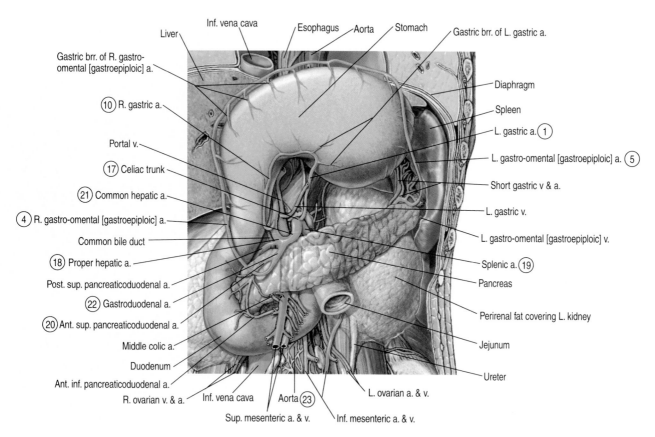

Liver — Inf. vena cava — Esophagus — Aorta — Stomach — Gastric brr. of L. gastric a.

Gastric brr. of R. gastro-omental [gastroepiploic] a.

Diaphragm

Spleen

(10) R. gastric a.

L. gastric a. (1)

Portal v.

L. gastro-omental [gastroepiploic] a. (5)

(17) Celiac trunk

Short gastric v & a.

(21) Common hepatic a.

L. gastric v.

(4) R. gastro-omental [gastroepiploic] a.

L. gastro-omental [gastroepiploic] v.

Common bile duct

Splenic a. (19)

(18) Proper hepatic a.

Pancreas

Post. sup. pancreaticoduodenal a.

Perirenal fat covering L. kidney

(22) Gastroduodenal a.

Jejunum

(20) Ant. sup. pancreaticoduodenal a.

Middle colic a.

Duodenum

Ureter

Ant. inf. pancreaticoduodenal a.

L. ovarian a. & v.

R. ovarian v. & a. — Inf. vena cava — Aorta (23)

Sup. mesenteric a. & v. — Inf. mesenteric a. & v.

**ANTERIOR VIEW—STOMACH REFLECTED SUPERIORLY
AND POSTERIOR PARIETAL PERITONEUM REMOVED**

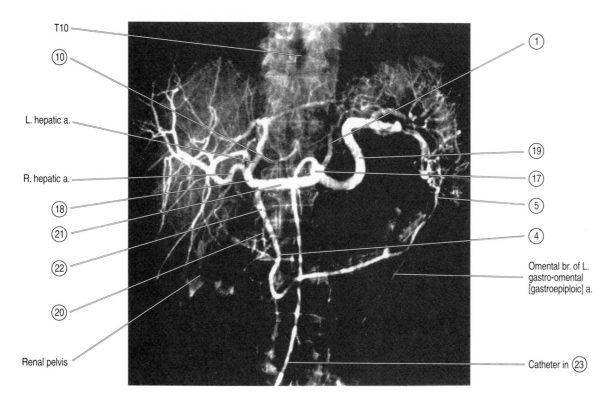

T10

(1)

(10)

L. hepatic a.

(19)

R. hepatic a.

(17)

(18)

(5)

(21)

(4)

(22)

Omental br. of L. gastro-omental [gastroepiploic] a.

(20)

Renal pelvis

Catheter in (23)

ARTERIOGRAPH OF CELIAC TRUNK & BRANCHES

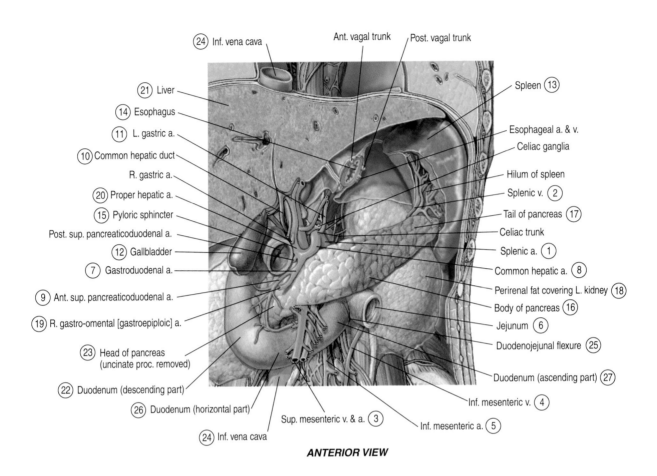

(24) Inf. vena cava   Ant. vagal trunk   Post. vagal trunk

(21) Liver

(14) Esophagus

(11) L. gastric a.

(10) Common hepatic duct

R. gastric a.

(20) Proper hepatic a.

(15) Pyloric sphincter

Post. sup. pancreaticoduodenal a.

(12) Gallbladder

(7) Gastroduodenal a.

(9) Ant. sup. pancreaticoduodenal a.

(19) R. gastro-omental [gastroepiploic] a.

(23) Head of pancreas
(uncinate proc. removed)

(22) Duodenum (descending part)

(26) Duodenum (horizontal part)

(24) Inf. vena cava

Spleen (13)

Esophageal a. & v.

Celiac ganglia

Hilum of spleen

Splenic v. (2)

Tail of pancreas (17)

Celiac trunk

Splenic a. (1)

Common hepatic a. (8)

Perirenal fat covering L. kidney (18)

Body of pancreas (16)

Jejunum (6)

Duodenojejunal flexure (25)

Duodenum (ascending part) (27)

Inf. mesenteric v. (4)

Sup. mesenteric v. & a. (3)

Inf. mesenteric a. (5)

ANTERIOR VIEW

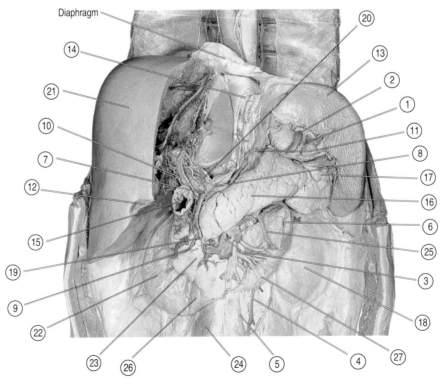

Diaphragm

(14)

(21)

(10)

(7)

(12)

(15)

(19)

(9)

(22)

(23) (26) (24) (5)

(20)

(13)

(2)

(1)

(11)

(8)

(17)

(16)

(6)

(25)

(3)

(18)

(27)

ANTERIOR VIEW

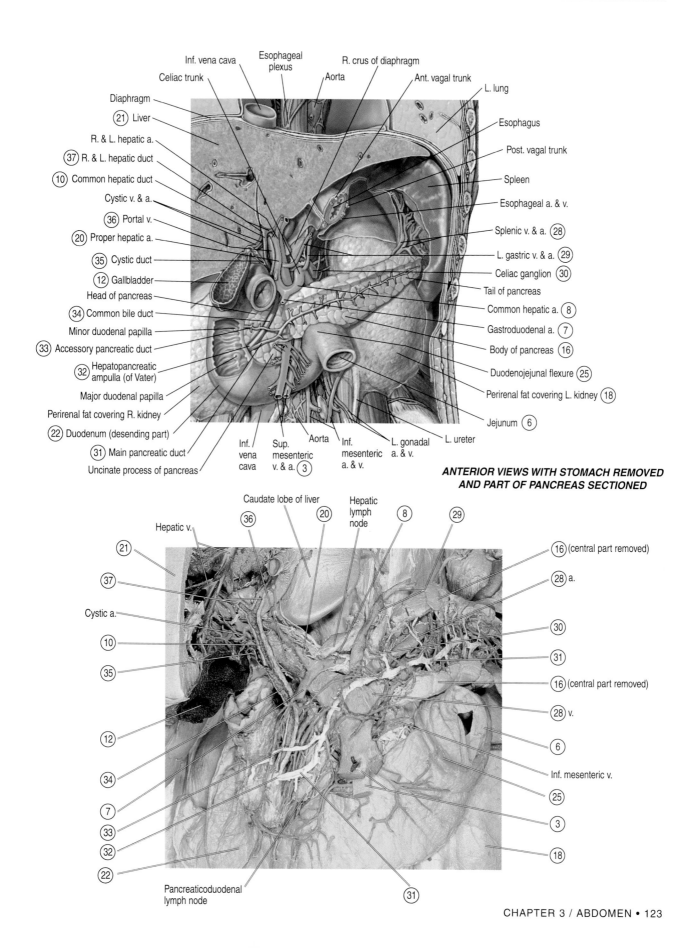

Inf. vena cava
Esophageal plexus
Celiac trunk
R. crus of diaphragm
Aorta
Ant. vagal trunk
L. lung
Diaphragm
(21) Liver
R. & L. hepatic a.
(37) R. & L. hepatic duct
(10) Common hepatic duct
Cystic v. & a.
(36) Portal v.
(20) Proper hepatic a.
(35) Cystic duct
(12) Gallbladder
Head of pancreas
(34) Common bile duct
Minor duodenal papilla
(33) Accessory pancreatic duct
(32) Hepatopancreatic ampulla (of Vater)
Major duodenal papilla
Perirenal fat covering R. kidney
(22) Duodenum (desending part)
(31) Main pancreatic duct
Uncinate process of pancreas

Esophagus
Post. vagal trunk
Spleen
Esophageal a. & v.
Splenic v. & a. (28)
L. gastric v. & a. (29)
Celiac ganglion (30)
Tail of pancreas
Common hepatic a. (8)
Gastroduodenal a. (7)
Body of pancreas (16)
Duodenojejunal flexure (25)
Perirenal fat covering L. kidney (18)
Jejunum (6)

Inf. vena cava
Sup. mesenteric v. & a. (3)
Aorta
Inf. mesenteric a. & v.
L. gonadal a. & v.
L. ureter

ANTERIOR VIEWS WITH STOMACH REMOVED AND PART OF PANCREAS SECTIONED

Caudate lobe of liver
Hepatic lymph node
(36)
(20)
(8)
(29)
Hepatic v.
(21)
(37)
Cystic a.
(10)
(35)
(12)
(34)
(7)
(33)
(32)
(22)

(16) (central part removed)
(28) a.
(30)
(31)
(16) (central part removed)
(28) v.
(6)
Inf. mesenteric v.
(25)
(3)
(18)

Pancreaticoduodenal lymph node
(31)

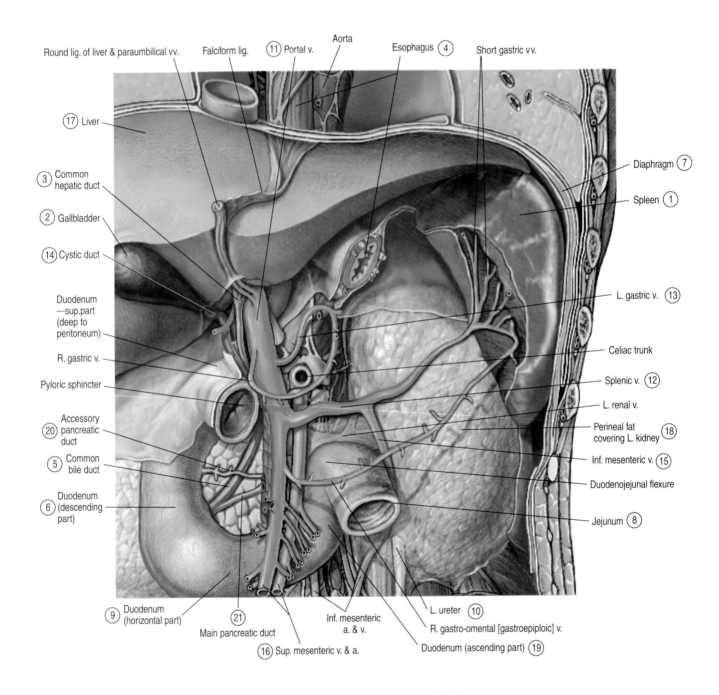

Round lig. of liver & paraumbilical vv.

Falciform lig.

(11) Portal v.

Aorta

Esophagus (4)

Short gastric vv.

(17) Liver

Diaphragm (7)

Spleen (1)

(3) Common hepatic duct

(2) Gallbladder

(14) Cystic duct

L. gastric v. (13)

Duodenum —sup.part (deep to peritoneum)

Celiac trunk

R. gastric v.

Splenic v. (12)

Pyloric sphincter

L. renal v.

(20) Accessory pancreatic duct

Perineal fat covering L. kidney (18)

(5) Common bile duct

Inf. mesenteric v. (15)

Duodenojejunal flexure

(6) Duodenum (descending part)

Jejunum (8)

(9) Duodenum (horizontal part)

(21)

Inf. mesenteric a. & v.

L. ureter (10)

R. gastro-omental [gastroepiploic] v.

Main pancreatic duct

(16) Sup. mesenteric v. & a.

Duodenum (ascending part) (19)

ANTERIOR VIEW WITH STOMACH REMOVED

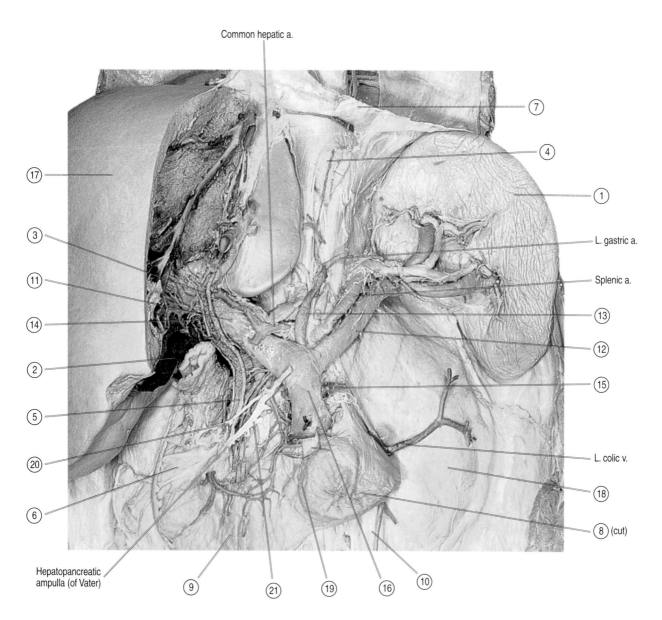

Common hepatic a.

⑦

④

①

L. gastric a.

Splenic a.

⑬

⑫

⑮

L. colic v.

⑱

⑧ (cut)

⑰

③

⑪

⑭

②

⑤

⑳

⑥

Hepatopancreatic
ampulla (of Vater)

⑨ ㉑ ⑲ ⑯ ⑩

*ANTERIOR VIEW WITH STOMACH, LEFT HALF OF LIVER,
AND PANCREAS REMOVED*

Liver
Plate 3.17

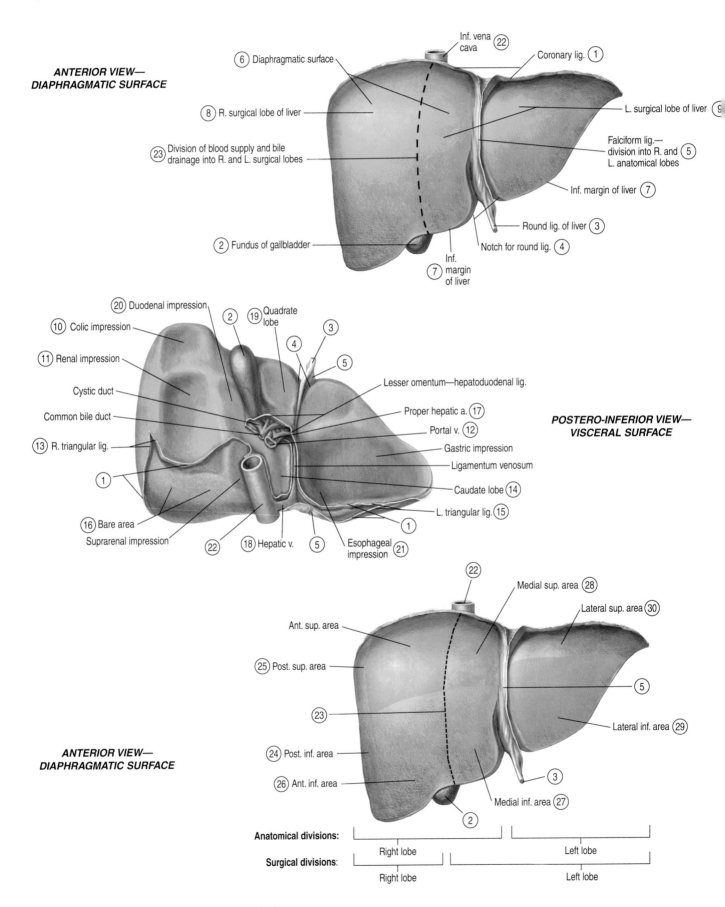

ANTERIOR VIEW—DIAPHRAGMATIC SURFACE

6 Diaphragmatic surface

Inf. vena cava 22

Coronary lig. 1

8 R. surgical lobe of liver

L. surgical lobe of liver 9

23 Division of blood supply and bile drainage into R. and L. surgical lobes

Falciform lig.—division into R. and L. anatomical lobes 5

Inf. margin of liver 7

Round lig. of liver 3

2 Fundus of gallbladder

Notch for round lig. 4

7 Inf. margin of liver

POSTERO-INFERIOR VIEW—VISCERAL SURFACE

20 Duodenal impression

2

19 Quadrate lobe

3

10 Colic impression

4

5

11 Renal impression

Lesser omentum—hepatoduodenal lig.

Cystic duct

Proper hepatic a. 17

Common bile duct

Portal v. 12

13 R. triangular lig.

Gastric impression

Ligamentum venosum

1

Caudate lobe 14

L. triangular lig. 15

16 Bare area

1

Suprarenal impression

22

18 Hepatic v.

5

Esophageal impression 21

ANTERIOR VIEW—DIAPHRAGMATIC SURFACE

22

Medial sup. area 28

Lateral sup. area 30

Ant. sup. area

25 Post. sup. area

5

23

Lateral inf. area 29

24 Post. inf. area

3

26 Ant. inf. area

Medial inf. area 27

2

Anatomical divisions:

Right lobe

Left lobe

Surgical divisions:

Right lobe

Left lobe

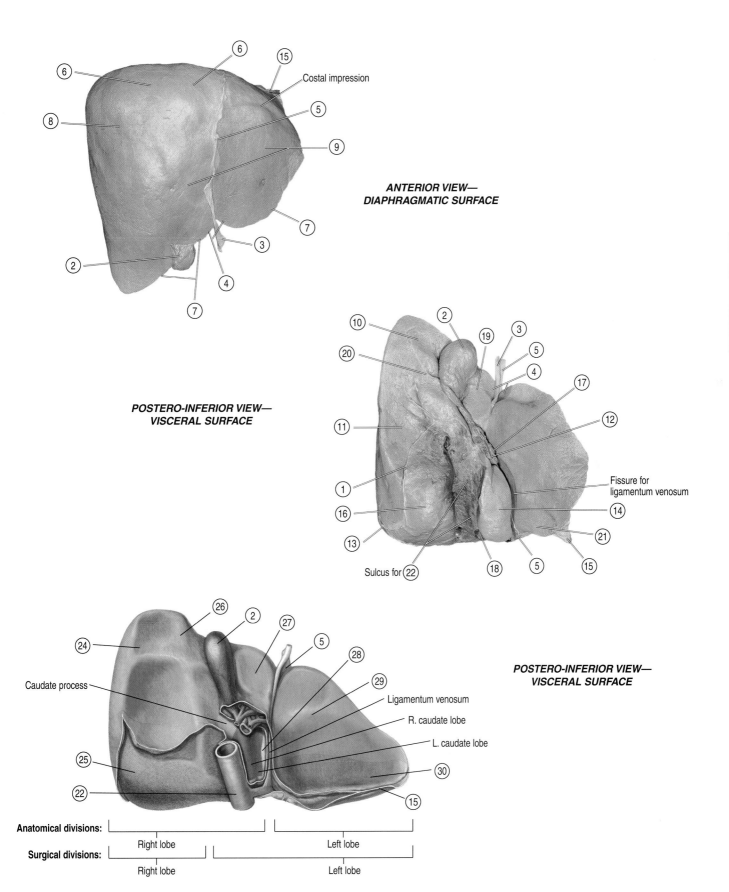

ANTERIOR VIEW—
DIAPHRAGMATIC SURFACE

Costal impression

POSTERO-INFERIOR VIEW—
VISCERAL SURFACE

Fissure for
ligamentum venosum

Sulcus for (22)

POSTERO-INFERIOR VIEW—
VISCERAL SURFACE

Caudate process

Ligamentum venosum

R. caudate lobe

L. caudate lobe

Anatomical divisions:

Right lobe   Left lobe

Surgical divisions:

Right lobe   Left lobe

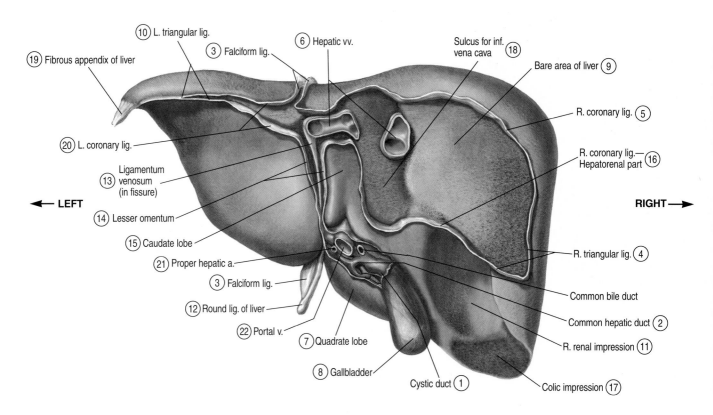

(10) L. triangular lig.

(19) Fibrous appendix of liver

(3) Falciform lig.

(6) Hepatic vv.

Sulcus for inf. vena cava (18)

Bare area of liver (9)

(20) L. coronary lig.

R. coronary lig. (5)

Ligamentum
(13) venosum
(in fissure)

R. coronary lig.—
Hepatorenal part (16)

◄— LEFT

RIGHT —►

(14) Lesser omentum

(15) Caudate lobe

(21) Proper hepatic a.

R. triangular lig. (4)

(3) Falciform lig.

Common bile duct

(12) Round lig. of liver

Common hepatic duct (2)

(22) Portal v.

R. renal impression (11)

(7) Quadrate lobe

(8) Gallbladder

Cystic duct (1)

Colic impression (17)

POSTERIOR VIEWS—VISCERO-DIAPHRAGMATIC SURFACE

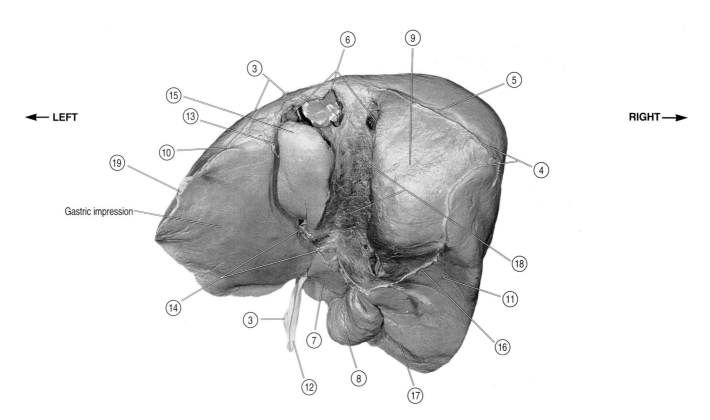

(6)

(9)

(3)

(5)

(15)

◄— LEFT

RIGHT —►

(13)

(10)

(19)

(4)

Gastric impression

(18)

(14)

(11)

(3)

(16)

(7)

(12)

(8)

(17)

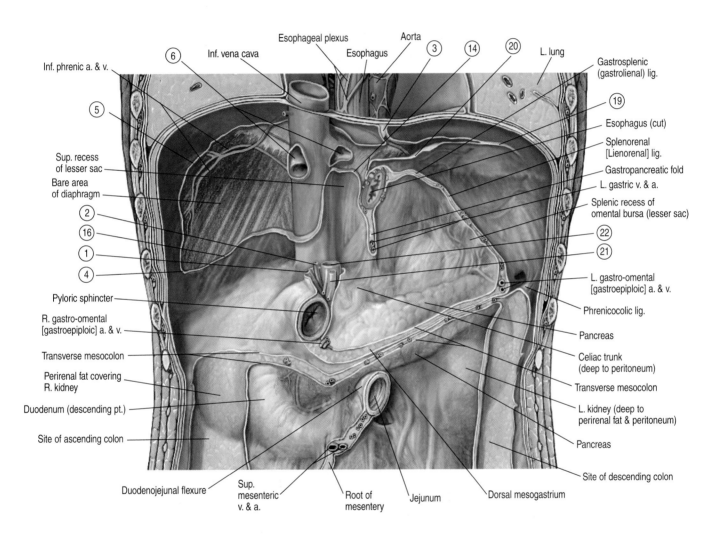

Esophageal plexus

Aorta

Inf. vena cava

Esophagus

⑥

⑤

Inf. phrenic a. & v.

③ ⑭ ⑳ L. lung

Gastrosplenic (gastrolienal) lig.

⑲

Esophagus (cut)

Splenorenal [Lienorenal] lig.

Gastropancreatic fold

L. gastric v. & a.

Splenic recess of omental bursa (lesser sac)

Sup. recess of lesser sac

Bare area of diaphragm

②

⑯

①

④

Pyloric sphincter

R. gastro-omental [gastroepiploic] a. & v.

Transverse mesocolon

Perirenal fat covering R. kidney

Duodenum (descending pt.)

Site of ascending colon

Duodenojejunal flexure

Sup. mesenteric v. & a.

Root of mesentery

Jejunum

Dorsal mesogastrium

⑳

②

②

L. gastro-omental [gastroepiploic] a. & v.

Phrenicocolic lig.

Pancreas

Celiac trunk (deep to peritoneum)

Transverse mesocolon

L. kidney (deep to perirenal fat & peritoneum)

Pancreas

Site of descending colon

ANTERIOR VIEW—POSTERIOR ABDOMINAL WALL

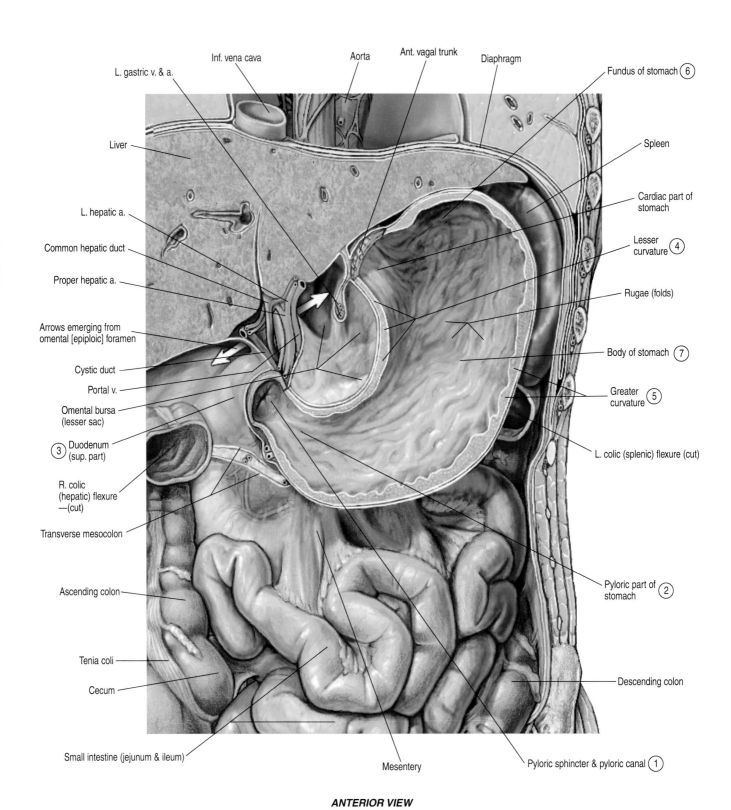

Inf. vena cava

Aorta

Ant. vagal trunk

Diaphragm

L. gastric v. & a.

Fundus of stomach 6

Liver

Spleen

Cardiac part of stomach

L. hepatic a.

Lesser curvature 4

Common hepatic duct

Proper hepatic a.

Rugae (folds)

Arrows emerging from omental [epiploic] foramen

Body of stomach 7

Cystic duct

Portal v.

Greater curvature 5

Omental bursa (lesser sac)

3 Duodenum (sup. part)

L. colic (splenic) flexure (cut)

R. colic (hepatic) flexure —(cut)

Transverse mesocolon

Ascending colon

Pyloric part of stomach 2

Tenia coli

Cecum

Descending colon

Small intestine (jejunum & ileum)

Mesentery

Pyloric sphincter & pyloric canal 1

ANTERIOR VIEW

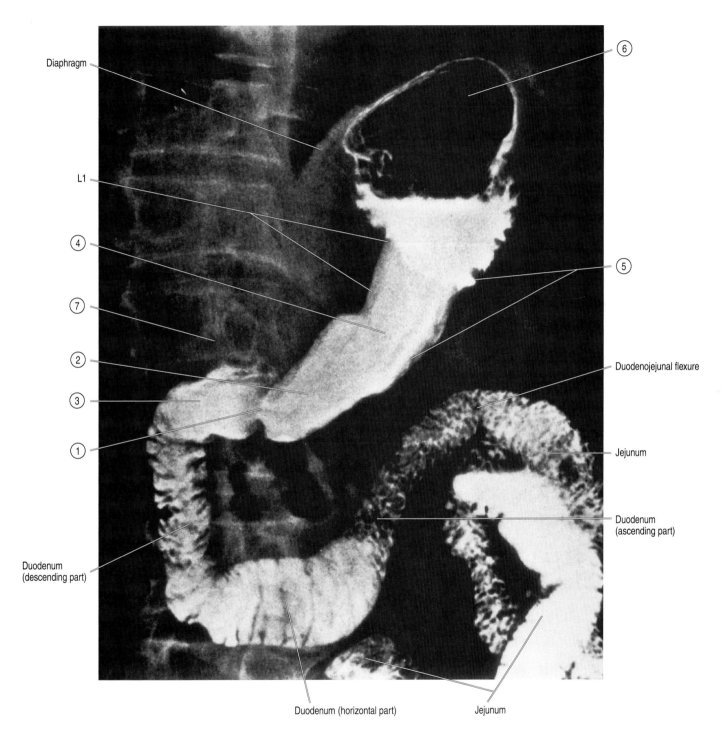

Diaphragm

L1

④

⑦

②

③

①

Duodenum
(descending part)

⑥

⑤

Duodenojejunal flexure

Jejunum

Duodenum
(ascending part)

Duodenum (horizontal part)

Jejunum

RADIOGRAPH OF UPPER G.I. TRACT FOLLOWING BARIUM SWALLOW

Small Intestines—Vasculature
Plate 3.23

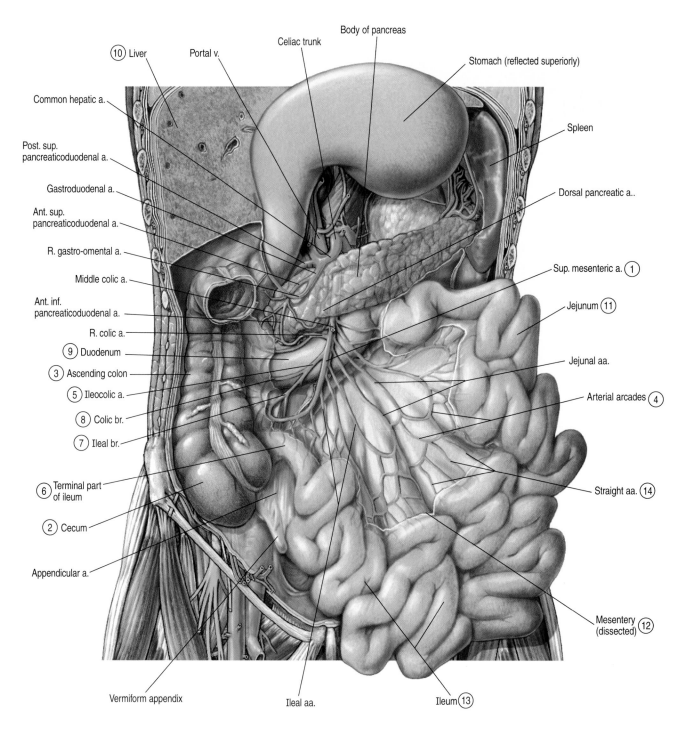

Body of pancreas

Celiac trunk

⑩ Liver   Portal v.

Stomach (reflected superiorly)

Common hepatic a.

Spleen

Post. sup.
pancreaticoduodenal a.

Dorsal pancreatic a..

Gastroduodenal a.

Ant. sup.
pancreaticoduodenal a.

R. gastro-omental a.

Sup. mesenteric a. ①

Middle colic a.

Jejunum ⑪

Ant. inf.
pancreaticoduodenal a.

Jejunal aa.

R. colic a.

⑨ Duodenum

Arterial arcades ④

③ Ascending colon

⑤ Ileocolic a.

⑧ Colic br.

⑦ Ileal br.

Straight aa. ⑭

⑥ Terminal part
of ileum

② Cecum

Appendicular a.

Mesentery ⑫
(dissected)

Vermiform appendix   Ileal aa.   Ileum ⑬

ANTERIOR VIEW—STOMACH REFLECTED SUPERIORLY

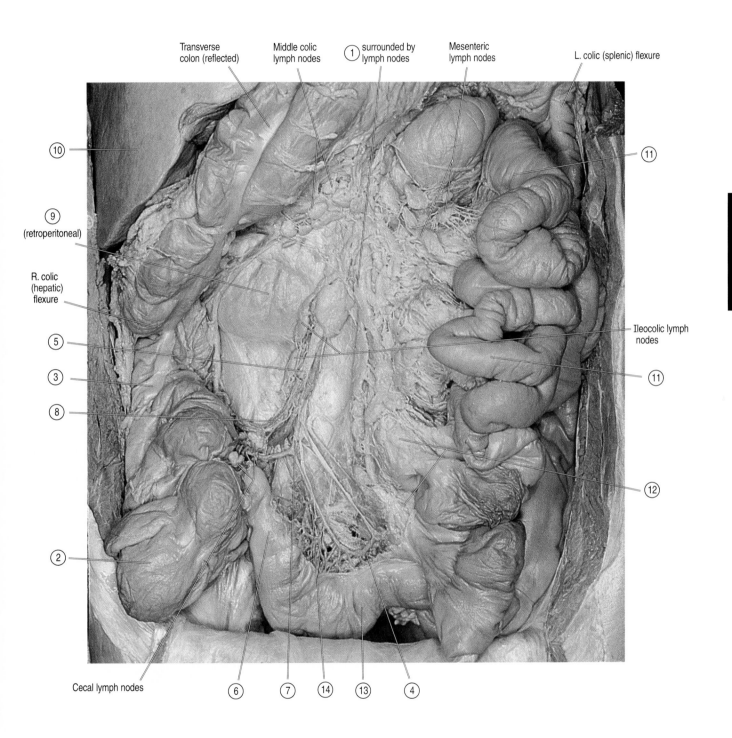

Transverse colon (reflected)

Middle colic lymph nodes

① surrounded by lymph nodes

Mesenteric lymph nodes

L. colic (splenic) flexure

⑩

⑪

⑨ (retroperitoneal)

R. colic (hepatic) flexure

Ileocolic lymph nodes

⑤

⑪

③

⑧

⑫

②

Cecal lymph nodes

⑥   ⑦   ⑭   ⑬   ④

ANTERIOR VIEW—TRANSVERSE COLON REFLECTED SUPERIORLY

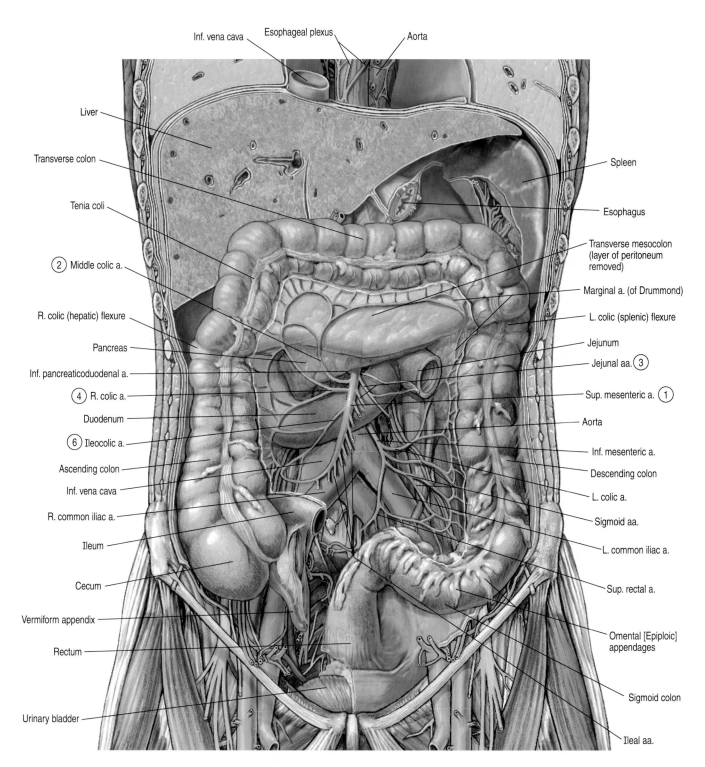

Inf. vena cava

Esophageal plexus

Aorta

Liver

Transverse colon

Tenia coli

② Middle colic a.

R. colic (hepatic) flexure

Pancreas

Inf. pancreaticoduodenal a.

④ R. colic a.

Duodenum

⑥ Ileocolic a.

Ascending colon

Inf. vena cava

R. common iliac a.

Ileum

Cecum

Vermiform appendix

Rectum

Urinary bladder

Spleen

Esophagus

Transverse mesocolon
(layer of peritoneum
removed)

Marginal a. (of Drummond)

L. colic (splenic) flexure

Jejunum

Jejunal aa. ③

Sup. mesenteric a. ①

Aorta

Inf. mesenteric a.

Descending colon

L. colic a.

Sigmoid aa.

L. common iliac a.

Sup. rectal a.

Omental [Epiploic]
appendages

Sigmoid colon

Ileal aa.

*ANTERIOR VIEW—TRANSVERSE COLON REFLECTED SUPERIORLY
& THE MESENTERY PROPER REMOVED*

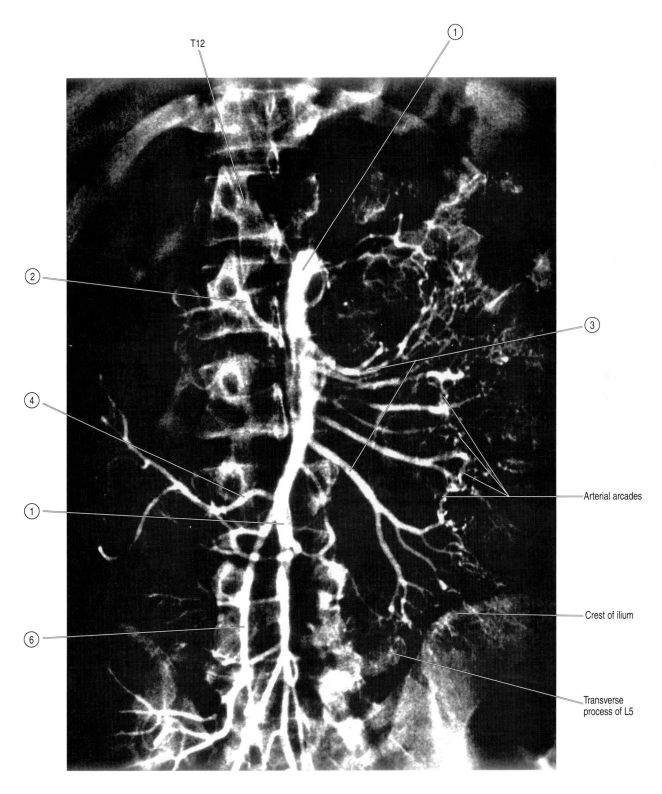

T12

1

2

3

4

1

Arterial arcades

6

Crest of ilium

Transverse
process of L5

ARTERIOGRAPH OF SUPERIOR MESENTERIC ARTERY & BRANCHES

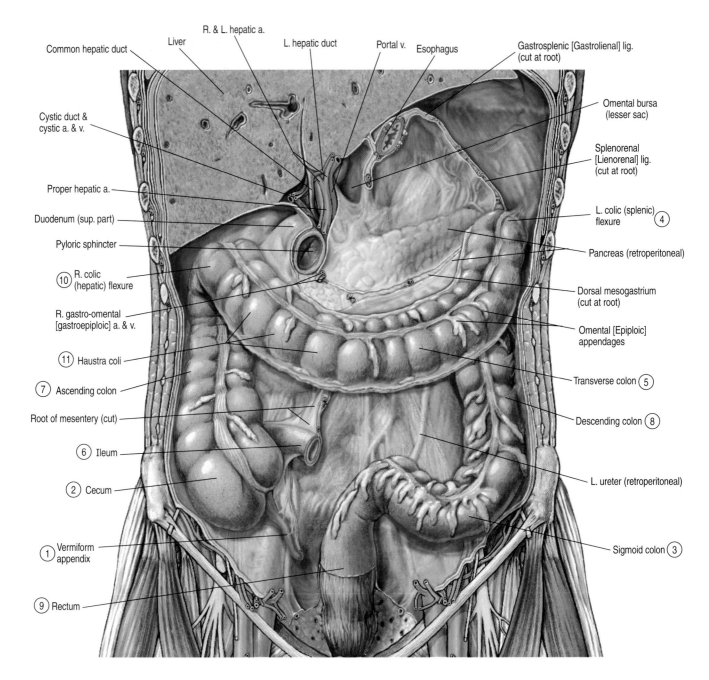

Common hepatic duct

R. & L. hepatic a.

Liver

L. hepatic duct

Portal v.

Esophagus

Gastrosplenic [Gastrolienal] lig. (cut at root)

Cystic duct & cystic a. & v.

Omental bursa (lesser sac)

Splenorenal [Lienorenal] lig. (cut at root)

Proper hepatic a.

Duodenum (sup. part)

L. colic (splenic) flexure ④

Pyloric sphincter

Pancreas (retroperitoneal)

⑩ R. colic (hepatic) flexure

Dorsal mesogastrium (cut at root)

R. gastro-omental [gastroepiploic] a. & v.

Omental [Epiploic] appendages

⑪ Haustra coli

⑦ Ascending colon

Transverse colon ⑤

Root of mesentery (cut)

Descending colon ⑧

⑥ Ileum

② Cecum

L. ureter (retroperitoneal)

① Vermiform appendix

Sigmoid colon ③

⑨ Rectum

ANTERIOR VIEW—SMALL INTESTINES REMOVED

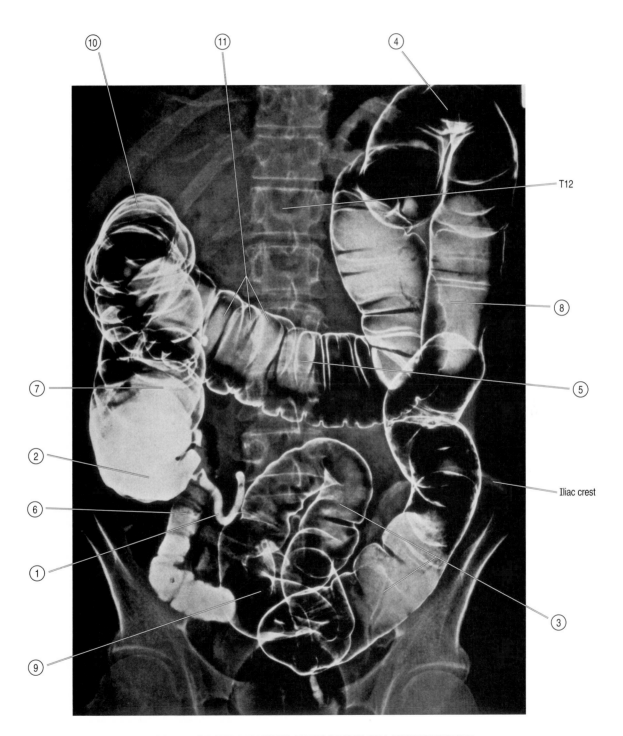

DOUBLE CONTRAST (AIR & BARIUM) RADIOGRAPH OF LARGE INTESTINE

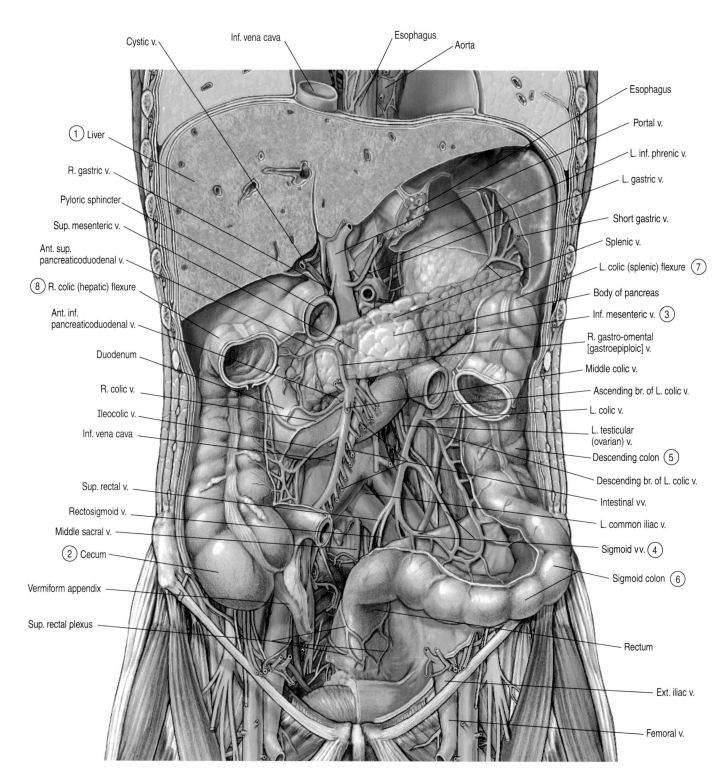

Cystic v.

Inf. vena cava

Esophagus

Aorta

① Liver

R. gastric v.

Pyloric sphincter

Sup. mesenteric v.

Ant. sup. pancreaticoduodenal v.

⑧ R. colic (hepatic) flexure

Ant. inf. pancreaticoduodenal v.

Duodenum

R. colic v.

Ileocolic v.

Inf. vena cava

Sup. rectal v.

Rectosigmoid v.

Middle sacral v.

② Cecum

Vermiform appendix

Sup. rectal plexus

Esophagus

Portal v.

L. inf. phrenic v.

L. gastric v.

Short gastric v.

Splenic v.

L. colic (splenic) flexure ⑦

Body of pancreas

Inf. mesenteric v. ③

R. gastro-omental [gastroepiploic] v.

Middle colic v.

Ascending br. of L. colic v.

L. colic v.

L. testicular (ovarian) v.

Descending colon ⑤

Descending br. of L. colic v.

Intestinal vv.

L. common iliac v.

Sigmoid vv. ④

Sigmoid colon ⑥

Rectum

Ext. iliac v.

Femoral v.

ANTERIOR VIEW

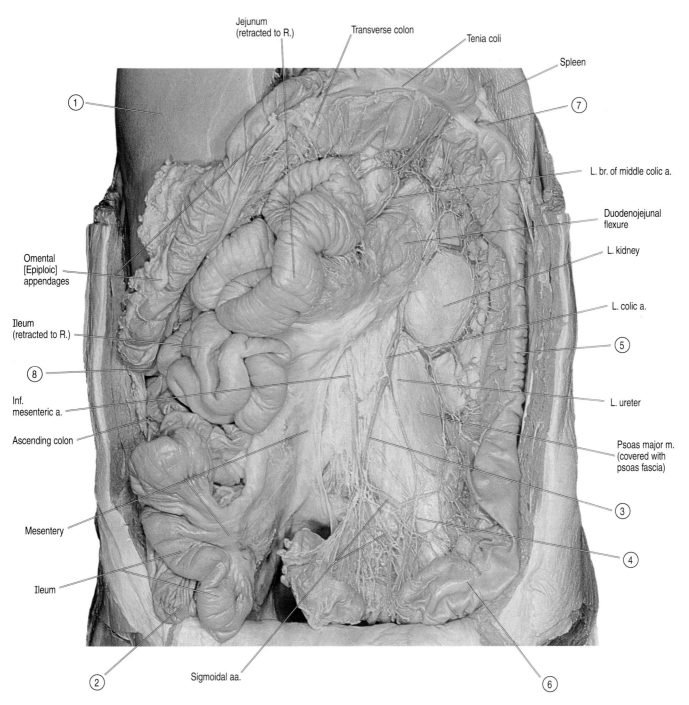

Jejunum
(retracted to R.)

Transverse colon

Tenia coli

Spleen

1

7

L. br. of middle colic a.

Duodenojejunal
flexure

L. kidney

Omental
[Epiploic]
appendages

L. colic a.

Ileum
(retracted to R.)

5

8

L. ureter

Inf.
mesenteric a.

Ascending colon

Psoas major m.
(covered with
psoas fascia)

3

Mesentery

4

Ileum

2

Sigmoidal aa.

6

ANTERIOR VIEW—TRANSVERSE COLON REFLECTED SUPERIORLY

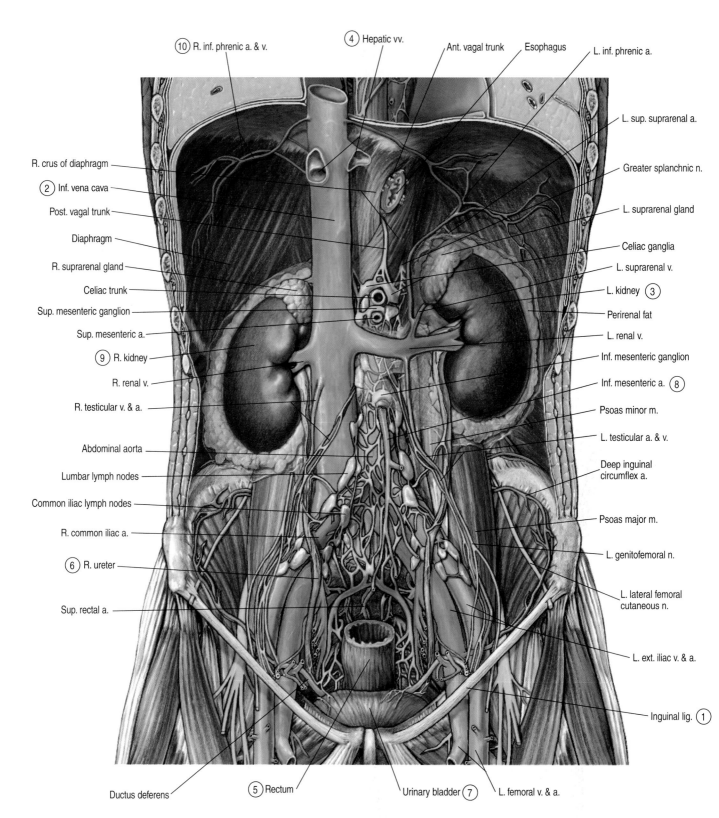

⑩ R. inf. phrenic a. & v.

④ Hepatic vv.

Ant. vagal trunk

Esophagus

L. inf. phrenic a.

L. sup. suprarenal a.

R. crus of diaphragm

② Inf. vena cava

Post. vagal trunk

Diaphragm

R. suprarenal gland

Celiac trunk

Sup. mesenteric ganglion

Sup. mesenteric a.

⑨ R. kidney

R. renal v.

R. testicular v. & a.

Abdominal aorta

Lumbar lymph nodes

Common iliac lymph nodes

R. common iliac a.

⑥ R. ureter

Sup. rectal a.

Greater splanchnic n.

L. suprarenal gland

Celiac ganglia

L. suprarenal v.

L. kidney ③

Perirenal fat

L. renal v.

Inf. mesenteric ganglion

Inf. mesenteric a. ⑧

Psoas minor m.

L. testicular a. & v.

Deep inguinal circumflex a.

Psoas major m.

L. genitofemoral n.

L. lateral femoral cutaneous n.

L. ext. iliac v. & a.

Inguinal lig. ①

Ductus deferens

⑤ Rectum

Urinary bladder ⑦

L. femoral v. & a.

ANTERIOR VIEW WITH VISCERA AND PERITONEUM REMOVED

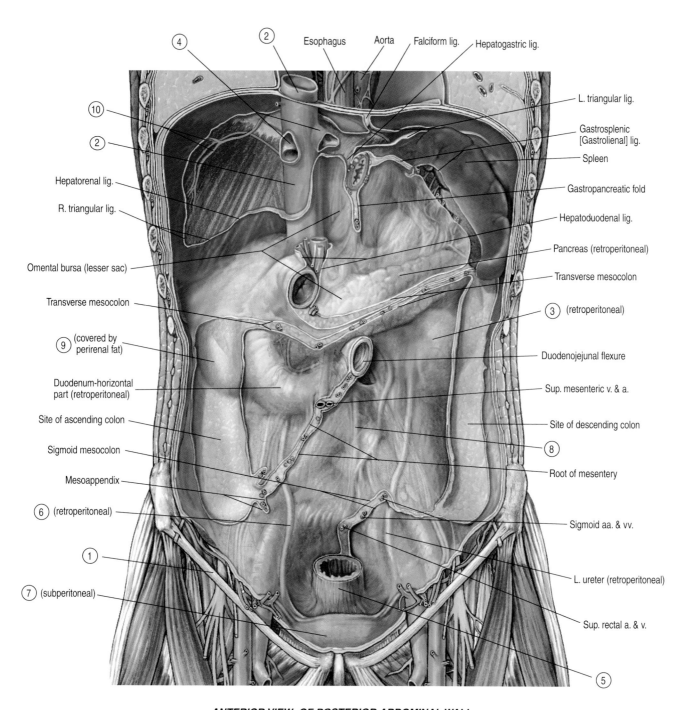

④ ② Esophagus Aorta Falciform lig. Hepatogastric lig.

L. triangular lig.

⑩

Gastrosplenic [Gastrolienal] lig.

②

Spleen

Hepatorenal lig.

Gastropancreatic fold

R. triangular lig.

Hepatoduodenal lig.

Pancreas (retroperitoneal)

Omental bursa (lesser sac)

Transverse mesocolon

Transverse mesocolon

③ (retroperitoneal)

⑨ (covered by perirenal fat)

Duodenojejunal flexure

Duodenum-horizontal part (retroperitoneal)

Sup. mesenteric v. & a.

Site of ascending colon

Site of descending colon

Sigmoid mesocolon

⑧

Mesoappendix

Root of mesentery

⑥ (retroperitoneal)

Sigmoid aa. & vv.

①

L. ureter (retroperitoneal)

⑦ (subperitoneal)

Sup. rectal a. & v.

⑤

**ANTERIOR VIEW OF POSTERIOR ABDOMINAL WALL
SHOWING PERITONEAL COVERINGS AND MESENTERY ORIGINS**

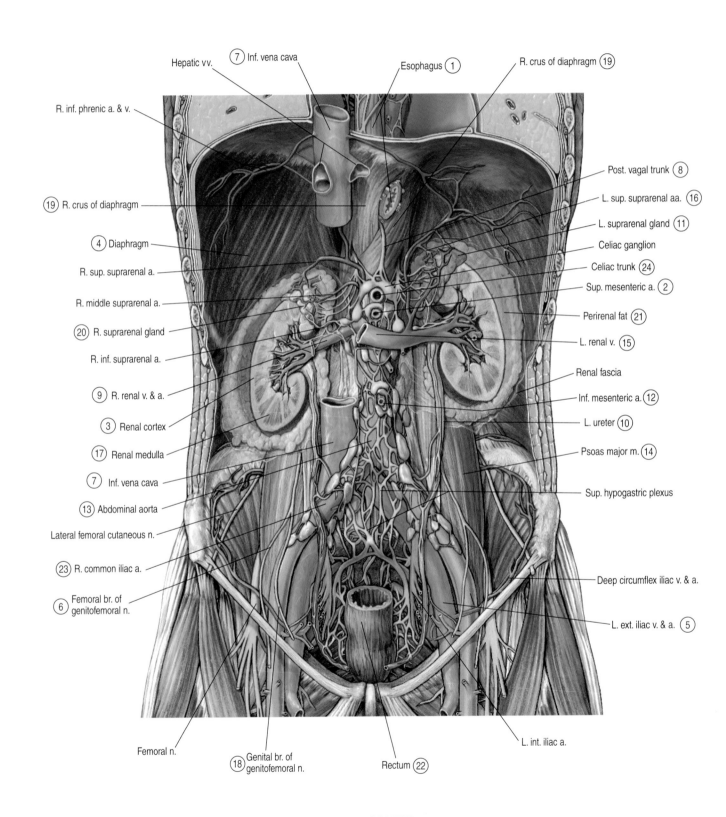

Hepatic vv.

(7) Inf. vena cava

Esophagus (1)

R. crus of diaphragm (19)

R. inf. phrenic a. & v.

(19) R. crus of diaphragm

(4) Diaphragm

R. sup. suprarenal a.

R. middle suprarenal a.

(20) R. suprarenal gland

R. inf. suprarenal a.

(9) R. renal v. & a.

(3) Renal cortex

(17) Renal medulla

(7) Inf. vena cava

(13) Abdominal aorta

Lateral femoral cutaneous n.

(23) R. common iliac a.

(6) Femoral br. of genitofemoral n.

Post. vagal trunk (8)

L. sup. suprarenal aa. (16)

L. suprarenal gland (11)

Celiac ganglion

Celiac trunk (24)

Sup. mesenteric a. (2)

Perirenal fat (21)

L. renal v. (15)

Renal fascia

Inf. mesenteric a. (12)

L. ureter (10)

Psoas major m. (14)

Sup. hypogastric plexus

Deep circumflex iliac v. & a.

L. ext. iliac v. & a. (5)

Femoral n.

(18) Genital br. of genitofemoral n.

Rectum (22)

L. int. iliac a.

ANTERIOR VIEW

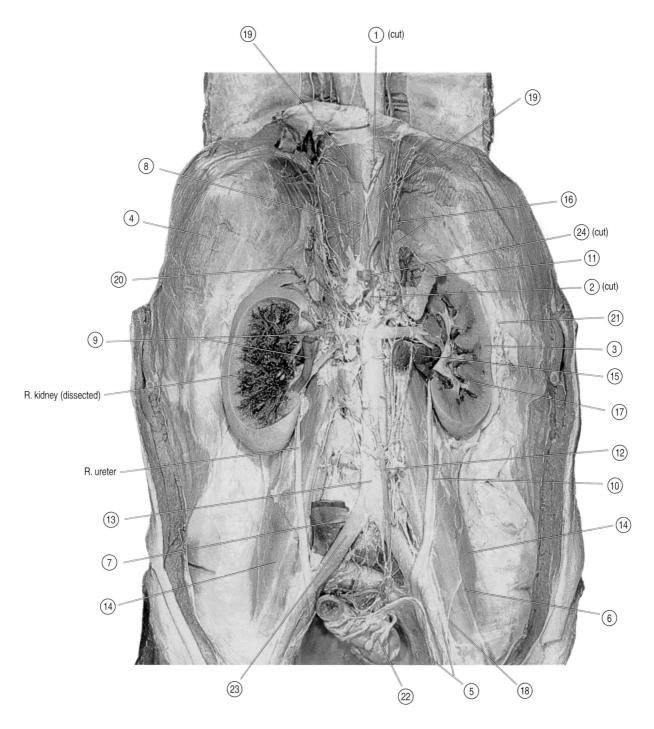

(19) (1) (cut)

(19)

(8)

(4)

(16)

(24) (cut)

(11)

(2) (cut)

(20)

(21)

(9)

(3)

(15)

R. kidney (dissected)

(17)

(12)

R. ureter

(10)

(13)

(14)

(7)

(14)

(6)

(23) (22) (5) (18)

ANTERIOR VIEW

Kidneys
Plate 3.35

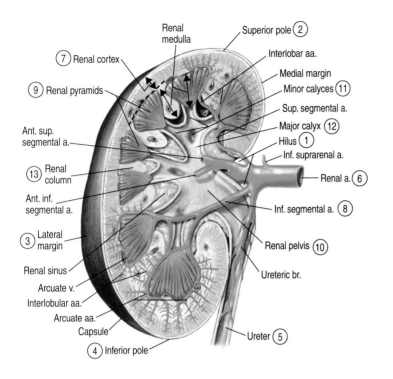

Renal medulla

⑦ Renal cortex

Superior pole ②

Interlobar aa.

⑨ Renal pyramids

Medial margin

Minor calyces ⑪

Sup. segmental a.

Ant. sup. segmental a.

Major calyx ⑫

Hilus ①

Inf. suprarenal a.

⑬ Renal column

Renal a. ⑥

Ant. inf. segmental a.

Inf. segmental a. ⑧

③ Lateral margin

Renal pelvis ⑩

Renal sinus

Ureteric br.

Arcuate v.

Interlobular aa.

Arcuate aa.

Capsule

Ureter ⑤

④ Inferior pole

*POSTERIOR VIEWS OF CORONALLY
SECTIONED L. KIDNEY*

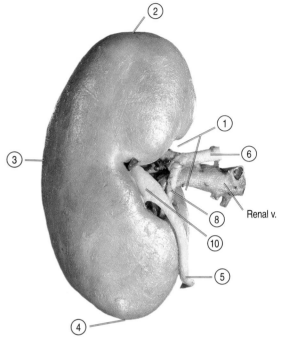

POSTERIOR SURFACE OF LEFT KIDNEY

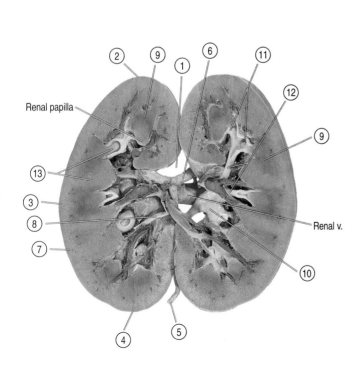

Renal papilla

Renal v.

(bottom-left section labels: ② ⑨ ① ⑥ ⑪ ⑫ ⑨ ⑬ ③ ⑧ ⑦ ⑩ ④ ⑤)

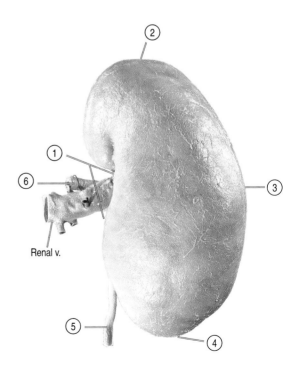

Renal v.

ANTERIOR SURFACE OF LEFT KIDNEY

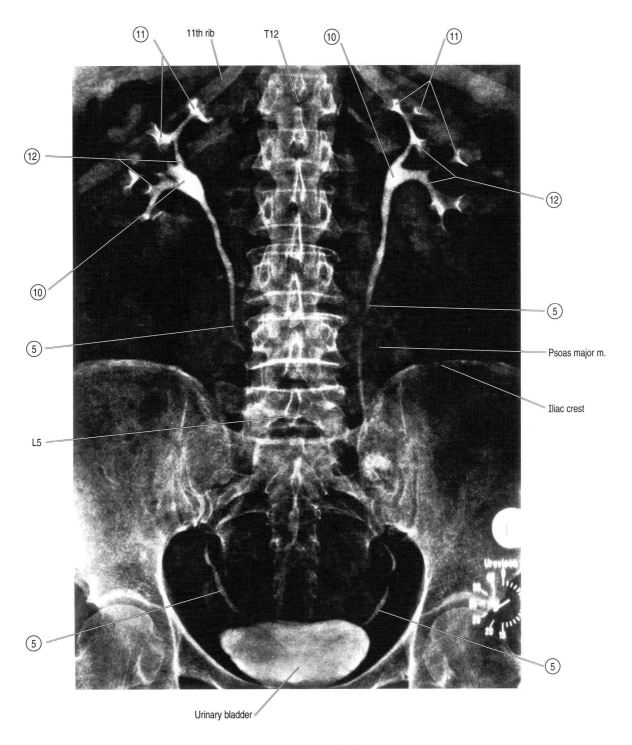

11th rib   T12

Psoas major m.

Iliac crest

L5

Urinary bladder

INTRAVENOUS UROGRAM

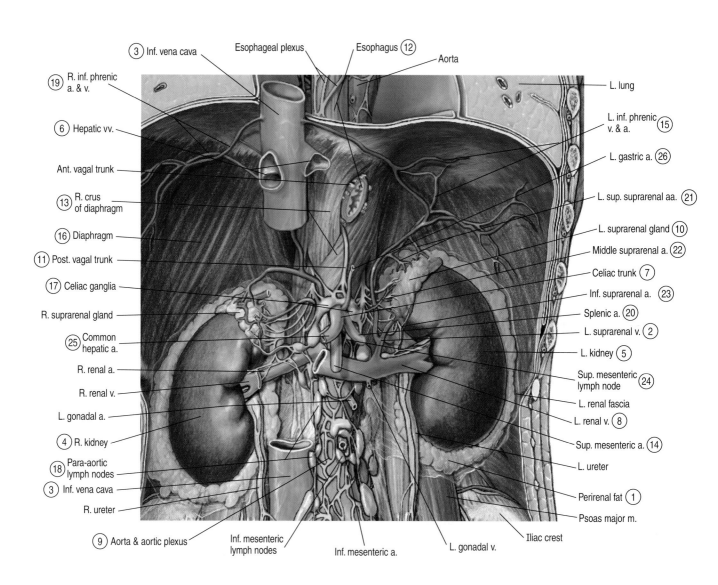

③ Inf. vena cava

Esophageal plexus

Esophagus ⑫

Aorta

⑲ R. inf. phrenic a. & v.

⑥ Hepatic vv.

Ant. vagal trunk

⑬ R. crus of diaphragm

⑯ Diaphragm

⑪ Post. vagal trunk

⑰ Celiac ganglia

R. suprarenal gland

㉕ Common hepatic a.

R. renal a.

R. renal v.

L. gonadal a.

④ R. kidney

⑱ Para-aortic lymph nodes

③ Inf. vena cava

R. ureter

⑨ Aorta & aortic plexus

Inf. mesenteric lymph nodes

Inf. mesenteric a.

L. gonadal v.

L. lung

L. inf. phrenic v. & a. ⑮

L. gastric a. ㉖

L. sup. suprarenal aa. ㉑

L. suprarenal gland ⑩

Middle suprarenal a. ㉒

Celiac trunk ⑦

Inf. suprarenal a. ㉓

Splenic a. ⑳

L. suprarenal v. ②

L. kidney ⑤

Sup. mesenteric lymph node ㉔

L. renal fascia

L. renal v. ⑧

Sup. mesenteric a. ⑭

L. ureter

Perirenal fat ①

Psoas major m.

Iliac crest

ANTERIOR VIEW

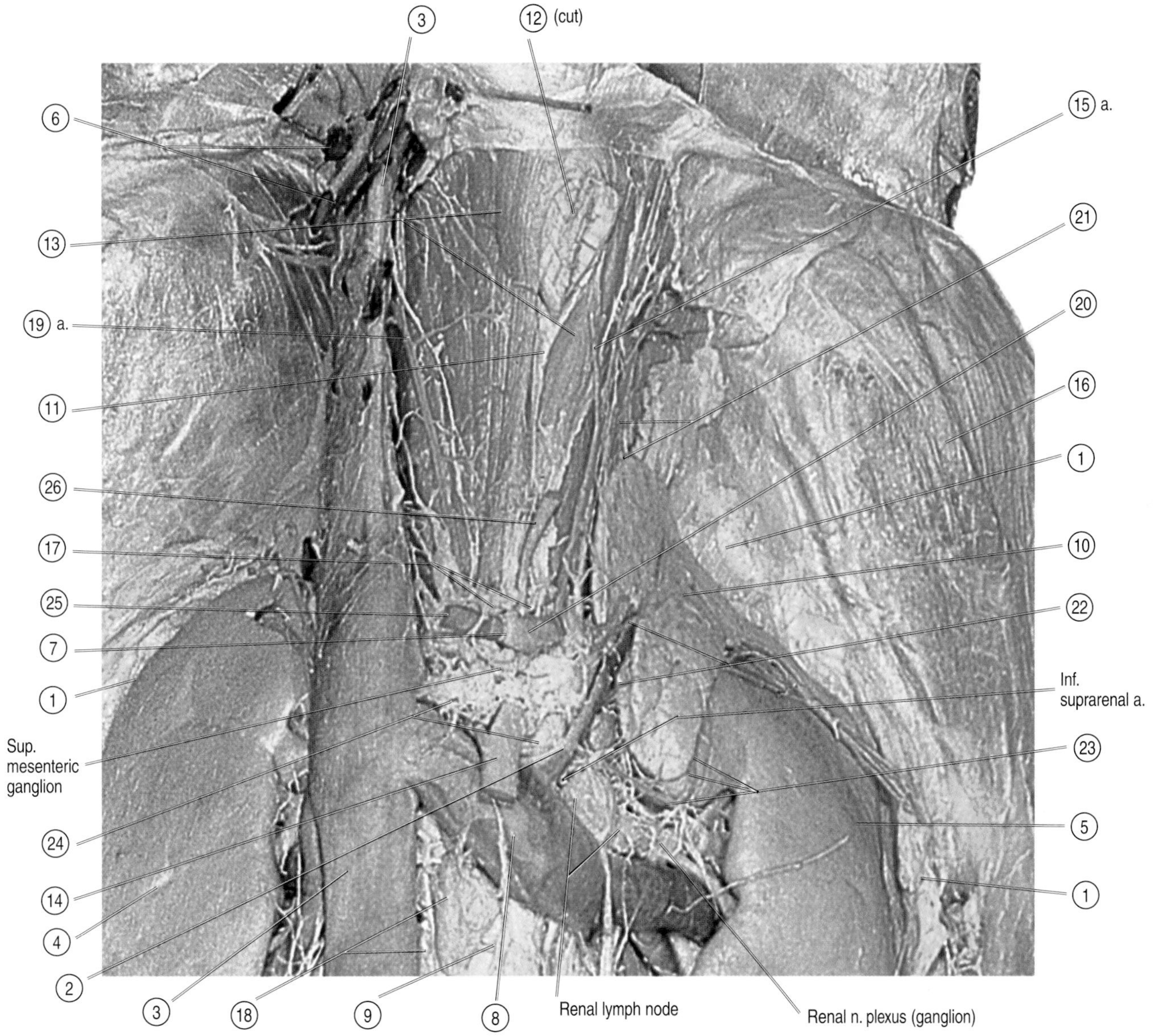
3
12 (cut)
15 a.
6
21
13
20
19 a.
11
16
1
26
10
17
25
22
7
1
Inf.
suprarenal a.
Sup.
mesenteric
ganglion
23
5
24
14
1
4
2
3
18
9
8
Renal lymph node
Renal n. plexus (ganglion)

ANTERIOR VIEW OF SUPERIOR POLE OF L. KIDNEY

Pelvis and Perineum

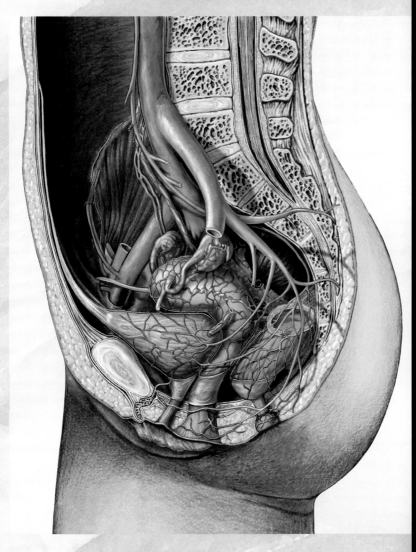

Chapter **4**

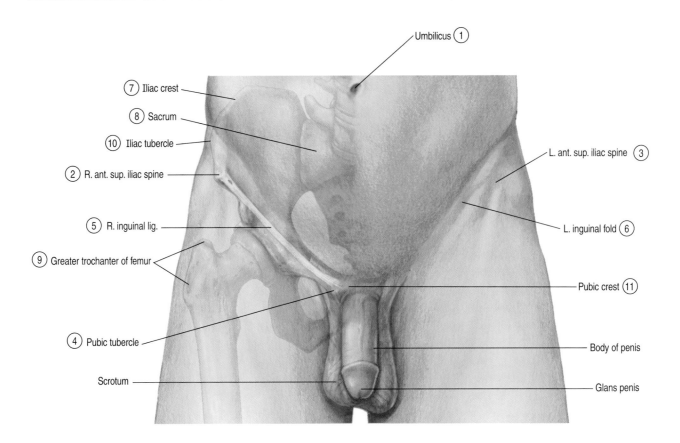

Umbilicus ①

⑦ Iliac crest

⑧ Sacrum

⑩ Iliac tubercle

② R. ant. sup. iliac spine

⑤ R. inguinal lig.

⑨ Greater trochanter of femur

④ Pubic tubercle

Scrotum

L. ant. sup. iliac spine ③

L. inguinal fold ⑥

Pubic crest ⑪

Body of penis

Glans penis

ANTERIOR VIEW

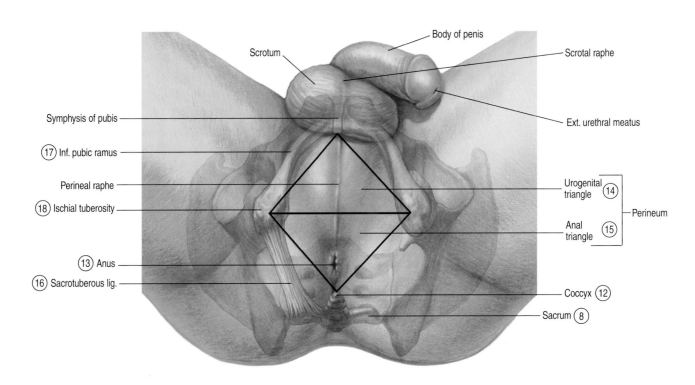

Scrotum

Body of penis

Scrotal raphe

Symphysis of pubis

⑰ Inf. pubic ramus

Perineal raphe

⑱ Ischial tuberosity

⑬ Anus

⑯ Sacrotuberous lig.

Ext. urethral meatus

Urogenital triangle ⑭

Anal triangle ⑮

Perineum

Coccyx ⑫

Sacrum ⑧

LITHOTOMY VIEW

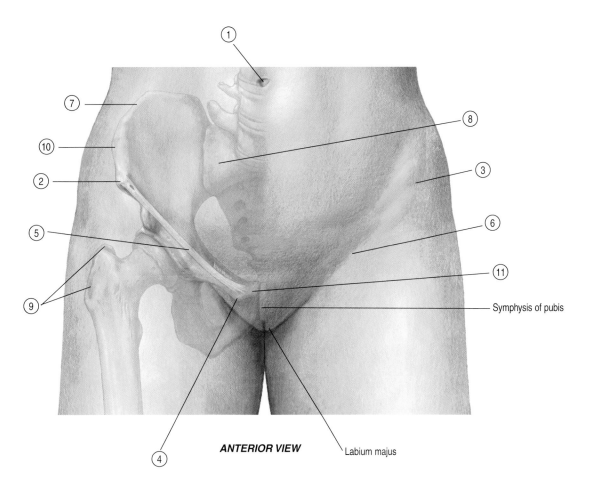

Symphysis of pubis

ANTERIOR VIEW

Labium majus

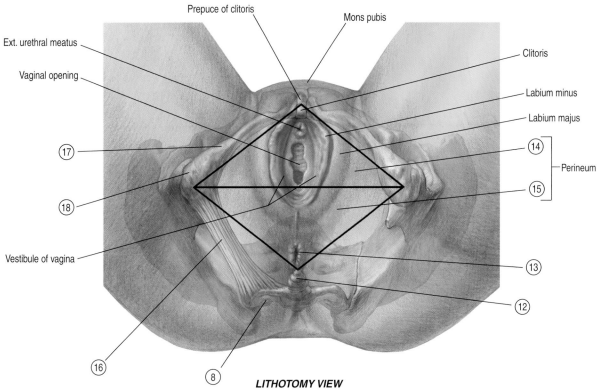

Prepuce of clitoris

Mons pubis

Ext. urethral meatus

Clitoris

Vaginal opening

Labium minus

Labium majus

Perineum

Vestibule of vagina

LITHOTOMY VIEW

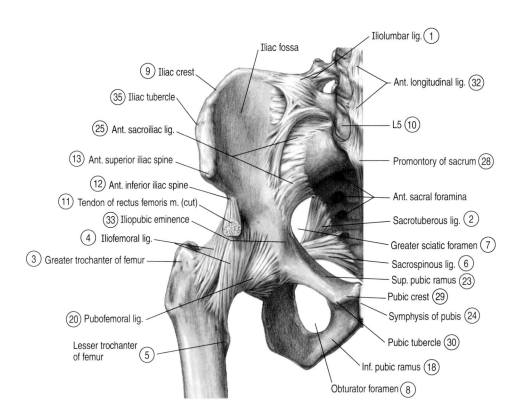

Iliac fossa

Iliolumbar lig. ① 1

⑨ Iliac crest

Ant. longitudinal lig. ㉘ 32

㉟ Iliac tubercle

L5 ⑩ 10

㉕ Ant. sacroiliac lig.

Promontory of sacrum ㉘ 28

⑬ Ant. superior iliac spine

⑫ Ant. inferior iliac spine

Ant. sacral foramina

⑪ Tendon of rectus femoris m. (cut)

Sacrotuberous lig. ② 2

㉝ Iliopubic eminence

Greater sciatic foramen ⑦ 7

④ Iliofemoral lig.

Sacrospinous lig. ⑥ 6

③ Greater trochanter of femur

Sup. pubic ramus ㉓ 23

Pubic crest ㉙ 29

⑳ Pubofemoral lig.

Symphysis of pubis ㉔ 24

Lesser trochanter
of femur ⑤ 5

Pubic tubercle ㉚ 30

Inf. pubic ramus ⑱ 18

Obturator foramen ⑧ 8

ANTERIOR VIEW

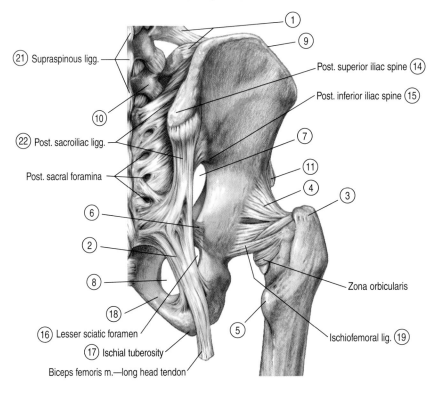

① 1

⑨ 9

㉑ Supraspinous ligg.

Post. superior iliac spine ⑭ 14

Post. inferior iliac spine ⑮ 15

⑩ 10

㉒ Post. sacroiliac ligg.

⑦ 7

Post. sacral foramina

⑪ 11

④ 4

⑥ 6

③ 3

② 2

⑧ 8

Zona orbicularis

⑱ 18

⑯ Lesser sciatic foramen

⑤ 5

⑰ Ischial tuberosity

Ischiofemoral lig. ⑲ 19

Biceps femoris m.—long head tendon

POSTERIOR VIEW

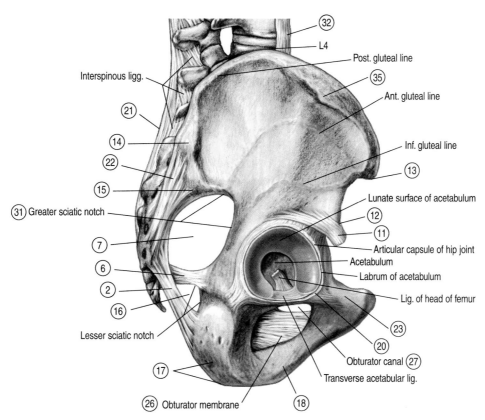

Interspinous ligg.

Post. gluteal line

Ant. gluteal line

Inf. gluteal line

L4

(32)

(35)

(21)

(14)

(22)

(15)

(31) Greater sciatic notch

(7)

(6)

(2)

(16)

Lesser sciatic notch

(17)

(26) Obturator membrane

(18)

(13)

Lunate surface of acetabulum

(12)

(11)

Articular capsule of hip joint

Acetabulum

Labrum of acetabulum

Lig. of head of femur

(23)

(20)

Obturator canal (27)

Transverse acetabular lig.

RIGHT LATERAL VIEW

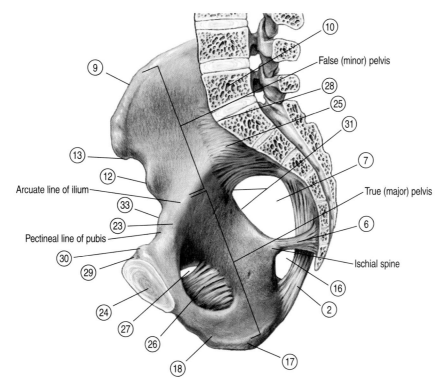

(9)

(10)

False (minor) pelvis

(28)

(25)

(31)

(7)

(13)

(12)

Arcuate line of ilium

(33)

(23)

Pectineal line of pubis

(30)

(29)

(24)

(27)

(26)

(18)

(17)

True (major) pelvis

(6)

Ischial spine

(16)

(2)

RIGHT SIDE OF HEMISECTED PELVIS—MEDIAL VIEW

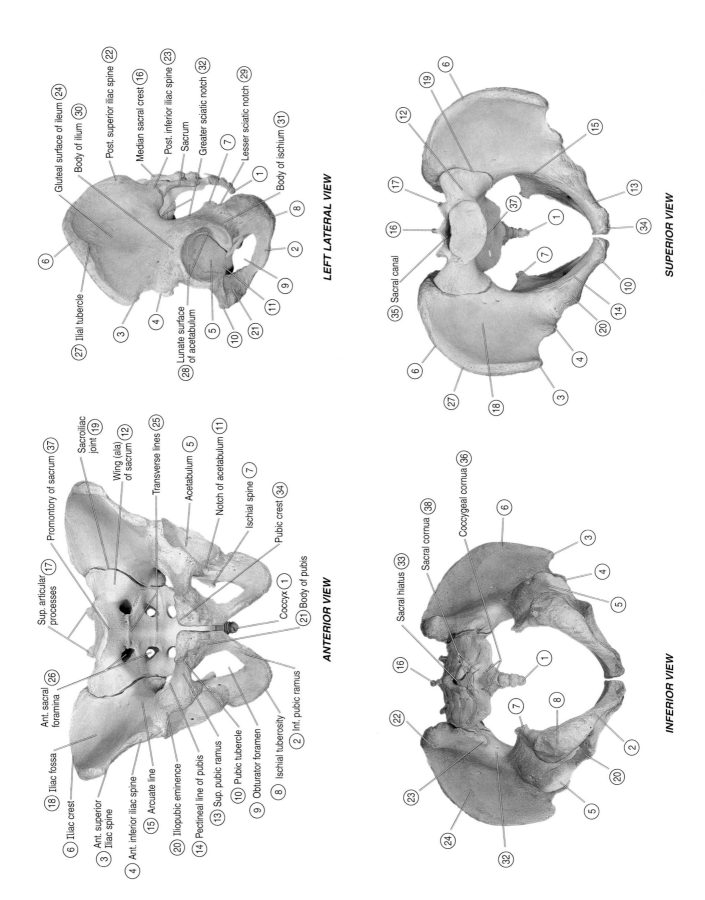

LEFT LATERAL VIEW

24 Gluteal surface of ileum
30 Body of ilium
22 Post. superior iliac spine
16 Median sacral crest
23 Post. inferior iliac spine
Sacrum
32 Greater sciatic notch
29 Lesser sciatic notch
7
1
Body of ischium 31
8
2
9
11
10
5
21
28 Lunate surface of acetabulum
4
3
27 Ilial tubercle
6

SUPERIOR VIEW

12
19
6
17
16
35 Sacral canal
37
1
7
10
14
20
4
3
18
27
6
15
13
34

ANTERIOR VIEW

37 Promontory of sacrum
17 Sup. articular processes
19 Sacroiliac joint
12 Wing (ala) of sacrum
25 Transverse lines
5 Acetabulum
11 Notch of acetabulum
7 Ischial spine
34 Pubic crest
Body of pubis
21 Body of pubis
1 Coccyx
2 Inf. pubic ramus
8 Ischial tuberosity
9 Obturator foramen
10 Pubic tubercle
13 Sup. pubic ramus
14 Pectineal line of pubis
20 Iliopubic eminence
15 Arcuate line
4 Ant. inferior iliac spine
3 Ant. superior iliac spine
6 Iliac crest
18 Iliac fossa
26 Ant. sacral foramina

INFERIOR VIEW

33 Sacral hiatus
38 Sacral cornua
36 Coccygeal cornua
6
3
4
5
16
1
7
8
2
22
23
24
32
20
5

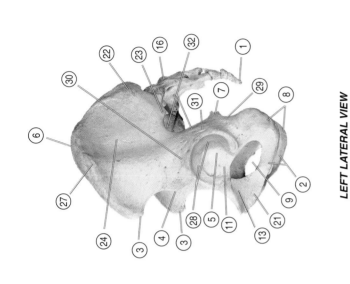

LEFT LATERAL VIEW

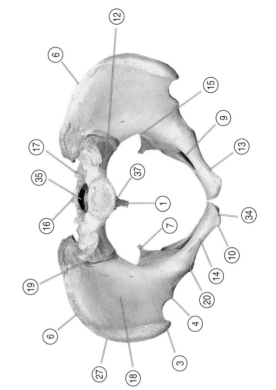

SUPERIOR VIEW

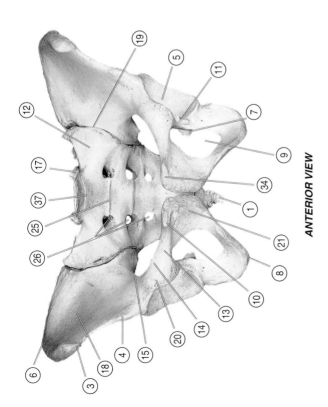

ANTERIOR VIEW

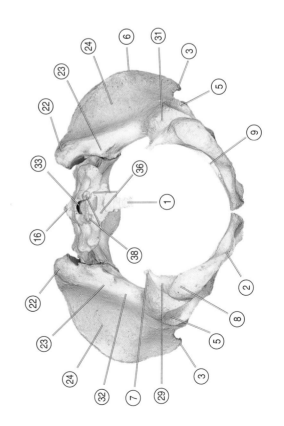

INFERIOR VIEW

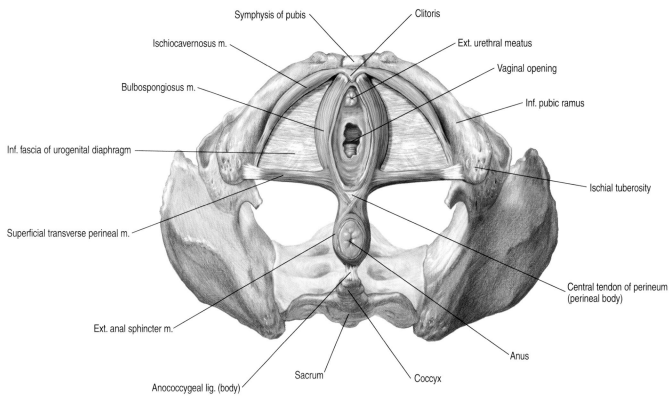

Symphysis of pubis

Clitoris

Ischiocavernosus m.

Ext. urethral meatus

Bulbospongiosus m.

Vaginal opening

Inf. pubic ramus

Inf. fascia of urogenital diaphragm

Ischial tuberosity

Superficial transverse perineal m.

Central tendon of perineum (perineal body)

Ext. anal sphincter m.

Anus

Anococcygeal lig. (body)

Sacrum

Coccyx

FEMALE—INFERIOR VIEW

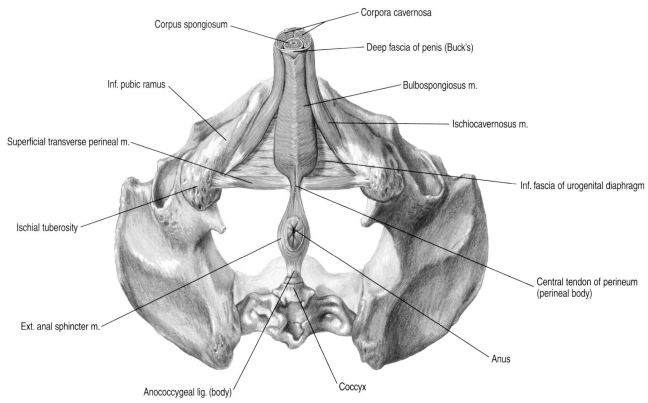

Corpora cavernosa

Corpus spongiosum

Deep fascia of penis (Buck's)

Inf. pubic ramus

Bulbospongiosus m.

Ischiocavernosus m.

Superficial transverse perineal m.

Inf. fascia of urogenital diaphragm

Ischial tuberosity

Central tendon of perineum (perineal body)

Ext. anal sphincter m.

Anus

Anococcygeal lig. (body)

Coccyx

MALE—INFERIOR VIEW

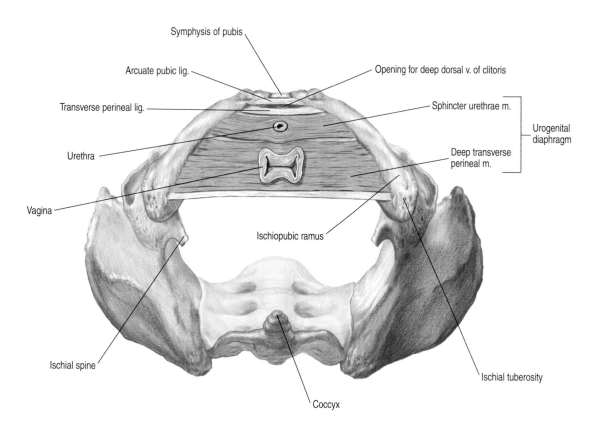

Symphysis of pubis

Arcuate pubic lig.

Opening for deep dorsal v. of clitoris

Transverse perineal lig.

Sphincter urethrae m.

Urogenital diaphragm

Urethra

Deep transverse perineal m.

Vagina

Ischiopubic ramus

Ischial spine

Ischial tuberosity

Coccyx

FEMALE—INFERIOR VIEW

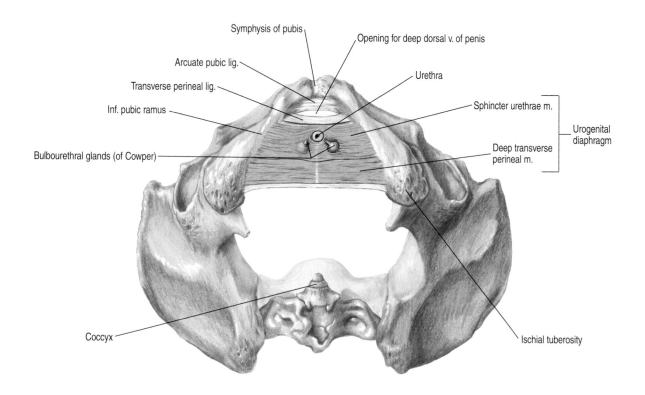

Symphysis of pubis

Opening for deep dorsal v. of penis

Arcuate pubic lig.

Urethra

Transverse perineal lig.

Sphincter urethrae m.

Inf. pubic ramus

Urogenital diaphragm

Bulbourethral glands (of Cowper)

Deep transverse perineal m.

Coccyx

Ischial tuberosity

MALE—INFERIOR VIEW

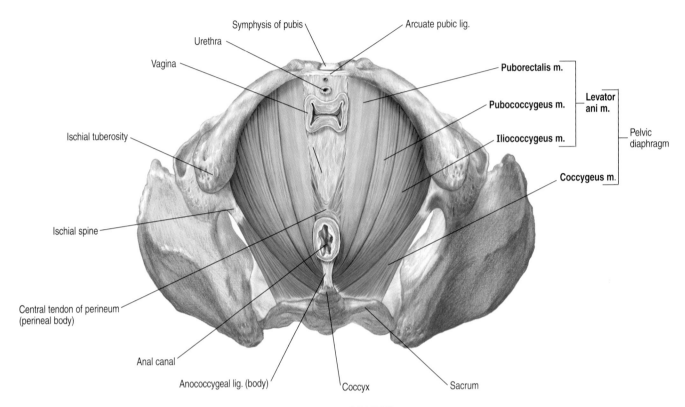

Symphysis of pubis

Urethra

Vagina

Arcuate pubic lig.

Ischial tuberosity

Puborectalis m.

Pubococcygeus m.

Iliococcygeus m.

Levator ani m.

Pelvic diaphragm

Coccygeus m.

Ischial spine

Central tendon of perineum (perineal body)

Anal canal

Anococcygeal lig. (body)

Coccyx

Sacrum

FEMALE—INFERIOR VIEW

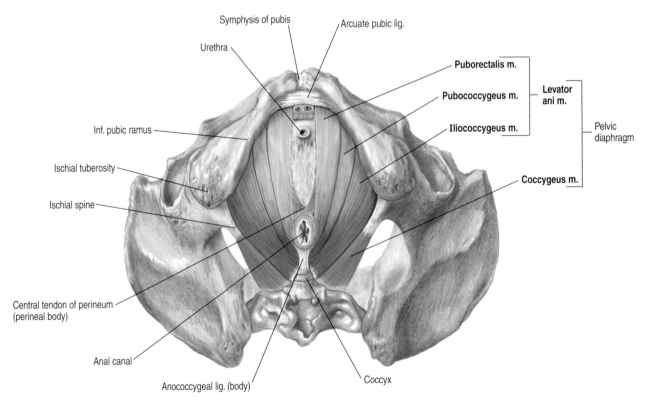

Symphysis of pubis

Urethra

Arcuate pubic lig.

Inf. pubic ramus

Puborectalis m.

Pubococcygeus m.

Iliococcygeus m.

Levator ani m.

Pelvic diaphragm

Ischial tuberosity

Ischial spine

Coccygeus m.

Central tendon of perineum (perineal body)

Anal canal

Anococcygeal lig. (body)

Coccyx

MALE—INFERIOR VIEW

Muscle	Superior or Lateral Attachment	Inferior or Medial Attachment	Innervation	Action(s)
Ischiocavernosus	Int. surface of ischial ramus & tuberosity laterally	Sides & ventrum of crus of penis in ♂ or clitoris medially in ♀	Perineal brr. of pudendal n. (S2–4)	Maintains erection of penis or clitoris
Bulbospongiosus	Dorsum of clitoris in ♀; inf. fascia of urogenital diaphragm, sides & dorsum of penile bulb in ♂	Perineal body, inf. fascia of urogenital diaphragm & median raphe of penile bulb in ♂	Perineal brr. of pudendal n. (S2–4)	Compresses vaginal orifice & erection of clitoris in ♀; compresses urethra, assist in erection & ejaculation in ♂
Superficial transverse perineal	Int. surface of ischial tuberosity laterally	Perineal body (central perineal tendon) medially	Perineal brr. of pudendal n. (S2–4)	Supports pelvic viscera
Ext. anal sphincter	Anococcygeal lig. to coccyx & int. anal sphincter m. superiorly	Perineal body anteriorly & skin superficially	Inf. rectal n. (S2–3) and perineal br. of S4 spinal n.	Compresses anus
Sphincter urethrae	Inf. pubic ramus laterally	Perineal body posteriorly & fibers from opposite side medially	Perineal brr. of pudendal n. (S2–4)	Compresses urethra in ♂ & ♀ & vagina in ♀
Deep transverse perineal	Ischial ramus laterally	Perineal body medially	Perineal brr. of pudendal n. (S2–4)	Supports pelvic viscera

**FEMALE PERINEUM & MUSCLES—
LEFT LATERAL VIEW**

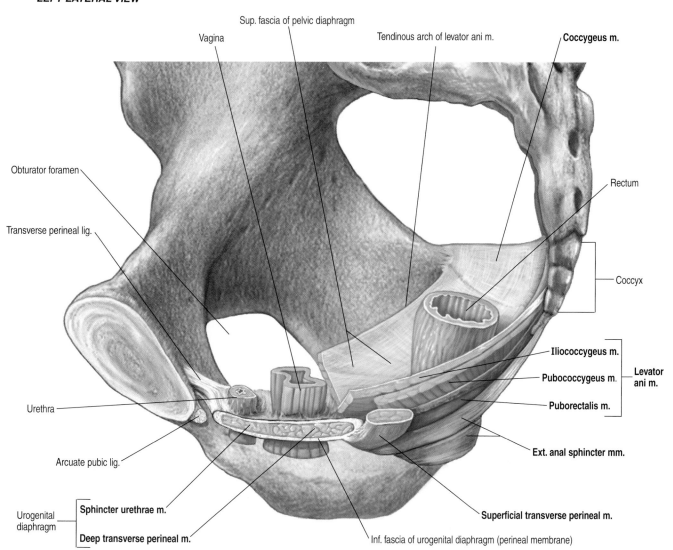

Pelvic Muscles—Male
Plate 4.10

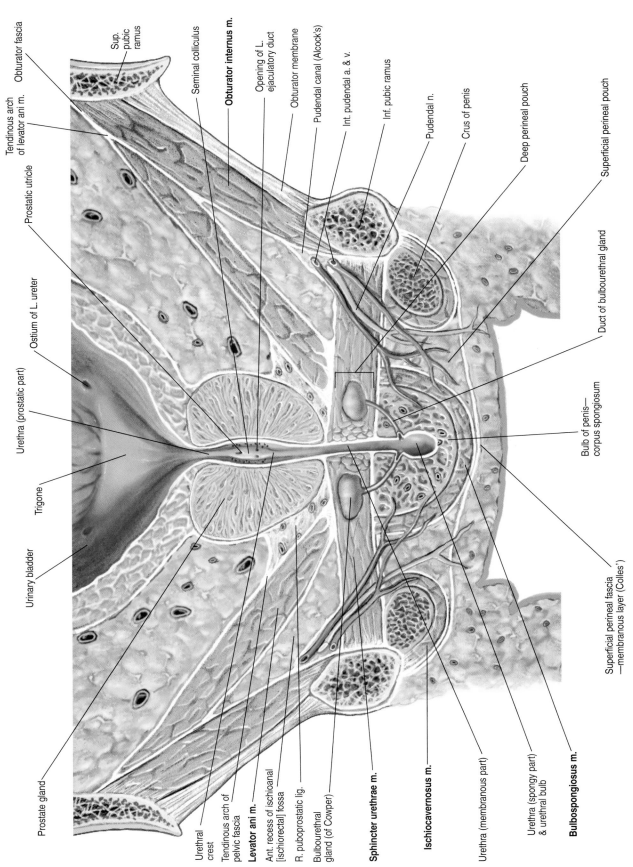

Tendinous arch of levator ani m.

Obturator fascia

Sup. pubic ramus

Seminal colliculus

Obturator internus m.

Opening of L. ejaculatory duct

Obturator membrane

Pudendal canal (Alcock's)

Int. pudendal a. & v.

Inf. pubic ramus

Pudendal n.

Crus of penis

Deep perineal pouch

Superficial perineal pouch

Prostatic utricle

Ostium of L. ureter

Urethra (prostatic part)

Trigone

Urinary bladder

Prostate gland

Urethral crest

Tendinous arch of pelvic fascia

Levator ani m.

Ant. recess of ischioanal [ischiorectal] fossa

R. puboprostatic lig.

Bulbourethral gland (of Cowper)

Sphincter urethrae m.

Ischiocavernosus m.

Urethra (membranous part)

Urethra (spongy part) & urethral bulb

Bulbospongiosus m.

Superficial perineal fascia—membranous layer (Colles')

Bulb of penis—corpus spongiosum

Duct of bulbourethral gland

MALE CORONAL SECTION—ANTERIOR VIEW

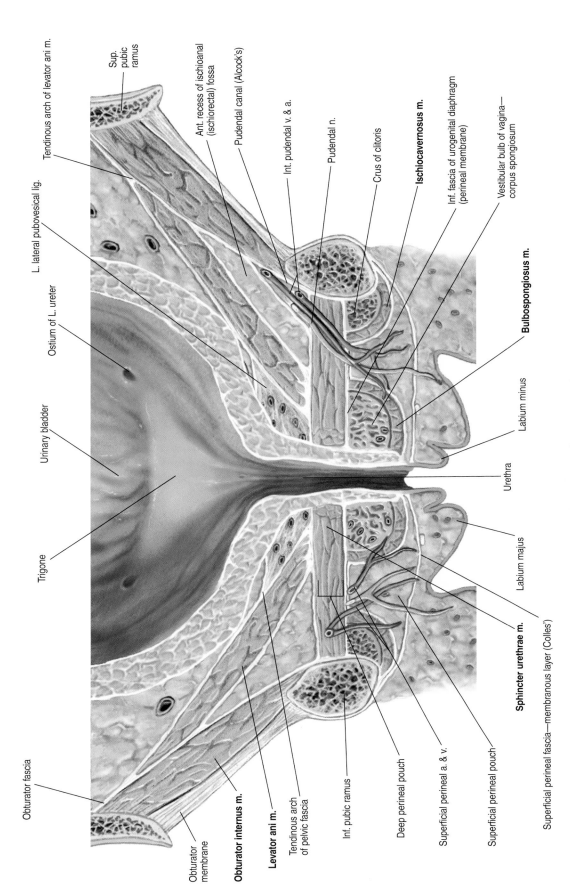

FEMALE CORONAL SECTION—ANTERIOR VIEW

Tendinous arch of levator ani m.

Sup. pubic ramus

Ant. recess of ischioanal (ischiorectal) fossa

Pudendal canal (Alcock's)

Int. pudendal v. & a.

Pudendal n.

Crus of clitoris

Ischiocavernosus m.

Inf. fascia of urogenital diaphragm (perineal membrane)

Vestibular bulb of vagina— corpus spongiosum

Bulbospongiosus m.

L. lateral pubovesical lig.

Ostium of L. ureter

Urinary bladder

Trigone

Labium minus

Urethra

Labium majus

Sphincter urethrae m.

Superficial perineal fascia—membranous layer (Colles')

Obturator fascia

Obturator membrane

Obturator internus m.

Levator ani m.

Tendinous arch of pelvic fascia

Inf. pubic ramus

Deep perineal pouch

Superficial perineal a. & v.

Superficial perineal pouch

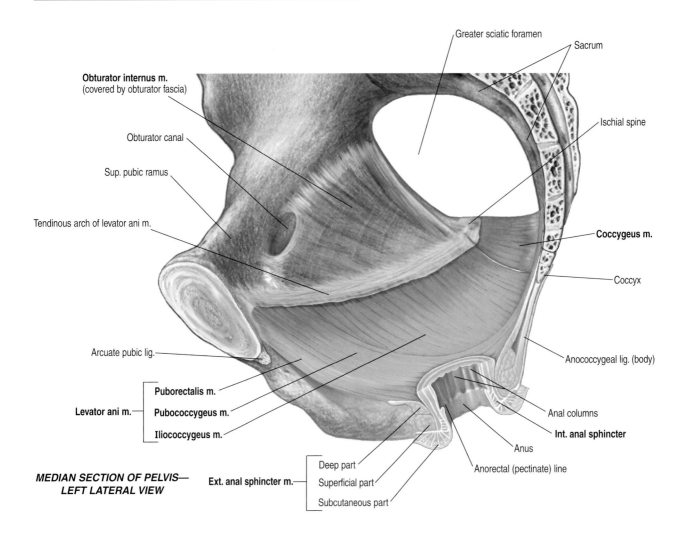

Greater sciatic foramen

Sacrum

Ischial spine

Obturator internus m.
(covered by obturator fascia)

Obturator canal

Sup. pubic ramus

Tendinous arch of levator ani m.

Coccygeus m.

Coccyx

Arcuate pubic lig.

Anococcygeal lig. (body)

Anal columns

Puborectalis m.

Levator ani m. — **Pubococcygeus m.**

Iliococcygeus m.

Int. anal sphincter

Anus

Anorectal (pectinate) line

Deep part

Ext. anal sphincter m. — Superficial part

Subcutaneous part

MEDIAN SECTION OF PELVIS—
LEFT LATERAL VIEW

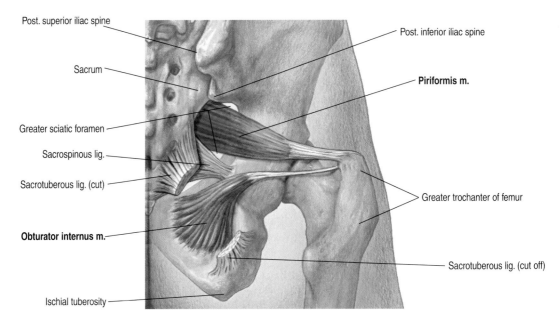

Post. superior iliac spine

Post. inferior iliac spine

Sacrum

Piriformis m.

Greater sciatic foramen

Sacrospinous lig.

Sacrotuberous lig. (cut)

Greater trochanter of femur

Obturator internus m.

Sacrotuberous lig. (cut off)

Ischial tuberosity

RIGHT GLUTEAL REGION—POSTERIOR VIEW

Muscles of the Pelvic Diaphragm

Muscle	Superior or Lateral Attachment	Inferior or Medial Attachment	Innervation	Action(s)
Puborectalis	Body of pubis anteriorly	Fibers of opposite side post. to rectum	Inf. rectal n. (S2, 3) & perineal brr. of S3, 4 spinal n.	Maintains anorectal flexure by drawing anal canal anteriorly
Pubococcygeus	Body of pubis and obturator fascia anteriorly	Coccyx & anococcygeal lig. posteriorly	Inf. rectal n. (S2, 3) & perineal brr. of S3, 4 spinal n.	Supports pelvic viscera
Iliococcygeus	Ischial spine & tendinous arch of pelvic fascia laterally	Coccyx & anococcygeal lig. posteriorly	Inf. rectal n. (S2, 3) & perineal brr. of S3, 4 spinal n.	Supports pelvic viscera
Coccygeus	Ischial spine & sacrospinous lig. laterally	Coccyx & S5 vertebra medially	Brr. of S3–5 spinal nn.	Supports pelvic viscera

Muscles of the Pelvic Walls

Muscle	Superior or Medial Attachment	Inferior or Lateral Attachment	Innervation	Action(s)
Obturator internus	Pelvic surfaces of ilium & ischium; obturator membrane	Greater trochanter of femur	N. to obturator internus (L5–S2)	Rotates thigh laterally
Piriformis	Pelvic surface of 2nd–4th sacral segments; sup. margin of greater sciatic notch, & sacrotuberous lig.	Greater trochanter of femur	Ventral rami of S1 & S2	Rotates thigh laterally

MEDIAN VIEW—RIGHT SIDE OF MEDIAL SECTION

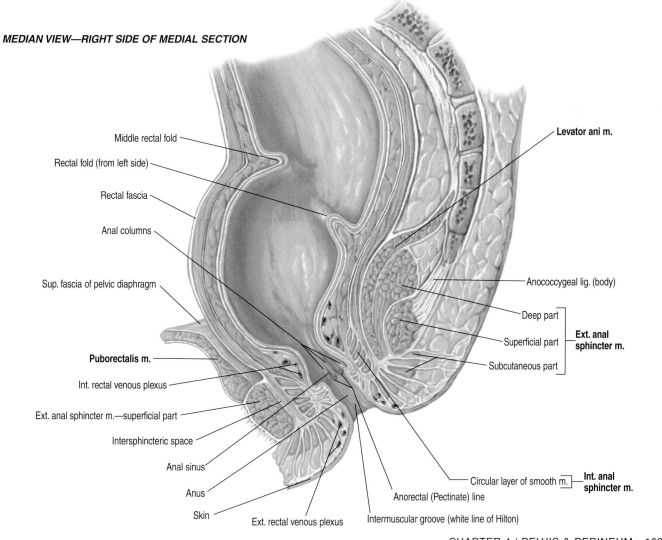

Middle rectal fold

Rectal fold (from left side)

Rectal fascia

Anal columns

Sup. fascia of pelvic diaphragm

Puborectalis m.

Int. rectal venous plexus

Ext. anal sphincter m.—superficial part

Intersphincteric space

Anal sinus

Anus

Skin

Ext. rectal venous plexus

Anorectal (Pectinate) line

Intermuscular groove (white line of Hilton)

Circular layer of smooth m.

Int. anal sphincter m.

Levator ani m.

Anococcygeal lig. (body)

Deep part

Superficial part

Subcutaneous part

Ext. anal sphincter m.

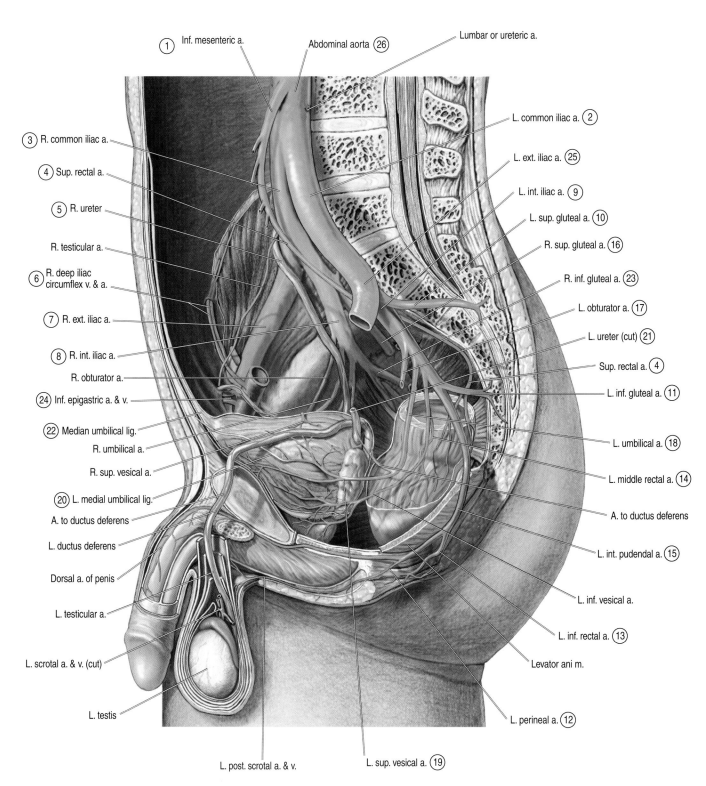

① Inf. mesenteric a.

Abdominal aorta ㉖

Lumbar or ureteric a.

L. common iliac a. ②

③ R. common iliac a.

L. ext. iliac a. ㉕

④ Sup. rectal a.

L. int. iliac a. ⑨

⑤ R. ureter

L. sup. gluteal a. ⑩

R. testicular a.

R. sup. gluteal a. ⑯

⑥ R. deep iliac circumflex v. & a.

R. inf. gluteal a. ㉓

⑦ R. ext. iliac a.

L. obturator a. ⑰

L. ureter (cut) ㉑

⑧ R. int. iliac a.

Sup. rectal a. ④

R. obturator a.

L. inf. gluteal a. ⑪

㉔ Inf. epigastric a. & v.

㉒ Median umbilical lig.

L. umbilical a. ⑱

R. umbilical a.

R. sup. vesical a.

L. middle rectal a. ⑭

㉔ L. medial umbilical lig.

A. to ductus deferens

A. to ductus deferens

L. ductus deferens

L. int. pudendal a. ⑮

Dorsal a. of penis

L. inf. vesical a.

L. testicular a.

L. inf. rectal a. ⑬

L. scrotal a. & v. (cut)

Levator ani m.

L. testis

L. perineal a. ⑫

L. post. scrotal a. & v.

L. sup. vesical a. ⑲

MEDIAL VIEW WITH PERITONEUM REMOVED

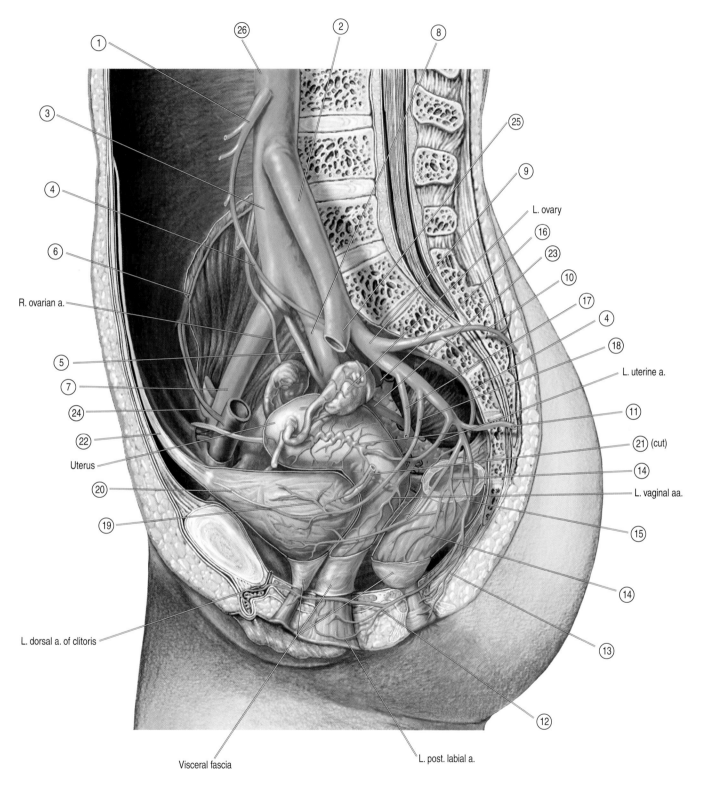

R. ovarian a.

L. ovary

L. uterine a.

Uterus

L. vaginal aa.

L. dorsal a. of clitoris

(21) (cut)

Visceral fascia

L. post. labial a.

MEDIAL VIEW WITH PERITONEUM REMOVED

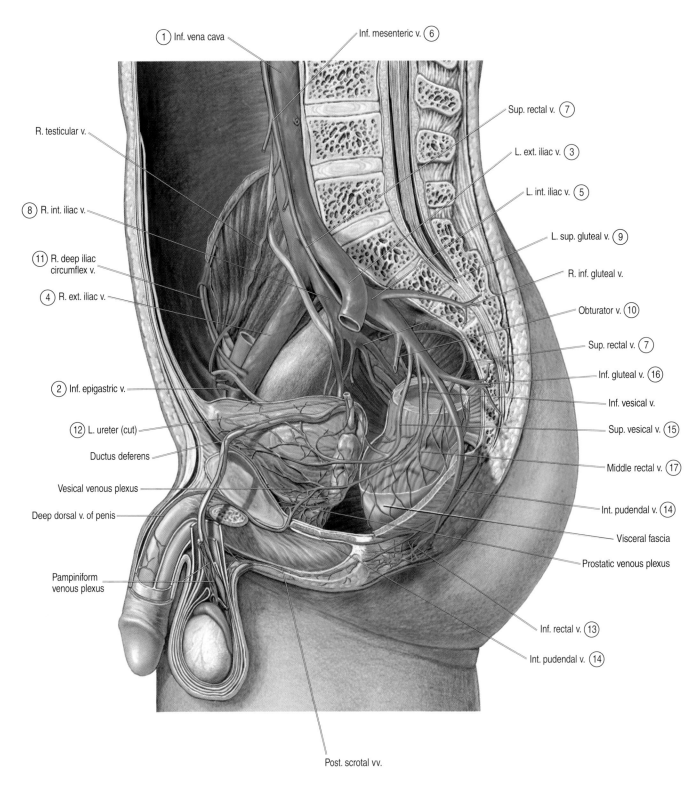

① Inf. vena cava

Inf. mesenteric v. ⑥

Sup. rectal v. ⑦

L. ext. iliac v. ③

L. int. iliac v. ⑤

L. sup. gluteal v. ⑨

R. inf. gluteal v.

Obturator v. ⑩

Sup. rectal v. ⑦

Inf. gluteal v. ⑯

Inf. vesical v.

Sup. vesical v. ⑮

Middle rectal v. ⑰

Int. pudendal v. ⑭

Visceral fascia

Prostatic venous plexus

Inf. rectal v. ⑬

Int. pudendal v. ⑭

R. testicular v.

⑧ R. int. iliac v.

⑪ R. deep iliac circumflex v.

④ R. ext. iliac v.

② Inf. epigastric v.

⑫ L. ureter (cut)

Ductus deferens

Vesical venous plexus

Deep dorsal v. of penis

Pampiniform venous plexus

Post. scrotal vv.

MEDIAL VIEW WITH PERITONEUM REMOVED

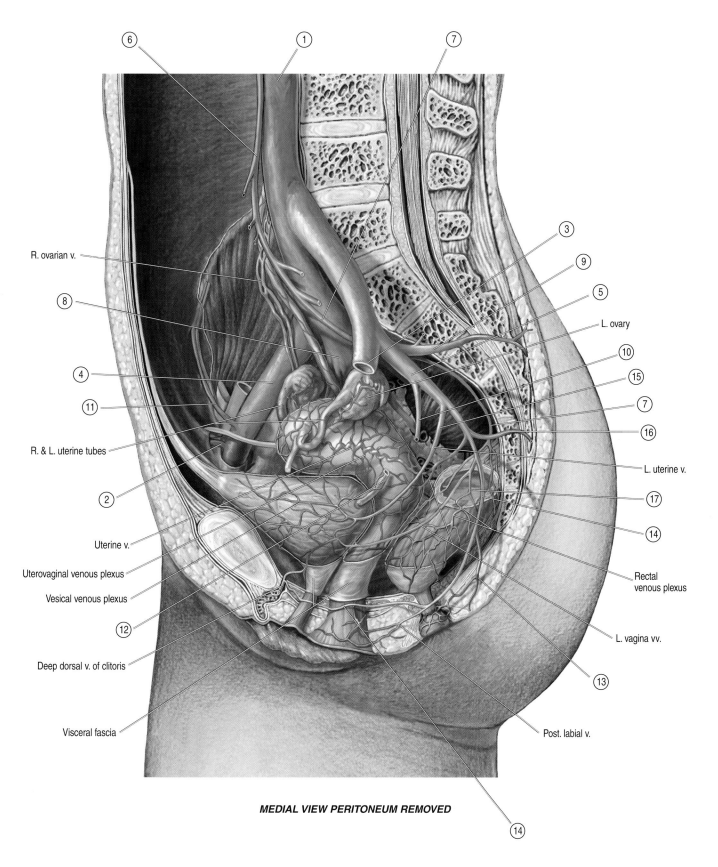

6 1 7

R. ovarian v.

8

3

9

5

L. ovary

10

15

7

16

4

11

L. uterine v.

R. & L. uterine tubes

17

2

14

Uterine v.

Uterovaginal venous plexus

Vesical venous plexus

12

Rectal venous plexus

Deep dorsal v. of clitoris

L. vagina vv.

13

Visceral fascia

Post. labial v.

14

MEDIAL VIEW PERITONEUM REMOVED

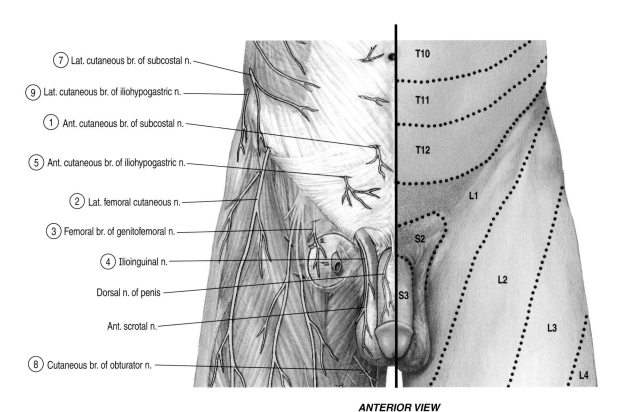

7 Lat. cutaneous br. of subcostal n.

9 Lat. cutaneous br. of iliohypogastric n.

1 Ant. cutaneous br. of subcostal n.

5 Ant. cutaneous br. of iliohypogastric n.

2 Lat. femoral cutaneous n.

3 Femoral br. of genitofemoral n.

4 Ilioinguinal n.

Dorsal n. of penis

Ant. scrotal n.

8 Cutaneous br. of obturator n.

T10
T11
T12
L1
S2
L2
S3
L3
L4

ANTERIOR VIEW

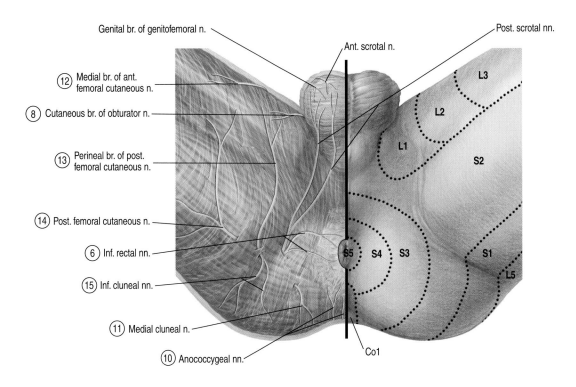

Genital br. of genitofemoral n.

Ant. scrotal n.

Post. scrotal nn.

12 Medial br. of ant. femoral cutaneous n.

8 Cutaneous br. of obturator n.

13 Perineal br. of post. femoral cutaneous n.

14 Post. femoral cutaneous n.

6 Inf. rectal nn.

15 Inf. cluneal nn.

11 Medial cluneal n.

10 Anococcygeal nn.

L3
L2
L1
S2
S5
S4
S3
S1
L5
Co1

LITHOTOMY VIEW

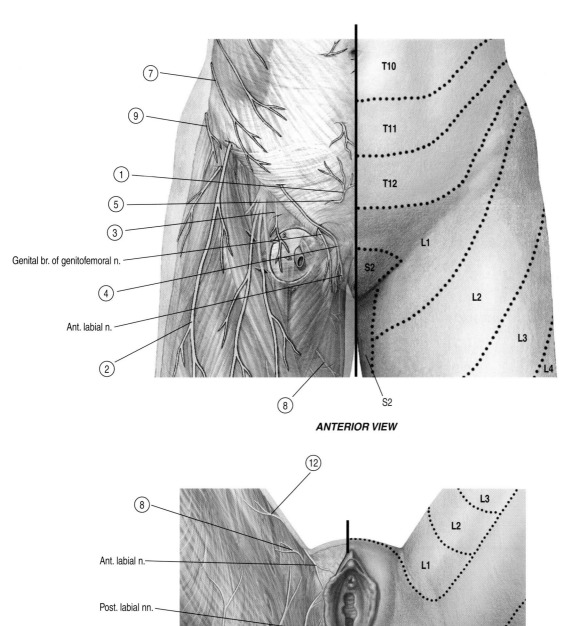

7

9

1

5

3

Genital br. of genitofemoral n.

4

Ant. labial n.

2

T10

T11

T12

L1

S2

L2

L3

L4

8

S2

ANTERIOR VIEW

12

8

Ant. labial n.

Post. labial nn.

14

6

13

15

11

10

Co1

L3

L2

L1

S2

S1

L5

S5

S4

S3

LITHOTOMY VIEW

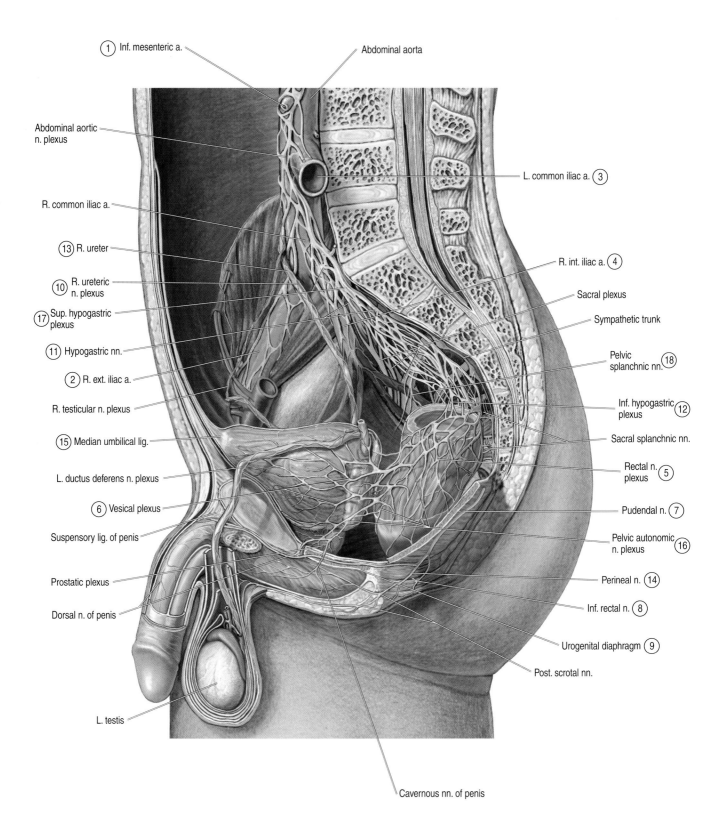

① Inf. mesenteric a.

Abdominal aorta

Abdominal aortic
n. plexus

L. common iliac a. ③

R. common iliac a.

⑬ R. ureter

R. int. iliac a. ④

⑩ R. ureteric
n. plexus

Sacral plexus

⑰ Sup. hypogastric
plexus

Sympathetic trunk

⑪ Hypogastric nn.

Pelvic
splanchnic nn. ⑱

② R. ext. iliac a.

Inf. hypogastric
plexus ⑫

R. testicular n. plexus

⑮ Median umbilical lig.

Sacral splanchnic nn.

L. ductus deferens n. plexus

Rectal n.
plexus ⑤

⑥ Vesical plexus

Pudendal n. ⑦

Suspensory lig. of penis

Pelvic autonomic
n. plexus ⑯

Prostatic plexus

Perineal n. ⑭

Dorsal n. of penis

Inf. rectal n. ⑧

Urogenital diaphragm ⑨

Post. scrotal nn.

L. testis

Cavernous nn. of penis

MEDIAL VIEW WITH PERITONEUM REMOVED

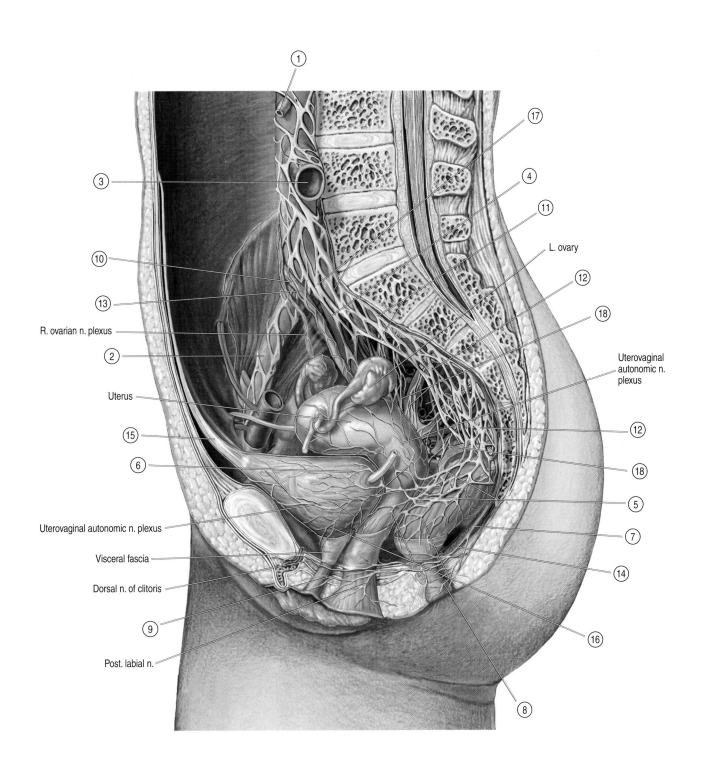

R. ovarian n. plexus

L. ovary

Uterovaginal autonomic n. plexus

Uterus

Uterovaginal autonomic n. plexus

Visceral fascia

Dorsal n. of clitoris

Post. labial n.

MEDIAL VIEW PERITONEUM REMOVED

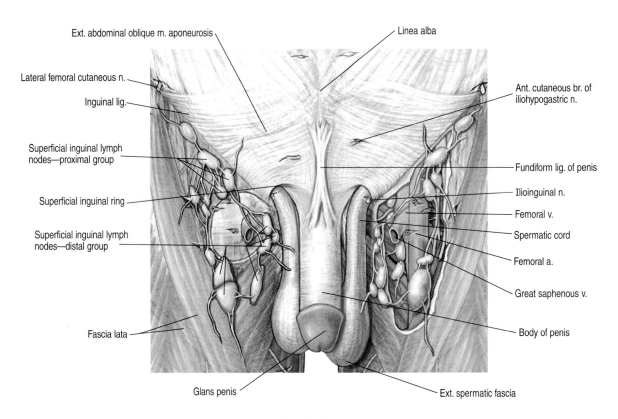

Ext. abdominal oblique m. aponeurosis

Linea alba

Lateral femoral cutaneous n.

Inguinal lig.

Superficial inguinal lymph nodes—proximal group

Superficial inguinal ring

Superficial inguinal lymph nodes—distal group

Fascia lata

Glans penis

Ant. cutaneous br. of iliohypogastric n.

Fundiform lig. of penis

Ilioinguinal n.

Femoral v.

Spermatic cord

Femoral a.

Great saphenous v.

Body of penis

Ext. spermatic fascia

MALE ANTERIOR VIEW

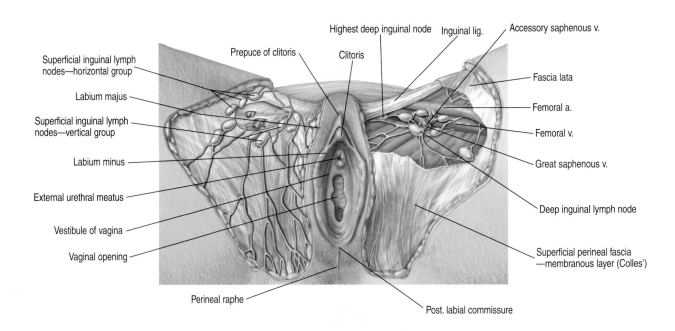

Highest deep inguinal node

Inguinal lig.

Accessory saphenous v.

Prepuce of clitoris

Clitoris

Superficial inguinal lymph nodes—horizontal group

Labium majus

Superficial inguinal lymph nodes—vertical group

Labium minus

External urethral meatus

Vestibule of vagina

Vaginal opening

Fascia lata

Femoral a.

Femoral v.

Great saphenous v.

Deep inguinal lymph node

Superficial perineal fascia —membranous layer (Colles')

Perineal raphe

Post. labial commissure

FEMALE LITHOTOMY VIEW

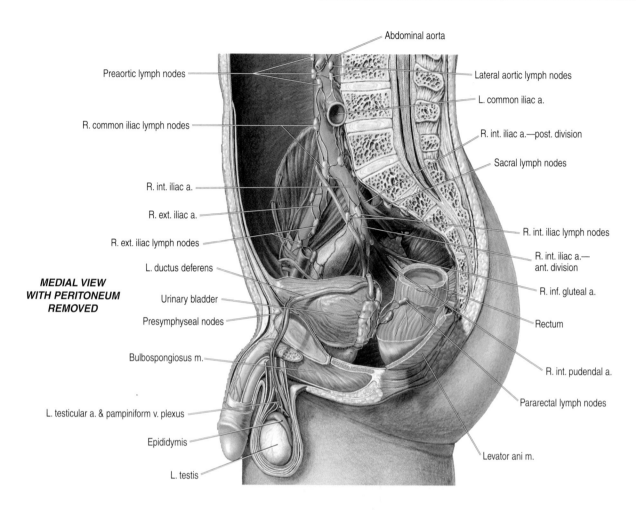

Abdominal aorta

Preaortic lymph nodes

Lateral aortic lymph nodes

L. common iliac a.

R. common iliac lymph nodes

R. int. iliac a.—post. division

Sacral lymph nodes

R. int. iliac a.

R. ext. iliac a.

R. int. iliac lymph nodes

R. ext. iliac lymph nodes

R. int. iliac a.—
ant. division

L. ductus deferens

R. inf. gluteal a.

**MEDIAL VIEW
WITH PERITONEUM
REMOVED**

Urinary bladder

Presymphyseal nodes

Rectum

Bulbospongiosus m.

R. int. pudendal a.

L. testicular a. & pampiniform v. plexus

Pararectal lymph nodes

Epididymis

L. testis

Levator ani m.

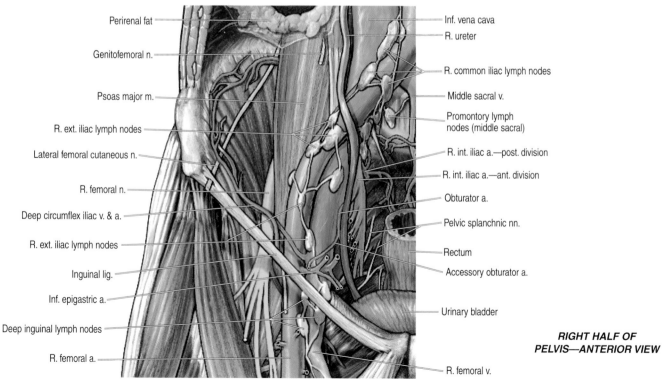

Perirenal fat

Inf. vena cava

R. ureter

Genitofemoral n.

R. common iliac lymph nodes

Psoas major m.

Middle sacral v.

Promontory lymph
nodes (middle sacral)

R. ext. iliac lymph nodes

Lateral femoral cutaneous n.

R. int. iliac a.—post. division

R. femoral n.

R. int. iliac a.—ant. division

Obturator a.

Deep circumflex iliac v. & a.

Pelvic splanchnic nn.

R. ext. iliac lymph nodes

Rectum

Inguinal lig.

Accessory obturator a.

Inf. epigastric a.

Deep inguinal lymph nodes

Urinary bladder

**RIGHT HALF OF
PELVIS—ANTERIOR VIEW**

R. femoral a.

R. femoral v.

♀ = **Characteristic Female Structures**

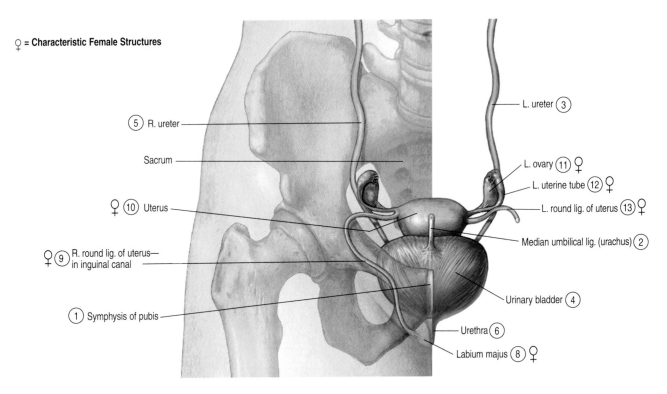

⑤ R. ureter

Sacrum

♀ ⑩ Uterus

♀ ⑨ R. round lig. of uterus—
in inguinal canal

① Symphysis of pubis

L. ureter ③

L. ovary ⑪ ♀

L. uterine tube ⑫ ♀

L. round lig. of uterus ⑬ ♀

Median umbilical lig. (urachus) ②

Urinary bladder ④

Urethra ⑥

Labium majus ⑧ ♀

ANTERIOR VIEW

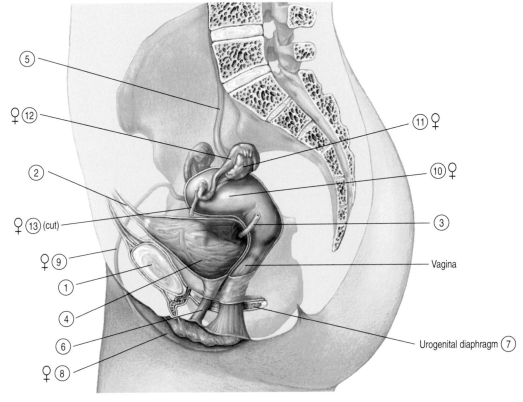

⑤

♀ ⑫

②

♀ ⑬ (cut)

♀ ⑨

①

④

⑥

♀ ⑧

⑪ ♀

⑩ ♀

③

Vagina

Urogenital diaphragm ⑦

MEDIAL VIEW

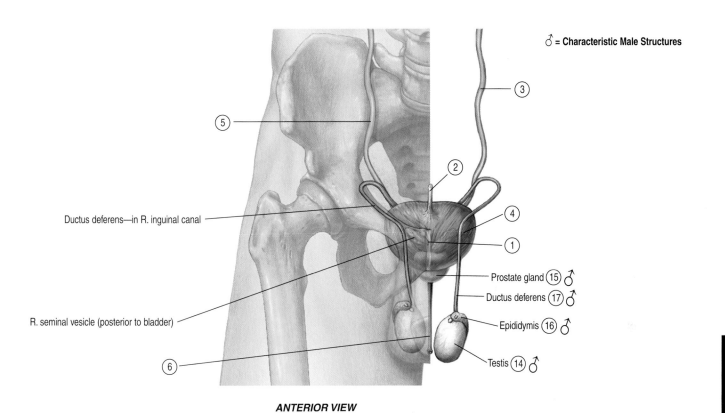

♂ = Characteristic Male Structures

Ductus deferens—in R. inguinal canal

R. seminal vesicle (posterior to bladder)

Prostate gland (15) ♂
Ductus deferens (17) ♂
Epididymis (16) ♂
Testis (14) ♂

ANTERIOR VIEW

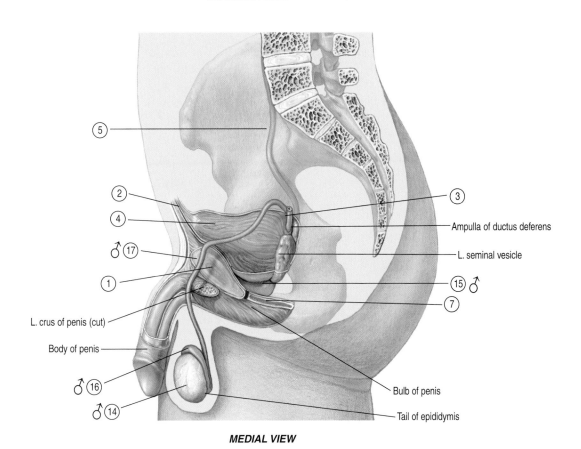

Ampulla of ductus deferens

L. seminal vesicle

(15) ♂

L. crus of penis (cut)

Body of penis

♂ (16)

♂ (14)

Bulb of penis

Tail of epididymis

MEDIAL VIEW

TRANSVERSE SECTION AT L4—SUPERIOR VIEW

LEFT ← →

RIGHT →

Medial umbilical lig. & fold

Linea alba

Vesicouterine pouch (11)

Lateral umbilical fold & inf. epigastric v. & a. (3)

Lig. of ovary

R. ovary (12)

Cecum

Vermiform appendix

Uterosacral fold (8)

Ascending colon

Suspensory lig. of ovary

Ileum

Gluteus medius m.

Iliacus m.

R. ureter

Gluteus maximus m.

Rectum (4)

Median umbilical lig. & fold

Rectus abdominis m.

(5) Urinary bladder—empty

(7) Round lig. of uterus

(9) Fundus of uterus

(6) Uterine tube

(13) Broad lig. of uterus

(2) Sigmoid colon

(10) Omental [Epiploic] appendages

Tenia coli

Descending colon

Body of uterus

Rectouterine pouch (of Douglas)

Psoas minor & major mm.

L. sympathetic trunk

Abdominal aorta

L4

Inf. vena cava

Erector spinae m.

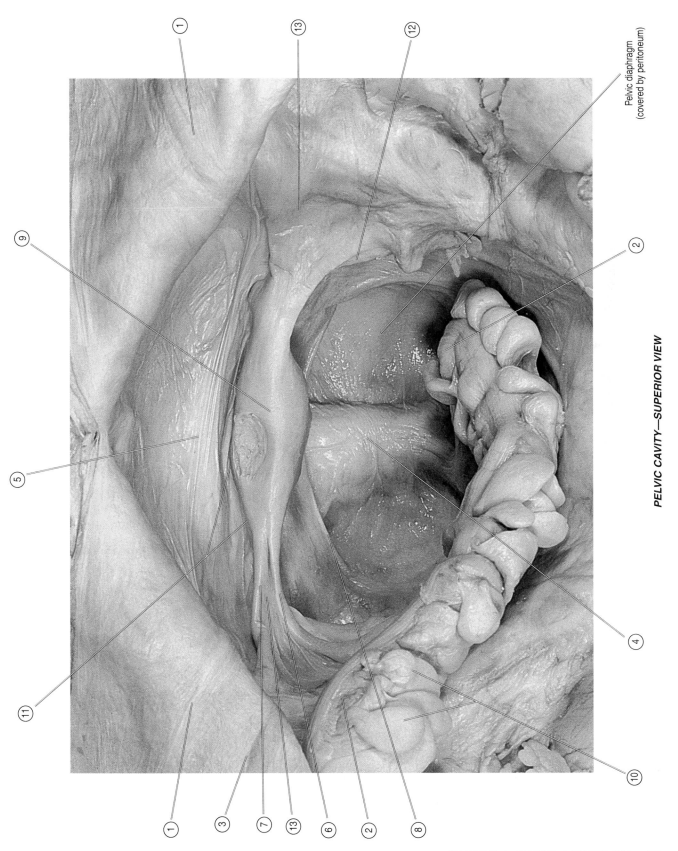

Pelvic diaphragm
(covered by peritoneum)

PELVIC CAVITY—SUPERIOR VIEW

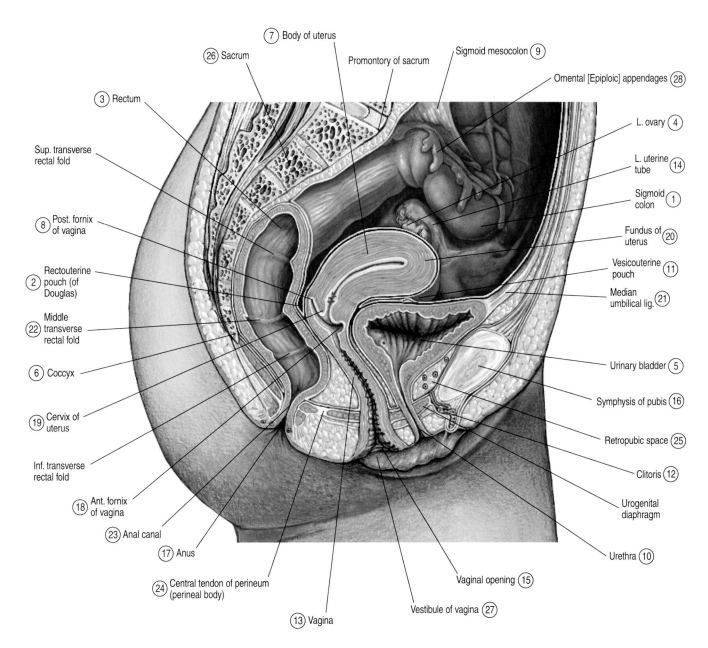

7 Body of uterus

26 Sacrum

Promontory of sacrum

Sigmoid mesocolon 9

Omental [Epiploic] appendages 28

3 Rectum

L. ovary 4

Sup. transverse rectal fold

L. uterine tube 14

Sigmoid colon 1

8 Post. fornix of vagina

Fundus of uterus 20

2 Rectouterine pouch (of Douglas)

Vesicouterine pouch 11

Median umbilical lig. 21

22 Middle transverse rectal fold

6 Coccyx

Urinary bladder 5

19 Cervix of uterus

Symphysis of pubis 16

Retropubic space 25

Inf. transverse rectal fold

Clitoris 12

18 Ant. fornix of vagina

Urogenital diaphragm

23 Anal canal

17 Anus

Urethra 10

24 Central tendon of perineum (perineal body)

Vaginal opening 15

Vestibule of vagina 27

13 Vagina

MEDIAN SECTION—RIGHT LATERAL VIEW

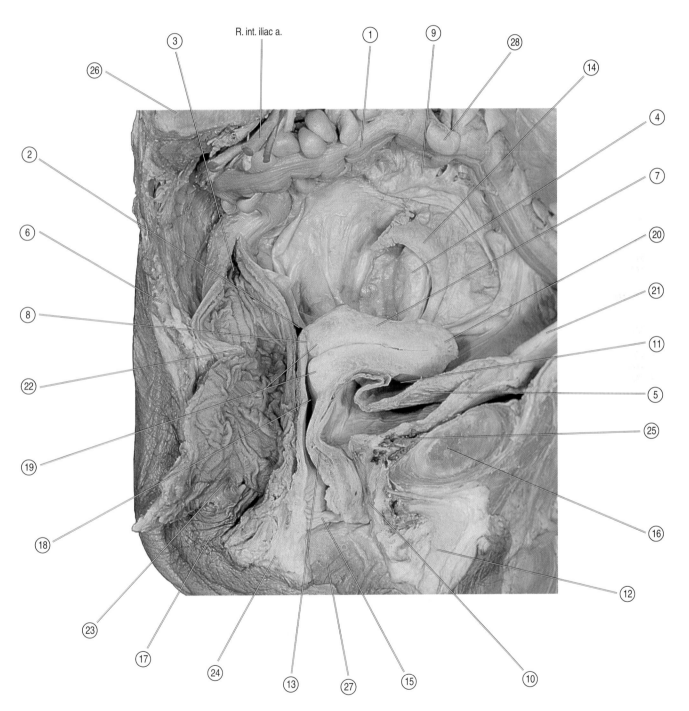

R. int. iliac a.

MEDIAN SECTION—RIGHT LATERAL VIEW OF LEFT PELVIS

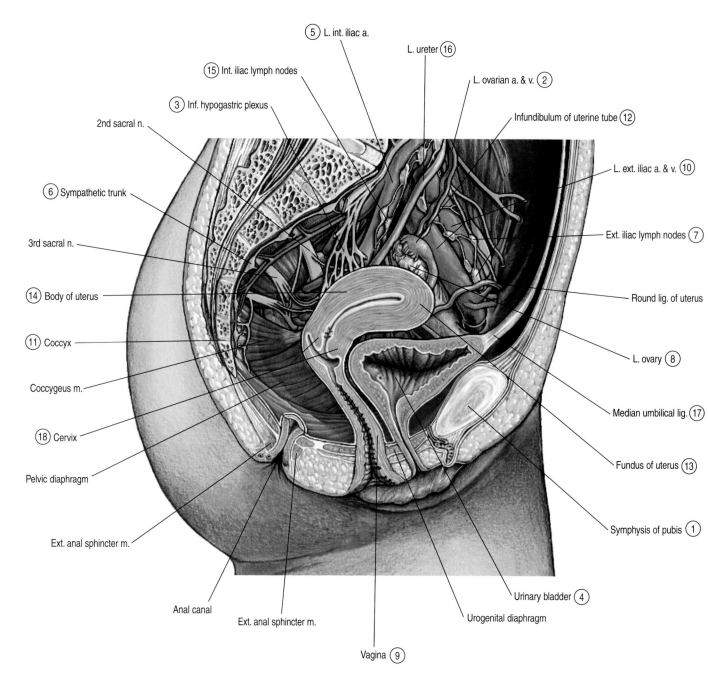

5 L. int. iliac a.

L. ureter 16

15 Int. iliac lymph nodes

L. ovarian a. & v. 2

3 Inf. hypogastric plexus

Infundibulum of uterine tube 12

2nd sacral n.

6 Sympathetic trunk

L. ext. iliac a. & v. 10

3rd sacral n.

Ext. iliac lymph nodes 7

14 Body of uterus

Round lig. of uterus

11 Coccyx

L. ovary 8

Coccygeus m.

Median umbilical lig. 17

18 Cervix

Fundus of uterus 13

Pelvic diaphragm

Symphysis of pubis 1

Ext. anal sphincter m.

Urinary bladder 4

Anal canal

Urogenital diaphragm

Ext. anal sphincter m.

Vagina 9

MEDIAN SECTION—RIGHT LATERAL VIEW

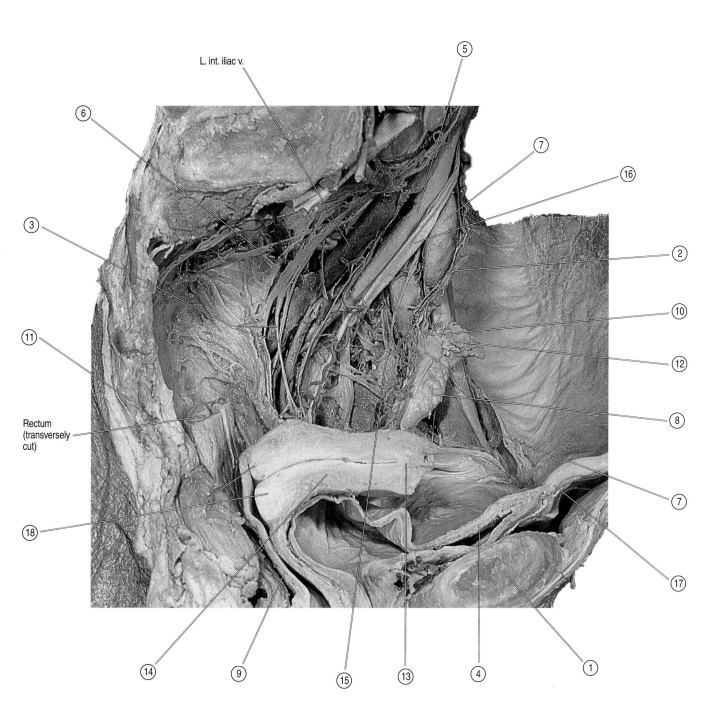

L. int. iliac v.

Rectum
(transversely
cut)

LEFT HALF OF HEMISECTED PELVIS—MEDIAL VIEW

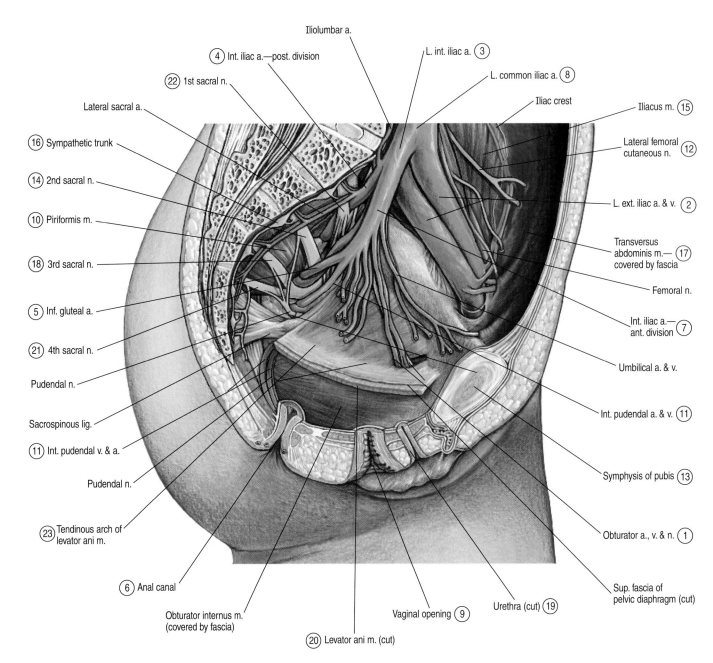

Iliolumbar a.

④ Int. iliac a.—post. division

㉒ 1st sacral n.

L. int. iliac a. ③

L. common iliac a. ⑧

Iliac crest

Iliacus m. ⑮

Lateral sacral a.

⑯ Sympathetic trunk

⑭ 2nd sacral n.

⑩ Piriformis m.

⑱ 3rd sacral n.

⑤ Inf. gluteal a.

㉑ 4th sacral n.

Pudendal n.

Sacrospinous lig.

⑪ Int. pudendal v. & a.

Pudendal n.

㉓ Tendinous arch of levator ani m.

⑥ Anal canal

Obturator internus m. (covered by fascia)

㉔ Levator ani m. (cut)

Vaginal opening ⑨

Urethra (cut) ⑲

Lateral femoral cutaneous n. ⑫

L. ext. iliac a. & v. ②

Transversus abdominis m.— ⑰ covered by fascia

Femoral n.

Int. iliac a.— ⑦ ant. division

Umbilical a. & v.

Int. pudendal a. & v. ⑪

Symphysis of pubis ⑬

Obturator a., v. & n. ①

Sup. fascia of pelvic diaphragm (cut)

MEDIAN SECTION—RIGHT LATERAL VIEW

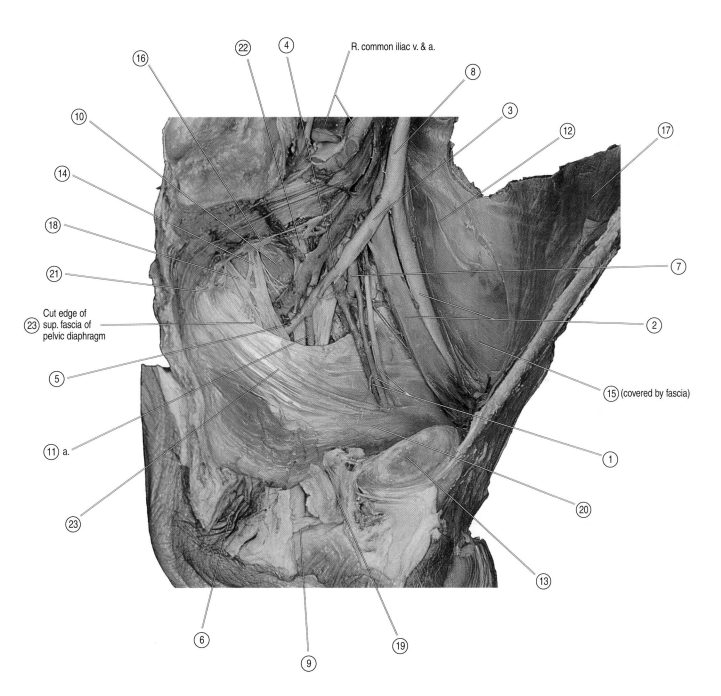

R. common iliac v. & a.

Cut edge of
sup. fascia of
pelvic diaphragm

(15) (covered by fascia)

(11) a.

MEDIAN SECTION—RIGHT LATERAL VIEW

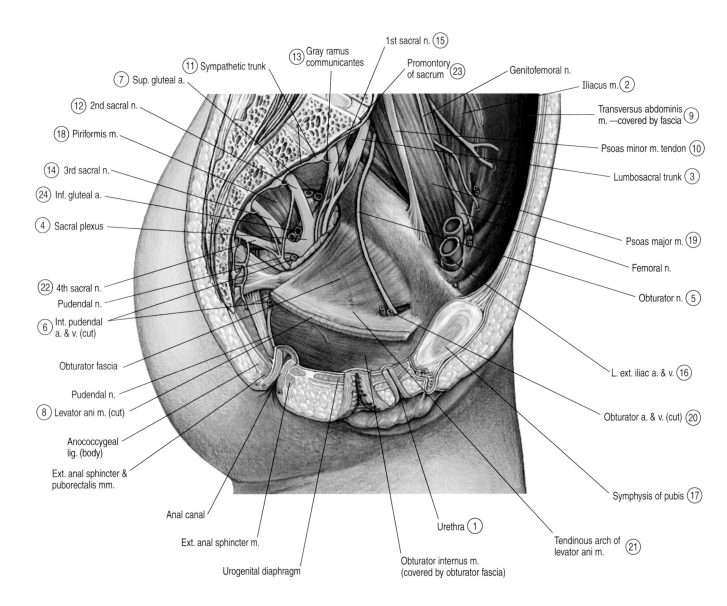

1st sacral n. (15)

(13) Gray ramus communicantes

(11) Sympathetic trunk

Promontory of sacrum (23)

Genitofemoral n.

(7) Sup. gluteal a.

Iliacus m. (2)

(12) 2nd sacral n.

Transversus abdominis m. —covered by fascia (9)

(18) Piriformis m.

Psoas minor m. tendon (10)

(14) 3rd sacral n.

Lumbosacral trunk (3)

(24) Inf. gluteal a.

(4) Sacral plexus

Psoas major m. (19)

Femoral n.

(22) 4th sacral n.

Obturator n. (5)

Pudendal n.

(6) Int. pudendal a. & v. (cut)

Obturator fascia

L. ext. iliac a. & v. (16)

Pudendal n.

(8) Levator ani m. (cut)

Obturator a. & v. (cut) (20)

Anococcygeal lig. (body)

Ext. anal sphincter & puborectalis mm.

Symphysis of pubis (17)

Anal canal

Urethra (1)

Ext. anal sphincter m.

Tendinous arch of levator ani m. (21)

Urogenital diaphragm

Obturator internus m. (covered by obturator fascia)

MEDIAN SECTION—RIGHT LATERAL VIEW

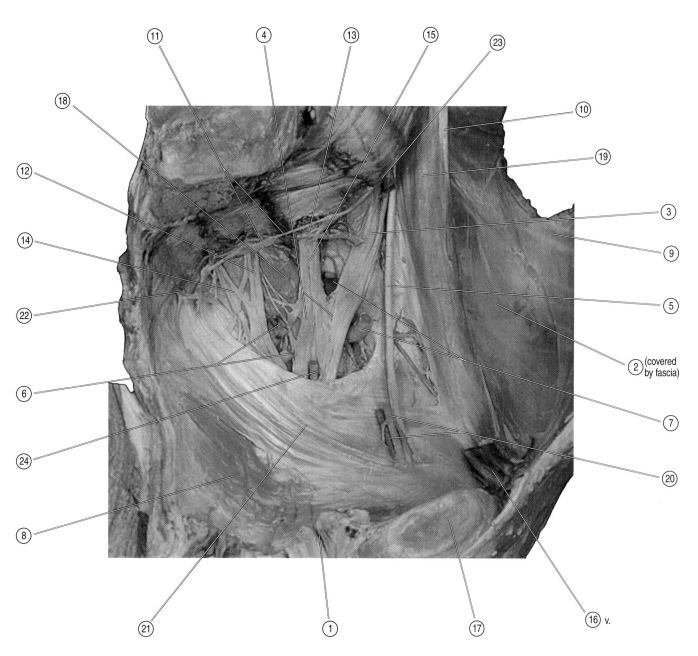

MEDIAN SECTION—RIGHT LATERAL VIEW

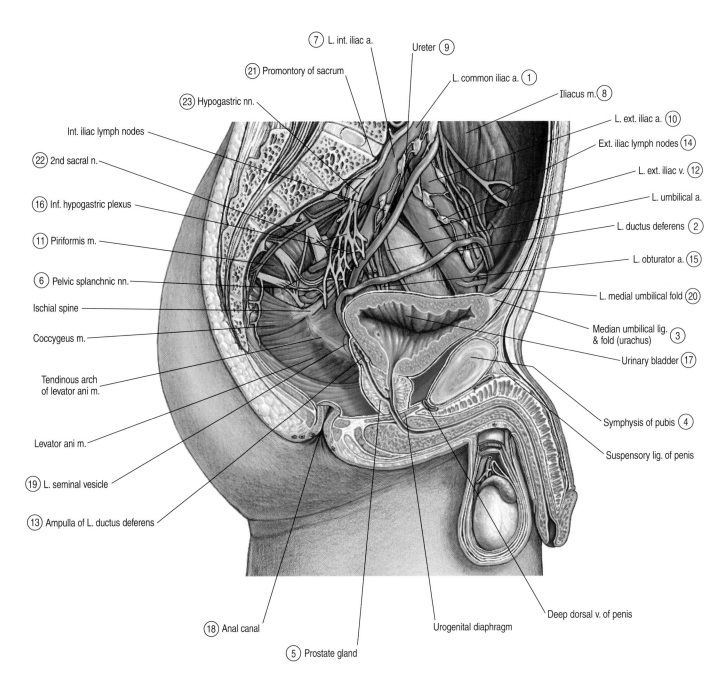

⑦ L. int. iliac a.

Ureter ⑨

㉑ Promontory of sacrum

L. common iliac a. ①

㉓ Hypogastric nn.

Iliacus m. ⑧

Int. iliac lymph nodes

L. ext. iliac a. ⑩

Ext. iliac lymph nodes ⑭

㉒ 2nd sacral n.

L. ext. iliac v. ⑫

L. umbilical a.

⑯ Inf. hypogastric plexus

L. ductus deferens ②

⑪ Piriformis m.

L. obturator a. ⑮

⑥ Pelvic splanchnic nn.

L. medial umbilical fold ⑳

Ischial spine

Median umbilical lig.
& fold (urachus) ③

Coccygeus m.

Urinary bladder ⑰

Tendinous arch
of levator ani m.

Levator ani m.

Symphysis of pubis ④

Suspensory lig. of penis

⑲ L. seminal vesicle

⑬ Ampulla of L. ductus deferens

Deep dorsal v. of penis

⑱ Anal canal

Urogenital diaphragm

⑤ Prostate gland

MEDIAN SECTION—RIGHT LATERAL VIEW

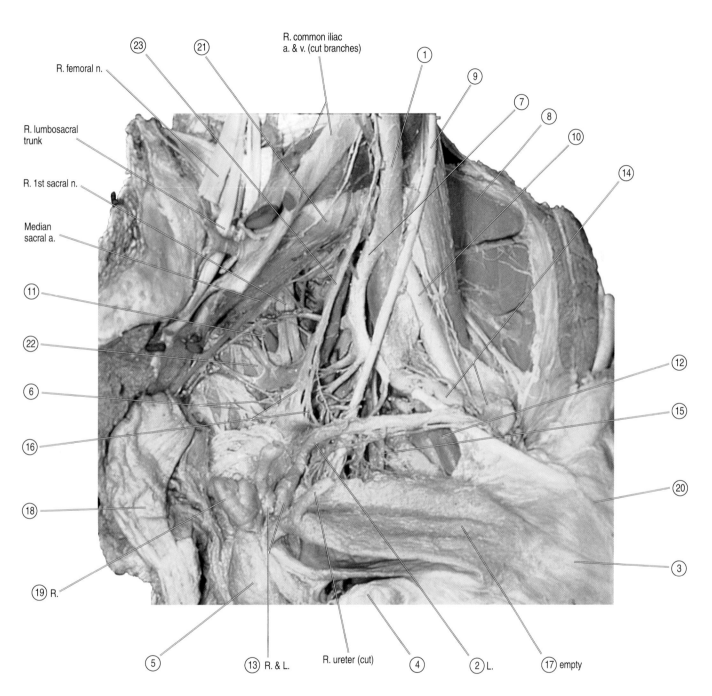

R. common iliac
a. & v. (cut branches)

R. femoral n.

R. lumbosacral
trunk

R. 1st sacral n.

Median
sacral a.

R. ureter (cut)

**LEFT HALF OF HEMISECTED PELVIS WITH
BLADDER PULLED ANTERIORLY—MEDIAL VIEW**

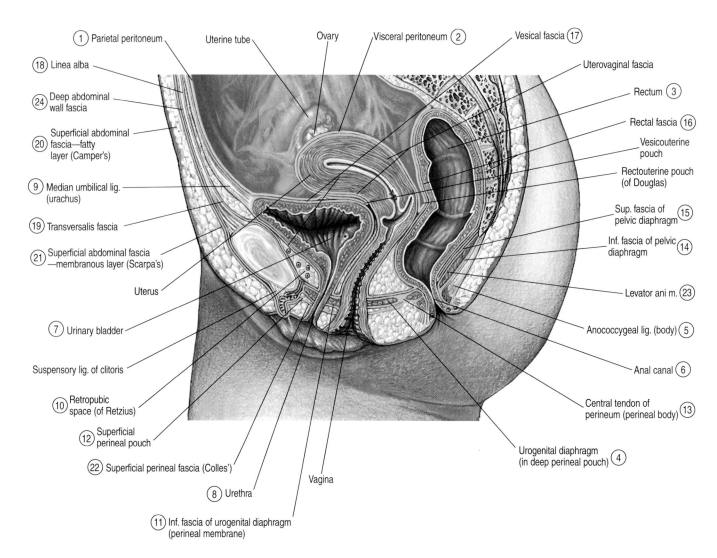

① Parietal peritoneum

Uterine tube

Ovary

Visceral peritoneum ②

Vesical fascia ⑰

⑱ Linea alba

Uterovaginal fascia

㉔ Deep abdominal wall fascia

Rectum ③

⑳ Superficial abdominal fascia—fatty layer (Camper's)

Rectal fascia ⑯

Vesicouterine pouch

⑨ Median umbilical lig. (urachus)

Rectouterine pouch (of Douglas)

⑲ Transversalis fascia

Sup. fascia of pelvic diaphragm ⑮

㉑ Superficial abdominal fascia —membranous layer (Scarpa's)

Inf. fascia of pelvic diaphragm ⑭

Uterus

Levator ani m. ㉓

⑦ Urinary bladder

Anococcygeal lig. (body) ⑤

Suspensory lig. of clitoris

Anal canal ⑥

⑩ Retropubic space (of Retzius)

Central tendon of perineum (perineal body) ⑬

⑫ Superficial perineal pouch

㉒ Superficial perineal fascia (Colles')

Urogenital diaphragm (in deep perineal pouch) ④

Vagina

⑧ Urethra

⑪ Inf. fascia of urogenital diaphragm (perineal membrane)

MEDIAN SECTION—LEFT LATERAL VIEW

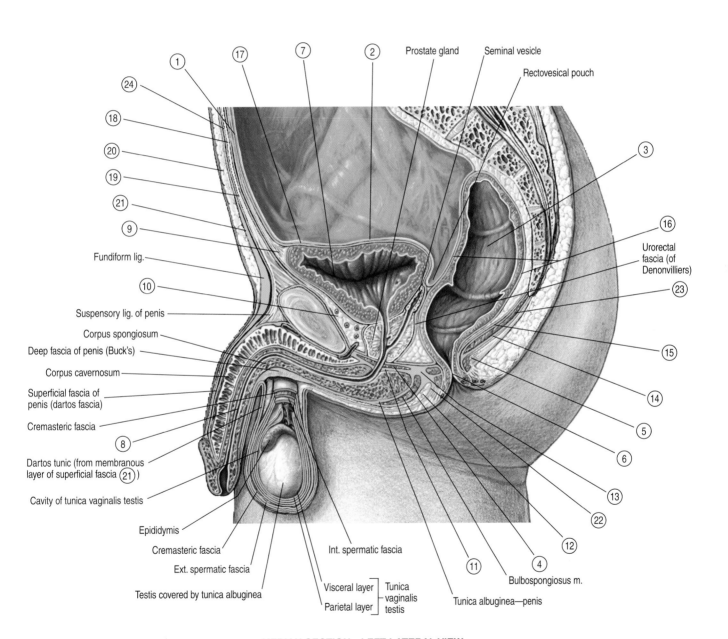

Fundiform lig.

Suspensory lig. of penis

Corpus spongiosum

Deep fascia of penis (Buck's)

Corpus cavernosum

Superficial fascia of penis (dartos fascia)

Cremasteric fascia

Dartos tunic (from membranous layer of superficial fascia (21))

Cavity of tunica vaginalis testis

Epididymis

Cremasteric fascia

Ext. spermatic fascia

Testis covered by tunica albuginea

Int. spermatic fascia

Visceral layer ⎤ Tunica
Parietal layer ⎦ vaginalis testis

Bulbospongiosus m.

Tunica albuginea—penis

Prostate gland   Seminal vesicle

Rectovesical pouch

Urorectal fascia (of Denonvilliers)

MEDIAN SECTION—LEFT LATERAL VIEW

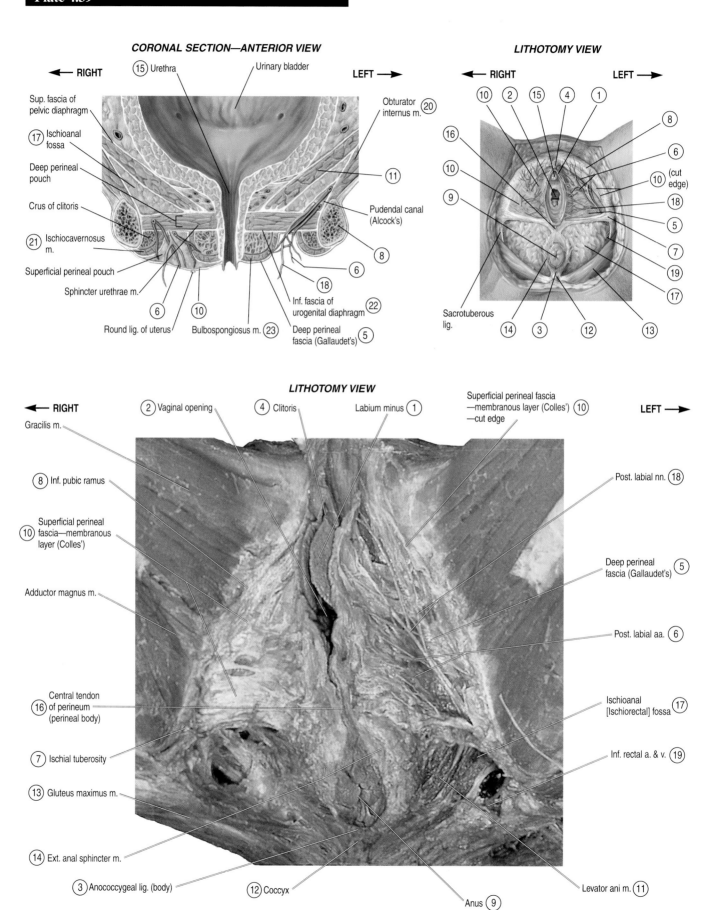

CORONAL SECTION—ANTERIOR VIEW

← RIGHT   LEFT →

⑮ Urethra   Urinary bladder

Sup. fascia of pelvic diaphragm

⑰ Ischioanal fossa

Deep perineal pouch

Crus of clitoris

㉑ Ischiocavernosus m.

Superficial perineal pouch

Sphincter urethrae m.

Round lig. of uterus

Bulbospongiosus m. ㉓

Obturator internus m. ⑳

⑪

Pudendal canal (Alcock's)

⑧

⑥

⑱

Inf. fascia of urogenital diaphragm ㉒

⑥   ⑩

Deep perineal fascia (Gallaudet's) ⑤

LITHOTOMY VIEW

← RIGHT   LEFT →

⑩ ② ⑮ ④ ①

⑯   ⑧

⑩   ⑥

⑨   ⑩ (cut edge)

Sacrotuberous lig.   ⑱

⑤

⑦

⑲

⑰

⑭ ③ ⑫ ⑬

LITHOTOMY VIEW

← RIGHT

② Vaginal opening   ④ Clitoris   Labium minus ①   Superficial perineal fascia —membranous layer (Colles') ⑩ —cut edge   LEFT →

Gracilis m.

⑧ Inf. pubic ramus

⑩ Superficial perineal fascia—membranous layer (Colles')

Adductor magnus m.

Central tendon ⑯ of perineum (perineal body)

⑦ Ischial tuberosity

⑬ Gluteus maximus m.

⑭ Ext. anal sphincter m.

③ Anococcygeal lig. (body)   ⑫ Coccyx   Anus ⑨

Post. labial nn. ⑱

Deep perineal fascia (Gallaudet's) ⑤

Post. labial aa. ⑥

Ischioanal [Ischiorectal] fossa ⑰

Inf. rectal a. & v. ⑲

Levator ani m. ⑪

LITHOTOMY VIEW

← RIGHT   LEFT →

CORONAL SECTION—ANTERIOR VIEW

← RIGHT   LEFT →

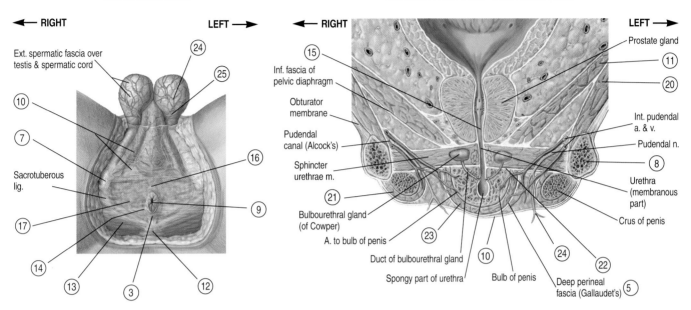

Ext. spermatic fascia over testis & spermatic cord

(24)

(25)

(10)

(7)

Sacrotuberous lig.

(17)

(14)

(13)

(3)

(16)

(9)

(12)

(15)

Inf. fascia of pelvic diaphragm

Obturator membrane

Pudendal canal (Alcock's)

Sphincter urethrae m.

(21)

Bulbourethral gland (of Cowper)

A. to bulb of penis

(23)

Duct of bulbourethral gland

Spongy part of urethra

(10)

Bulb of penis

Prostate gland

(11)

(20)

Int. pudendal a. & v.

Pudendal n.

(8)

Urethra (membranous part)

Crus of penis

(24)

Deep perineal fascia (Gallaudet's) (5)

(22)

LITHOTOMY VIEW

← RIGHT   LEFT →

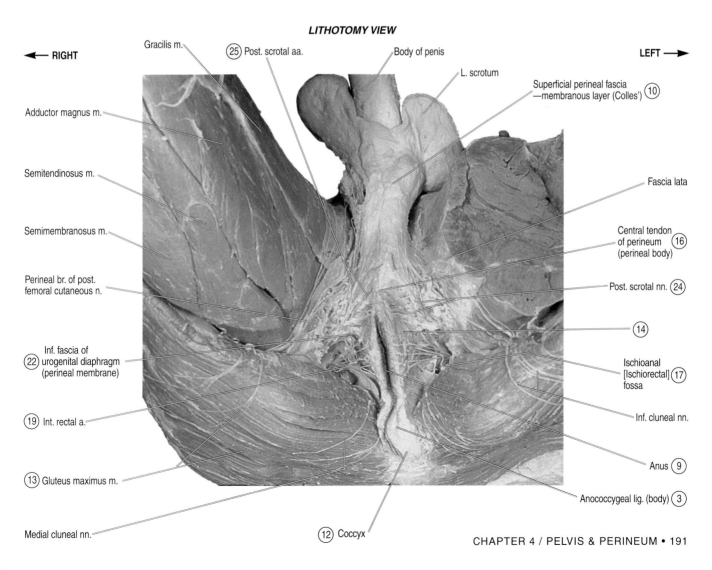

Gracilis m.

(25) Post. scrotal aa.

Body of penis

L. scrotum

Superficial perineal fascia —membranous layer (Colles') (10)

Adductor magnus m.

Semitendinosus m.

Semimembranosus m.

Perineal br. of post. femoral cutaneous n.

(22) Inf. fascia of urogenital diaphragm (perineal membrane)

(19) Int. rectal a.

(13) Gluteus maximus m.

Medial cluneal nn.

(12) Coccyx

Fascia lata

Central tendon of perineum (16) (perineal body)

Post. scrotal nn. (24)

(14)

Ischioanal [Ischiorectal] (17) fossa

Inf. cluneal nn.

Anus (9)

Anococcygeal lig. (body) (3)

Perineum—Female II
Plate 4.41

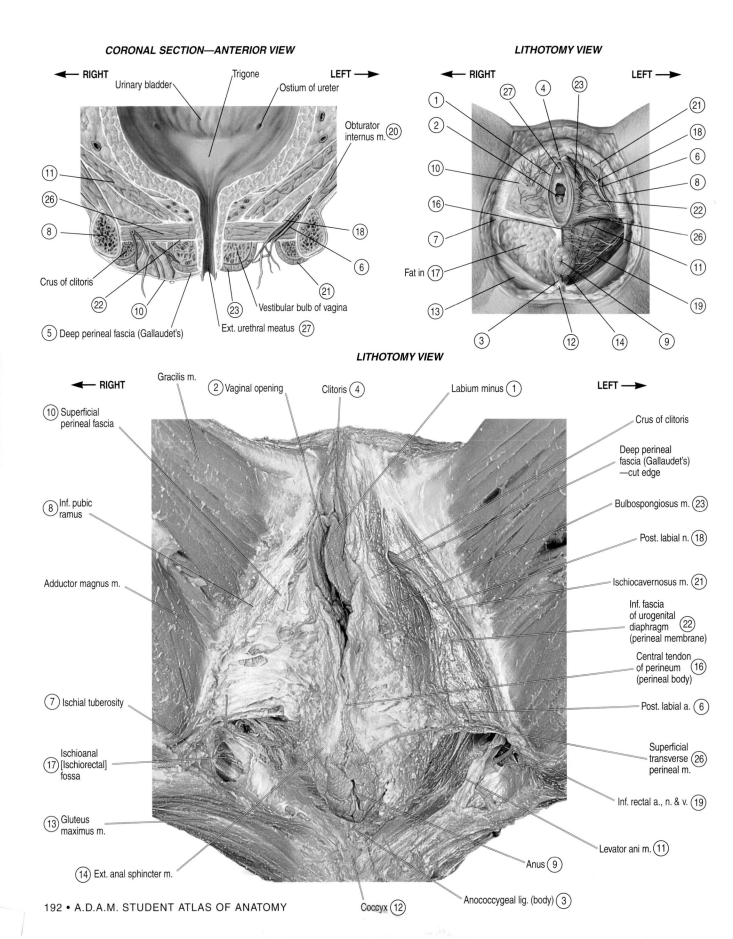

CORONAL SECTION—ANTERIOR VIEW

← RIGHT   LEFT →

Trigone
Urinary bladder
Ostium of ureter

Obturator internus m. ⑳

⑪
㉖
⑧

Crus of clitoris

㉒ ⑩

⑤ Deep perineal fascia (Gallaudet's)

Ext. urethral meatus ㉗

㉓

Vestibular bulb of vagina

⑱

⑥

㉑

LITHOTOMY VIEW

← RIGHT   LEFT →

㉗ ④ ㉓

①
②
⑩
⑯
⑦

Fat in ⑰

⑬

③ ⑫ ⑭ ⑨

㉑
⑱
⑥
⑧
㉒
㉖
⑪
⑲

LITHOTOMY VIEW

← RIGHT   LEFT →

Gracilis m.
② Vaginal opening
Clitoris ④
Labium minus ①

⑩ Superficial perineal fascia

Crus of clitoris

Deep perineal fascia (Gallaudet's) —cut edge

⑧ Inf. pubic ramus

Bulbospongiosus m. ㉓

Post. labial n. ⑱

Adductor magnus m.

Ischiocavernosus m. ㉑

Inf. fascia of urogenital diaphragm ㉒ (perineal membrane)

Central tendon of perineum ⑯ (perineal body)

⑦ Ischial tuberosity

Post. labial a. ⑥

⑰ Ischioanal [Ischiorectal] fossa

Superficial transverse ㉖ perineal m.

Inf. rectal a., n. & v. ⑲

⑬ Gluteus maximus m.

Levator ani m. ⑪

⑭ Ext. anal sphincter m.

Anus ⑨

Anococcygeal lig. (body) ③

Coccyx ⑫

LITHOTOMY VIEW

◄— RIGHT   LEFT —►

(28)
(15)
(23)   L. spermatic cord (cut)
(8)   (32)
(22)   (21)
(22)   (29)
(7)   (31)
(14)   (26)
                                 (19)
(3)   (12)   (13)   (9)

CORONAL SECTION—ANTERIOR VIEW

◄— LEFT   Prostate   Urinary   Lateral   Obturator   (20) RIGHT —►
          gland   bladder   puboprostatic lig. internus m.

(11)   (31)
(22)   (8)
(30)   (21)
(32) Perineal n.   Corpus spongiosum (28)
     (15) Urethra   (23)

LITHOTOMY VIEW

◄— RIGHT   Body of penis   L. scrotum   LEFT —►

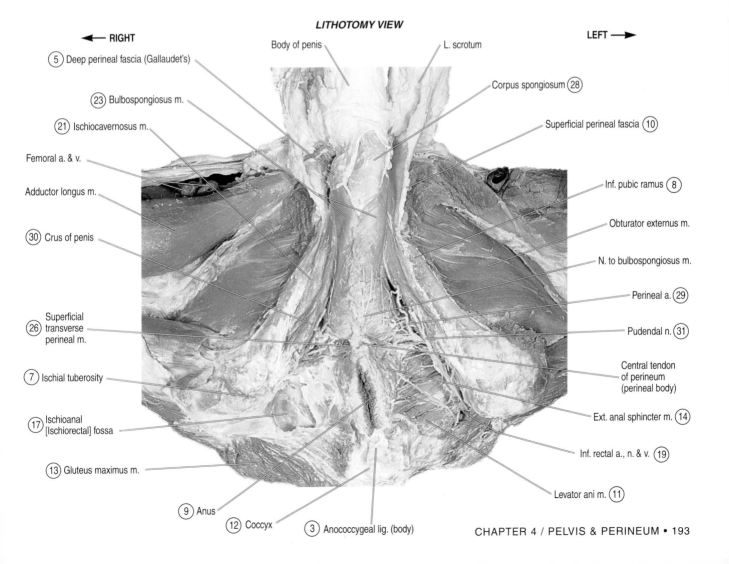

(5) Deep perineal fascia (Gallaudet's)   Corpus spongiosum (28)

(23) Bulbospongiosus m.   Superficial perineal fascia (10)

(21) Ischiocavernosus m.

Femoral a. & v.   Inf. pubic ramus (8)

Adductor longus m.   Obturator externus m.

(30) Crus of penis   N. to bulbospongiosus m.

                                                        Perineal a. (29)

Superficial
(26) transverse   Pudendal n. (31)
     perineal m.
                                                        Central tendon
(7) Ischial tuberosity   of perineum
                                                        (perineal body)

(17) Ischioanal   Ext. anal sphincter m. (14)
     [Ischiorectal] fossa

                                                        Inf. rectal a., n. & v. (19)

(13) Gluteus maximus m.
                                                        Levator ani m. (11)

(9) Anus
        (12) Coccyx   (3) Anococcygeal lig. (body)   CHAPTER 4 / PELVIS & PERINEUM • 193

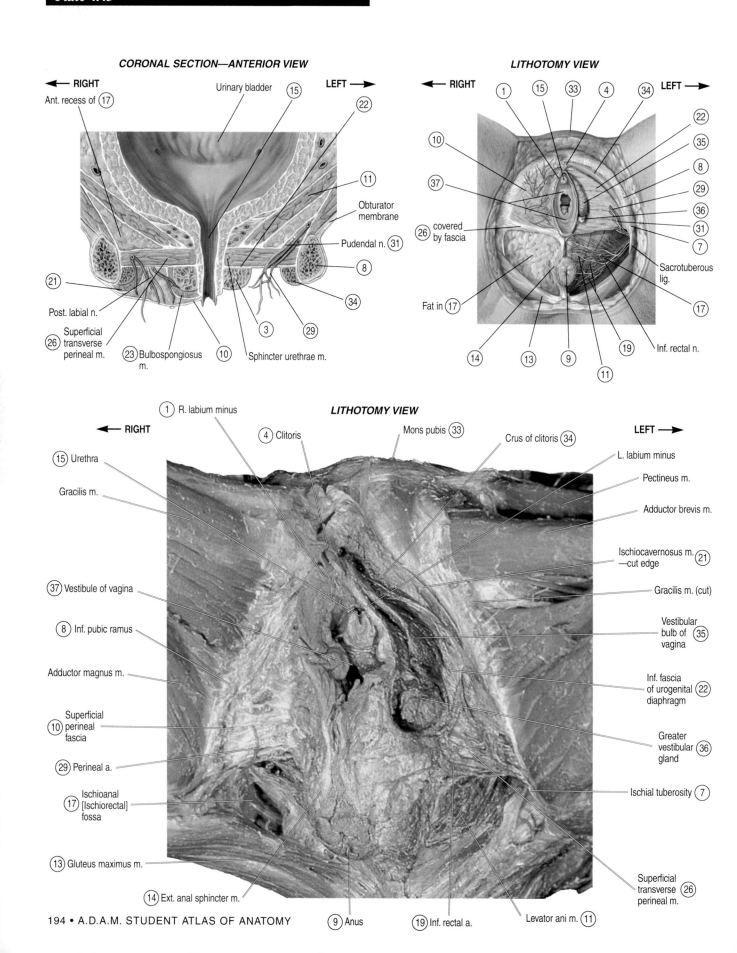

CORONAL SECTION—ANTERIOR VIEW

◄— RIGHT   LEFT —►

Ant. recess of (17)
Urinary bladder (15)
(22)
(11)
Obturator membrane
Pudendal n. (31)
(8)
(34)
(21)
Post. labial n.
(26) Superficial transverse perineal m.
(23) Bulbospongiosus m.
(10)
(3)
(29)
Sphincter urethrae m.

LITHOTOMY VIEW

◄— RIGHT   LEFT —►

(1) (15) (33) (4) (34)
(10)
(37)
(26) covered by fascia
Fat in (17)
(14) (13) (9) (11)
(22)
(35)
(8)
(29)
(36)
(31)
(7)
Sacrotuberous lig.
(17)
Inf. rectal n.
(19)

LITHOTOMY VIEW

(1) R. labium minus
(4) Clitoris
Mons pubis (33)
Crus of clitoris (34)

◄— RIGHT   LEFT —►

(15) Urethra
Gracilis m.
(37) Vestibule of vagina
(8) Inf. pubic ramus
Adductor magnus m.
(10) Superficial perineal fascia
(29) Perineal a.
(17) Ischioanal [Ischiorectal] fossa
(13) Gluteus maximus m.
(14) Ext. anal sphincter m.
(9) Anus

L. labium minus
Pectineus m.
Adductor brevis m.
Ischiocavernosus m. —cut edge (21)
Gracilis m. (cut)
Vestibular bulb of (35) vagina
Inf. fascia of urogenital (22) diaphragm
Greater vestibular (36) gland
Ischial tuberosity (7)
Superficial transverse (26) perineal m.
(19) Inf. rectal a.
Levator ani m. (11)

LITHOTOMY VIEW

← RIGHT   LEFT →

Deep fascia of penis
(15)
Corpus cavernosum
(28)
Spermatic cord (cut)
(23)
(30)
(21)
(28)
(8)
(22)
(31)
(7)
(19)
(11)
(38)
(9)
(14)

CORONAL SECTION—ANTERIOR VIEW

← RIGHT   Urinary bladder   LEFT →

Prostate gland
Urogenital diaphragm
(11)
(11)
(31)
Ant. recess of (17)
(8)
(30)
(29)
(21)
Urethra (15)
(24) Post. scrotal n.
(22)
(23)
(28)
Post. scrotal a. (25)
Bulbourethral gland (of Cowper)

LITHOTOMY VIEW

← RIGHT   LEFT →

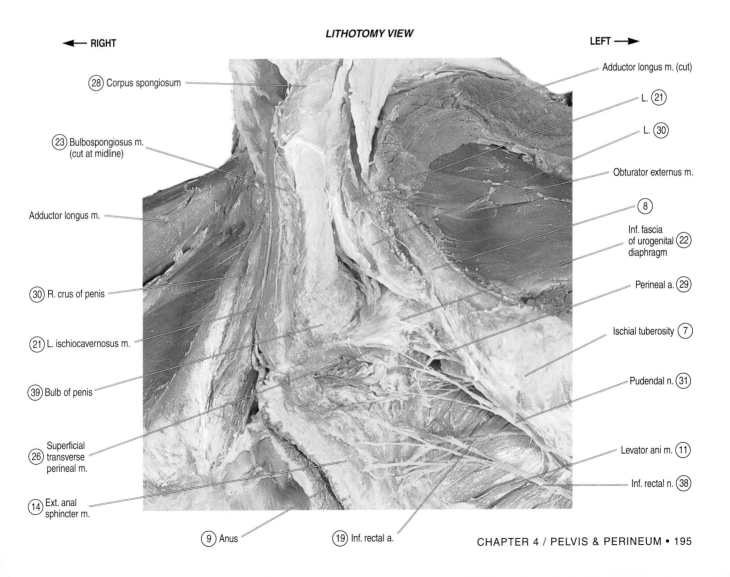

(28) Corpus spongiosum
Adductor longus m. (cut)
L. (21)
L. (30)
(23) Bulbospongiosus m. (cut at midline)
Obturator externus m.
(8)
Adductor longus m.
Inf. fascia of urogenital (22) diaphragm
(30) R. crus of penis
Perineal a. (29)
(21) L. ischiocavernosus m.
Ischial tuberosity (7)
(39) Bulb of penis
Pudendal n. (31)
(26) Superficial transverse perineal m.
Levator ani m. (11)
(14) Ext. anal sphincter m.
Inf. rectal n. (38)
(9) Anus
(19) Inf. rectal a.

CORONAL SECTION—ANTERIOR VIEW

← RIGHT

LEFT →

Urinary bladder

(15)

Obturator internus m.

(11)

(17)

(8)

(34) Crus of clitoris

(21)

(22)

(10)

(40)

(41)

Vestibular bulb of vagina (35)

LITHOTOMY VIEW

← RIGHT

LEFT →

Arcuate pubic lig.

(33) (40) (22)

(4)

(29)

(15)

(8)

(10)

(43)

(1)

(42)

(7)

(10)

(16)

(41)

Sacrotuberous lig.

(11)

(9)

(17)

(13)

(14) (3) (19)

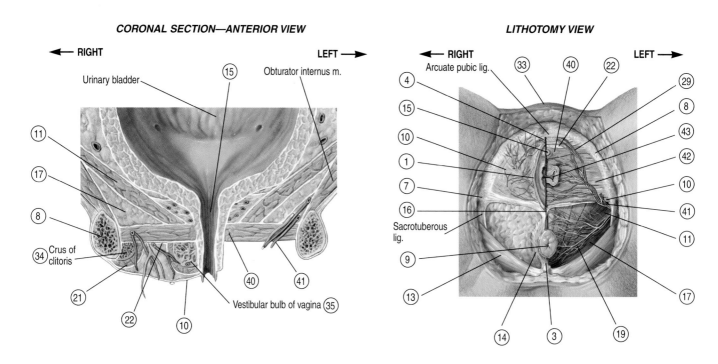

LITHOTOMY VIEW

← RIGHT

LEFT →

Adductor longus m.

(4) Clitoris

Suspensory lig. of clitoris

Mons pubis (33)

Intercavernosus septum

Gracilis m.

Inf. fascia of urogenital diaphragm (cut & reflected) (22)

(1) R. labium minus

Sphincter urethrae m. portion of urogenital diaphragm (40)

(15) Urethra

Inf. pubic ramus (8)

(21) Ischiocavernosus m. (visible through investing fascia)

Perineal a. (29)

Inf. pudendal a. (41)

(43) Vagina

Deep transverse perineal m. (42)

(10) Superficial perineal fascia

Central tendon of perineum (perineal body) (16)

(7) Ischial tuberosity

Levator ani m. (11)

(17) Ischioanal [Ischiorectal] fossa

(13) Gluteus maximus m.

Inf. rectal a. (19)

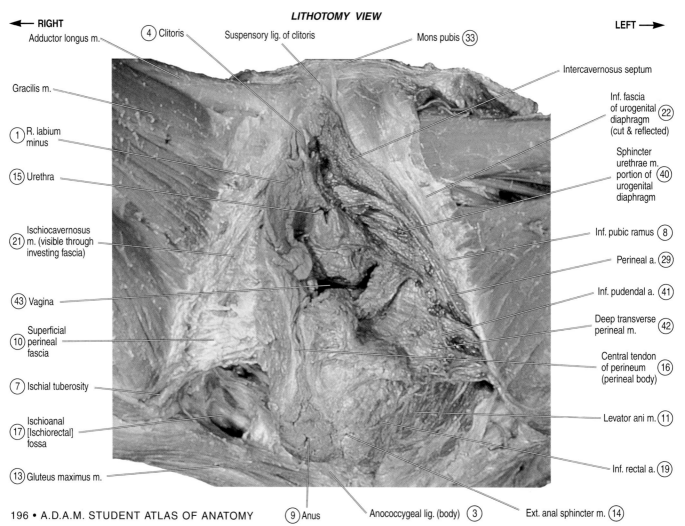

(9) Anus

Anococcygeal lig. (body) (3)

Ext. anal sphincter m. (14)

LITHOTOMY VIEW

← RIGHT   LEFT →

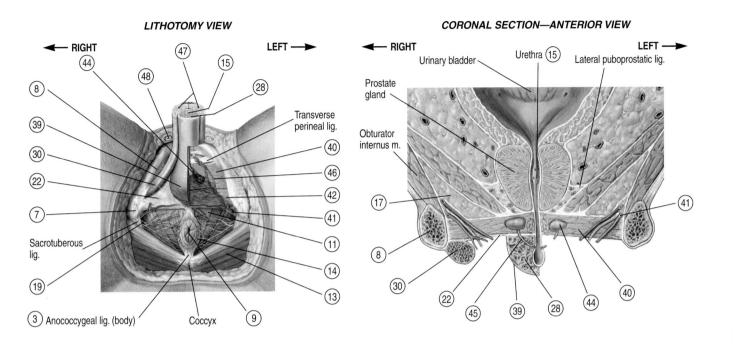

47
44 15
8 48 28
39
30 Transverse perineal lig.
22 40
7 46
42
Sacrotuberous lig. 41
11
19 14
13
3 Anococcygeal lig. (body)   Coccyx   9

CORONAL SECTION—ANTERIOR VIEW

← RIGHT   LEFT →

Urinary bladder   Urethra 15   Lateral puboprostatic lig.
Prostate gland
Obturator internus m.
17   41
8
30
22   40
45 39 28 44

LITHOTOMY VIEW

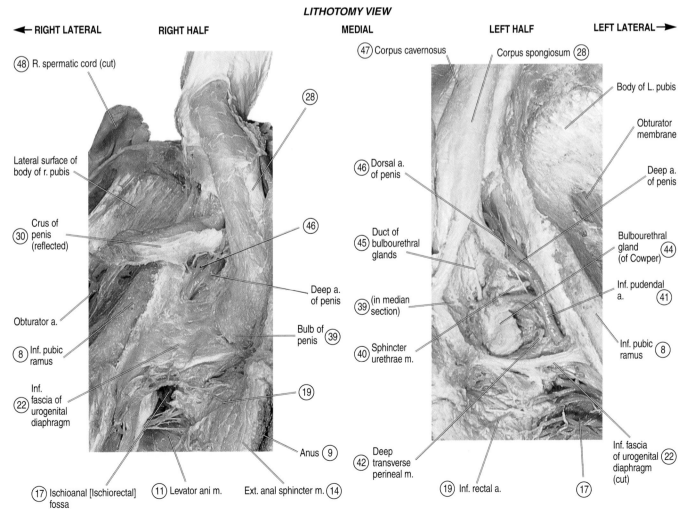

← RIGHT LATERAL   RIGHT HALF   MEDIAL   LEFT HALF   LEFT LATERAL →

47 Corpus cavernosus   Corpus spongiosum 28

48 R. spermatic cord (cut)   Body of L. pubis

28

Lateral surface of body of r. pubis   Obturator membrane

46 Dorsal a. of penis   Deep a. of penis

Crus of
30 penis (reflected)   46

Duct of
45 bulbourethral glands   Bulbourethral gland 44 (of Cowper)

Obturator a.   Deep a. of penis   39 (in median section)   Inf. pudendal a. 41

8 Inf. pubic ramus   Bulb of penis 39   40 Sphincter urethrae m.   Inf. pubic ramus 8

Inf.
22 fascia of urogenital diaphragm   19

Deep
42 transverse perineal m.   Inf. fascia of urogenital 22 diaphragm (cut)

Anus 9

17 Ischioanal [Ischiorectal] fossa   11 Levator ani m.   Ext. anal sphincter m. 14   19 Inf. rectal a.   17

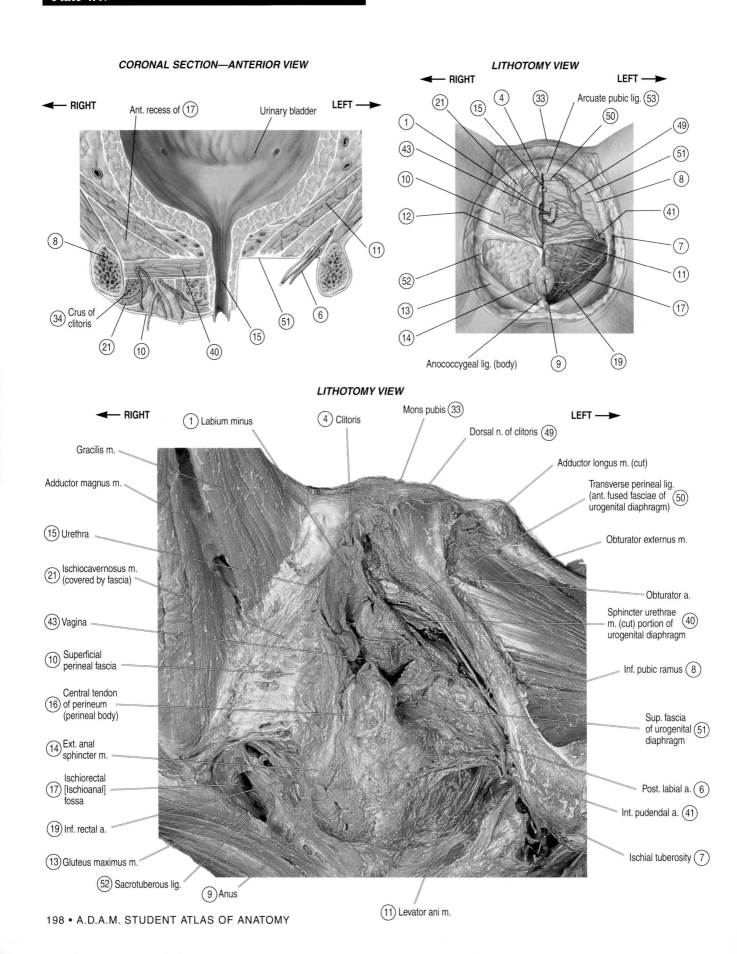

CORONAL SECTION—ANTERIOR VIEW

← RIGHT   LEFT →

Ant. recess of (17)   Urinary bladder

(8)   (11)

Crus of clitoris (34)   (51)   (6)

(21)   (10)   (40)   (15)

LITHOTOMY VIEW

← RIGHT   LEFT →

(21) (15) (4) (33)   Arcuate pubic lig. (53)

(1)   (50)   (49)

(43)   (51)

(10)   (8)

(12)   (41)

(52)   (7)

(13)   (11)

(14)   (17)

Anococcygeal lig. (body)   (9)   (19)

LITHOTOMY VIEW

← RIGHT   Mons pubis (33)   LEFT →

(1) Labium minus   (4) Clitoris   Dorsal n. of clitoris (49)

Gracilis m.   Adductor longus m. (cut)

Adductor magnus m.   Transverse perineal lig. (ant. fused fasciae of urogenital diaphragm) (50)

(15) Urethra   Obturator externus m.

(21) Ischiocavernosus m. (covered by fascia)   Obturator a.

(43) Vagina   Sphincter urethrae m. (cut) portion of urogenital diaphragm (40)

(10) Superficial perineal fascia   Inf. pubic ramus (8)

(16) Central tendon of perineum (perineal body)   Sup. fascia of urogenital diaphragm (51)

(14) Ext. anal sphincter m.   Post. labial a. (6)

(17) Ischiorectal [Ischioanal] fossa   Int. pudendal a. (41)

(19) Inf. rectal a.   Ischial tuberosity (7)

(13) Gluteus maximus m.

(52) Sacrotuberous lig.   (9) Anus   (11) Levator ani m.

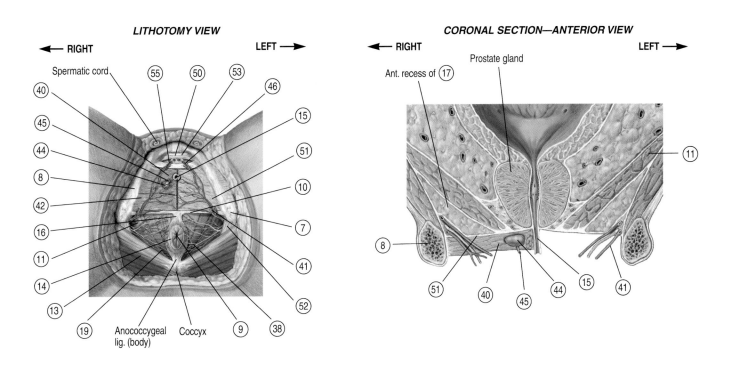

LITHOTOMY VIEW

← RIGHT   LEFT →

Spermatic cord — (55) (50) (53) (46)
(40)
(45)
(44)
(8)
(42)
(16)
(11)
(14)
(13)
(19)   Anococcygeal   Coccyx   (9)   (38)
lig. (body)

(15)
(51)
(10)
(7)
(41)
(52)

CORONAL SECTION—ANTERIOR VIEW

← RIGHT   LEFT →

Ant. recess of (17)   Prostate gland

(11)

(8)   (51) (40) (45) (44) (15) (41)

LITHOTOMY VIEWS

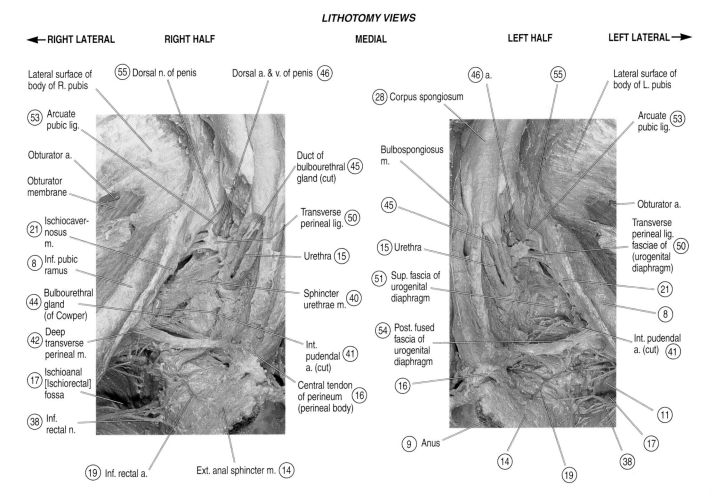

← RIGHT LATERAL   RIGHT HALF   MEDIAL   LEFT HALF   LEFT LATERAL →

Lateral surface of
body of R. pubis
(53) Arcuate
pubic lig.
Obturator a.
Obturator
membrane
(21) Ischiocaver-
nosus
m.
(8) Inf. pubic
ramus
(44) Bulbourethral
gland
(of Cowper)
(42) Deep
transverse
perineal m.
(17) Ischioanal
[Ischiorectal]
fossa
(38) Inf.
rectal n.

(55) Dorsal n. of penis   Dorsal a. & v. of penis (46)

Duct of
bulbourethral (45)
gland (cut)
Transverse (50)
perineal lig.
Urethra (15)
Sphincter (40)
urethrae m.
Int.
pudendal (41)
a. (cut)
Central tendon
of perineum (16)
(perineal body)

(19) Inf. rectal a.   Ext. anal sphincter m. (14)

(46) a.   (55)

(28) Corpus spongiosum

Bulbospongiosus
m.
(45)

(15) Urethra

(51) Sup. fascia of
urogenital
diaphragm

(54) Post. fused
fascia of
urogenital
diaphragm
(16)

(9) Anus   (14)   (19)   (38)

Lateral surface of
body of L. pubis
Arcuate (53)
pubic lig.
Obturator a.
Transverse
perineal lig.
fasciae of (50)
(urogenital
diaphragm)
(21)
(8)
Int. pudendal
a. (cut) (41)
(11)
(17)

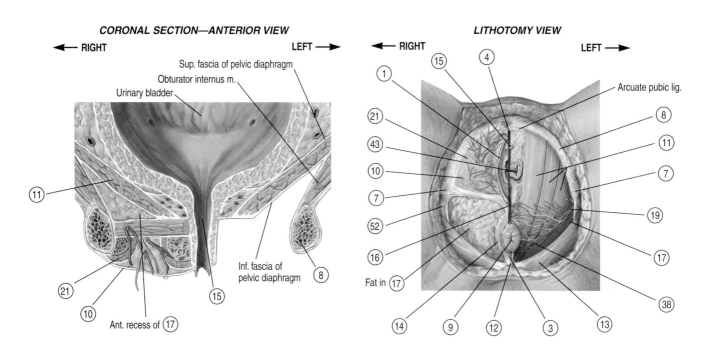

CORONAL SECTION—ANTERIOR VIEW

← RIGHT   LEFT →

Sup. fascia of pelvic diaphragm
Obturator internus m.
Urinary bladder

11
21
10
Ant. recess of 17
15
8
Inf. fascia of pelvic diaphragm

LITHOTOMY VIEW

← RIGHT   LEFT →

15
4
1
Arcuate pubic lig.
21
8
43
11
10
7
7
19
52
16
17
Fat in 17
38
14
9
12
3
13

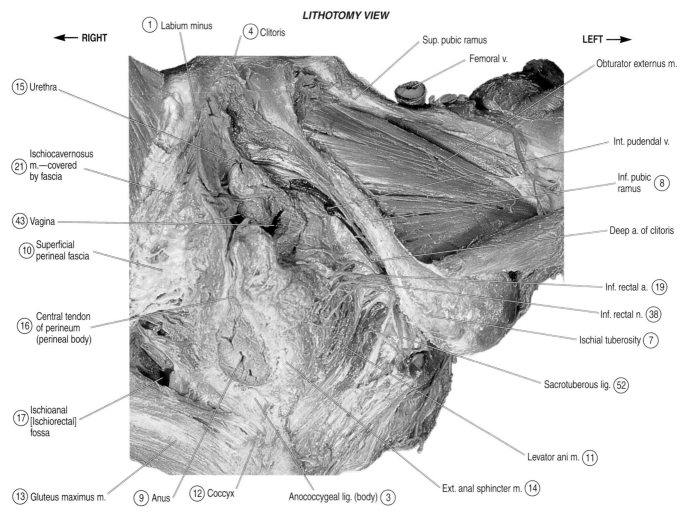

LITHOTOMY VIEW

← RIGHT   LEFT →

1 Labium minus   4 Clitoris   Sup. pubic ramus
Femoral v.
Obturator externus m.

15 Urethra

Int. pudendal v.

21 Ischiocavernosus m.—covered by fascia

Inf. pubic 8 ramus

43 Vagina

Deep a. of clitoris

10 Superficial perineal fascia

Inf. rectal a. 19

16 Central tendon of perineum (perineal body)

Inf. rectal n. 38

Ischial tuberosity 7

Sacrotuberous lig. 52

17 Ischioanal [Ischiorectal] fossa

Levator ani m. 11

13 Gluteus maximus m.   9 Anus   12 Coccyx   Anococcygeal lig. (body) 3   Ext. anal sphincter m. 14

LITHOTOMY VIEW

◄— RIGHT   LEFT —►

Spermatic cord   53   57   Deep dorsal vv. of penis

15

56

8

11

9

3

13   12   14   53   Coccygeus m.

58

7

52

17

CORONAL SECTION—ANTERIOR VIEW

◄— RIGHT   LEFT —►

56   Urinary bladder

20

58

8

17

15

11

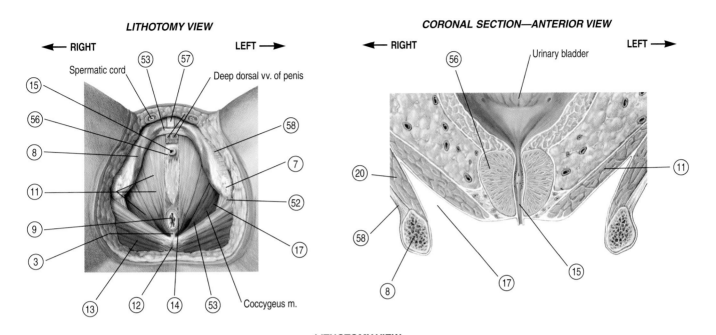

LITHOTOMY VIEW

◄— RIGHT   Puboprostatic m.   57 Pubic symphysis   Arcuate pubic lig. 53   LEFT —►

15 Urethra   Obturator membrane 58

Obturator canal

56 Prostate gland

Puborectalis m. part of 11

11 Levator ani m.

Inf. pubic ramus 8

Obturator internus m. fascia

20 Obturator internus m.

16 Central tendon of perineum (perineal body)

Ischial tuberosity 7

Ischioanal [Ischiorectal] 17 fossa

52 Sacrotuberous lig.

Pubococcygeal m. part of 11

14 Ext. anal sphincter m.

Iliococcygeal m. part of 11

9 Anus   Coccyx 12   Anococcygeal lig. (body) 3

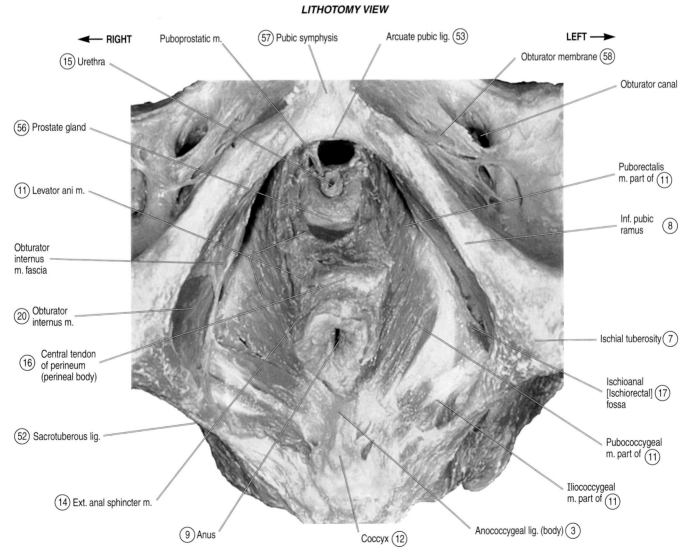

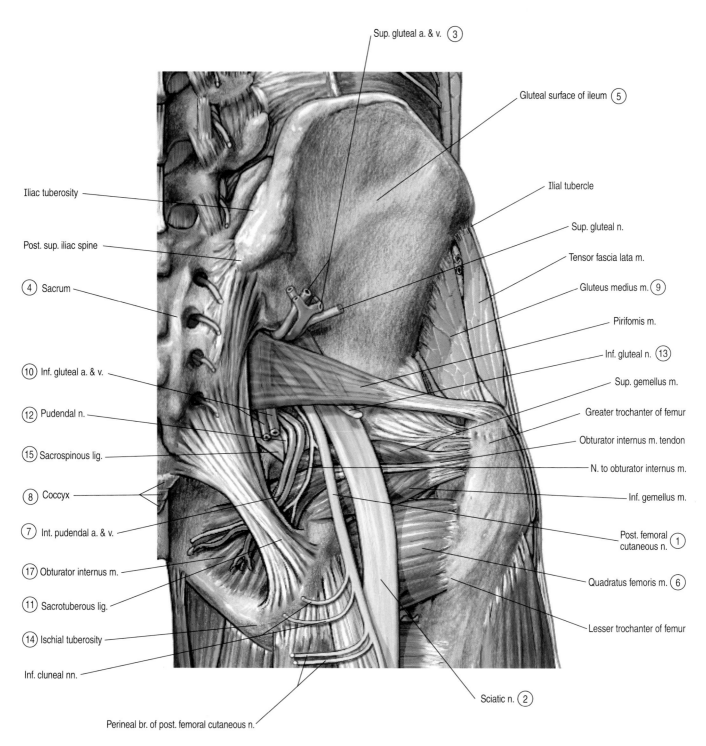

Sup. gluteal a. & v. ③

Gluteal surface of ileum ⑤

Ilial tubercle

Sup. gluteal n.

Tensor fascia lata m.

Gluteus medius m. ⑨

Pirifomis m.

Inf. gluteal n. ⑬

Sup. gemellus m.

Greater trochanter of femur

Obturator internus m. tendon

N. to obturator internus m.

Inf. gemellus m.

Post. femoral cutaneous n. ①

Quadratus femoris m. ⑥

Lesser trochanter of femur

Iliac tuberosity

Post. sup. iliac spine

④ Sacrum

⑩ Inf. gluteal a. & v.

⑫ Pudendal n.

⑮ Sacrospinous lig.

⑧ Coccyx

⑦ Int. pudendal a. & v.

⑰ Obturator internus m.

⑪ Sacrotuberous lig.

⑭ Ischial tuberosity

Inf. cluneal nn.

Perineal br. of post. femoral cutaneous n.

Sciatic n. ②

GLUTEAL REGION—POSTERIOR VIEW

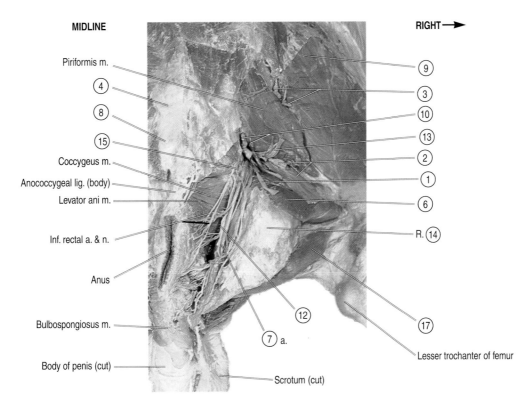

MIDLINE   RIGHT ➡

Piriformis m.
④
⑧
⑮
Coccygeus m.
Anococcygeal lig. (body)
Levator ani m.

Inf. rectal a. & n.

Anus

Bulbospongiosus m.

Body of penis (cut)

⑨
③
⑩
⑬
②
①
⑥
R. ⑭

⑫
⑦ a.

Scrotum (cut)

⑰
Lesser trochanter of femur

INFERIOR OBLIQUE VIEW OF RIGHT MALE PERINEUM & PUDENDAL CANAL

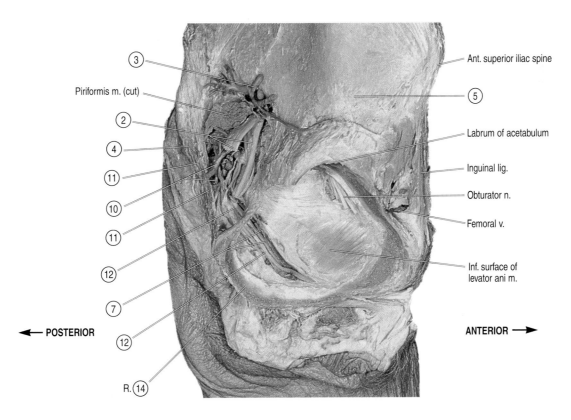

③
Piriformis m. (cut)
②
④
⑪
⑩
⑪
⑫
⑦
⑫

◀ POSTERIOR

R. ⑭

Ant. superior iliac spine
⑤
Labrum of acetabulum
Inguinal lig.
Obturator n.
Femoral v.
Inf. surface of
levator ani m.

ANTERIOR ➡

DISSECTION OF FEMALE PERINEUM FROM LATERAL APPROACH (ACETABULUM REMOVED)

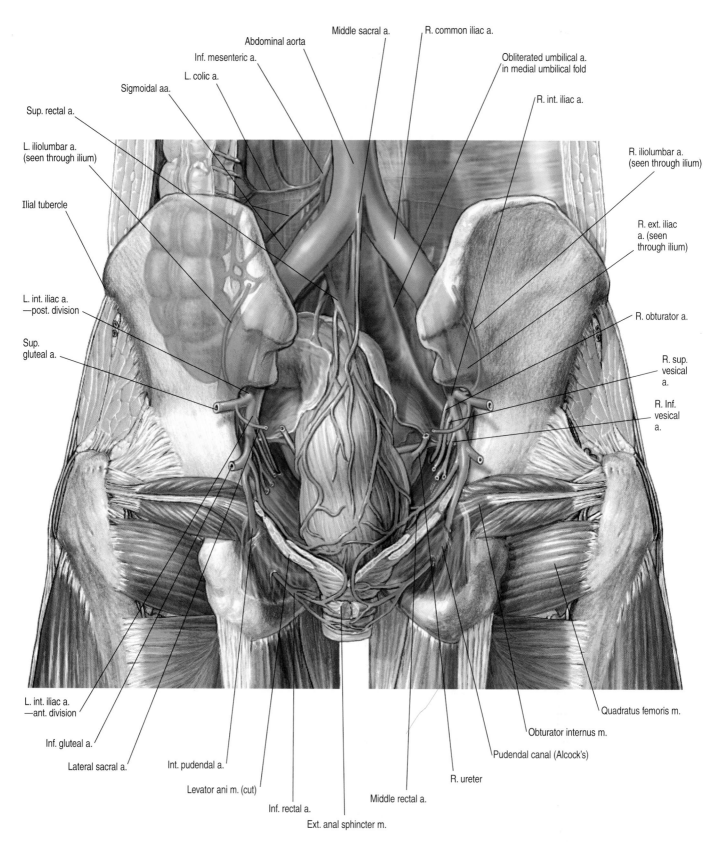

Middle sacral a.

Abdominal aorta

R. common iliac a.

Inf. mesenteric a.

Obliterated umbilical a. in medial umbilical fold

L. colic a.

Sigmoidal aa.

R. int. iliac a.

Sup. rectal a.

L. iliolumbar a. (seen through ilium)

R. iliolumbar a. (seen through ilium)

Ilial tubercle

R. ext. iliac a. (seen through ilium)

L. int. iliac a. —post. division

R. obturator a.

Sup. gluteal a.

R. sup. vesical a.

R. Inf. vesical a.

L. int. iliac a. —ant. division

Quadratus femoris m.

Inf. gluteal a.

Obturator internus m.

Lateral sacral a.

Pudendal canal (Alcock's)

Int. pudendal a.

R. ureter

Levator ani m. (cut)

Middle rectal a.

Inf. rectal a.

Ext. anal sphincter m.

POSTERIOR VIEW WITH SACRUM REMOVED

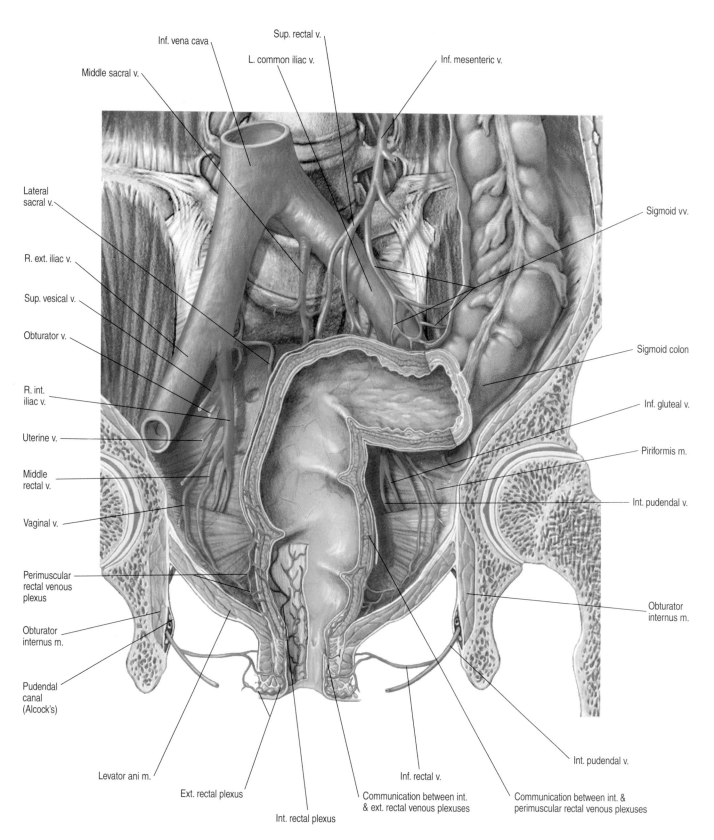

Inf. vena cava

Sup. rectal v.

Middle sacral v.

L. common iliac v.

Inf. mesenteric v.

Lateral sacral v.

Sigmoid vv.

R. ext. iliac v.

Sup. vesical v.

Obturator v.

Sigmoid colon

R. int. iliac v.

Inf. gluteal v.

Uterine v.

Piriformis m.

Middle rectal v.

Int. pudendal v.

Vaginal v.

Perimuscular rectal venous plexus

Obturator internus m.

Obturator internus m.

Pudendal canal (Alcock's)

Levator ani m.

Int. pudendal v.

Ext. rectal plexus

Inf. rectal v.

Communication between int. & ext. rectal venous plexuses

Communication between int. & perimuscular rectal venous plexuses

Int. rectal plexus

CORONAL SECTION—ANTERIOR VIEW

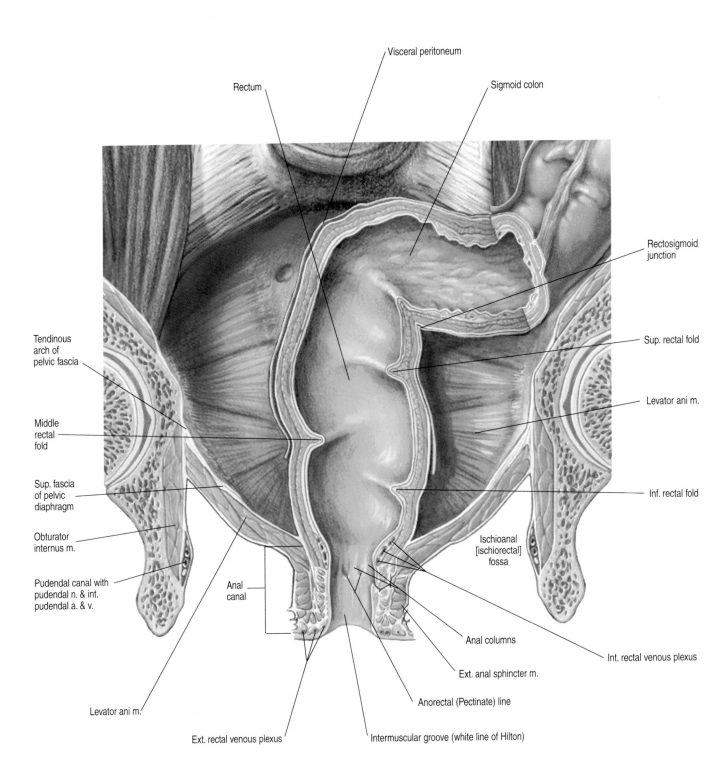

Visceral peritoneum

Rectum

Sigmoid colon

Rectosigmoid junction

Tendinous arch of pelvic fascia

Sup. rectal fold

Middle rectal fold

Levator ani m.

Sup. fascia of pelvic diaphragm

Inf. rectal fold

Obturator internus m.

Ischioanal [ischiorectal] fossa

Pudendal canal with pudendal n. & int. pudendal a. & v.

Anal canal

Anal columns

Int. rectal venous plexus

Ext. anal sphincter m.

Levator ani m.

Anorectal (Pectinate) line

Ext. rectal venous plexus

Intermuscular groove (white line of Hilton)

CORONAL SECTION—ANTERIOR VIEW

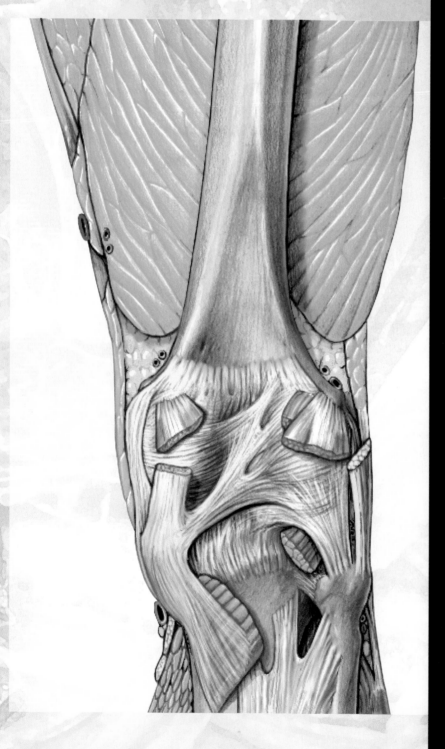

Lower Limb

Chapter **5**

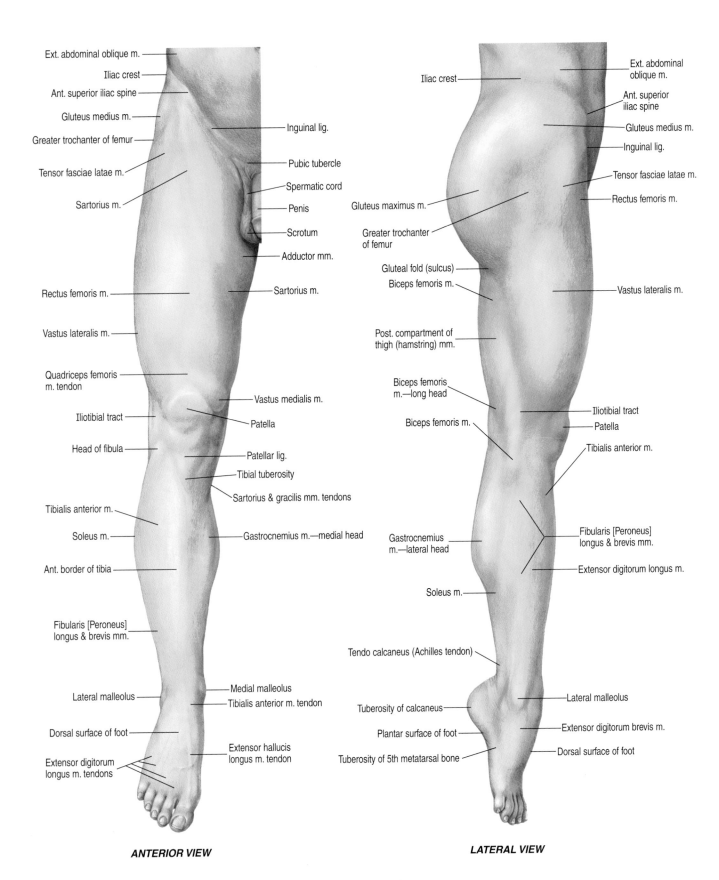

Ext. abdominal oblique m.
Iliac crest
Ant. superior iliac spine
Gluteus medius m.
Greater trochanter of femur
Tensor fasciae latae m.
Sartorius m.

Inguinal lig.
Pubic tubercle
Spermatic cord
Penis
Scrotum
Adductor mm.
Sartorius m.

Rectus femoris m.
Vastus lateralis m.
Quadriceps femoris m. tendon
Iliotibial tract
Head of fibula

Vastus medialis m.
Patella
Patellar lig.
Tibial tuberosity
Sartorius & gracilis mm. tendons

Tibialis anterior m.
Soleus m.
Ant. border of tibia

Gastrocnemius m.—medial head

Fibularis [Peroneus] longus & brevis mm.

Lateral malleolus
Dorsal surface of foot
Extensor digitorum longus m. tendons

Medial malleolus
Tibialis anterior m. tendon

Extensor hallucis longus m. tendon

ANTERIOR VIEW

Iliac crest

Ext. abdominal oblique m.
Ant. superior iliac spine
Gluteus medius m.
Inguinal lig.
Tensor fasciae latae m.
Rectus femoris m.

Gluteus maximus m.
Greater trochanter of femur
Gluteal fold (sulcus)
Biceps femoris m.

Vastus lateralis m.

Post. compartment of thigh (hamstring) mm.

Biceps femoris m.—long head
Biceps femoris m.

Iliotibial tract
Patella
Tibialis anterior m.

Gastrocnemius m.—lateral head

Fibularis [Peroneus] longus & brevis mm.
Extensor digitorum longus m.

Soleus m.

Tendo calcaneus (Achilles tendon)

Tuberosity of calcaneus
Plantar surface of foot
Tuberosity of 5th metatarsal bone

Lateral malleolus
Extensor digitorum brevis m.
Dorsal surface of foot

LATERAL VIEW

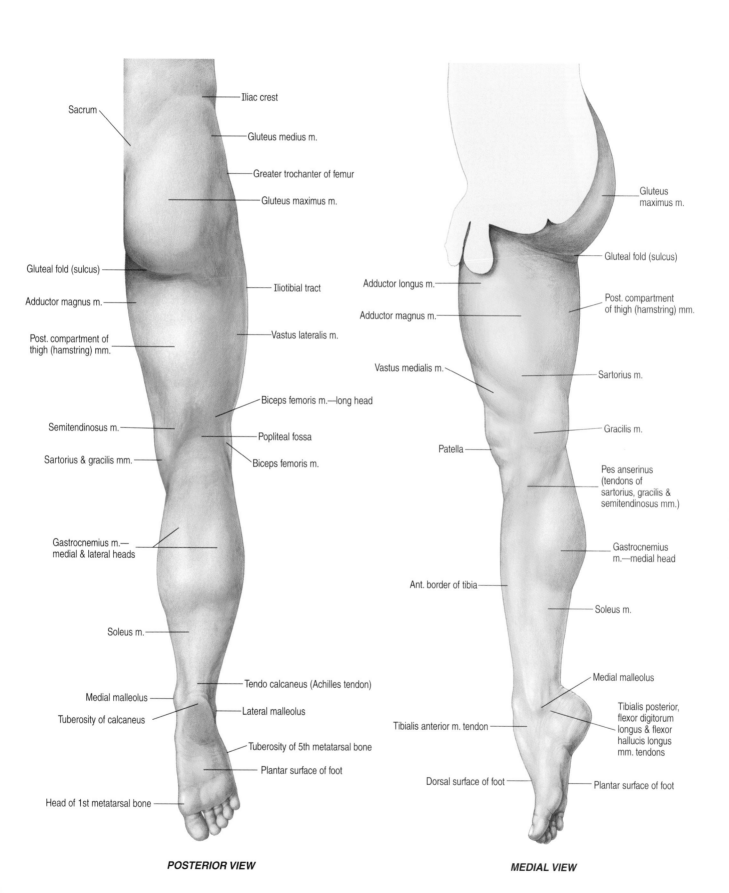

Iliac crest

Sacrum

Gluteus medius m.

Greater trochanter of femur

Gluteus maximus m.

Gluteal fold (sulcus)

Adductor magnus m.

Iliotibial tract

Post. compartment of thigh (hamstring) mm.

Vastus lateralis m.

Biceps femoris m.—long head

Semitendinosus m.

Popliteal fossa

Sartorius & gracilis mm.

Biceps femoris m.

Gastrocnemius m.— medial & lateral heads

Soleus m.

Tendo calcaneus (Achilles tendon)

Medial malleolus

Lateral malleolus

Tuberosity of calcaneus

Tuberosity of 5th metatarsal bone

Plantar surface of foot

Head of 1st metatarsal bone

Gluteus maximus m.

Gluteal fold (sulcus)

Post. compartment of thigh (hamstring) mm.

Adductor longus m.

Adductor magnus m.

Vastus medialis m.

Sartorius m.

Gracilis m.

Patella

Pes anserinus (tendons of sartorius, gracilis & semitendinosus mm.)

Gastrocnemius m.—medial head

Ant. border of tibia

Soleus m.

Medial malleolus

Tibialis posterior, flexor digitorum longus & flexor hallucis longus mm. tendons

Tibialis anterior m. tendon

Dorsal surface of foot

Plantar surface of foot

POSTERIOR VIEW

MEDIAL VIEW

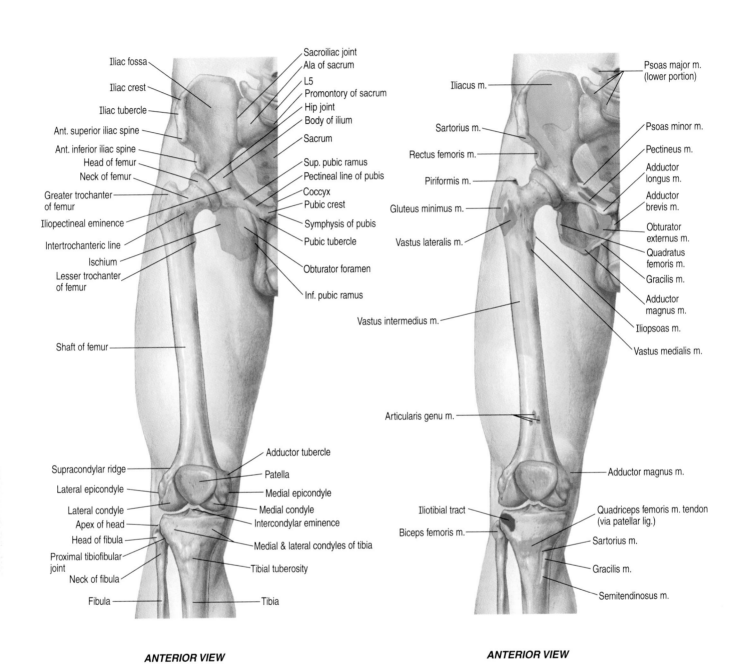

Iliac fossa
Iliac crest
Iliac tubercle
Ant. superior iliac spine
Ant. inferior iliac spine
Head of femur
Neck of femur
Greater trochanter of femur
Iliopectineal eminence
Intertrochanteric line
Ischium
Lesser trochanter of femur

Shaft of femur

Supracondylar ridge
Lateral epicondyle
Lateral condyle
Apex of head
Head of fibula
Proximal tibiofibular joint
Neck of fibula
Fibula

Sacroiliac joint
Ala of sacrum
L5
Promontory of sacrum
Hip joint
Body of ilium
Sacrum
Sup. pubic ramus
Pectineal line of pubis
Coccyx
Pubic crest
Symphysis of pubis
Pubic tubercle
Obturator foramen
Inf. pubic ramus

Adductor tubercle
Patella
Medial epicondyle
Medial condyle
Intercondylar eminence
Medial & lateral condyles of tibia
Tibial tuberosity
Tibia

ANTERIOR VIEW

Iliacus m.
Sartorius m.
Rectus femoris m.
Piriformis m.
Gluteus minimus m.
Vastus lateralis m.

Vastus intermedius m.

Articularis genu m.

Iliotibial tract
Biceps femoris m.

Psoas major m. (lower portion)
Psoas minor m.
Pectineus m.
Adductor longus m.
Adductor brevis m.
Obturator externus m.
Quadratus femoris m.
Gracilis m.
Adductor magnus m.
Iliopsoas m.
Vastus medialis m.

Adductor magnus m.

Quadriceps femoris m. tendon (via patellar lig.)
Sartorius m.
Gracilis m.
Semitendinosus m.

ANTERIOR VIEW

- Gluteus minimus
- Vastus lateralis
- Vastus medialis
- Iliopsoas
- Vastus intermedius
- Obturator externus

- Adductor longus
- Iliotibial tract
- Piriformis
- Articularis genu
- Patellar ligament
- Sartorius

- Gracilis
- Adductor brevis
- Quadratus femoris
- Biceps femoris
- Semitendinosus
- Iliacus

- Psoas major
- Rectus femoris
- Psoas minor
- Adductor magnus
- Pectineus

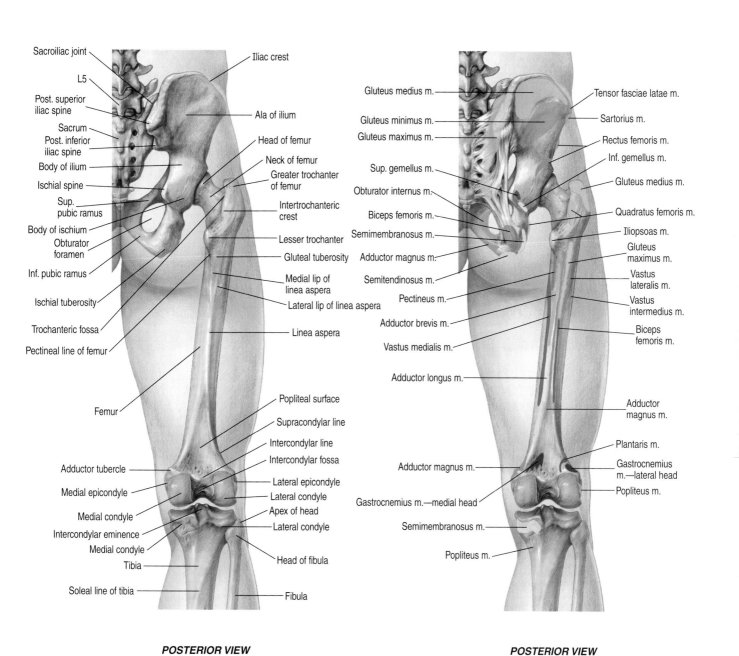

POSTERIOR VIEW

Sacroiliac joint
L5
Post. superior iliac spine
Sacrum
Post. inferior iliac spine
Body of ilium
Ischial spine
Sup. pubic ramus
Body of ischium
Obturator foramen
Inf. pubic ramus
Ischial tuberosity
Trochanteric fossa
Pectineal line of femur
Femur
Adductor tubercle
Medial epicondyle
Medial condyle
Intercondylar eminence
Medial condyle
Tibia
Soleal line of tibia

Iliac crest
Ala of ilium
Head of femur
Neck of femur
Greater trochanter of femur
Intertrochanteric crest
Lesser trochanter
Gluteal tuberosity
Medial lip of linea aspera
Lateral lip of linea aspera
Linea aspera
Popliteal surface
Supracondylar line
Intercondylar line
Intercondylar fossa
Lateral epicondyle
Lateral condyle
Apex of head
Lateral condyle
Head of fibula
Fibula

POSTERIOR VIEW

Gluteus medius m.
Gluteus minimus m.
Gluteus maximus m.
Sup. gemellus m.
Obturator internus m.
Biceps femoris m.
Semimembranosus m.
Adductor magnus m.
Semitendinosus m.
Pectineus m.
Adductor brevis m.
Vastus medialis m.
Adductor longus m.
Adductor magnus m.
Gastrocnemius m.—medial head
Semimembranosus m.
Popliteus m.

Tensor fasciae latae m.
Sartorius m.
Rectus femoris m.
Inf. gemellus m.
Gluteus medius m.
Quadratus femoris m.
Iliopsoas m.
Gluteus maximus m.
Vastus lateralis m.
Vastus intermedius m.
Biceps femoris m.
Adductor magnus m.
Plantaris m.
Gastrocnemius m.—lateral head
Popliteus m.

POSTERIOR VIEW

- Sartorius
- Rectus femoris
- Tensor fasciae latae
- Gluteus medius
- Gluteus minimus
- Obturator internus
- Semimembranosus
- Popliteus
- Adductor magnus
- Gluteus maximus
- Quadratus femoris
- Inferior gemellus
- Superior gemellus
- Semitendinosus
- Biceps femoris
- Gastrocnemius
- Iliopsoas
- Pectineus
- Vastus medialis
- Adductor brevis
- Adductor longus
- Vastus lateralis
- Vastus intermedius
- Plantaris

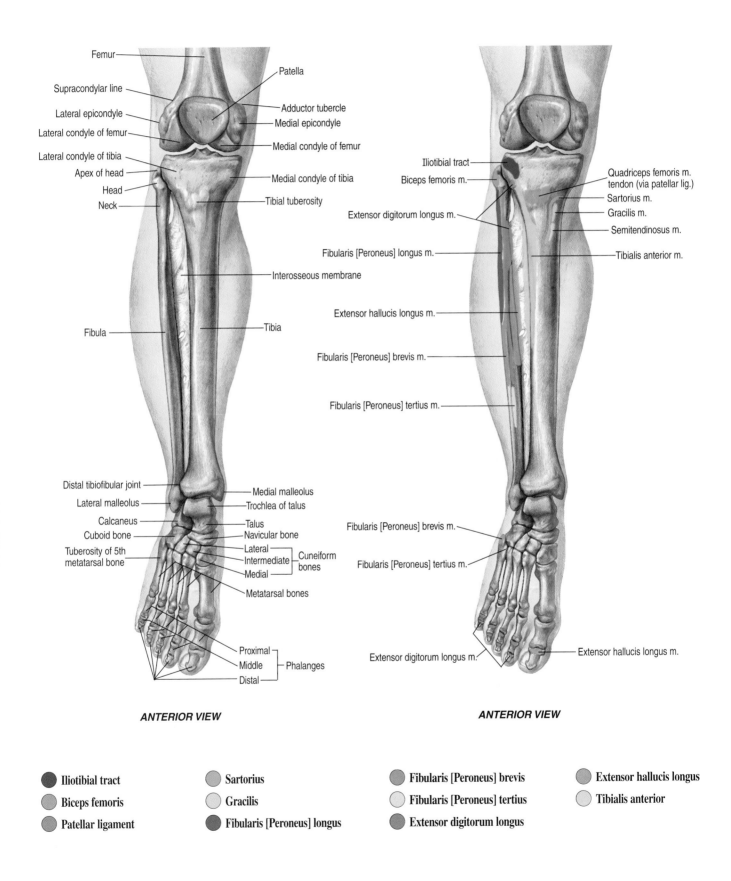

Femur

Supracondylar line

Lateral epicondyle

Lateral condyle of femur

Lateral condyle of tibia

Apex of head

Head

Neck

Fibula

Patella

Adductor tubercle

Medial epicondyle

Medial condyle of femur

Medial condyle of tibia

Tibial tuberosity

Interosseous membrane

Tibia

Distal tibiofibular joint

Lateral malleolus

Calcaneus

Cuboid bone

Tuberosity of 5th metatarsal bone

Medial malleolus

Trochlea of talus

Talus

Navicular bone

Lateral

Intermediate — Cuneiform bones

Medial

Metatarsal bones

Proximal

Middle — Phalanges

Distal

ANTERIOR VIEW

Iliotibial tract

Biceps femoris m.

Extensor digitorum longus m.

Fibularis [Peroneus] longus m.

Extensor hallucis longus m.

Fibularis [Peroneus] brevis m.

Fibularis [Peroneus] tertius m.

Quadriceps femoris m. tendon (via patellar lig.)

Sartorius m.

Gracilis m.

Semitendinosus m.

Tibialis anterior m.

Fibularis [Peroneus] brevis m.

Fibularis [Peroneus] tertius m.

Extensor digitorum longus m.

Extensor hallucis longus m.

ANTERIOR VIEW

Iliotibial tract

Biceps femoris

Patellar ligament

Sartorius

Gracilis

Fibularis [Peroneus] longus

Fibularis [Peroneus] brevis

Fibularis [Peroneus] tertius

Extensor digitorum longus

Extensor hallucis longus

Tibialis anterior

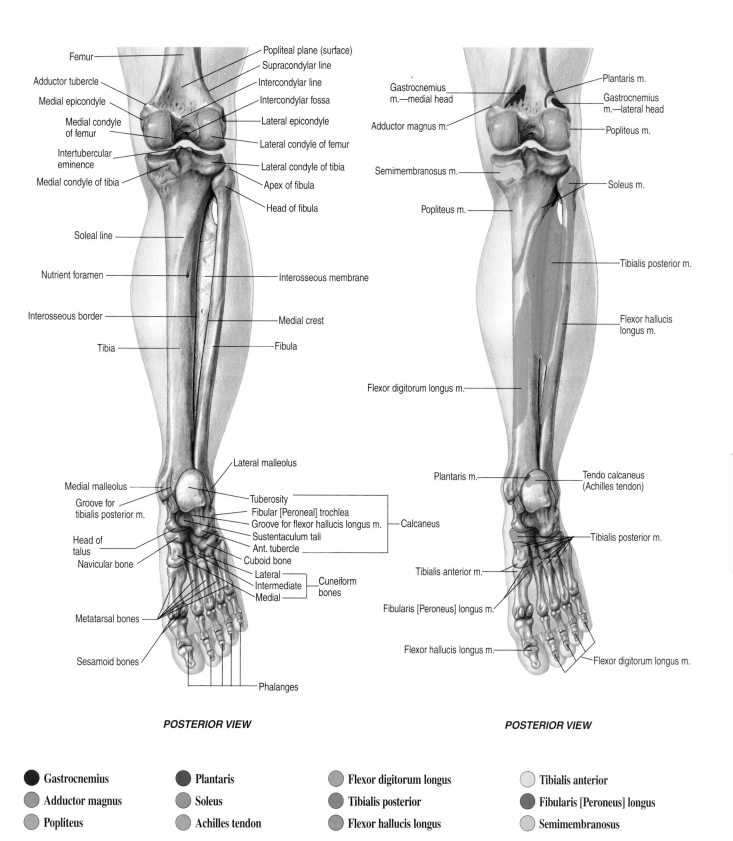

Femur — Popliteal plane (surface)
Supracondylar line
Adductor tubercle — Intercondylar line
Medial epicondyle — Intercondylar fossa
Medial condyle of femur — Lateral epicondyle
Lateral condyle of femur
Intertubercular eminence — Lateral condyle of tibia
Medial condyle of tibia — Apex of fibula
Head of fibula
Soleal line
Nutrient foramen — Interosseous membrane
Interosseous border — Medial crest
Tibia — Fibula

Gastrocnemius m.—medial head — Plantaris m.
Adductor magnus m. — Gastrocnemius m.—lateral head
Popliteus m.
Semimembranosus m. — Soleus m.
Popliteus m. — Tibialis posterior m.
Flexor hallucis longus m.
Flexor digitorum longus m.

Lateral malleolus
Medial malleolus
Groove for tibialis posterior m. — Tuberosity
Fibular [Peroneal] trochlea
Groove for flexor hallucis longus m. — Calcaneus
Head of talus — Sustentaculum tali
Navicular bone — Ant. tubercle
Cuboid bone
Lateral
Intermediate — Cuneiform bones
Medial
Metatarsal bones
Sesamoid bones
Phalanges

Plantaris m. — Tendo calcaneus (Achilles tendon)
Tibialis posterior m.
Tibialis anterior m.
Fibularis [Peroneus] longus m.
Flexor hallucis longus m. — Flexor digitorum longus m.

POSTERIOR VIEW

POSTERIOR VIEW

● **Gastrocnemius**

● **Plantaris**

● **Flexor digitorum longus**

○ **Tibialis anterior**

● **Adductor magnus**

● **Soleus**

● **Tibialis posterior**

● **Fibularis [Peroneus] longus**

● **Popliteus**

● **Achilles tendon**

● **Flexor hallucis longus**

○ **Semimembranosus**

Anterior Thigh Muscles
Table 5.1

Muscle	Proximal Attachment	Distal Attachment	Innervation	Main Actions
Iliopsoas Psoas major	Sides of T12 to L5 vertebral bodies, intervertebral discs between them & transverse processes of L1–L5	Lesser trochanter of femur	Ventral rami of lumbar nn. (**L1, L2** & L3)[a]	Act conjointly in flexing thigh at hip joint and in stabilizing this joint.
Psoas minor	Sides of T12 & L1 vertebrae & intervertebral disc	Pectineal line, iliopectineal eminence via iliopectineal arch lig.	Ventral rami of lumbar nn. (L1 & L2)	
Iliacus	Iliac crest, iliac fossa, ala of sacrum, ant. sacroiliac ligg. & capsule of hip joint	Tendon of psoas major & body of femur, inf. to lesser trochanter	Femoral n. (**L2** & L3)	
Tensor fasciae latae	Ant. sup. iliac spine & ant. part of ext. lip of iliac crest	Anterolateral aspect of lateral tibial condyle via iliotibial tract	Sup. gluteal n. (L4 & L5)	Abducts, medially rotates, and flexes thigh; helps to keep knee extended
Sartorius	Ant. sup. iliac spine & sup. part of notch inf. to it	Sup. part of medial surface of tibia	Femoral n. (L2 & L3)	Flexes, abducts & laterally rotates thigh at hip joint & flexes leg at knee joint
Quadriceps femoris Rectus femoris	Ant. inf. iliac spine & groove sup. to acetabulum	Base of patella & via patellar lig. to tibial tuberosity	Femoral n. (L2, **L3** & **L4**)	Extend leg at knee joint; rectus femoris also helps iliopsoas to flex thigh
Vastus lateralis	Greater trochanter & lateral lip of linea aspera of femur			
Vastus medialis	Intertrochanteric line & medial lip of linea aspera of femur			
Vastus intermedius	Ant. & lateral surfaces of shaft of femur			

[a]In this and subsequent tables, the numbers indicate the spinal cord segmental innervation of the nerves. For example, **L1, L2**, and L3 indicate that the nerves supplying the psoas major muscle are derived from the first three lumbar segments of the spinal cord; the boldface (**L1, L2**) indicates the main segmental innervation. Damage to one or more of these spinal cord segments or to the motor nerve roots arising from them results in paralysis of the muscles concerned.

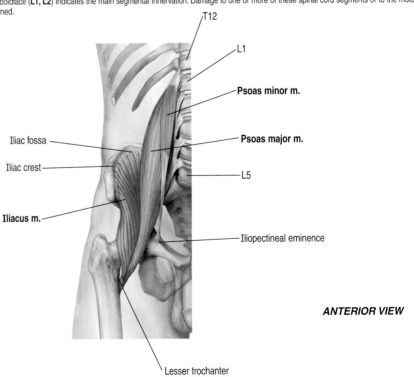

T12
L1
Psoas minor m.
Psoas major m.
L5
Iliopectineal eminence
Iliac fossa
Iliac crest
Iliacus m.
Lesser trochanter

ANTERIOR VIEW

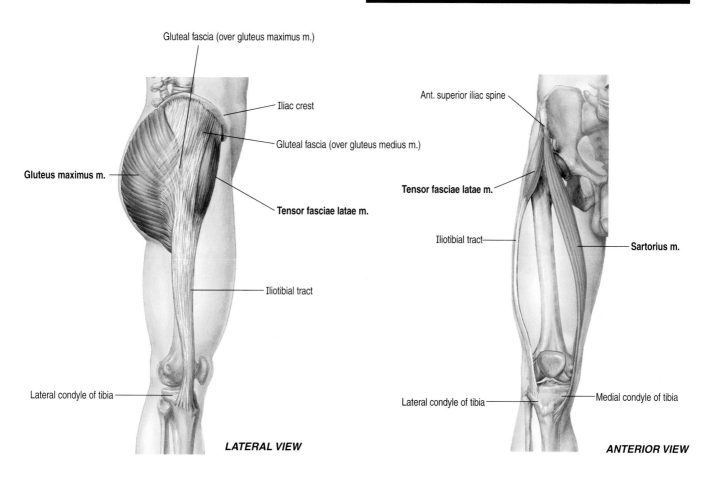

Gluteal fascia (over gluteus maximus m.)

Iliac crest

Gluteal fascia (over gluteus medius m.)

Gluteus maximus m.

Tensor fasciae latae m.

Iliotibial tract

Lateral condyle of tibia

LATERAL VIEW

Ant. superior iliac spine

Tensor fasciae latae m.

Iliotibial tract

Sartorius m.

Lateral condyle of tibia

Medial condyle of tibia

ANTERIOR VIEW

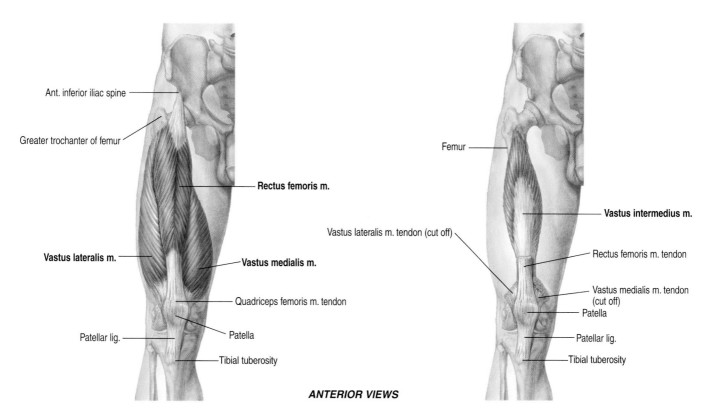

Ant. inferior iliac spine

Greater trochanter of femur

Rectus femoris m.

Vastus lateralis m.

Vastus medialis m.

Quadriceps femoris m. tendon

Patellar lig.

Patella

Tibial tuberosity

ANTERIOR VIEWS

Femur

Vastus intermedius m.

Vastus lateralis m. tendon (cut off)

Rectus femoris m. tendon

Vastus medialis m. tendon (cut off)

Patella

Patellar lig.

Tibial tuberosity

Gluteal & Posterior Thigh Muscles
Table 5.2

Gluteal Muscle	Proximal Attachment	Distal Attachment	Innervation	Main Actions
Gluteus maximus	Ext. surface of ala of ilium, including iliac crest, dorsal surface of sacrum & coccyx, and sacrotuberous lig.	Most fibers end in iliotibial tract which inserts into lateral condyle of tibia; some fibers insert on gluteal tuberosity of femur	Inf. gluteal n. (L5, **S1** & **S2**)	Extends thigh & assists in its lat. rotation; also assists in raising trunk from flexed position
Gluteus medius	Ext. surface of ilium between ant. & post. gluteal lines	Lateral surface of greater trochanter of femur	Sup. gluteal n. (**L5** & S1)	Abduct & medially rotate thigh; steady pelvis
Gluteus minimus	Ext. surface of ilium between ant. & inf. gluteal lines	Ant. surface of greater trochanter of femur		
Piriformis	Ant. surface of sacrum between S2 & S4	Superior border of greater trochanter of femur	Brr. from ventral rami of **S1** & S2	Laterally rotate extended thigh & abduct flexed thigh
Obturator internus	Pelvic surface of obturator membrane & surrounding bones	Trochanteric fossa[a]	N. to obturator internus (L5 & **S1**)	
Gemelli, superior & inferior	*Sup.:* ischial spine *Inf.:* ischial tuberosity		*Sup. gemellus,* same nerve supply as obturator internus *Inf. gemellus,* same nerve supply as quadratus femoris	
Quadratus femoris	Lateral border of ischial tuberosity	Quadrate tubercle on intertrochanteric crest of femur & inf. to it	N. to quadratus femoris (L5 & S1)	Laterally rotates thigh[b]

[a]The gemelli muscles blend with the tendon of the obturator internus muscle as it attaches to the trochanteric fossa.
[b]There are six lateral rotators of the thigh: piriformis, obturator internus, gemelli (superior and inferior), quadratus femoris, and obturator externus. These muscles also stabilize the hip joint.

Post. Thigh Muscle	Proximal Attachment	Distal Attachment	Innervation	Main Actions
Semitendinosus	Ischial tuberosity	Medial surface of sup. part of tibia	Tibial division of sciatic n. (**L5, S1** & S2)	Extend thigh; flex leg and rotate it medially; when thigh & leg are flexed, they can extend trunk
Semimembranous		Post. part of medial condyle of tibia		
Biceps femoris	*Long head:* Ischial tuberosity *Short head:* Lateral lip of distal half of linea aspera & lateral supracondylar line	Lateral side of head of fibular	*Long head:* Tibial division of sciatic n. (L5, **S1** & S2) *Short head:* Common fibular (peroneal) division of sciatic n. (L5, **S1** & S2)	Flexes leg & rotates it laterally; extends thigh (*e.g.,* when starting to walk)

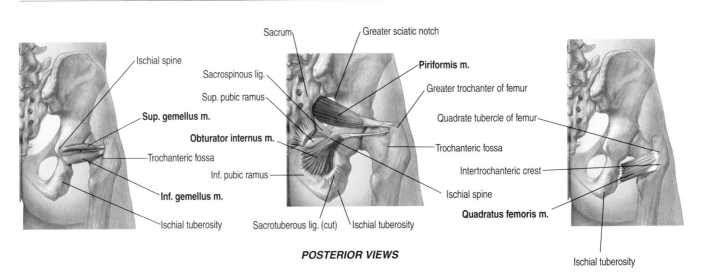

POSTERIOR VIEWS

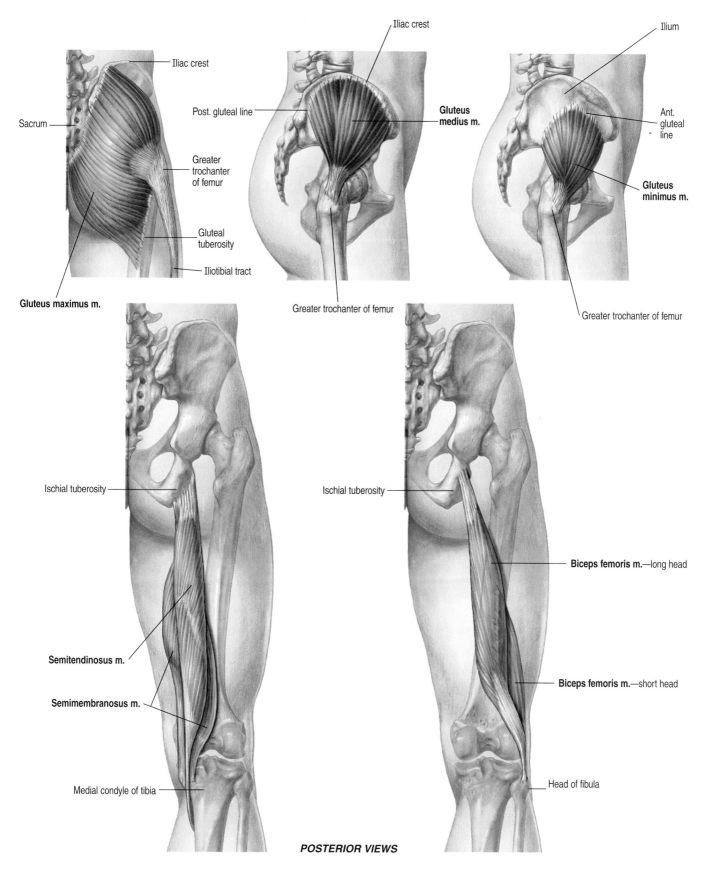

POSTERIOR VIEW

LATERAL VIEWS

Iliac crest

Iliac crest

Ilium

Sacrum

Post. gluteal line

**Gluteus
medius m.**

Ant.
gluteal
line

Greater
trochanter
of femur

Gluteus
tuberosity

**Gluteus
minimus m.**

Iliotibial tract

Gluteus maximus m.

Greater trochanter of femur

Greater trochanter of femur

Ischial tuberosity

Ischial tuberosity

Biceps femoris m.—long head

Semitendinosus m.

Semimembranosus m.

Biceps femoris m.—short head

Medial condyle of tibia

Head of fibula

POSTERIOR VIEWS

Medial Thigh Muscles
Table 5.3

Muscle[a]	Proximal Attachment	Distal Attachment	Innervation	Main Actions
Pectineus	Pecten pubis	Pectineal line of femur	Femoral nerve (**L2** & L3) & br. from obturator n. (L2, L3)	Adducts; flexes & laterally rotates thigh
Adductor longus	Body of pubis, inf. to pubic crest	Middle third of linea aspera of femur	Obturator n. ant. br. (L2, **L3** & L4)	Adducts thigh
Adductor brevis	Body & inf. ramus of pubis	Pectineal line & proximal part of linea aspera of femur	Obturator n. (L2, **L3** & L4)	Adducts thigh & to some extent flexes it
Adductor magnus	Inf. ramus of pubis, ramus of ischium (adductor part) & ischial tuberosity	Gluteal tuberosity, linea aspera med., supracondylar line (adductor part) & adductor tubercle of femur (hamstring part)	*Adductor part,* obturator n. (L2, **L3** & L4) *Hamstring part,* tibial portion of sciatic n. (**L4**)	Adducts thigh; its adductor part also flexes thigh & its hamstring part extends it
Gracilis	Body & inf. ramus of pubis	Sup. part of med. surface of tibia	Obturator n. (**L2**, L3 & L4)	Adducts thigh, flexes leg & helps to rotate it medially
Obturator externus	Margins of obturator foramen & ext. surface of obturator membrane	Trochanteric fossa of femur	Obturator n. (L3 & **L4**)	Laterally rotates thigh

[a]Collectively, the first five muscles listed are known as the *adductors of the thigh,* but their actions are more complex than this, *e.g.,* they act as *fixors of the hip* during flexion of the knee joint and are active during walking.

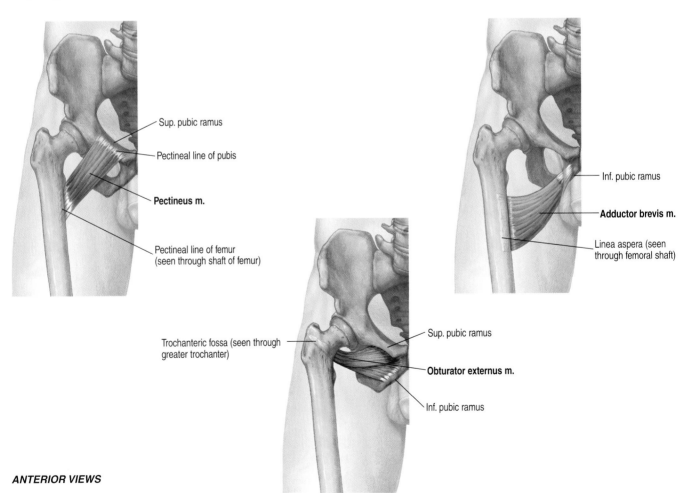

Sup. pubic ramus

Pectineal line of pubis

Pectineus m.

Pectineal line of femur (seen through shaft of femur)

Inf. pubic ramus

Adductor brevis m.

Linea aspera (seen through femoral shaft)

Trochanteric fossa (seen through greater trochanter)

Sup. pubic ramus

Obturator externus m.

Inf. pubic ramus

ANTERIOR VIEWS

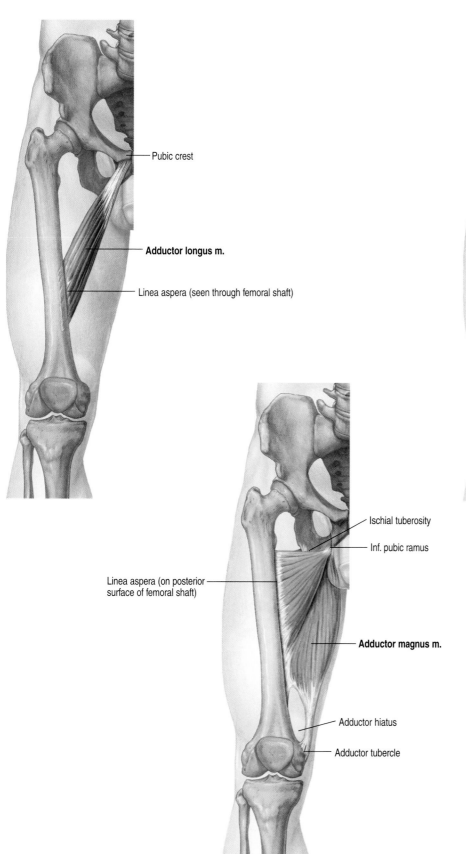

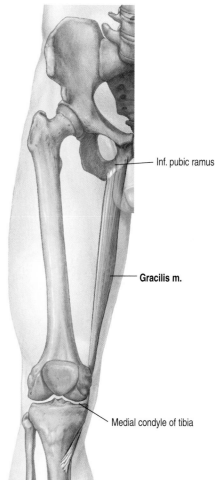

Pubic crest

Adductor longus m.

Linea aspera (seen through femoral shaft)

Inf. pubic ramus

Gracilis m.

Medial condyle of tibia

Ischial tuberosity

Inf. pubic ramus

Linea aspera (on posterior
surface of femoral shaft)

Adductor magnus m.

Adductor hiatus

Adductor tubercle

ANTERIOR VIEWS

Anterior Muscle	Proximal Attachment	Distal Attachment	Innervation	Main Actions
Tibialis anterior	Lateral condyle & sup. half of lateral surface of tibia	Medial & inf. surfaces of medial cuneiform bone & base of 1st metatarsal bone	Deep fibular [peroneal] n. (**L4** & **L5**)	Dorsiflexes & inverts foot
Extensor hallucis longus	Middle part of ant. surface of fibula & interosseous membrane	Dorsal aspect of base of distal phalanx of 1st digit (hallux)		Extends 1st digit & dorsiflexes foot
Extensor digitorum longus	Lateral condyle of tibia, sup. 3/4 of ant. surface of fibula & interosseous membrane	Middle & distal phalanges of lateral 4 digits	Deep fibular [peroneal] n. (**L5** & **S1**)	Extends lateral 4 digits dorsiflexes foot
Fibularis [Peroneus] tertius	Inferior third of ant. surface of fibula & interosseous membrane	Dorsum of base of 5th metatarsal bone		Dorsiflexes foot & aids in eversion of it

Lateral Muscle[a]	Proximal Attachment	Distal Attachment	Innervation	Main Actions
Fibularis [Peroneus] longus	Head & sup. 2/3 of lateral surface of fibula	Base of metatarsal 1st bone & medial cuneiform bone	Superficial fibular (peroneal) n. (**L5**, **S1** & **S2**)	Everts & plantar flexes foot
Fibularis [Peroneus] brevis	Inf. 2/3 of lateral surface of fibula	Dorsal surface of tuberosity of 5th metatarsal bone		Everts foot & weakly plantarflexes foot

[a]The fibularis [peroneus] longus and brevis were named because their proximal attachment is to the fibula. *Peroneus* is the Greek word for the Latin term *fibula* and was formerly used to describe these muscles.

ANTERIOR VIEWS

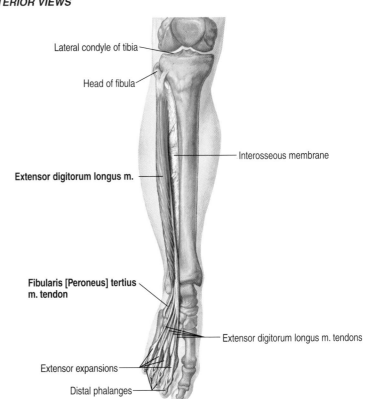

Lateral condyle of tibia

Tibialis anterior m.

Medial cuneiform bone

Base of 1st metatarsal bone

Lateral condyle of tibia

Head of fibula

Interosseous membrane

Extensor digitorum longus m.

Fibularis [Peroneus] tertius m. tendon

Extensor digitorum longus m. tendons

Extensor expansions

Distal phalanges

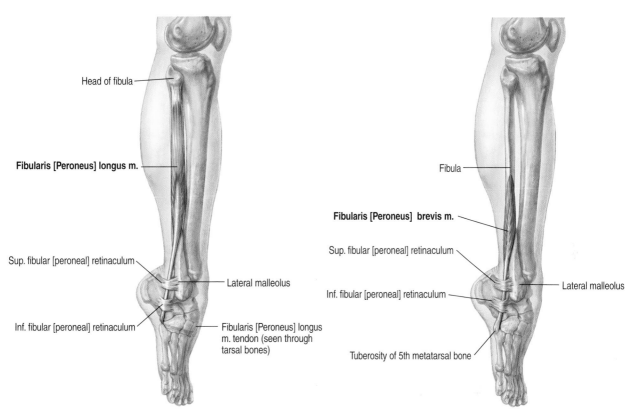

Head of fibula

Fibularis [Peroneus] longus m.

Sup. fibular [peroneal] retinaculum

Lateral malleolus

Inf. fibular [peroneal] retinaculum

Fibularis [Peroneus] longus m. tendon (seen through tarsal bones)

Fibula

Fibularis [Peroneus] brevis m.

Sup. fibular [peroneal] retinaculum

Inf. fibular [peroneal] retinaculum

Lateral malleolus

Tuberosity of 5th metatarsal bone

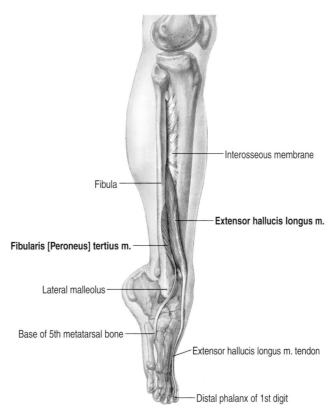

Interosseous membrane

Fibula

Extensor hallucis longus m.

Fibularis [Peroneus] tertius m.

Lateral malleolus

Base of 5th metatarsal bone

Extensor hallucis longus m. tendon

Distal phalanx of 1st digit

LATERAL VIEWS

Posterior Leg Muscles
Table 5.5

Superficial Muscle	Proximal Attachment	Distal Attachment	Innervation	Main Actions
Gastrocnemius	*Lateral head:* Lateral aspect of lateral condyle of femur *Medial head:* Popliteal surface of femur, sup. to medial condyle	Post. surface of tuberosity of calcaneus via tendo calcaneus	Tibial n. (L5, S1 & **S2**)	Plantarflexes foot, raises heel during walking & flexes knee joint
Soleus	Post. aspect of head of fibula, sup. 4th of post. surface of fibula, soleal line & medial border of tibia			Plantarflexes foot
Plantaris	Inf. end of lat. supracondylar line of femur & oblique popliteal lig.	Medial side of tendo calcaneus		Weakly assists gastrocnemius in plantarflexing foot & flexing knee joint

Deep Muscle	Proximal Attachment	Distal Attachment	Innervation	Main Actions
Popliteus	Lateral epicondyle of femur & lateral meniscus	Post. surface of tibia, sup. to soleal line	Tibial n. (**L4, L5** & S1)	Weakly flexes knee & unlocks it
Flexor hallucis longus	Inf. 2/3 of post. surface of fibula & inf. part of interosseous membrane	Base of distal phalanx of 1st digit (hallux)	Tibial n. (**S2**–S3)	Flexes 1st digit at all joints and plantarflexes foot
Flexor digitorum longus	Medial part of post. surface of tibia, inf. to soleal line & by a broad aponeurosis to fibula	Bases of distal phalanges of lateral 4 digits		Flexes 4 digits & plantarflexes foot
Tibialis posterior	Interosseous membrane, post. surface of tibia inf. to soleal line & post. surface of fibula	Tuberosity of navicular, cuneiform & cuboid bones, & bases of 2nd, 3rd & 4th metatarsal bones	Tibial n. (L4–L5)	Plantarflexes & inverts foot

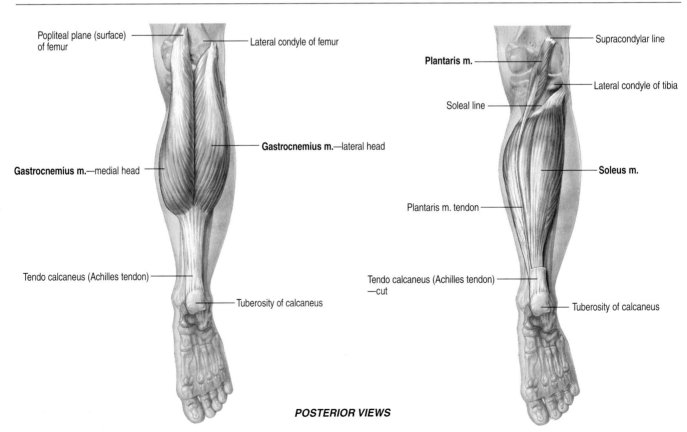

Popliteal plane (surface) of femur

Lateral condyle of femur

Gastrocnemius m.—lateral head

Gastrocnemius m.—medial head

Tendo calcaneus (Achilles tendon)

Tuberosity of calcaneus

Supracondylar line

Plantaris m.

Lateral condyle of tibia

Soleal line

Soleus m.

Plantaris m. tendon

Tendo calcaneus (Achilles tendon) —cut

Tuberosity of calcaneus

POSTERIOR VIEWS

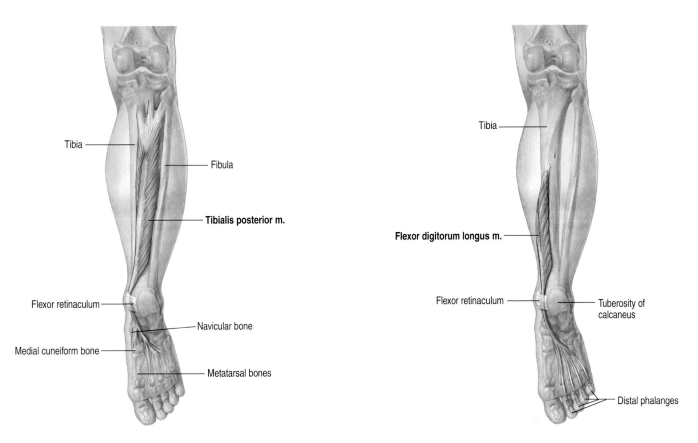

Tibia

Fibula

Tibialis posterior m.

Flexor retinaculum

Medial cuneiform bone

Navicular bone

Metatarsal bones

Tibia

Flexor digitorum longus m.

Flexor retinaculum

Tuberosity of calcaneus

Distal phalanges

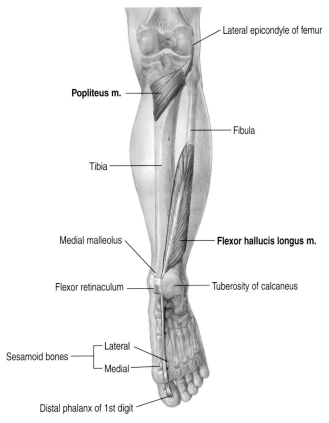

Lateral epicondyle of femur

Popliteus m.

Fibula

Tibia

Medial malleolus

Flexor hallucis longus m.

Flexor retinaculum

Tuberosity of calcaneus

Sesamoid bones — Lateral

Medial

Distal phalanx of 1st digit

POSTERIOR VIEWS

Intrinsic Foot Muscles
Table 5.6

Muscle	Proximal Attachment	Distal Attachment	Innervation	Main Actions
FIRST LAYER[a]				
Abductor hallucis	Medial process of tuber calcanei, flexor retinaculum & plantar aponeurosis	Medial side of base of proximal phalanx & medial sesamoid bone of 1st digit (hallux)	Medial plantar n. (S2 & **S3**)	Abducts & flexes 1st digit
Flexor digitorum brevis	Medial process of tuber calcanei, plantar aponeurosis & intermuscular septa	Both sides of middle phalanges of lateral 4 digits		Flexes lateral 4 digits (toes)
Abductor digiti minimi	Medial & lateral processes of tuber calcanei, plantar aponeurosis & intermuscular septa	Lateral side of base of proximal phalanx of 5th digit (little toe)	Lateral plantar n. (S2 & **S3**)	Abducts & flexes 5th digit
SECOND LAYER				
Quadratus plantae	Medial surface & lateral margin of plantar surface of calcaneus	Posterolateral margin of tendon of flexor digitorum longus	Lateral plantar n. (S2 & **S3**)	Assists flexor digitorum longus in flexing lateral 4 digits
Lumbricalis	Tendons of flexor digitorum longus	Medial sides of bases of proximal phalanges of lateral 4 digits & extensor expansions of tendons of extensor digitorum longus	*Medial one:* medial plantar n. (S2 & **S3**) *Lateral three:* lateral plantar n. (S2 & **S3**)	Flex proximal phalanges & extend middle & distal phalanges of lateral 4 digits
THIRD LAYER				
Flexor hallucis brevis	Plantar surfaces of cuboid & lateral cuneiform bones	Both sides of base of proximal phalanx of 1st digit	Medial plantar n. (S2 & **S3**)	Flexes proximal phalanx of 1st digit (hallux)
Adductor hallucis	*Oblique head:* Bases of metatarsal bones 2–4 *Transverse head:* Plantar ligg. of metatarsophalangeal joints 2–5	*Tendons of both heads* attached to lateral side of base of proximal phalanx & lat. sesamoid bone of 1st digit (hallux)	Deep br. of lateral plantar n. (S2 & **S3**)	Adducts 1st digit; assists in maintaining transverse arch of foot
Flexor digiti minimi brevis	Base of 5th metatarsal bone	Base of proximal phalanx of 5th digit	Superficial br. of lateral plantar n. (S2 & **S3**)	Flexes proximal phalanx of 5th digit, thereby assisting with its flexion
FOURTH LAYER				
Plantar interossei (3 muscles)	Bases & medial sides of metatarsal bones 3–5	Medial sides of bases of proximal phalanges of digits 3–5	Lateral plantar n. (S2 & **S3**)	Adduct digits (2–4) & flex metatarsophalangeal joints
Dorsal interossei (4 muscles)	Adjacent side of metatarsal bones 1–5	*1st:* medial side of proximal phalanx of 2nd digit *2nd–4th:* lateral sides of digits 2–4		Abduct digits (2–4) & flex metatarsorphalangeal joints

[a]In spite of the individual actions ascribed to them, the primary function of the first layer of intrinsic muscles of the foot is to provide dynamic support of the longitudinal arch of the foot (i.e., resisting forces tending to spread or flatten it).

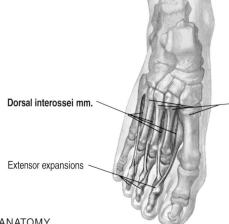

Dorsal interossei mm.

Metatarsal bones

Extensor expansions

DORSAL SURFACE VIEW

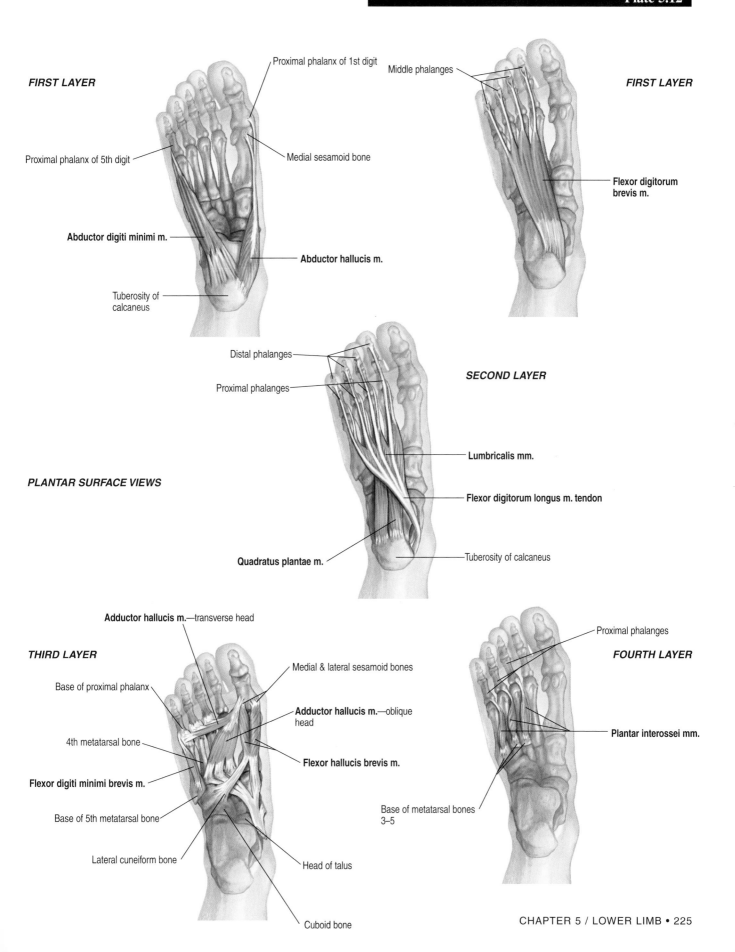

FIRST LAYER

Proximal phalanx of 1st digit

Middle phalanges

FIRST LAYER

Proximal phalanx of 5th digit

Medial sesamoid bone

Flexor digitorum brevis m.

Abductor digiti minimi m.

Abductor hallucis m.

Tuberosity of calcaneus

Distal phalanges

SECOND LAYER

Proximal phalanges

PLANTAR SURFACE VIEWS

Lumbricalis mm.

Flexor digitorum longus m. tendon

Quadratus plantae m.

Tuberosity of calcaneus

Adductor hallucis m.—transverse head

THIRD LAYER

Medial & lateral sesamoid bones

Base of proximal phalanx

Adductor hallucis m.—oblique head

4th metatarsal bone

FOURTH LAYER

Proximal phalanges

Flexor digiti minimi brevis m.

Flexor hallucis brevis m.

Plantar interossei mm.

Base of 5th metatarsal bone

Lateral cuneiform bone

Head of talus

Base of metatarsal bones 3–5

Cuboid bone

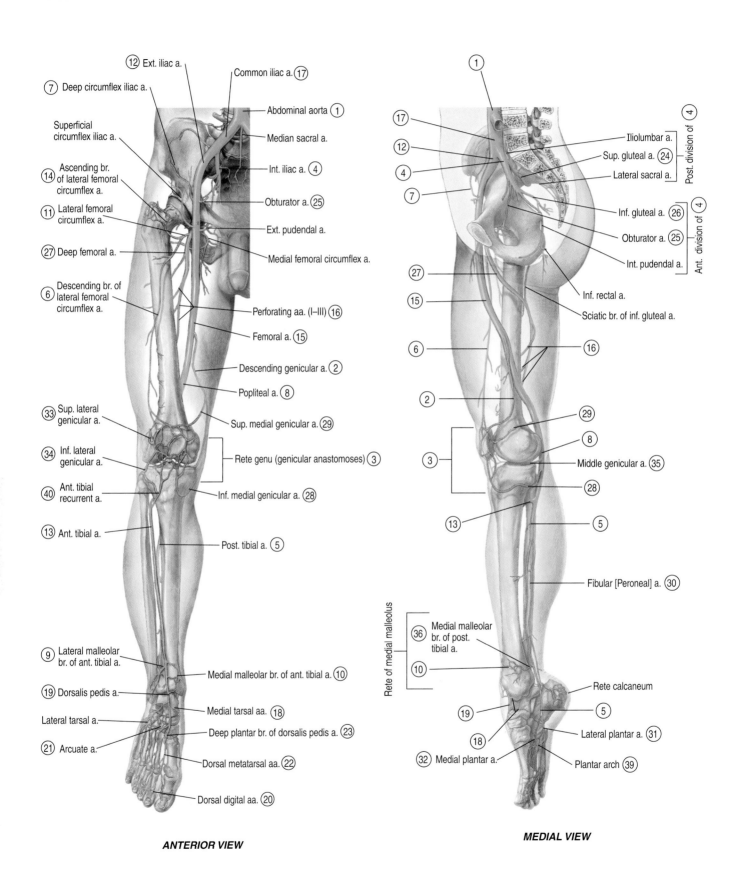

⑫ Ext. iliac a.

Common iliac a. ⑰

⑦ Deep circumflex iliac a.

Abdominal aorta ①

Median sacral a.

Superficial circumflex iliac a.

Int. iliac a. ④

⑭ Ascending br. of lateral femoral circumflex a.

Obturator a. ㉕

⑪ Lateral femoral circumflex a.

Ext. pudendal a.

㉗ Deep femoral a.

Medial femoral circumflex a.

⑥ Descending br. of lateral femoral circumflex a.

Perforating aa. (I–III) ⑯

Femoral a. ⑮

Descending genicular a. ②

Popliteal a. ⑧

㉝ Sup. lateral genicular a.

Sup. medial genicular a. ㉙

㉞ Inf. lateral genicular a.

Rete genu (genicular anastomoses) ③

㊵ Ant. tibial recurrent a.

Inf. medial genicular a. ㉘

⑬ Ant. tibial a.

Post. tibial a. ⑤

⑨ Lateral malleolar br. of ant. tibial a.

Medial malleolar br. of ant. tibial a. ⑩

⑲ Dorsalis pedis a.

Medial tarsal aa. ⑱

Lateral tarsal a.

Deep plantar br. of dorsalis pedis a. ㉓

㉑ Arcuate a.

Dorsal metatarsal aa. ㉒

Dorsal digital aa. ⑳

ANTERIOR VIEW

①

⑰

⑫

④

⑦

Iliolumbar a.

Sup. gluteal a. ㉔

Lateral sacral a.

Post. division of ④

Inf. gluteal a. ㉖

Obturator a. ㉕

Int. pudendal a.

Ant. division of ④

㉗

⑮

Inf. rectal a.

Sciatic br. of inf. gluteal a.

⑥

⑯

②

㉙

③

⑧

Middle genicular a. ㉟

㉘

⑬

⑤

Fibular [Peroneal] a. ㉚

Rete of medial malleolus

㊱ Medial malleolar br. of post. tibial a.

⑩

Rete calcaneum

⑲

⑤

⑱

Lateral plantar a. ㉛

㉜ Medial plantar a.

Plantar arch ㊴

MEDIAL VIEW

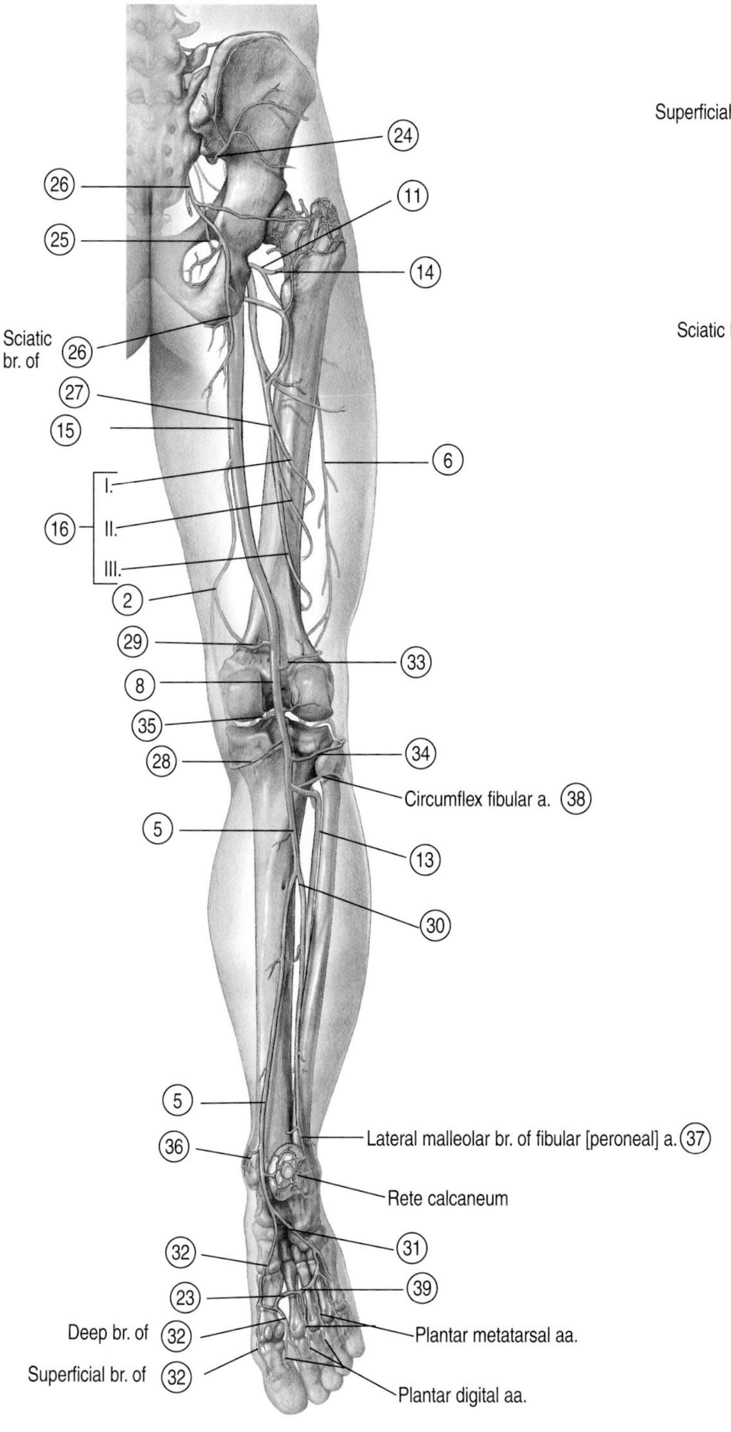
24
26
11
25
14
Sciatic br. of 26
27
15
6
16
I.
II.
III.
2
29
33
8
35
34
28
Circumflex fibular a. 38
5
13
30
5
Lateral malleolar br. of fibular [peroneal] a. 37
36
Rete calcaneum
31
32
23
39
Deep br. of 32
Plantar metatarsal aa.
Superficial br. of 32
Plantar digital aa.

POSTERIOR VIEW

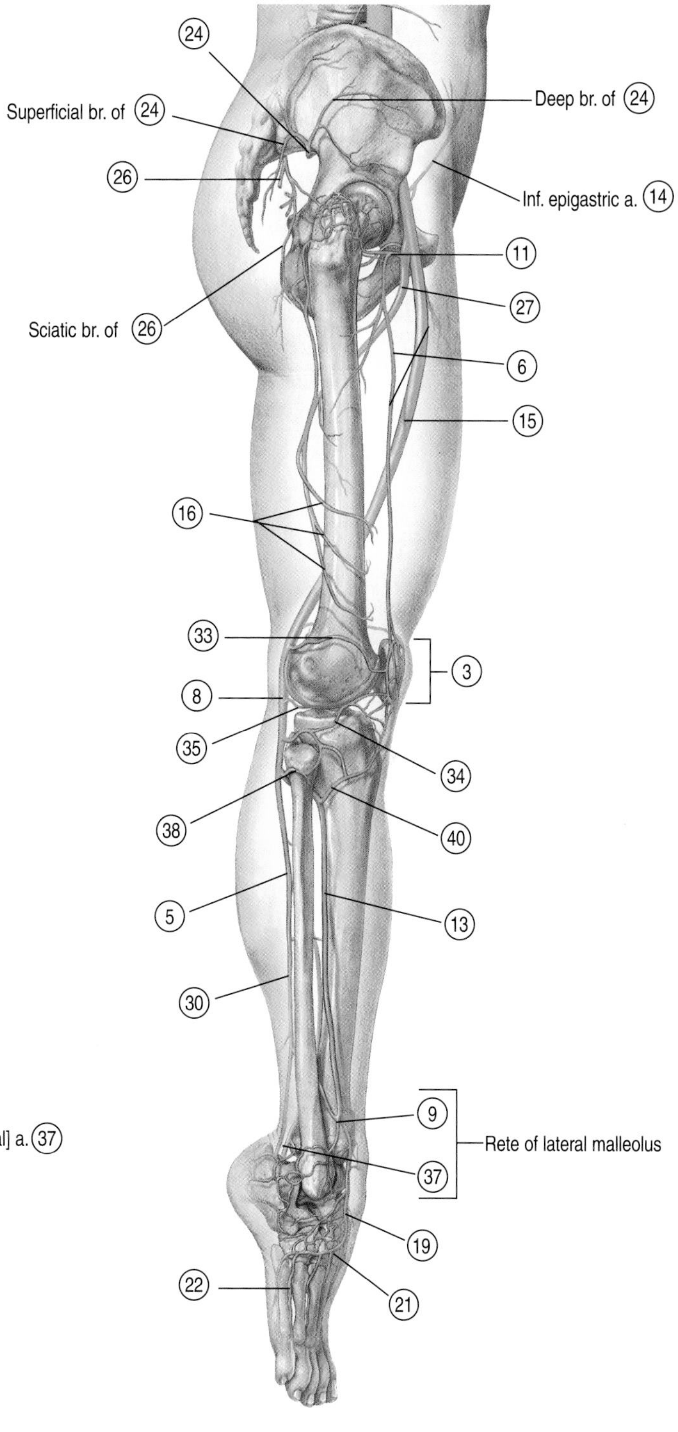
24
Superficial br. of 24
Deep br. of 24
26
Inf. epigastric a. 14
11
27
Sciatic br. of 26
6
15
16
33
3
8
35
34
38
40
5
13
30
9
Rete of lateral malleolus
37
19
22
21

LATERAL VIEW

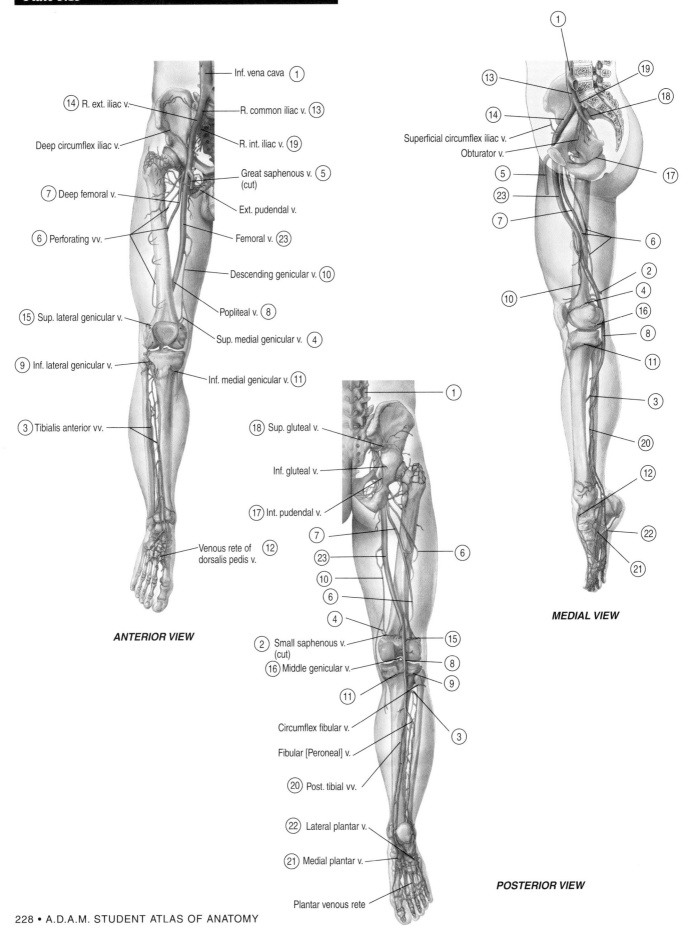

Inf. vena cava ①

⑭ R. ext. iliac v.

R. common iliac v. ⑬

Deep circumflex iliac v.

R. int. iliac v. ⑲

⑦ Deep femoral v.

Great saphenous v. ⑤
(cut)

Ext. pudendal v.

⑥ Perforating vv.

Femoral v. ㉓

Descending genicular v. ⑩

⑮ Sup. lateral genicular v.

Popliteal v. ⑧

Sup. medial genicular v. ④

⑨ Inf. lateral genicular v.

Inf. medial genicular v. ⑪

③ Tibialis anterior vv.

Venous rete of ⑫
dorsalis pedis v.

ANTERIOR VIEW

① Inf. vena cava

⑬

⑲

⑭

⑱

Superficial circumflex iliac v.

Obturator v.

⑰

⑤

㉓

⑦

⑥

⑩

②

④

⑯

⑧

⑪

③

⑳

⑫

㉒

㉑

MEDIAL VIEW

⑱ Sup. gluteal v.

Inf. gluteal v.

⑰ Int. pudendal v.

⑦

㉓

⑩

⑥

④

② Small saphenous v.
(cut)

⑯ Middle genicular v.

⑪

⑥

⑮

⑧

⑨

③

Circumflex fibular v.

Fibular [Peroneal] v.

⑳ Post. tibial vv.

㉒ Lateral plantar v.

㉑ Medial plantar v.

Plantar venous rete

POSTERIOR VIEW

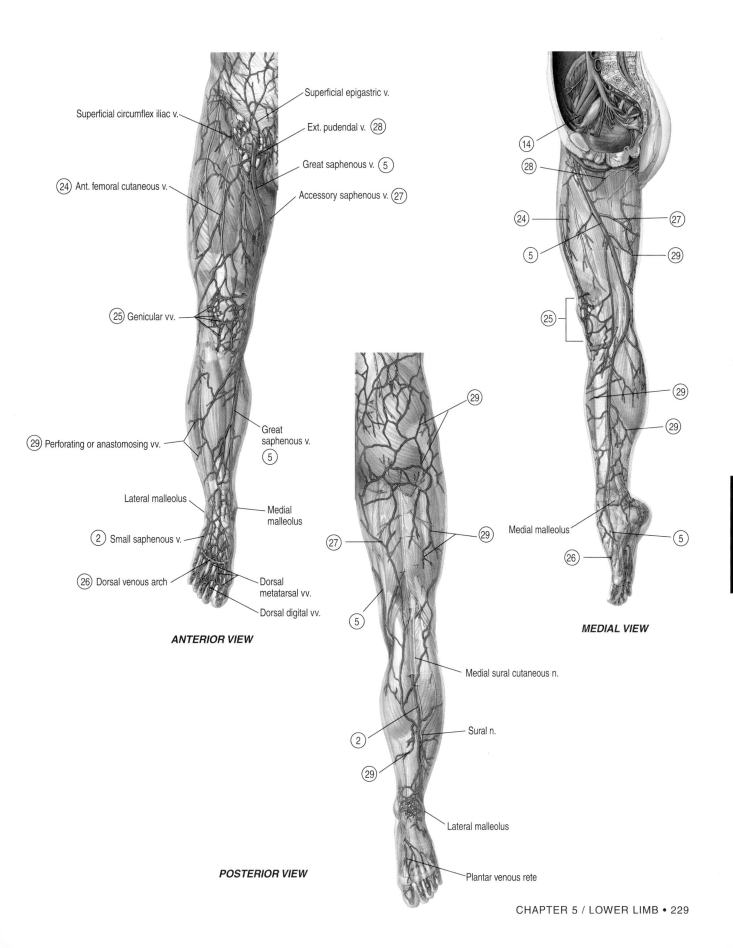

Superficial epigastric v.

Superficial circumflex iliac v.

Ext. pudendal v. (28)

Great saphenous v. (5)

(24) Ant. femoral cutaneous v.

Accessory saphenous v. (27)

(25) Genicular vv.

(29) Perforating or anastomosing vv.

Great
saphenous v.
(5)

Lateral malleolus

Medial
malleolus

(2) Small saphenous v.

(26) Dorsal venous arch

Dorsal
metatarsal vv.

Dorsal digital vv.

ANTERIOR VIEW

(14)

(28)

(24)

(27)

(5)

(29)

(25)

(29)

(29)

Medial malleolus

(5)

(26)

MEDIAL VIEW

(29)

(29)

(27)

(29)

(5)

Medial sural cutaneous n.

(2)

Sural n.

(29)

Lateral malleolus

POSTERIOR VIEW

Plantar venous rete

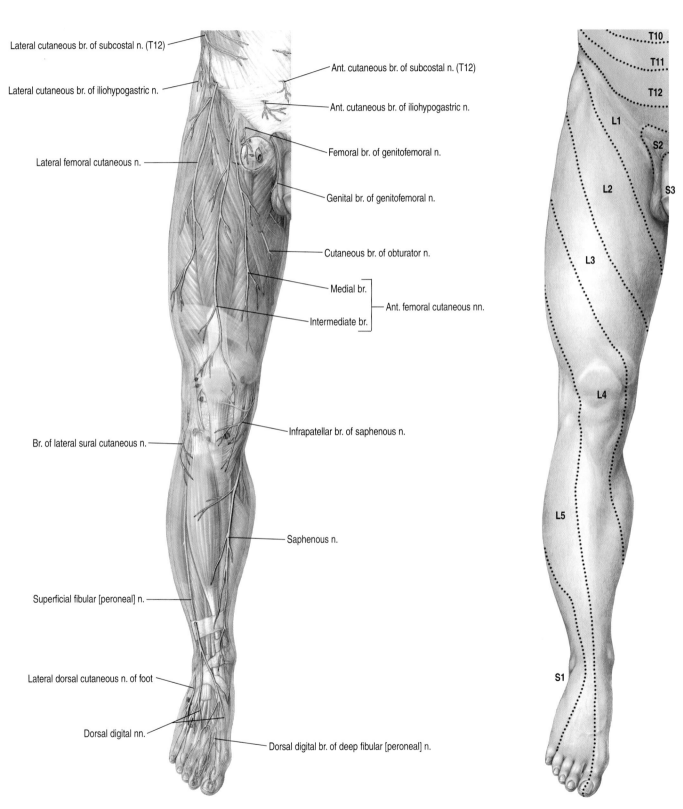

Lateral cutaneous br. of subcostal n. (T12)

Lateral cutaneous br. of iliohypogastric n.

Lateral femoral cutaneous n.

Ant. cutaneous br. of subcostal n. (T12)

Ant. cutaneous br. of iliohypogastric n.

Femoral br. of genitofemoral n.

Genital br. of genitofemoral n.

Cutaneous br. of obturator n.

Medial br.

Intermediate br.

Ant. femoral cutaneous nn.

Br. of lateral sural cutaneous n.

Infrapatellar br. of saphenous n.

Saphenous n.

Superficial fibular [peroneal] n.

Lateral dorsal cutaneous n. of foot

Dorsal digital nn.

Dorsal digital br. of deep fibular [peroneal] n.

T10

T11

T12

L1

S2

L2

S3

L3

L4

L5

S1

ANTERIOR VIEWS

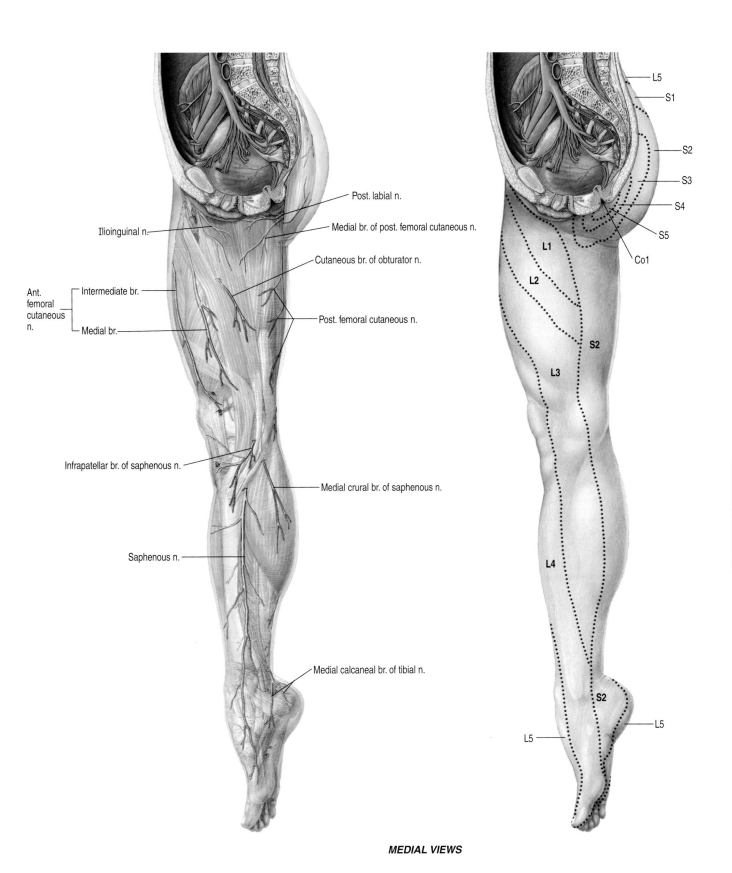

Post. labial n.

Medial br. of post. femoral cutaneous n.

Ilioinguinal n.

Cutaneous br. of obturator n.

Ant. femoral cutaneous n.

Intermediate br.

Medial br.

Post. femoral cutaneous n.

Infrapatellar br. of saphenous n.

Medial crural br. of saphenous n.

Saphenous n.

Medial calcaneal br. of tibial n.

L5
S1
S2
S3
S4
S5
Co1
L1
L2
S2
L3
L4
S2
L5
L5

MEDIAL VIEWS

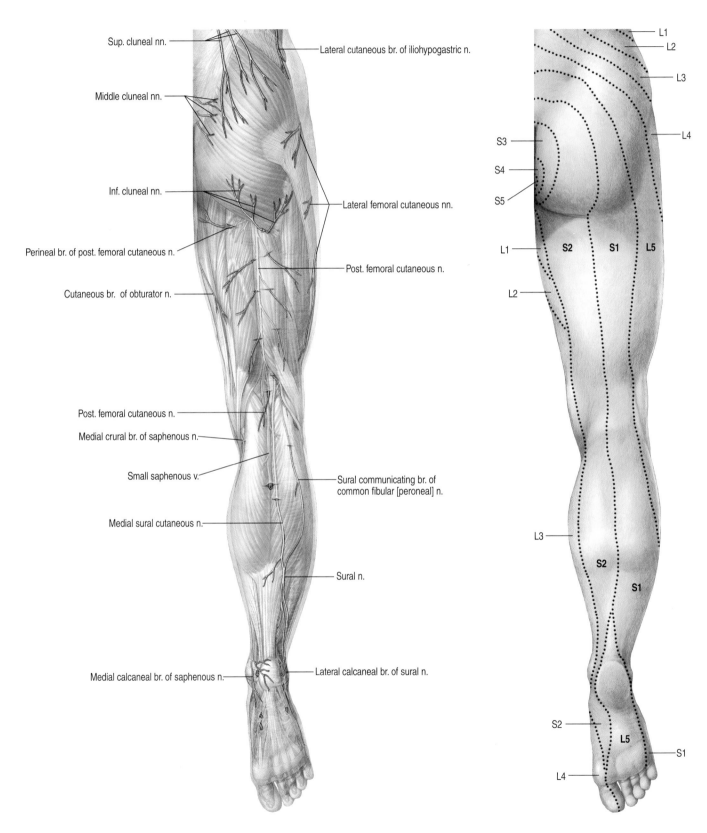

Sup. cluneal nn.

Lateral cutaneous br. of iliohypogastric n.

Middle cluneal nn.

Inf. cluneal nn.

Lateral femoral cutaneous nn.

Perineal br. of post. femoral cutaneous n.

Post. femoral cutaneous n.

Cutaneous br. of obturator n.

Post. femoral cutaneous n.

Medial crural br. of saphenous n.

Small saphenous v.

Sural communicating br. of common fibular [peroneal] n.

Medial sural cutaneous n.

Sural n.

Medial calcaneal br. of saphenous n.

Lateral calcaneal br. of sural n.

L1
L2
L3
L4
S3
S4
S5
L1
L2
S2
S1
L5
L3
S2
S1
S2
L5
S1
L4

POSTERIOR VIEWS

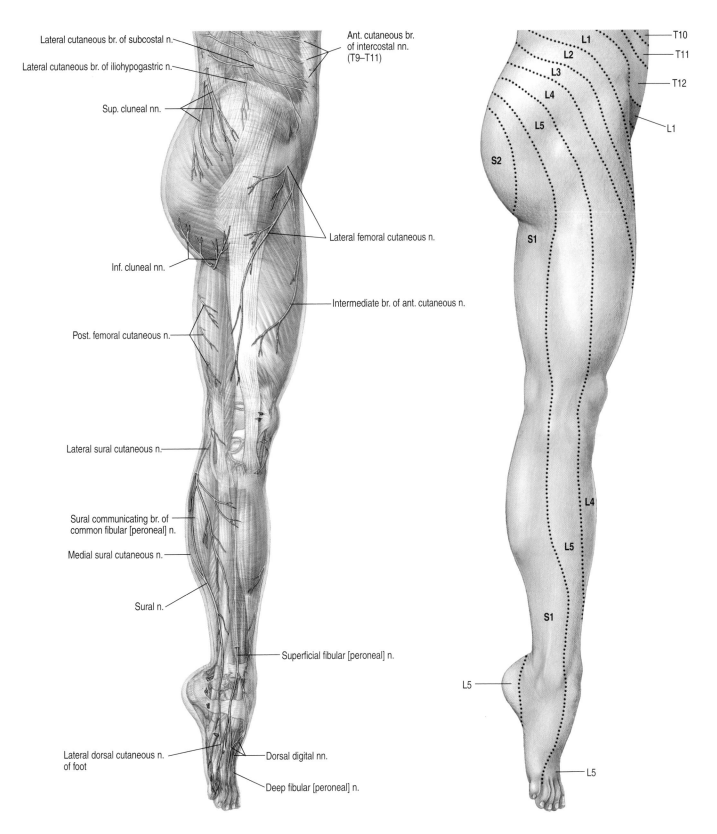

Lateral cutaneous br. of subcostal n.

Lateral cutaneous br. of iliohypogastric n.

Sup. cluneal nn.

Inf. cluneal nn.

Post. femoral cutaneous n.

Lateral sural cutaneous n.

Sural communicating br. of common fibular [peroneal] n.

Medial sural cutaneous n.

Sural n.

Lateral dorsal cutaneous n. of foot

Ant. cutaneous br. of intercostal nn. (T9–T11)

Lateral femoral cutaneous n.

Intermediate br. of ant. cutaneous n.

Superficial fibular [peroneal] n.

Dorsal digital nn.

Deep fibular [peroneal] n.

T10
T11
T12
L1

L1
L2
L3
L4
L5

S2

S1

L4

L5

S1

L5

L5

LATERAL VIEWS

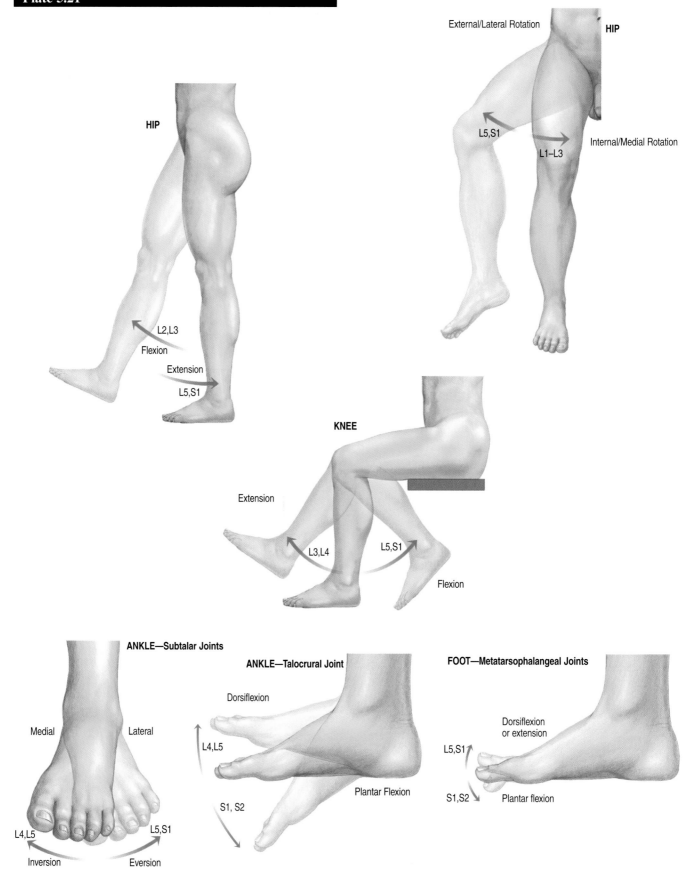

HIP

External/Lateral Rotation

HIP

L5,S1

Internal/Medial Rotation

L1–L3

L2,L3

Flexion

Extension

L5,S1

KNEE

Extension

L3,L4

L5,S1

Flexion

ANKLE—Subtalar Joints

Medial

Lateral

L4,L5

L5,S1

Inversion

Eversion

ANKLE—Talocrural Joint

Dorsiflexion

L4,L5

S1, S2

Plantar Flexion

FOOT—Metatarsophalangeal Joints

Dorsiflexion or extension

L5,S1

S1,S2

Plantar flexion

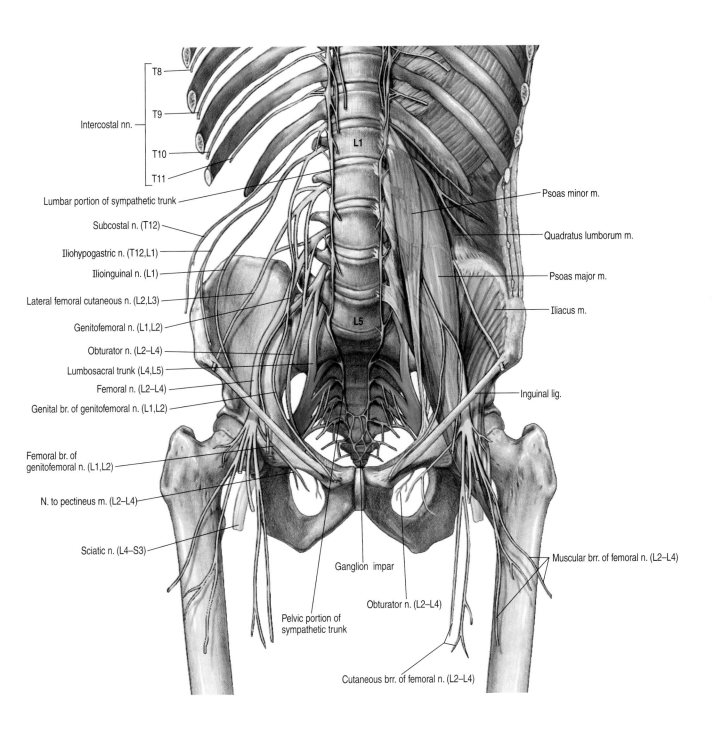

T8

T9

Intercostal nn.

T10

T11

Lumbar portion of sympathetic trunk

Subcostal n. (T12)

Iliohypogastric n. (T12,L1)

Ilioinguinal n. (L1)

Lateral femoral cutaneous n. (L2,L3)

Genitofemoral n. (L1,L2)

Obturator n. (L2–L4)

Lumbosacral trunk (L4,L5)

Femoral n. (L2–L4)

Genital br. of genitofemoral n. (L1,L2)

Femoral br. of genitofemoral n. (L1,L2)

N. to pectineus m. (L2–L4)

Sciatic n. (L4–S3)

L1

L5

Psoas minor m.

Quadratus lumborum m.

Psoas major m.

Iliacus m.

Inguinal lig.

Muscular brr. of femoral n. (L2–L4)

Ganglion impar

Obturator n. (L2–L4)

Pelvic portion of sympathetic trunk

Cutaneous brr. of femoral n. (L2–L4)

ANTERIOR VIEW

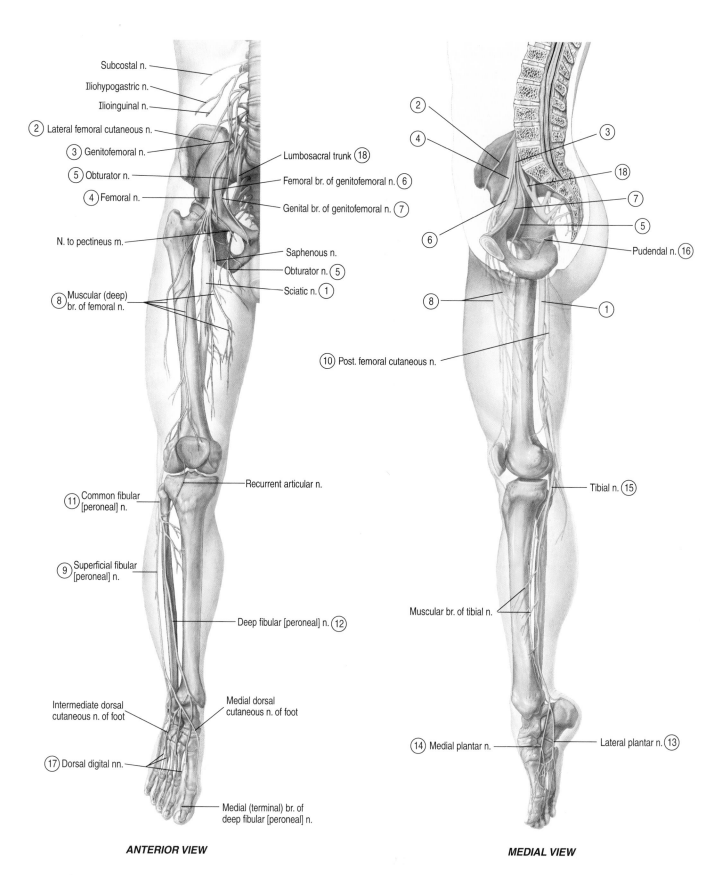

Subcostal n.

Iliohypogastric n.

Ilioinguinal n.

② Lateral femoral cutaneous n.

③ Genitofemoral n.

⑤ Obturator n.

④ Femoral n.

N. to pectineus m.

⑧ Muscular (deep) br. of femoral n.

Lumbosacral trunk ⑱

Femoral br. of genitofemoral n. ⑥

Genital br. of genitofemoral n. ⑦

Saphenous n.

Obturator n. ⑤

Sciatic n. ①

⑩ Post. femoral cutaneous n.

Pudendal n. ⑯

⑪ Common fibular [peroneal] n.

Recurrent articular n.

⑨ Superficial fibular [peroneal] n.

Deep fibular [peroneal] n. ⑫

Tibial n. ⑮

Muscular br. of tibial n.

Intermediate dorsal cutaneous n. of foot

Medial dorsal cutaneous n. of foot

⑰ Dorsal digital nn.

Medial (terminal) br. of deep fibular [peroneal] n.

⑭ Medial plantar n.

Lateral plantar n. ⑬

ANTERIOR VIEW

MEDIAL VIEW

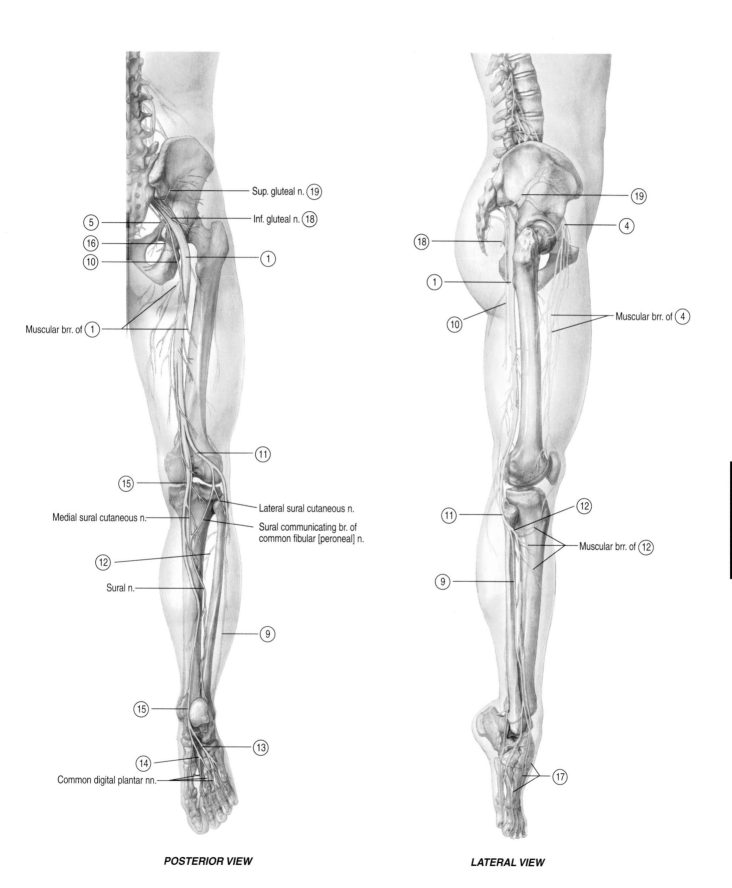

Sup. gluteal n. (19)

Inf. gluteal n. (18)

(5)

(16)

(10)

(1)

Muscular brr. of (1)

(19)

(4)

(18)

(1)

(10)

Muscular brr. of (4)

(11)

(15)

Lateral sural cutaneous n.

Medial sural cutaneous n.

Sural communicating br. of
common fibular [peroneal] n.

(12)

Sural n.

(9)

(15)

(13)

(14)

Common digital plantar nn.

(12)

Muscular brr. of (12)

(11)

(9)

(17)

POSTERIOR VIEW

LATERAL VIEW

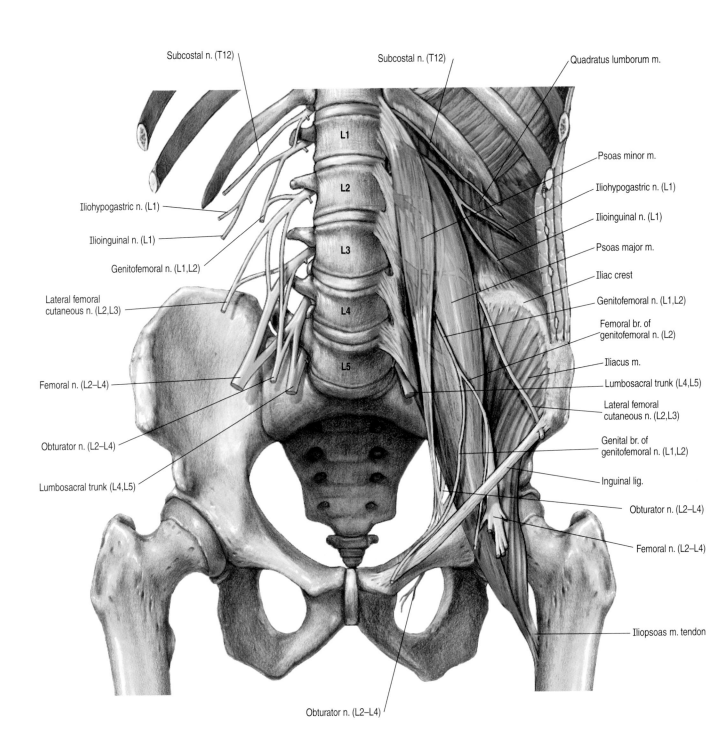

Subcostal n. (T12)

Subcostal n. (T12)

Quadratus lumborum m.

Iliohypogastric n. (L1)

Ilioinguinal n. (L1)

Genitofemoral n. (L1,L2)

Lateral femoral
cutaneous n. (L2,L3)

Femoral n. (L2–L4)

Obturator n. (L2–L4)

Lumbosacral trunk (L4,L5)

L1

L2

L3

L4

L5

Psoas minor m.

Iliohypogastric n. (L1)

Ilioinguinal n. (L1)

Psoas major m.

Iliac crest

Genitofemoral n. (L1,L2)

Femoral br. of
genitofemoral n. (L2)

Iliacus m.

Lumbosacral trunk (L4,L5)

Lateral femoral
cutaneous n. (L2,L3)

Genital br. of
genitofemoral n. (L1,L2)

Inguinal lig.

Obturator n. (L2–L4)

Femoral n. (L2–L4)

Iliopsoas m. tendon

Obturator n. (L2–L4)

ANTERIOR VIEW

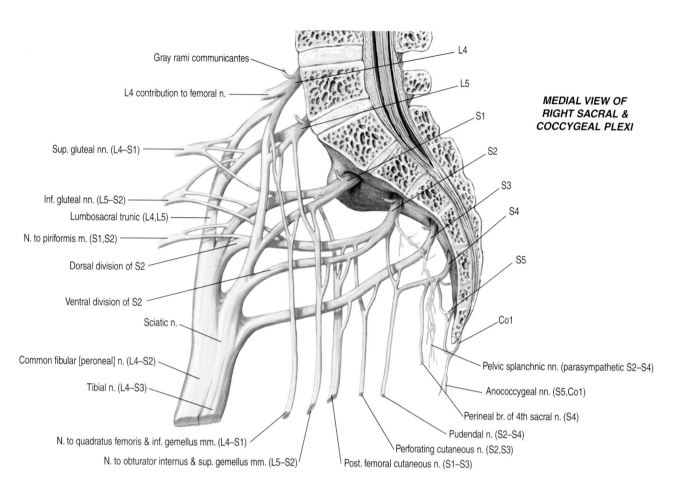

***MEDIAL VIEW OF
RIGHT SACRAL &
COCCYGEAL PLEXI***

Gray rami communicantes

L4 contribution to femoral n.

Sup. gluteal nn. (L4–S1)

Inf. gluteal nn. (L5–S2)

Lumbosacral trunic (L4,L5)

N. to piriformis m. (S1,S2)

Dorsal division of S2

Ventral division of S2

Sciatic n.

Common fibular [peroneal] n. (L4–S2)

Tibial n. (L4–S3)

N. to quadratus femoris & inf. gemellus mm. (L4–S1)

N. to obturator internus & sup. gemellus mm. (L5–S2)

Post. femoral cutaneous n. (S1–S3)

Perforating cutaneous n. (S2,S3)

Pudendal n. (S2–S4)

Perineal br. of 4th sacral n. (S4)

Anococcygeal nn. (S5,Co1)

Pelvic splanchnic nn. (parasympathetic S2–S4)

L4
L5
S1
S2
S3
S4
S5
Co1

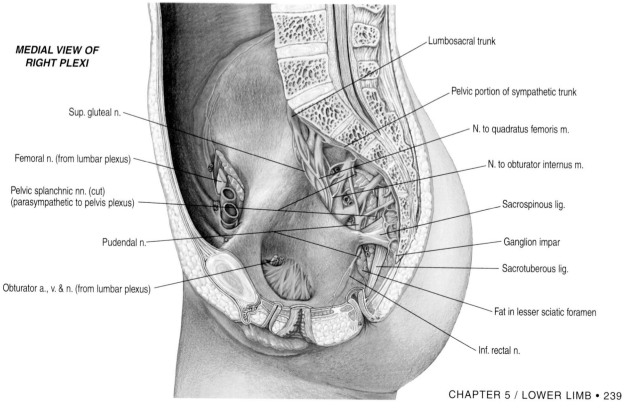

***MEDIAL VIEW OF
RIGHT PLEXI***

Sup. gluteal n.

Femoral n. (from lumbar plexus)

Pelvic splanchnic nn. (cut)
(parasympathetic to pelvis plexus)

Pudendal n.

Obturator a., v. & n. (from lumbar plexus)

Lumbosacral trunk

Pelvic portion of sympathetic trunk

N. to quadratus femoris m.

N. to obturator internus m.

Sacrospinous lig.

Ganglion impar

Sacrotuberous lig.

Fat in lesser sciatic foramen

Inf. rectal n.

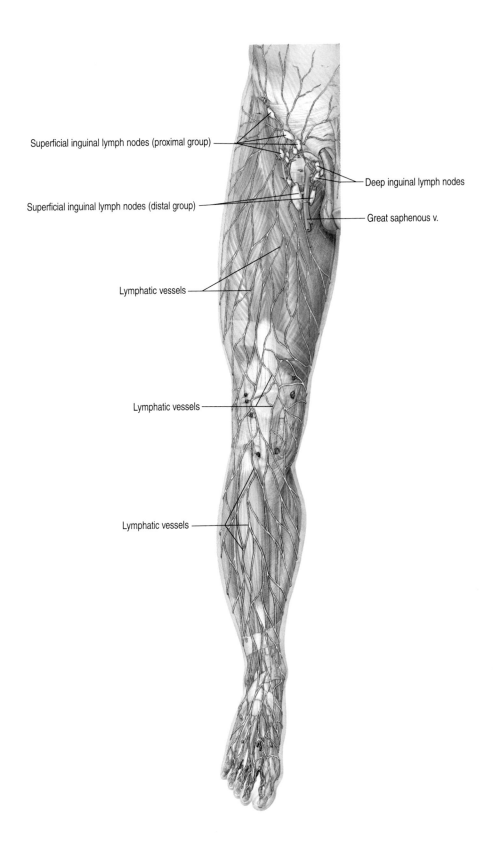

Superficial inguinal lymph nodes (proximal group)

Superficial inguinal lymph nodes (distal group)

Lymphatic vessels

Lymphatic vessels

Lymphatic vessels

Deep inguinal lymph nodes

Great saphenous v.

ANTERIOR VIEW

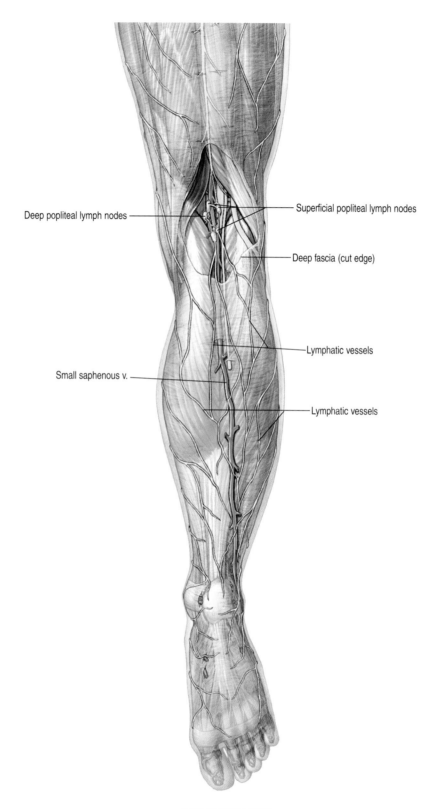

Deep popliteal lymph nodes

Superficial popliteal lymph nodes

Deep fascia (cut edge)

Lymphatic vessels

Small saphenous v.

Lymphatic vessels

POSTERIOR VIEW

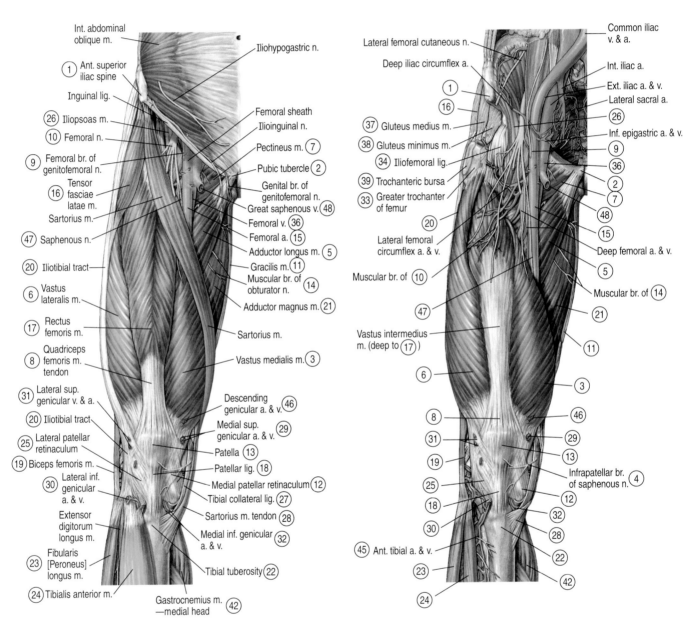

Int. abdominal oblique m.
Iliohypogastric n.
① Ant. superior iliac spine
Inguinal lig.
Femoral sheath
Ilioinguinal n.
㉖ Iliopsoas m.
⑩ Femoral n.
Pectineus m. ⑦
⑨ Femoral br. of genitofemoral n.
Pubic tubercle ②
⑯ Tensor fasciae latae m.
Genital br. of genitofemoral n.
Sartorius m.
Great saphenous v. ㊽
㊼ Saphenous n.
Femoral v. ㊱
Femoral a. ⑮
㉑ Iliotibial tract
Adductor longus m. ⑤
Gracilis m. ⑪
⑥ Vastus lateralis m.
Muscular br. of obturator n. ⑭
⑰ Rectus femoris m.
Adductor magnus m. ㉑
⑧ Quadriceps femoris m. tendon
Sartorius m.
Vastus medialis m. ③
㉛ Lateral sup. genicular v. & a.
㉒ Iliotibial tract
Descending genicular a. & v. ㊻
㉕ Lateral patellar retinaculum
Medial sup. genicular a. & v. ㉙
⑲ Biceps femoris m.
Patella ⑬
㉚ Lateral inf. genicular a. & v.
Patellar lig. ⑱
Medial patellar retinaculum ⑫
Extensor digitorum longus m.
Tibial collateral lig. ㉗
Sartorius m. tendon ㉘
㉓ Fibularis [Peroneus] longus m.
Medial inf. genicular a. & v. ㉜
㉔ Tibialis anterior m.
Tibial tuberosity ㉒
Gastrocnemius m. —medial head ㊷

Lateral femoral cutaneous n.
Common iliac v. & a.
Deep iliac circumflex a.
Int. iliac a.
① ⑯
Ext. iliac a. & v.
Lateral sacral a.
㉖
㊲ Gluteus medius m.
Inf. epigastric a. & v.
⑨
㊳ Gluteus minimus m.
㊱
㉞ Iliofemoral lig.
②
㊴ Trochanteric bursa
⑦
㉝ Greater trochanter of femur
㊽
⑮
㉑
Lateral femoral circumflex a. & v.
Deep femoral a. & v.
⑤
Muscular br. of ⑩
Muscular br. of ⑭
㊼
㉑
Vastus intermedius m. (deep to ⑰)
⑪
⑥
③
⑧
㊻
㉛
㉙
⑲
⑬
㉕
Infrapatellar br. of saphenous n. ④
⑱
⑫
㉚
㉜
㊺ Ant. tibial a. & v.
㉘
㉓
㉒
㉔
㊷

ANTERIOR VIEWS

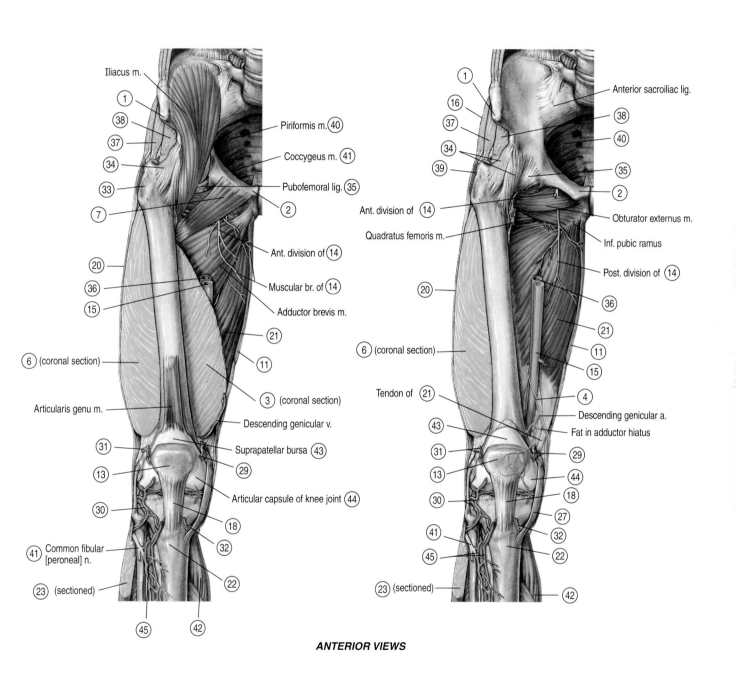

Iliacus m.

① ①
38
37
34
33
7

20
36
15

⑥ (coronal section)

Articularis genu m.

31
13
30

④① Common fibular
[peroneal] n.

② (sectioned)

45 42

Piriformis m. 40
Coccygeus m. 41
Pubofemoral lig. 35
②
Ant. division of 14
Muscular br. of 14
Adductor brevis m.
21
11
③ (coronal section)
Descending genicular v.
Suprapatellar bursa 43
29
Articular capsule of knee joint 44
18
32
22

① 16 37 34 39
Anterior sacroiliac lig.
38
40
35
②
Obturator externus m.
Inf. pubic ramus
Post. division of 14
36
21
11
15
④
Descending genicular a.
Fat in adductor hiatus
29
44
18
27
32
22
42

Ant. division of 14
Quadratus femoris m.

20

⑥ (coronal section)

Tendon of 21
43
31
13
30
41
45

② (sectioned)

ANTERIOR VIEWS

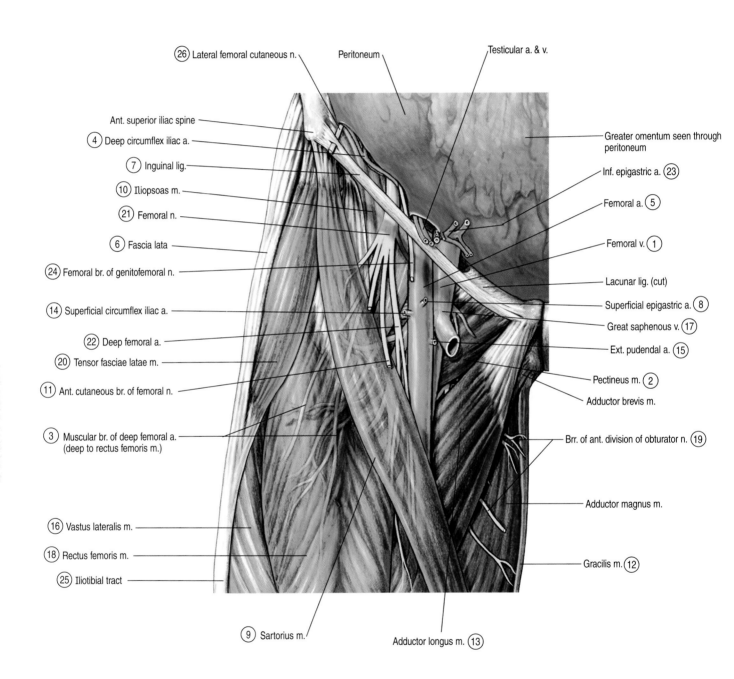

㉖ Lateral femoral cutaneous n.

Peritoneum

Testicular a. & v.

Ant. superior iliac spine

④ Deep circumflex iliac a.

⑦ Inguinal lig.

⑩ Iliopsoas m.

㉑ Femoral n.

⑥ Fascia lata

㉔ Femoral br. of genitofemoral n.

⑭ Superficial circumflex iliac a.

㉒ Deep femoral a.

⑳ Tensor fasciae latae m.

⑪ Ant. cutaneous br. of femoral n.

③ Muscular br. of deep femoral a.
(deep to rectus femoris m.)

⑯ Vastus lateralis m.

⑱ Rectus femoris m.

㉕ Iliotibial tract

⑨ Sartorius m.

Adductor longus m. ⑬

Greater omentum seen through
peritoneum

Inf. epigastric a. ㉓

Femoral a. ⑤

Femoral v. ①

Lacunar lig. (cut)

Superficial epigastric a. ⑧

Great saphenous v. ⑰

Ext. pudendal a. ⑮

Pectineus m. ②

Adductor brevis m.

Brr. of ant. division of obturator n. ⑲

Adductor magnus m.

Gracilis m. ⑫

ANTERIOR VIEW OF RIGHT PROXIMAL THIGH

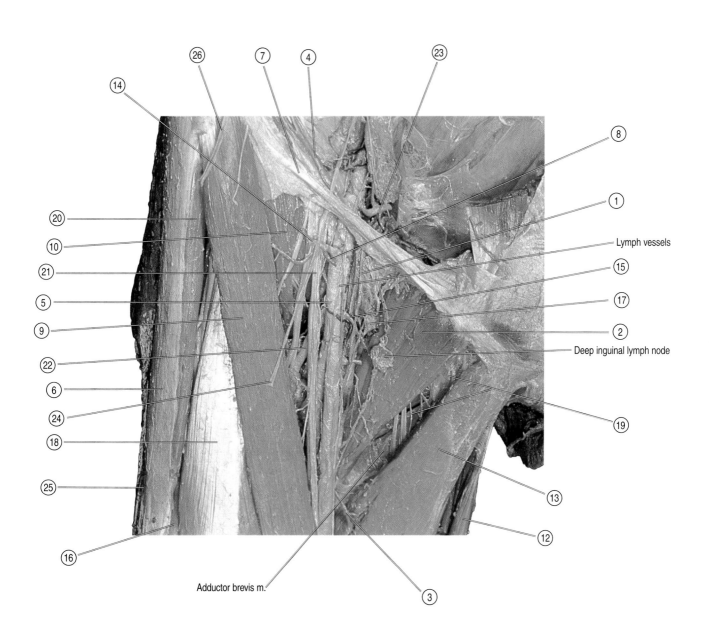

26 14 7 4 23

8

20

10

21

5

9

22

6

24

18

25

16

1

Lymph vessels

15

17

2

Deep inguinal lymph node

19

13

12

Adductor brevis m.

3

ANTERIOR VIEW OF RIGHT PROXIMAL THIGH

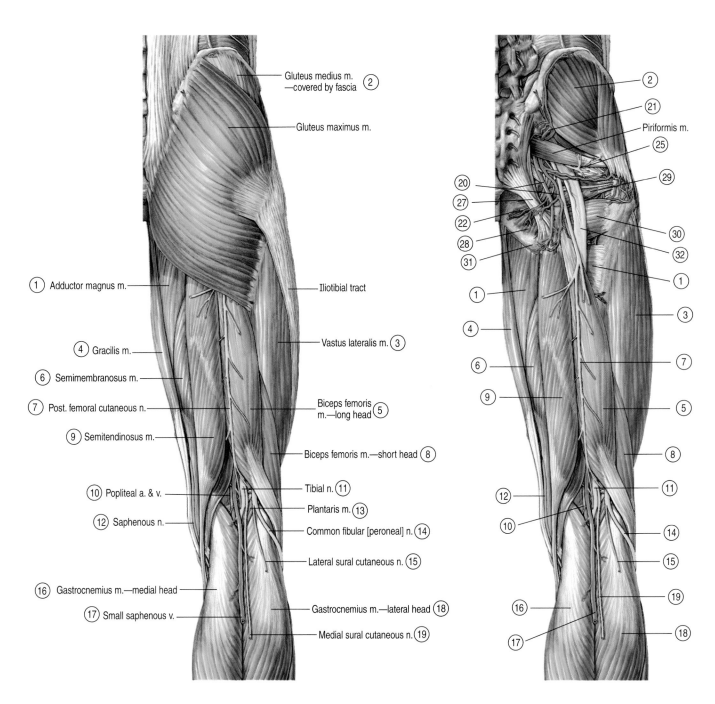

Gluteus medius m.
—covered by fascia (2)

Gluteus maximus m.

Piriformis m.

(2)
(21)
(25)
(29)
(20)
(27)
(22)
(28)
(31)
(30)
(32)

(1) Adductor magnus m.

Iliotibial tract

(4) Gracilis m.

Vastus lateralis m. (3)

(6) Semimembranosus m.

(7) Post. femoral cutaneous n.

Biceps femoris
m.—long head (5)

(9) Semitendinosus m.

Biceps femoris m.—short head (8)

(10) Popliteal a. & v.

Tibial n. (11)

Plantaris m. (13)

(12) Saphenous n.

Common fibular [peroneal] n. (14)

Lateral sural cutaneous n. (15)

(16) Gastrocnemius m.—medial head

(17) Small saphenous v.

Gastrocnemius m.—lateral head (18)

Medial sural cutaneous n. (19)

(1)
(4)
(6)
(9)
(12)
(10)
(16)
(17)

(2)
(3)
(7)
(5)
(8)
(11)
(14)
(15)
(19)
(18)

POSTERIOR VIEWS

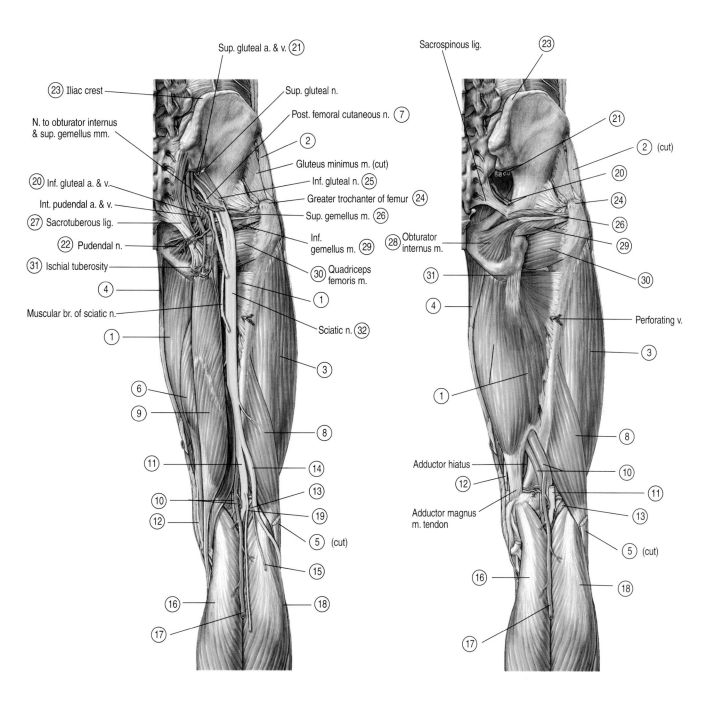

Sup. gluteal a. & v. (21)

Sacrospinous lig.   (23)

(23) Iliac crest

Sup. gluteal n.

N. to obturator internus
& sup. gemellus mm.

Post. femoral cutaneous n. (7)

(2)

Gluteus minimus m. (cut)

(20) Inf. gluteal a. & v.

Inf. gluteal n. (25)

Int. pudendal a. & v.

Greater trochanter of femur (24)

(27) Sacrotuberous lig.

Sup. gemellus m. (26)

(22) Pudendal n.

Inf.
gemellus m. (29)

(31) Ischial tuberosity

(30) Quadriceps
femoris m.

(4)

(1)

Muscular br. of sciatic n.

Sciatic n. (32)

(1)

(3)

(6)

(9)

(8)

(11)

(14)

(13)

(10)

(19)

(12)

(5) (cut)

(15)

(16)

(18)

(17)

(21)

(2) (cut)

(20)

(24)

(26)

(28) Obturator
internus m.

(29)

(31)

(30)

(4)

Perforating v.

(3)

(1)

(8)

Adductor hiatus

(10)

(12)

(11)

Adductor magnus
m. tendon

(13)

(5) (cut)

(16)

(18)

(17)

POSTERIOR VIEWS

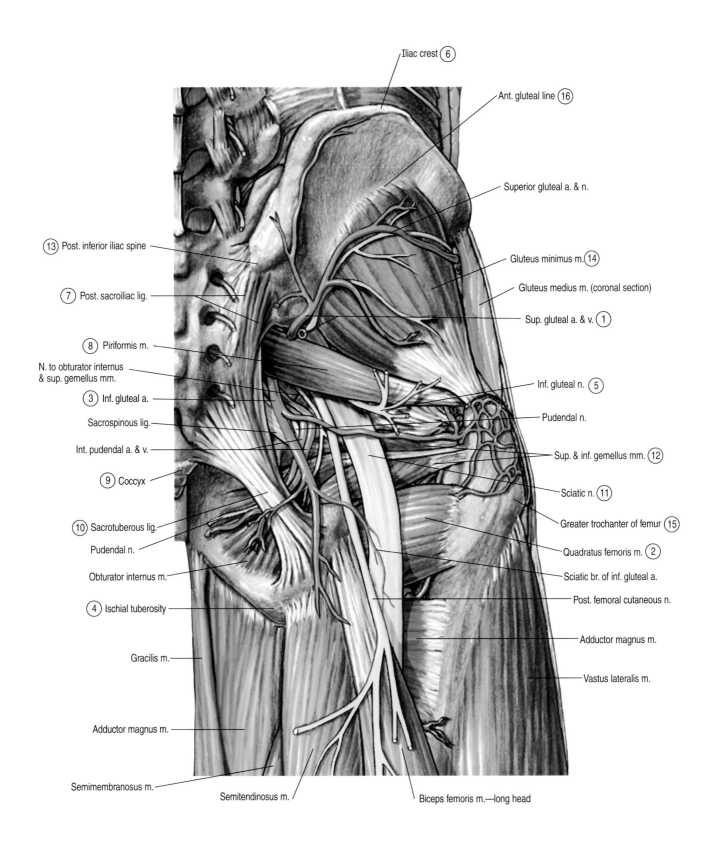

Iliac crest ⑥

Ant. gluteal line ⑯

Superior gluteal a. & n.

Gluteus minimus m.⑭

Gluteus medius m. (coronal section)

Sup. gluteal a. & v. ①

⑬ Post. inferior iliac spine

⑦ Post. sacroiliac lig.

⑧ Piriformis m.

N. to obturator internus
& sup. gemellus mm.

③ Inf. gluteal a.

Sacrospinous lig.

Int. pudendal a. & v.

⑨ Coccyx

⑩ Sacrotuberous lig.

Pudendal n.

Obturator internus m.

④ Ischial tuberosity

Gracilis m.

Adductor magnus m.

Semimembranosus m.

Inf. gluteal n. ⑤

Pudendal n.

Sup. & inf. gemellus mm. ⑫

Sciatic n. ⑪

Greater trochanter of femur ⑮

Quadratus femoris m. ②

Sciatic br. of inf. gluteal a.

Post. femoral cutaneous n.

Adductor magnus m.

Vastus lateralis m.

Semitendinosus m.

Biceps femoris m.—long head

POSTERIOR VIEW

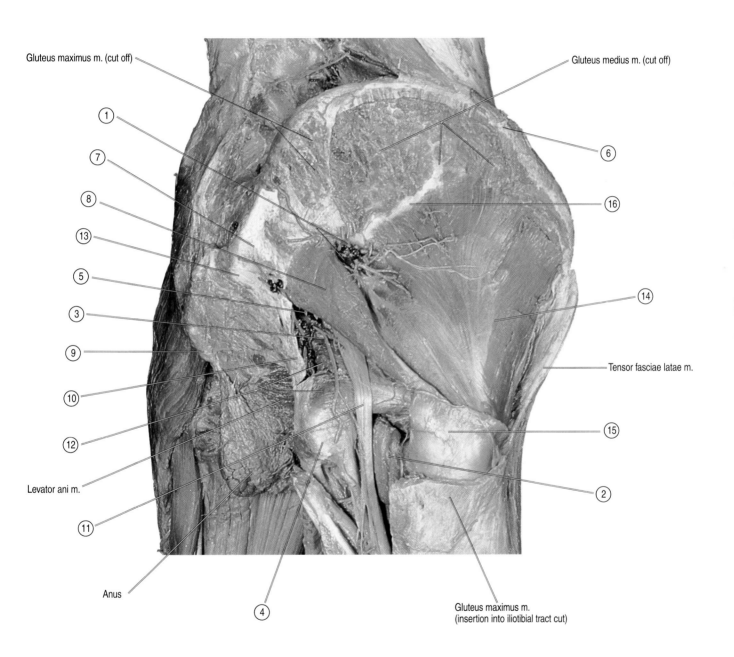

Gluteus maximus m. (cut off)

Gluteus medius m. (cut off)

① 7 8 13 5 3 9 10 12 11

⑥ ⑯ ⑭

Tensor fasciae latae m.

⑮ ②

Levator ani m.

Anus

④

Gluteus maximus m.
(insertion into iliotibial tract cut)

POSTEROLATERAL VIEW

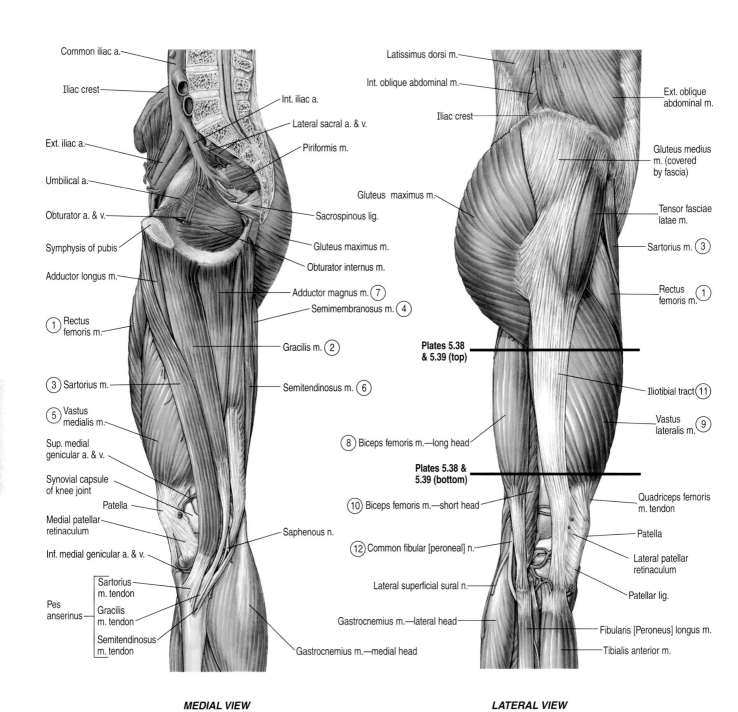

Common iliac a.

Iliac crest

Ext. iliac a.

Umbilical a.

Obturator a. & v.

Symphysis of pubis

Adductor longus m.

(1) Rectus femoris m.

(3) Sartorius m.

(5) Vastus medialis m.

Sup. medial genicular a. & v.

Synovial capsule of knee joint

Patella

Medial patellar retinaculum

Inf. medial genicular a. & v.

Pes anserinus
- Sartorius m. tendon
- Gracilis m. tendon
- Semitendinosus m. tendon

Int. iliac a.

Lateral sacral a. & v.

Piriformis m.

Sacrospinous lig.

Gluteus maximus m.

Obturator internus m.

Adductor magnus m. (7)

Semimembranosus m. (4)

Gracilis m. (2)

Semitendinosus m. (6)

Saphenous n.

Gastrocnemius m.—medial head

MEDIAL VIEW

Latissimus dorsi m.

Int. oblique abdominal m.

Iliac crest

Gluteus maximus m.

Plates 5.38 & 5.39 (top)

(8) Biceps femoris m.—long head

Plates 5.38 & 5.39 (bottom)

(10) Biceps femoris m.—short head

(12) Common fibular [peroneal] n.

Lateral superficial sural n.

Gastrocnemius m.—lateral head

Ext. oblique abdominal m.

Gluteus medius m. (covered by fascia)

Tensor fasciae latae m.

Sartorius m. (3)

Rectus femoris m. (1)

Iliotibial tract (11)

Vastus lateralis m. (9)

Quadriceps femoris m. tendon

Patella

Lateral patellar retinaculum

Patellar lig.

Fibularis [Peroneus] longus m.

Tibialis anterior m.

LATERAL VIEW

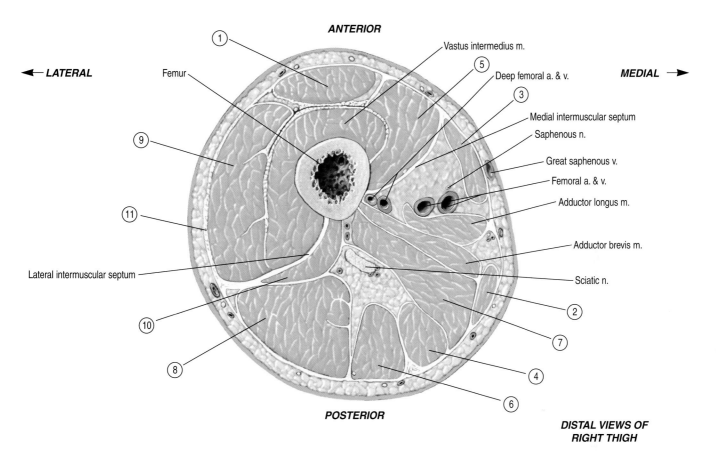

ANTERIOR

LATERAL

MEDIAL

1

Femur

Vastus intermedius m.

5

Deep femoral a. & v.

3

Medial intermuscular septum

Saphenous n.

9

Great saphenous v.

Femoral a. & v.

Adductor longus m.

11

Adductor brevis m.

Lateral intermuscular septum

Sciatic n.

2

10

7

8

4

6

POSTERIOR

DISTAL VIEWS OF
RIGHT THIGH

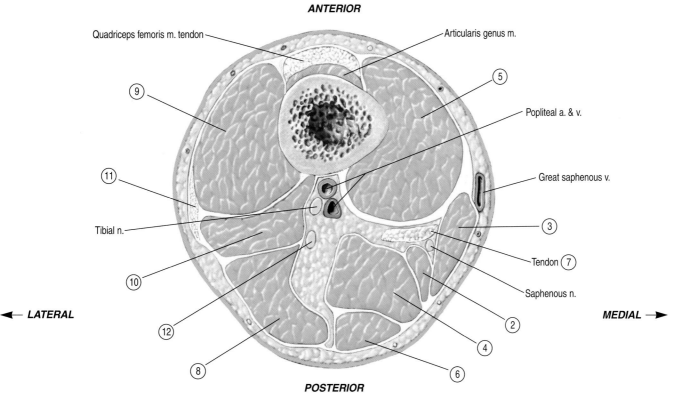

ANTERIOR

Quadriceps femoris m. tendon

Articularis genus m.

9

5

Popliteal a. & v.

11

Great saphenous v.

Tibial n.

3

10

Tendon 7

Saphenous n.

2

12

4

LATERAL

MEDIAL

8

6

POSTERIOR

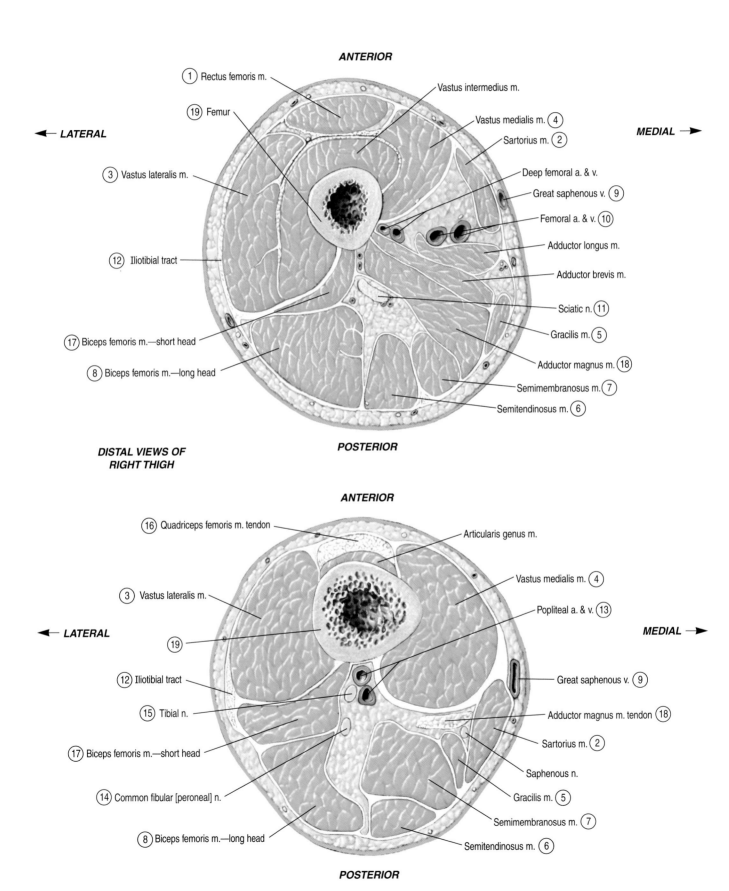

ANTERIOR

1 Rectus femoris m.

19 Femur

← *LATERAL*

3 Vastus lateralis m.

12 Iliotibial tract

17 Biceps femoris m.—short head

8 Biceps femoris m.—long head

Vastus intermedius m.

Vastus medialis m. 4

Sartorius m. 2

MEDIAL →

Deep femoral a. & v.

Great saphenous v. 9

Femoral a. & v. 10

Adductor longus m.

Adductor brevis m.

Sciatic n. 11

Gracilis m. 5

Adductor magnus m. 18

Semimembranosus m. 7

Semitendinosus m. 6

POSTERIOR

DISTAL VIEWS OF RIGHT THIGH

ANTERIOR

16 Quadriceps femoris m. tendon

3 Vastus lateralis m.

← *LATERAL*

19

12 Iliotibial tract

15 Tibial n.

17 Biceps femoris m.—short head

14 Common fibular [peroneal] n.

8 Biceps femoris m.—long head

Articularis genus m.

Vastus medialis m. 4

Popliteal a. & v. 13

MEDIAL →

Great saphenous v. 9

Adductor magnus m. tendon 18

Sartorius m. 2

Saphenous n.

Gracilis m. 5

Semimembranosus m. 7

Semitendinosus m. 6

POSTERIOR

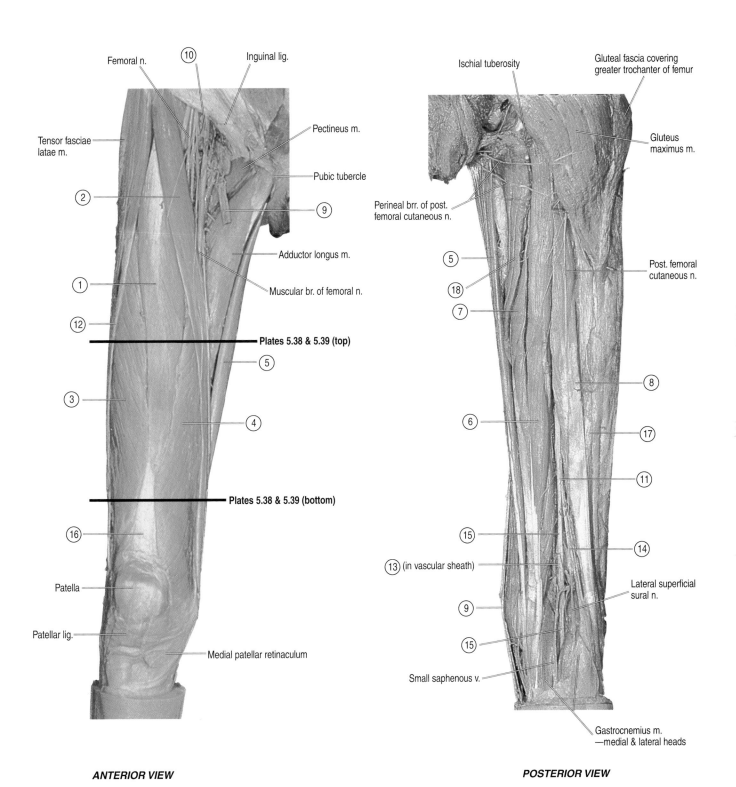

Femoral n.

⑩

Inguinal lig.

Tensor fasciae latae m.

Pectineus m.

Pubic tubercle

②

⑨

Adductor longus m.

Muscular br. of femoral n.

①

⑫

Plates 5.38 & 5.39 (top)

⑤

③

④

Plates 5.38 & 5.39 (bottom)

⑯

Patella

Patellar lig.

Medial patellar retinaculum

ANTERIOR VIEW

Ischial tuberosity

Gluteal fascia covering greater trochanter of femur

Gluteus maximus m.

Perineal brr. of post. femoral cutaneous n.

Post. femoral cutaneous n.

⑤

⑱

⑦

⑧

⑥

⑰

⑪

⑮

⑬ (in vascular sheath)

⑭

Lateral superficial sural n.

⑨

⑮

Small saphenous v.

Gastrocnemius m. —medial & lateral heads

POSTERIOR VIEW

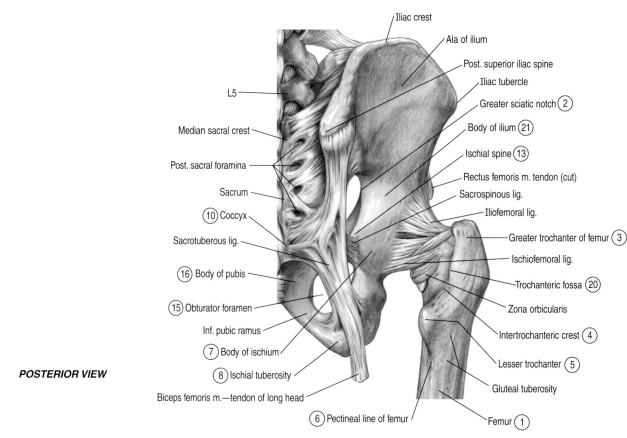

Iliac crest

Ala of ilium

Post. superior iliac spine

Iliac tubercle

Greater sciatic notch (2)

Body of ilium (21)

Ischial spine (13)

Rectus femoris m. tendon (cut)

Sacrospinous lig.

Iliofemoral lig.

Greater trochanter of femur (3)

Ischiofemoral lig.

Trochanteric fossa (20)

Zona orbicularis

Intertrochanteric crest (4)

Lesser trochanter (5)

Gluteal tuberosity

Femur (1)

L5

Median sacral crest

Post. sacral foramina

Sacrum

(10) Coccyx

Sacrotuberous lig.

(16) Body of pubis

(15) Obturator foramen

Inf. pubic ramus

(7) Body of ischium

POSTERIOR VIEW

(8) Ischial tuberosity

Biceps femoris m.—tendon of long head

(6) Pectineal line of femur

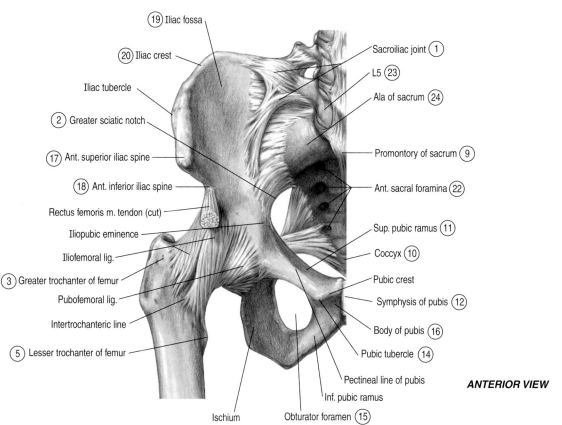

(19) Iliac fossa

(20) Iliac crest

Iliac tubercle

(2) Greater sciatic notch

(17) Ant. superior iliac spine

(18) Ant. inferior iliac spine

Rectus femoris m. tendon (cut)

Iliopubic eminence

Iliofemoral lig.

(3) Greater trochanter of femur

Pubofemoral lig.

Intertrochanteric line

(5) Lesser trochanter of femur

Sacroiliac joint (1)

L5 (23)

Ala of sacrum (24)

Promontory of sacrum (9)

Ant. sacral foramina (22)

Sup. pubic ramus (11)

Coccyx (10)

Pubic crest

Symphysis of pubis (12)

Body of pubis (16)

Pubic tubercle (14)

Pectineal line of pubis

ANTERIOR VIEW

Ischium

Obturator foramen (15)

Inf. pubic ramus

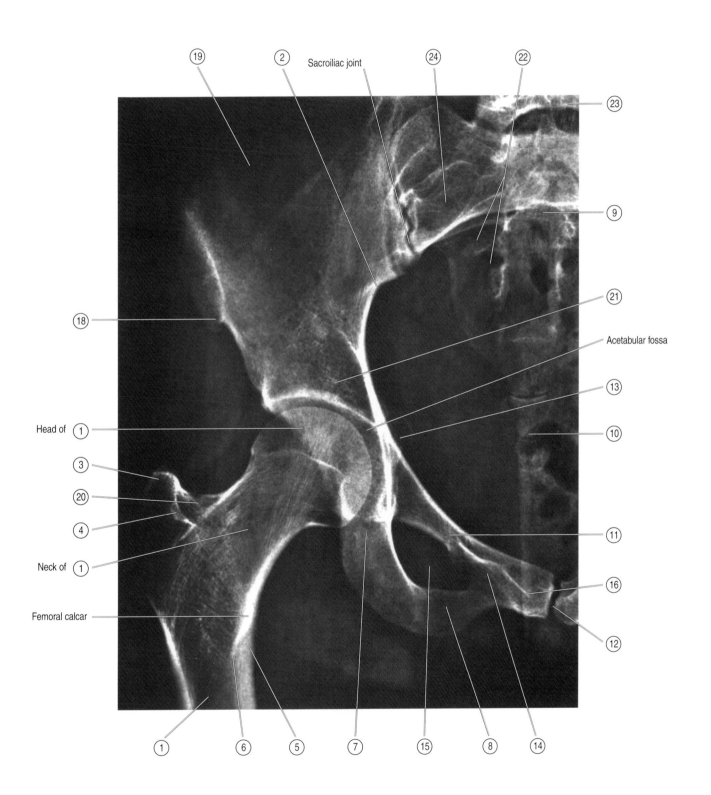

Sacroiliac joint

Head of ①

Neck of ①

Femoral calcar

Acetabular fossa

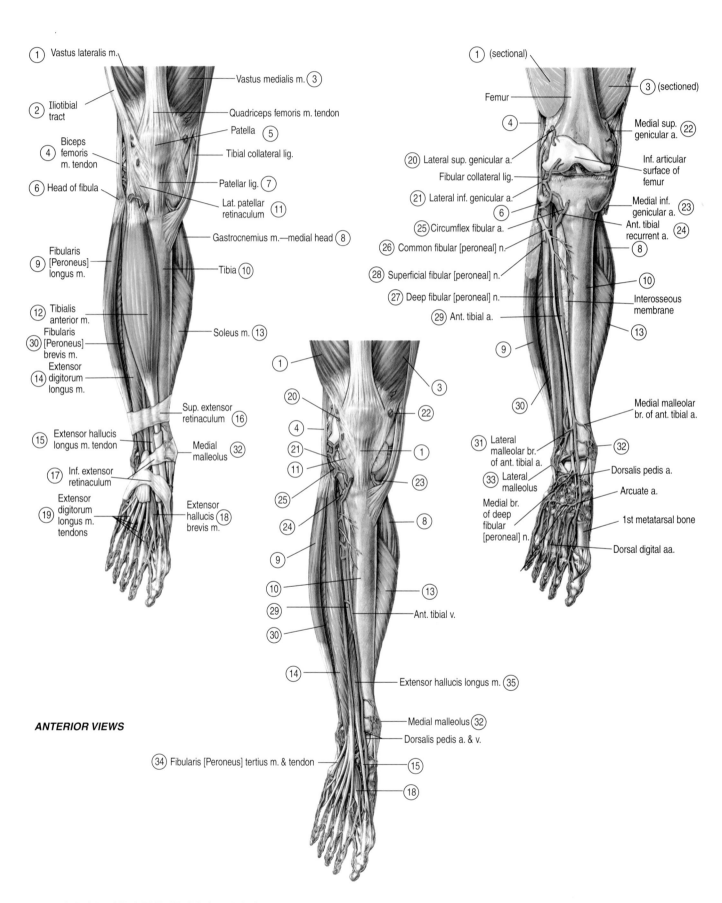

1. Vastus lateralis m.
2. Iliotibial tract
4. Biceps femoris m. tendon
6. Head of fibula
9. Fibularis [Peroneus] longus m.
12. Tibialis anterior m.
30. Fibularis [Peroneus] brevis m.
14. Extensor digitorum longus m.
15. Extensor hallucis longus m. tendon
17. Inf. extensor retinaculum
19. Extensor digitorum longus m. tendons

Vastus medialis m. 3
Quadriceps femoris m. tendon
Patella 5
Tibial collateral lig.
Patellar lig. 7
Lat. patellar retinaculum 11
Gastrocnemius m.—medial head 8
Tibia 10
Soleus m. 13
Sup. extensor retinaculum 16
Medial malleolus 32
Extensor hallucis 18 brevis m.

ANTERIOR VIEWS

1. (sectional)
Femur
4
20. Lateral sup. genicular a.
Fibular collateral lig.
21. Lateral inf. genicular a.
6
25. Circumflex fibular a.
26. Common fibular [peroneal] n.
28. Superficial fibular [peroneal] n.
27. Deep fibular [peroneal] n.
29. Ant. tibial a.
9
30
31. Lateral malleolar br. of ant. tibial a.
33. Lateral malleolus
Medial br. of deep fibular [peroneal] n.

3. (sectioned)
Medial sup. 22 genicular a.
Inf. articular surface of femur
Medial inf. 23 genicular a.
Ant. tibial recurrent a. 24
8
10
Interosseous membrane
13
Medial malleolar br. of ant. tibial a.
32
Dorsalis pedis a.
Arcuate a.
1st metatarsal bone
Dorsal digital aa.

1
20
4
21
11
25
24
9
10
29
30
14

3
22
1
23
8
13
Ant. tibial v.
Extensor hallucis longus m. 35
Medial malleolus 32
Dorsalis pedis a. & v.
15
18

34. Fibularis [Peroneus] tertius m. & tendon

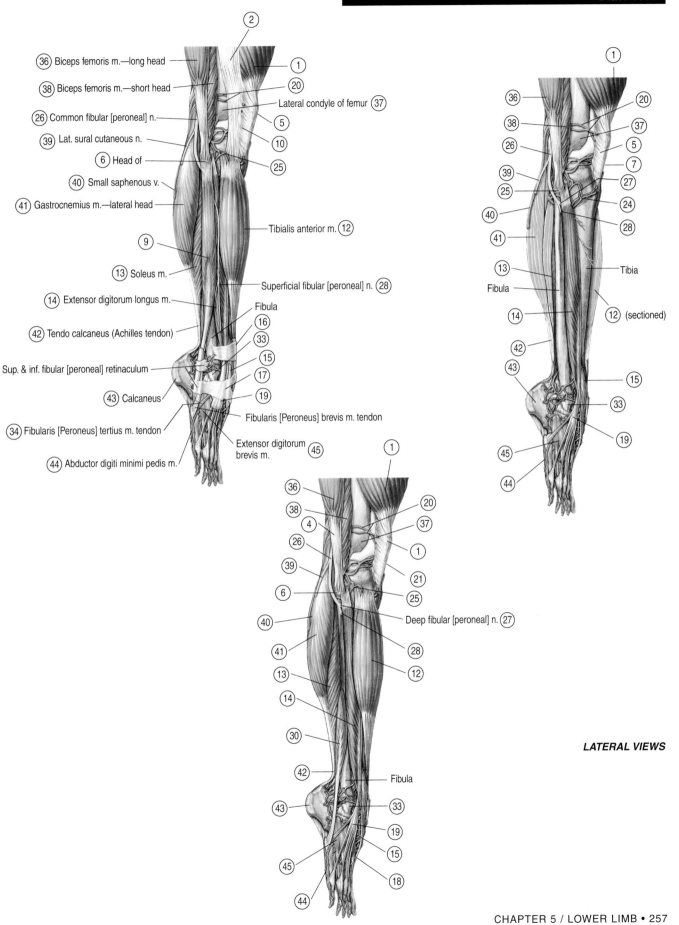

36 Biceps femoris m.—long head

38 Biceps femoris m.—short head

26 Common fibular [peroneal] n.

39 Lat. sural cutaneous n.

6 Head of

40 Small saphenous v.

41 Gastrocnemius m.—lateral head

9

13 Soleus m.

14 Extensor digitorum longus m.

42 Tendo calcaneus (Achilles tendon)

Sup. & inf. fibular [peroneal] retinaculum

43 Calcaneus

34 Fibularis [Peroneus] tertius m. tendon

44 Abductor digiti minimi pedis m.

2

1

20

Lateral condyle of femur 37

5

10

25

Tibialis anterior m. 12

Superficial fibular [peroneal] n. 28

Fibula

16

33

15

17

19

Fibularis [Peroneus] brevis m. tendon

Extensor digitorum brevis m. 45

1

36

20

38

37

26

5

39

7

25

27

40

24

41

28

13

Tibia

Fibula

14

42

12 (sectioned)

43

15

33

19

45

44

1

36

38

20

4

37

26

1

39

21

6

25

40

Deep fibular [peroneal] n. 27

41

28

13

12

14

30

42

Fibula

43

33

45

19

15

44

18

LATERAL VIEWS

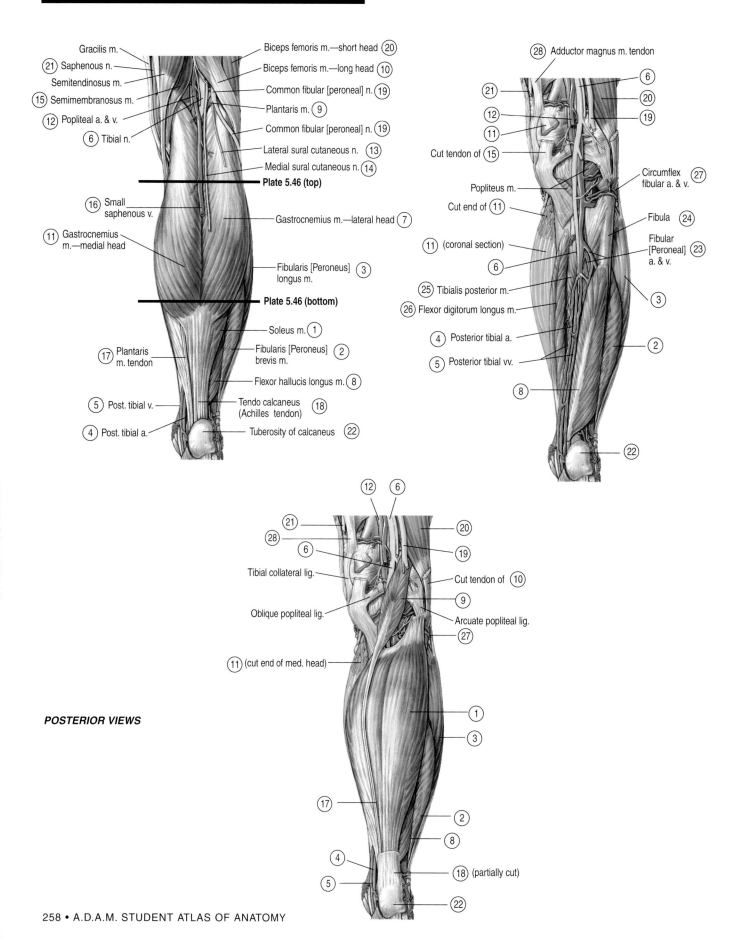

Gracilis m.

(21) Saphenous n.

Semitendinosus m.

(15) Semimembranosus m.

(12) Popliteal a. & v.

(6) Tibial n.

(16) Small saphenous v.

(11) Gastrocnemius m.—medial head

(17) Plantaris m. tendon

(5) Post. tibial v.

(4) Post. tibial a.

Biceps femoris m.—short head (20)

Biceps femoris m.—long head (10)

Common fibular [peroneal] n. (19)

Plantaris m. (9)

Common fibular [peroneal] n. (19)

Lateral sural cutaneous n. (13)

Medial sural cutaneous n. (14)

Plate 5.46 (top)

Gastrocnemius m.—lateral head (7)

Fibularis [Peroneus] longus m. (3)

Plate 5.46 (bottom)

Soleus m. (1)

Fibularis [Peroneus] brevis m. (2)

Flexor hallucis longus m. (8)

Tendo calcaneus (Achilles tendon) (18)

Tuberosity of calcaneus (22)

(28) Adductor magnus m. tendon

(21)

(12)

(11)

Cut tendon of (15)

Popliteus m.

Cut end of (11)

(11) (coronal section)

(6)

(25) Tibialis posterior m.

(26) Flexor digitorum longus m.

(4) Posterior tibial a.

(5) Posterior tibial vv.

(8)

6

20

19

Circumflex fibular a. & v. (27)

Fibula (24)

Fibular [Peroneal] a. & v. (23)

3

2

(22)

(12)   (6)

(21)

(28)

(6)

Tibial collateral lig.

Oblique popliteal lig.

(11) (cut end of med. head)

20

19

Cut tendon of (10)

9

Arcuate popliteal lig.

(27)

(1)

(3)

(17)

(2)

(8)

(4)

(18) (partially cut)

(5)

(22)

POSTERIOR VIEWS

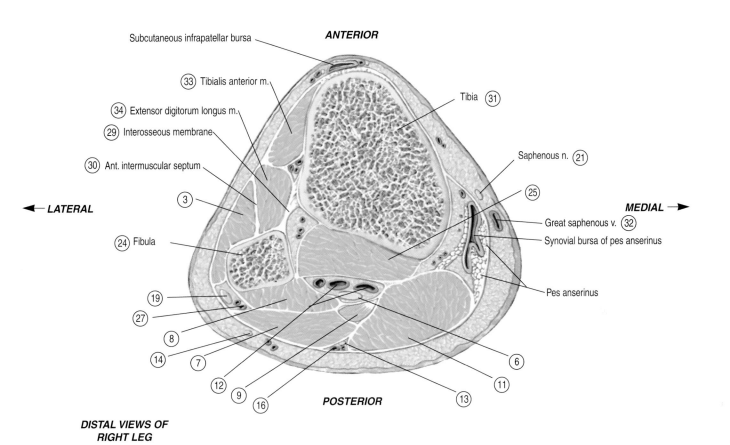

ANTERIOR

Subcutaneous infrapatellar bursa

(33) Tibialis anterior m.

(34) Extensor digitorum longus m.

(29) Interosseous membrane

(30) Ant. intermuscular septum

(3)

(24) Fibula

(19)

(27)

(8)

(14)   (7)

(12)   (9)

(16)

Tibia (31)

Saphenous n. (21)

(25)

Great saphenous v. (32)

Synovial bursa of pes anserinus

Pes anserinus

(6)

(11)

(13)

POSTERIOR

◄— LATERAL

MEDIAL —►

DISTAL VIEWS OF
RIGHT LEG

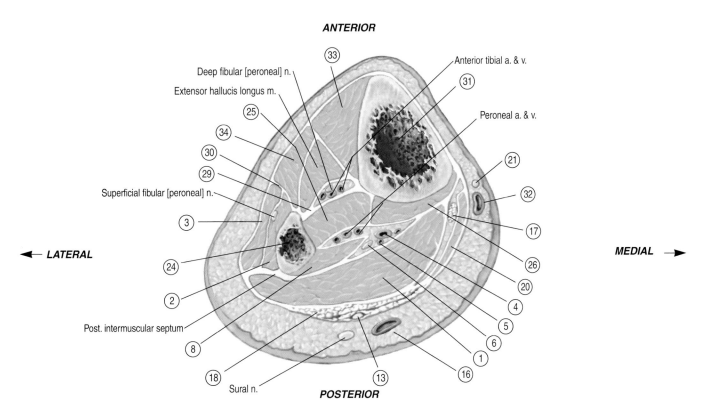

ANTERIOR

(33)

Deep fibular [peroneal] n.

Extensor hallucis longus m.

(25)

(34)

(30)

(29)

Superficial fibular [peroneal] n.

(3)

(24)

(2)

Post. intermuscular septum

(8)

(18)

Sural n.

Anterior tibial a. & v.

(31)

Peroneal a. & v.

(21)

(32)

(17)

(26)

(20)

(4)

(5)

(6)

(1)

(16)

(13)

POSTERIOR

◄— LATERAL

MEDIAL —►

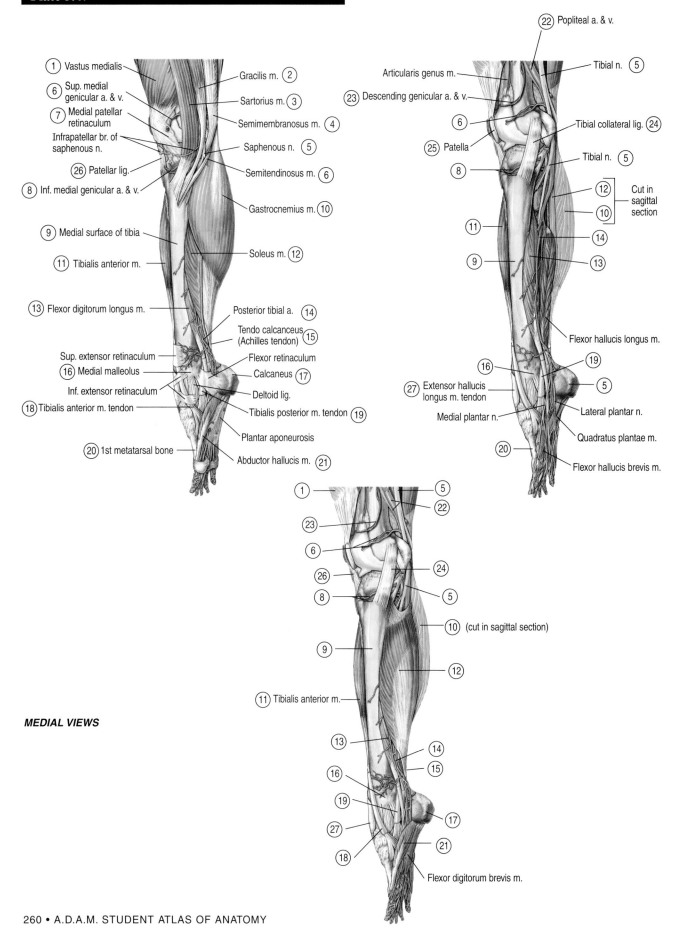

(22) Popliteal a. & v.

(1) Vastus medialis

Gracilis m. (2)

(6) Sup. medial genicular a. & v.

Sartorius m. (3)

(7) Medial patellar retinaculum

Semimembranosus m. (4)

Infrapatellar br. of saphenous n.

Saphenous n. (5)

(26) Patellar lig.

Semitendinosus m. (6)

(8) Inf. medial genicular a. & v.

Gastrocnemius m. (10)

(9) Medial surface of tibia

Soleus m. (12)

(11) Tibialis anterior m.

(13) Flexor digitorum longus m.

Posterior tibial a. (14)

Tendo calcanceus (Achilles tendon) (15)

Sup. extensor retinaculum

Flexor retinaculum

(16) Medial malleolus

Calcaneus (17)

Inf. extensor retinaculum

Deltoid lig.

(18) Tibialis anterior m. tendon

Tibialis posterior m. tendon (19)

Plantar aponeurosis

(20) 1st metatarsal bone

Abductor hallucis m. (21)

Articularis genus m.

Tibial n. (5)

(23) Descending genicular a. & v.

(6)

Tibial collateral lig. (24)

(25) Patella

Tibial n. (5)

(8)

(12) Cut in sagittal section
(10)

(11)

(14)

(9)

(13)

Flexor hallucis longus m.

(16)

(19)

(27) Extensor hallucis longus m. tendon

(5)

Medial plantar n.

Lateral plantar n.

Quadratus plantae m.

(20)

Flexor hallucis brevis m.

(1)

(5)

(22)

(23)

(6)

(26)

(24)

(8)

(5)

(10) (cut in sagittal section)

(9)

(12)

(11) Tibialis anterior m.

MEDIAL VIEWS

(13)

(14)

(15)

(16)

(19)

(17)

(27)

(18)

(21)

Flexor digitorum brevis m.

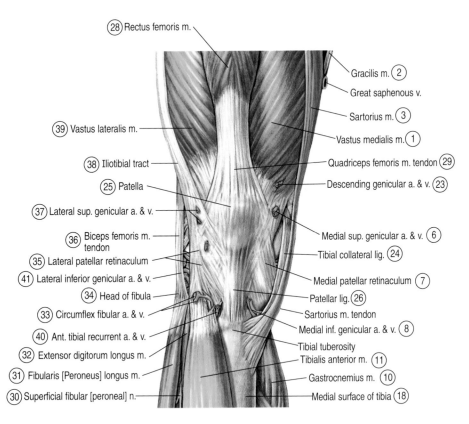

28 Rectus femoris m.

Gracilis m. 2
Great saphenous v.
Sartorius m. 3
39 Vastus lateralis m.
Vastus medialis m. 1
38 Iliotibial tract
Quadriceps femoris m. tendon 29
25 Patella
Descending genicular a. & v. 23
37 Lateral sup. genicular a. & v.
Medial sup. genicular a. & v. 6
36 Biceps femoris m. tendon
Tibial collateral lig. 24
35 Lateral patellar retinaculum
Medial patellar retinaculum 7
41 Lateral inferior genicular a. & v.
Patellar lig. 26
34 Head of fibula
Sartorius m. tendon
33 Circumflex fibular a. & v.
Medial inf. genicular a. & v. 8
40 Ant. tibial recurrent a. & v.
Tibial tuberosity
32 Extensor digitorum longus m.
Tibialis anterior m. 11
31 Fibularis [Peroneus] longus m.
Gastrocnemius m. 10
30 Superficial fibular [peroneal] n.
Medial surface of tibia 18

ANTERIOR VIEW

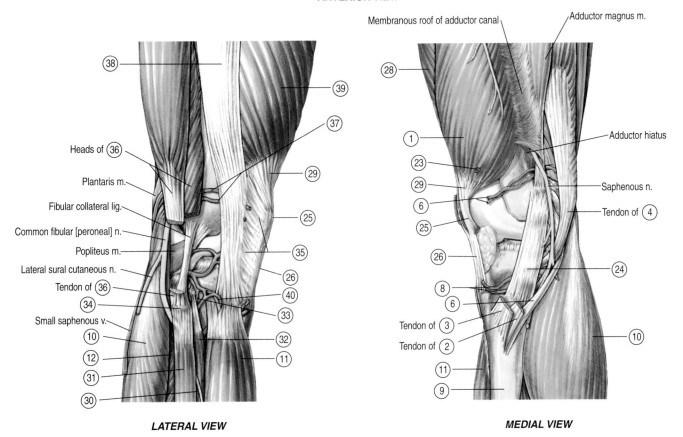

38
39
37
Heads of 36
29
Plantaris m.
Fibular collateral lig.
25
Common fibular [peroneal] n.
Popliteus m.
35
Lateral sural cutaneous n.
26
Tendon of 36
40
34
33
Small saphenous v.
10
32
12
11
31
30

LATERAL VIEW

Membranous roof of adductor canal
Adductor magnus m.
28
1
Adductor hiatus
23
29
Saphenous n.
6
Tendon of 4
25
26
24
8
6
Tendon of 3
10
Tendon of 2
11
9

MEDIAL VIEW

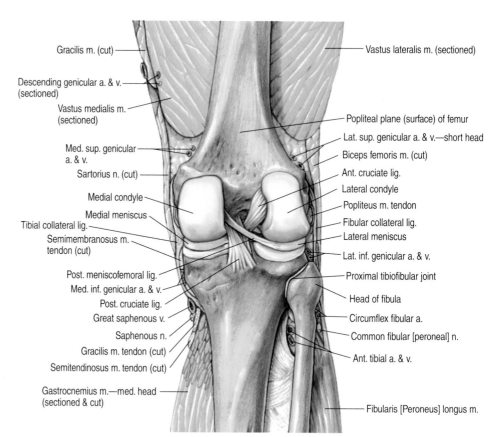

Gracilis m. (cut)

Descending genicular a. & v. (sectioned)

Vastus medialis m. (sectioned)

Med. sup. genicular a. & v.

Sartorius n. (cut)

Medial condyle

Medial meniscus

Tibial collateral lig.

Semimembranosus m. tendon (cut)

Post. meniscofemoral lig.

Med. inf. genicular a. & v.

Post. cruciate lig.

Great saphenous v.

Saphenous n.

Gracilis m. tendon (cut)

Semitendinosus m. tendon (cut)

Gastrocnemius m.—med. head (sectioned & cut)

Vastus lateralis m. (sectioned)

Popliteal plane (surface) of femur

Lat. sup. genicular a. & v.—short head

Biceps femoris m. (cut)

Ant. cruciate lig.

Lateral condyle

Popliteus m. tendon

Fibular collateral lig.

Lateral meniscus

Lat. inf. genicular a. & v.

Proximal tibiofibular joint

Head of fibula

Circumflex fibular a.

Common fibular [peroneal] n.

Ant. tibial a. & v.

Fibularis [Peroneus] longus m.

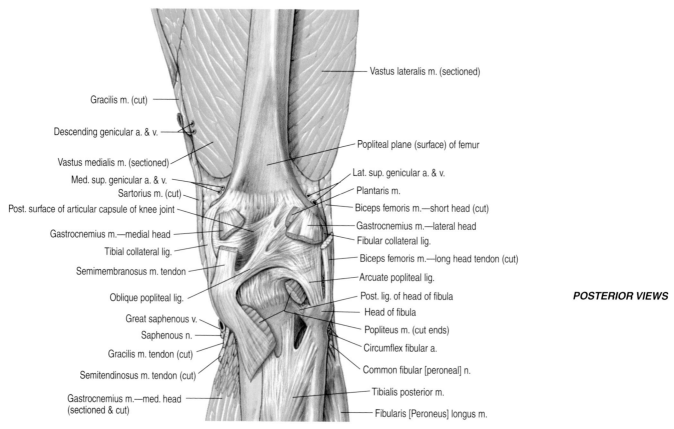

Gracilis m. (cut)

Descending genicular a. & v.

Vastus medialis m. (sectioned)

Med. sup. genicular a. & v.

Sartorius m. (cut)

Post. surface of articular capsule of knee joint

Gastrocnemius m.—medial head

Tibial collateral lig.

Semimembranosus m. tendon

Oblique popliteal lig.

Great saphenous v.

Saphenous n.

Gracilis m. tendon (cut)

Semitendinosus m. tendon (cut)

Gastrocnemius m.—med. head (sectioned & cut)

Vastus lateralis m. (sectioned)

Popliteal plane (surface) of femur

Lat. sup. genicular a. & v.

Plantaris m.

Biceps femoris m.—short head (cut)

Gastrocnemius m.—lateral head

Fibular collateral lig.

Biceps femoris m.—long head tendon (cut)

Arcuate popliteal lig.

Post. lig. of head of fibula

Head of fibula

Popliteus m. (cut ends)

Circumflex fibular a.

Common fibular [peroneal] n.

Tibialis posterior m.

Fibularis [Peroneus] longus m.

POSTERIOR VIEWS

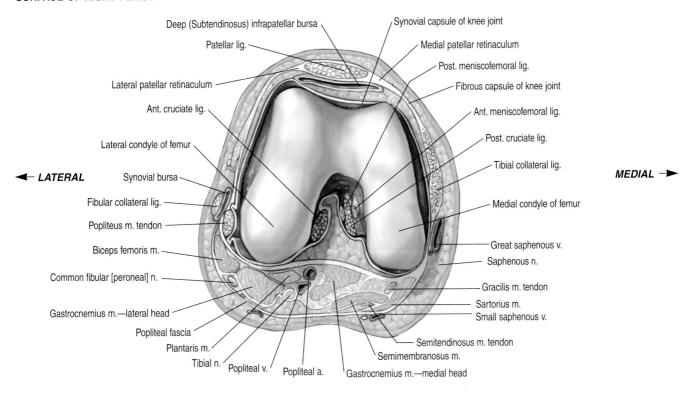

DISTAL VIEW OF ARTICULAR SURFACE OF RIGHT FEMUR

ANTERIOR

Deep (Subtendinosus) infrapatellar bursa

Patellar lig.

Lateral patellar retinaculum

Ant. cruciate lig.

Lateral condyle of femur

◄ LATERAL   Synovial bursa

Fibular collateral lig.

Popliteus m. tendon

Biceps femoris m.

Common fibular [peroneal] n.

Gastrocnemius m.—lateral head

Popliteal fascia

Plantaris m.

Tibial n.   Popliteal v.'   Popliteal a.

Synovial capsule of knee joint

Medial patellar retinaculum

Post. meniscofemoral lig.

Fibrous capsule of knee joint

Ant. meniscofemoral lig.

Post. cruciate lig.

Tibial collateral lig.

MEDIAL ►

Medial condyle of femur

Great saphenous v.

Saphenous n.

Gracilis m. tendon

Sartorius m.

Small saphenous v.

Semitendinosus m. tendon

Semimembranosus m.

Gastrocnemius m.—medial head

DISTAL VIEW OF ARTICULAR SURFACE OF RIGHT TIBIA

POSTERIOR

Popliteal v. & a.

Popliteal fascia

Tibial n.

Plantaris m.

Medial sural cutaneous n.

Gastrocnemius m.—lateral head

Common fibular [peroneal] n.

Post. meniscofemoral lig.

Biceps femoris m.

◄ LATERAL   Popliteus m. tendon

Post. cruciate ligament

Fibular collateral lig.

Lateral meniscus

Ant. meniscofemoral lig.

Sup. articular surface of tibia (lateral condyle)

Infrapatellar fat pad

Patellar lig.

Gastrocnemius m.—medial head

Semimembranosus m.

Small saphenous v.

Semitendinous m. tendon

Sartorius m.

Gracilis m.

Saphenous n.

Great saphenous v.

MEDIAL ►

Sup. articular surface of tibia

Med. meniscus

Tibial collateral lig.

Synovial capsule of knee joint

Intercondylar eminence

Ant. cruciate lig.

Transverse lig. of knee joint

ANTERIOR

Plane of Medial View below

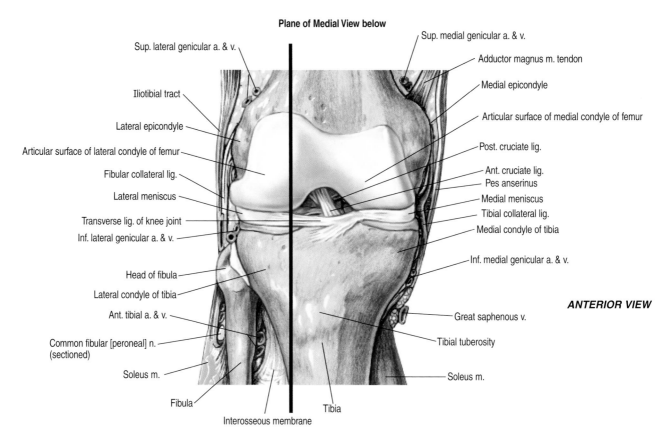

Sup. lateral genicular a. & v.

Iliotibial tract

Lateral epicondyle

Articular surface of lateral condyle of femur

Fibular collateral lig.

Lateral meniscus

Transverse lig. of knee joint

Inf. lateral genicular a. & v.

Head of fibula

Lateral condyle of tibia

Ant. tibial a. & v.

Common fibular [peroneal] n. (sectioned)

Soleus m.

Fibula

Interosseous membrane

Tibia

Sup. medial genicular a. & v.

Adductor magnus m. tendon

Medial epicondyle

Articular surface of medial condyle of femur

Post. cruciate lig.

Ant. cruciate lig.

Pes anserinus

Medial meniscus

Tibial collateral lig.

Medial condyle of tibia

Inf. medial genicular a. & v.

Great saphenous v.

Tibial tuberosity

Soleus m.

ANTERIOR VIEW

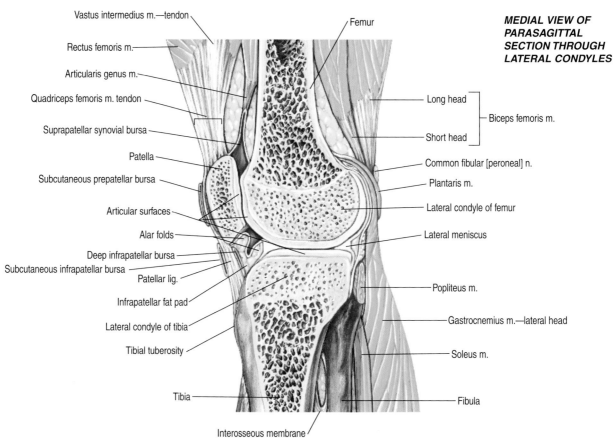

MEDIAL VIEW OF PARASAGITTAL SECTION THROUGH LATERAL CONDYLES

Vastus intermedius m.—tendon

Rectus femoris m.

Articularis genus m.

Quadriceps femoris m. tendon

Suprapatellar synovial bursa

Patella

Subcutaneous prepatellar bursa

Articular surfaces

Alar folds

Deep infrapatellar bursa

Subcutaneous infrapatellar bursa

Patellar lig.

Infrapatellar fat pad

Lateral condyle of tibia

Tibial tuberosity

Tibia

Interosseous membrane

Femur

Long head

Short head

Biceps femoris m.

Common fibular [peroneal] n.

Plantaris m.

Lateral condyle of femur

Lateral meniscus

Popliteus m.

Gastrocnemius m.—lateral head

Soleus m.

Fibula

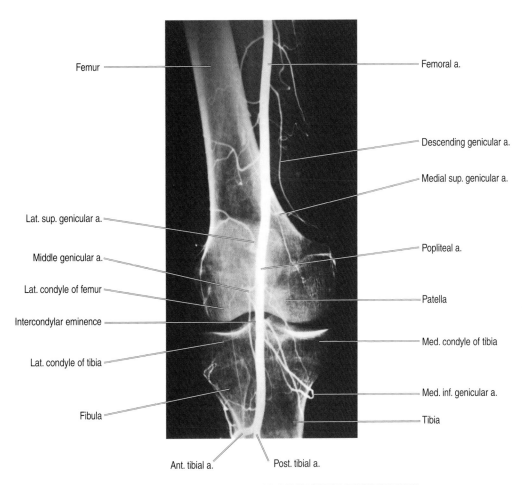

Femur

Femoral a.

Descending genicular a.

Medial sup. genicular a.

Lat. sup. genicular a.

Popliteal a.

Middle genicular a.

Lat. condyle of femur

Patella

Intercondylar eminence

Med. condyle of tibia

Lat. condyle of tibia

Med. inf. genicular a.

Fibula

Tibia

Ant. tibial a.

Post. tibial a.

ANTEROPOSTRIOR VIEW OF RIGHT KNEE ARTERIOGRAM

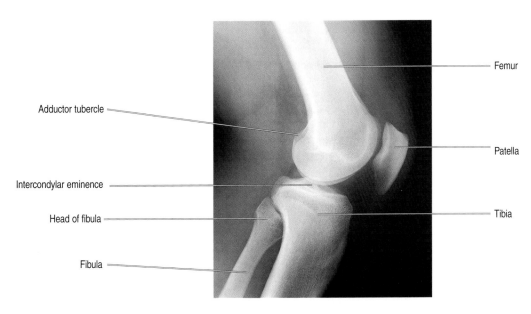

Femur

Adductor tubercle

Patella

Intercondylar eminence

Head of fibula

Tibia

Fibula

LATERAL VIEW OF RIGHT KNEE

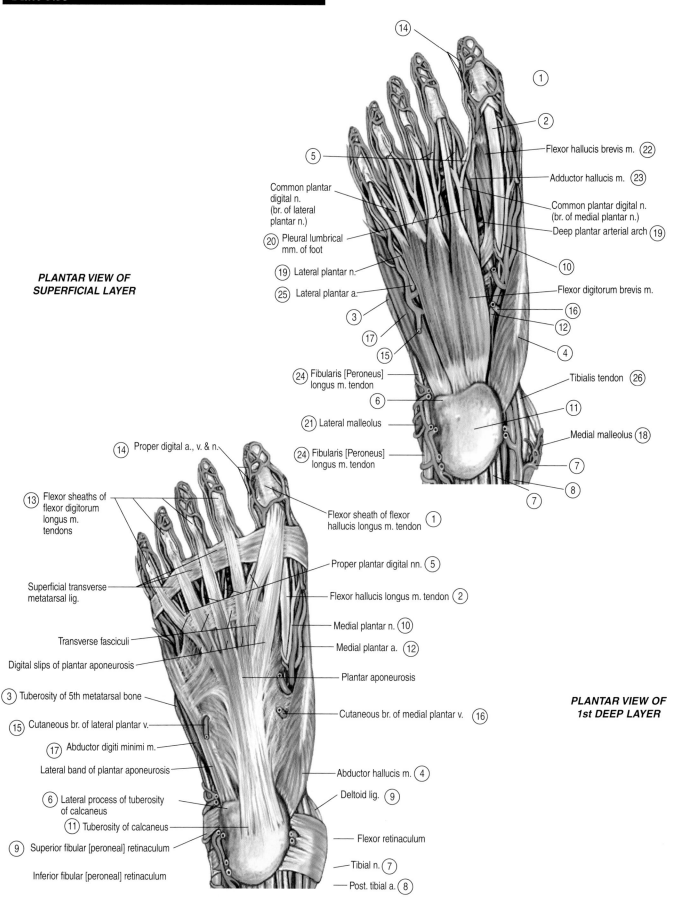

PLANTAR VIEW OF SUPERFICIAL LAYER

(14)

(1)

Flexor hallucis brevis m. (22)

Adductor hallucis m. (23)

(5)

Common plantar digital n. (br. of lateral plantar n.)

Common plantar digital n. (br. of medial plantar n.)

Deep plantar arterial arch (19)

(20) Pleural lumbrical mm. of foot

(10)

(19) Lateral plantar n.

(25) Lateral plantar a.

Flexor digitorum brevis m.

(3)

(16)

(12)

(17)

(4)

(15)

(24) Fibularis [Peroneus] longus m. tendon

Tibialis tendon (26)

(6)

(11)

(21) Lateral malleolus

Medial malleolus (18)

(24) Fibularis [Peroneus] longus m. tendon

(7)

(7)

(8)

PLANTAR VIEW OF 1st DEEP LAYER

(14) Proper digital a., v. & n.

(13) Flexor sheaths of flexor digitorum longus m. tendons

Flexor sheath of flexor hallucis longus m. tendon (1)

Proper plantar digital nn. (5)

Superficial transverse metatarsal lig.

Flexor hallucis longus m. tendon (2)

Medial plantar n. (10)

Transverse fasciculi

Medial plantar a. (12)

Digital slips of plantar aponeurosis

Plantar aponeurosis

(3) Tuberosity of 5th metatarsal bone

Cutaneous br. of medial plantar v. (16)

(15) Cutaneous br. of lateral plantar v.

(17) Abductor digiti minimi m.

Lateral band of plantar aponeurosis

Abductor hallucis m. (4)

Deltoid lig. (9)

(6) Lateral process of tuberosity of calcaneus

(11) Tuberosity of calcaneus

Flexor retinaculum

(9) Superior fibular [peroneal] retinaculum

Tibial n. (7)

Inferior fibular [peroneal] retinaculum

Post. tibial a. (8)

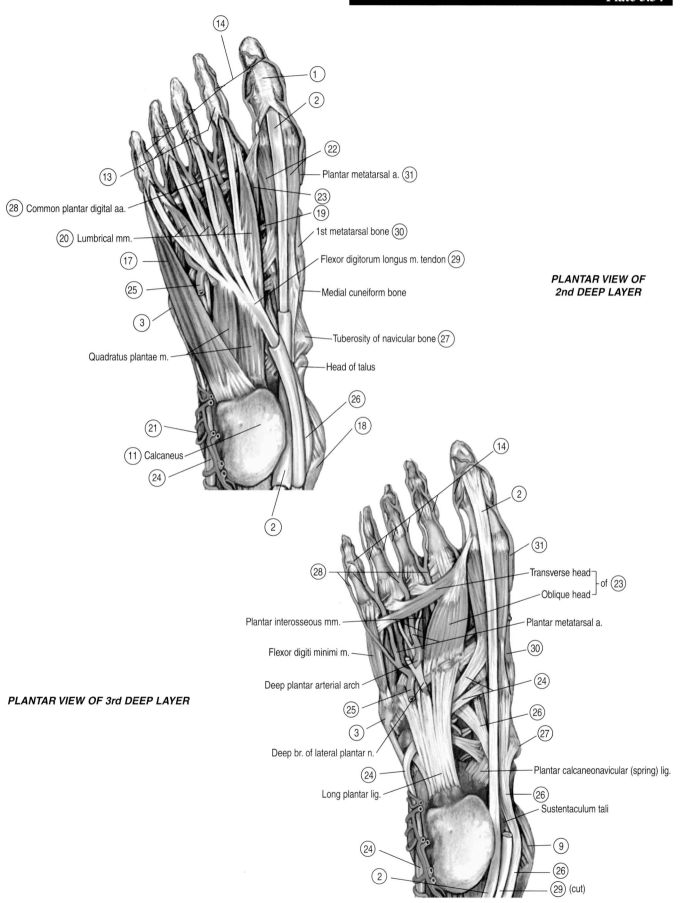

Sole of Foot
Plate 5.54

14

1

2

22

Plantar metatarsal a. 31

28 Common plantar digital aa.

23

19

1st metatarsal bone 30

13

20 Lumbrical mm.

Flexor digitorum longus m. tendon 29

17

Medial cuneiform bone

25

3

Tuberosity of navicular bone 27

Quadratus plantae m.

Head of talus

26

21

18

11 Calcaneus

24

2

**PLANTAR VIEW OF
2nd DEEP LAYER**

14

2

31

Transverse head ⎤
                      ⎬ of 23
Oblique head ⎦

28

Plantar metatarsal a.

Plantar interosseous mm.

30

Flexor digiti minimi m.

24

Deep plantar arterial arch

26

25

27

3

Deep br. of lateral plantar n.

Plantar calcaneonavicular (spring) lig.

24

26

Long plantar lig.

Sustentaculum tali

PLANTAR VIEW OF 3rd DEEP LAYER

9

24

2

26

29 (cut)

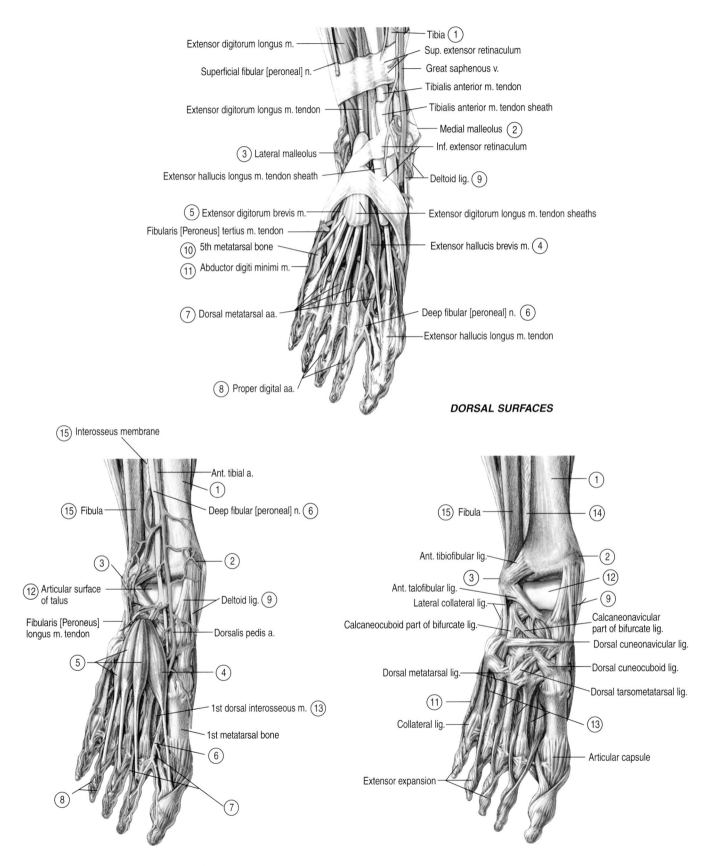

Extensor digitorum longus m.

Superficial fibular [peroneal] n.

Extensor digitorum longus m. tendon

③ Lateral malleolus

Extensor hallucis longus m. tendon sheath

⑤ Extensor digitorum brevis m.

Fibularis [Peroneus] tertius m. tendon

⑩ 5th metatarsal bone

⑪ Abductor digiti minimi m.

⑦ Dorsal metatarsal aa.

⑧ Proper digital aa.

Tibia ①

Sup. extensor retinaculum

Great saphenous v.

Tibialis anterior m. tendon

Tibialis anterior m. tendon sheath

Medial malleolus ②

Inf. extensor retinaculum

Deltoid lig. ⑨

Extensor digitorum longus m. tendon sheaths

Extensor hallucis brevis m. ④

Deep fibular [peroneal] n. ⑥

Extensor hallucis longus m. tendon

DORSAL SURFACES

⑮ Interosseus membrane

Ant. tibial a.

①

⑮ Fibula

Deep fibular [peroneal] n. ⑥

③

②

⑫ Articular surface of talus

Deltoid lig. ⑨

Fibularis [Peroneus] longus m. tendon

Dorsalis pedis a.

⑤

④

1st dorsal interosseous m. ⑬

1st metatarsal bone

⑥

⑧

⑦

⑮ Fibula

①

⑭

②

Ant. tibiofibular lig.

③

⑫

Ant. talofibular lig.

⑨

Lateral collateral lig.

Calcaneocuboid part of bifurcate lig.

Calcaneonavicular part of bifurcate lig.

Dorsal cuneonavicular lig.

Dorsal metatarsal lig.

Dorsal cuneocuboid lig.

Dorsal tarsometatarsal lig.

⑪

⑬

Collateral lig.

Articular capsule

Extensor expansion

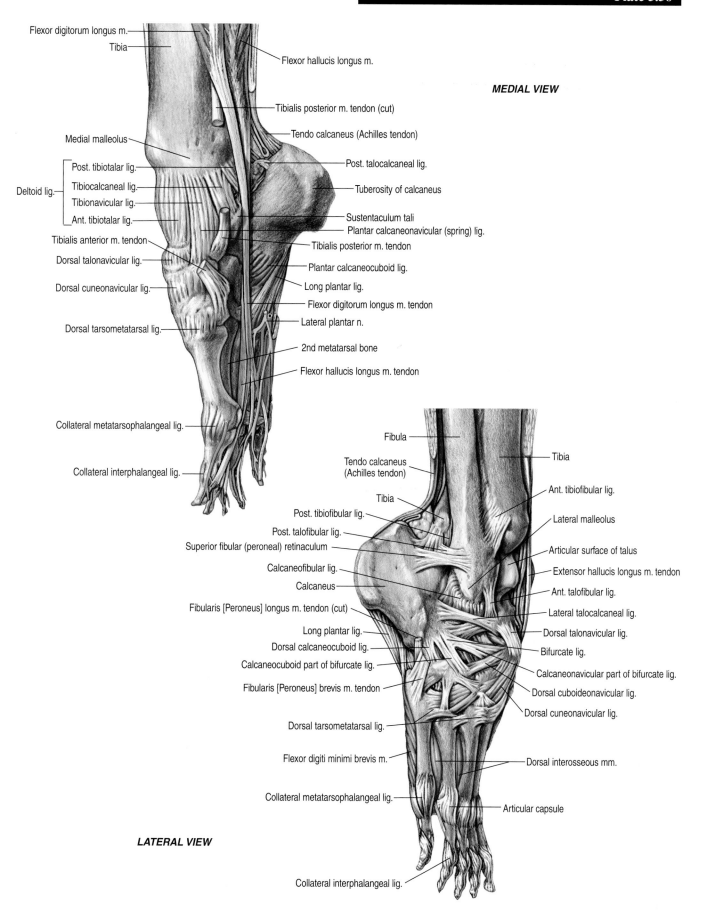

Flexor digitorum longus m.

Tibia

Flexor hallucis longus m.

MEDIAL VIEW

Tibialis posterior m. tendon (cut)

Tendo calcaneus (Achilles tendon)

Medial malleolus

Post. talocalcaneal lig.

Post. tibiotalar lig.

Tibiocalcaneal lig.

Tuberosity of calcaneus

Deltoid lig.

Tibionavicular lig.

Sustentaculum tali

Ant. tibiotalar lig.

Plantar calcaneonavicular (spring) lig.

Tibialis anterior m. tendon

Tibialis posterior m. tendon

Dorsal talonavicular lig.

Plantar calcaneocuboid lig.

Dorsal cuneonavicular lig.

Long plantar lig.

Flexor digitorum longus m. tendon

Dorsal tarsometatarsal lig.

Lateral plantar n.

2nd metatarsal bone

Flexor hallucis longus m. tendon

Collateral metatarsophalangeal lig.

Collateral interphalangeal lig.

Fibula

Tibia

Tendo calcaneus
(Achilles tendon)

Ant. tibiofibular lig.

Tibia

Post. tibiofibular lig.

Lateral malleolus

Post. talofibular lig.

Articular surface of talus

Superior fibular (peroneal) retinaculum

Extensor hallucis longus m. tendon

Calcaneofibular lig.

Ant. talofibular lig.

Calcaneus

Lateral talocalcaneal lig.

Fibularis [Peroneus] longus m. tendon (cut)

Dorsal talonavicular lig.

Long plantar lig.

Bifurcate lig.

Dorsal calcaneocuboid lig.

Calcaneonavicular part of bifurcate lig.

Calcaneocuboid part of bifurcate lig.

Dorsal cuboideonavicular lig.

Fibularis [Peroneus] brevis m. tendon

Dorsal cuneonavicular lig.

Dorsal tarsometatarsal lig.

Dorsal interosseous mm.

Flexor digiti minimi brevis m.

Collateral metatarsophalangeal lig.

Articular capsule

LATERAL VIEW

Collateral interphalangeal lig.

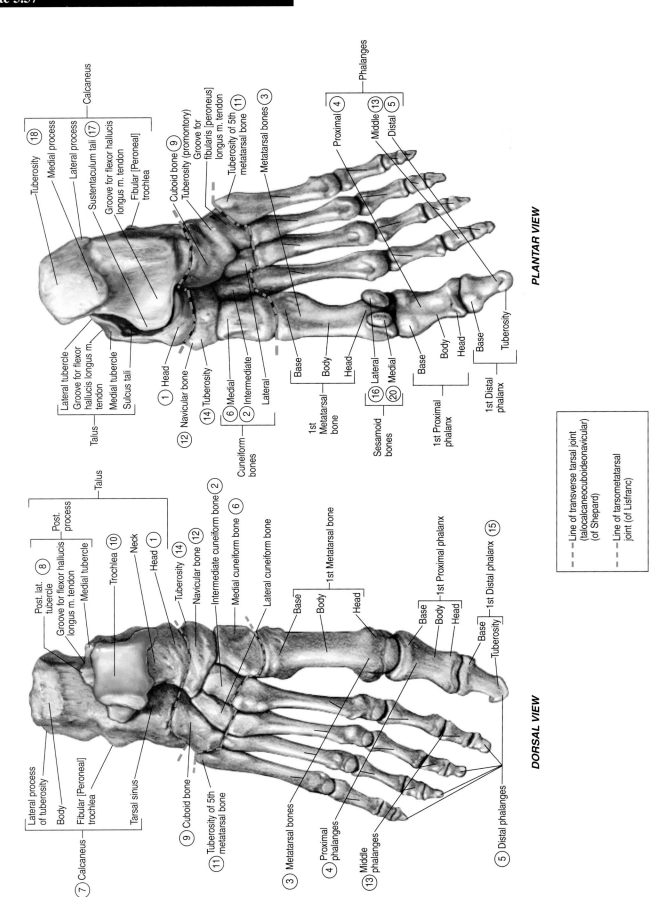

PLANTAR VIEW

Calcaneus
Tuberosity ⑱
Medial process
Lateral process
Sustentaculum tali ⑰
Groove for flexor hallucis longus m. tendon
Fibular [Peroneal] trochlea
Cuboid bone ⑨
Tuberosity (promontory)
Groove for fibularis [peroneus] longus m. tendon
Tuberosity of 5th metatarsal bone ⑪
Metatarsal bones ③
Phalanges
Proximal ④
Middle ⑬
Distal ⑤

Lateral tubercle
Groove for flexor hallucis longus m. tendon
Medial tubercle
Sulcus tali
Talus

① Head
Navicular bone ⑫
⑭ Tuberosity
⑥ Medial
② Intermediate
Lateral
Cuneiform bones

Base
Body
Head
1st Metatarsal bone

⑯ Lateral
⑳ Medial
Sesamoid bones

Base
Body
Head
1st Proximal phalanx

Base
Tuberosity
1st Distal phalanx

DORSAL VIEW

Talus
Post. lat. tubercle ⑧
Groove for flexor hallucis longus m. tendon
Medial tubercle
Post. process
Trochlea ⑩
Neck
Head ①
Tuberosity ⑭
Navicular bone ⑫
Intermediate cuneiform bone ②
Medial cuneiform bone ⑥
Lateral cuneiform bone

Base
Body
1st Metatarsal bone
Head

Base
Body
1st Proximal phalanx
Head

Base
1st Distal phalanx ⑮

Lateral process of tuberosity
Body
Fibular [Peroneal] trochlea
Tarsal sinus
⑦ Calcaneus

⑨ Cuboid bone
Tuberosity of 5th metatarsal bone ⑪

③ Metatarsal bones
④ Proximal phalanges
⑬ Middle phalanges
⑤ Distal phalanges

Base
Tuberosity

- - - Line of transverse tarsal joint (talocalcaneocuboideonavicular) (of Shepard)

- - - Line of tarsometatarsal joint (of Lisfranc)

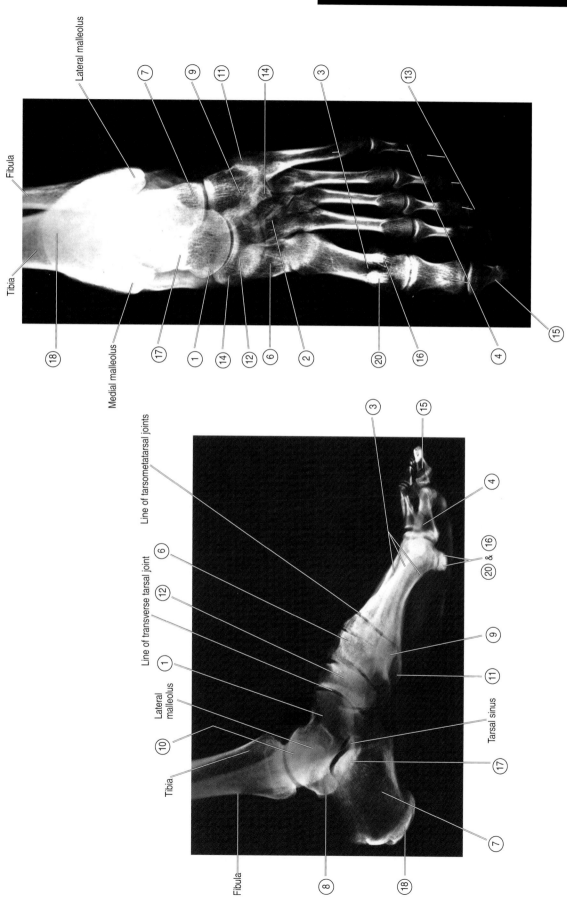

ANTEROPOSTERIOR VIEW

LATERAL VIEW

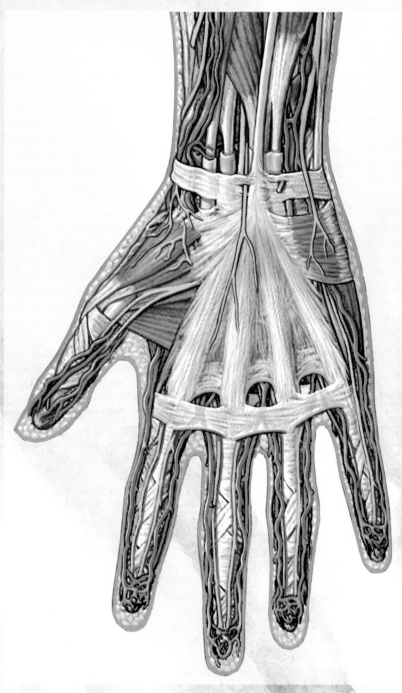

Upper Limb

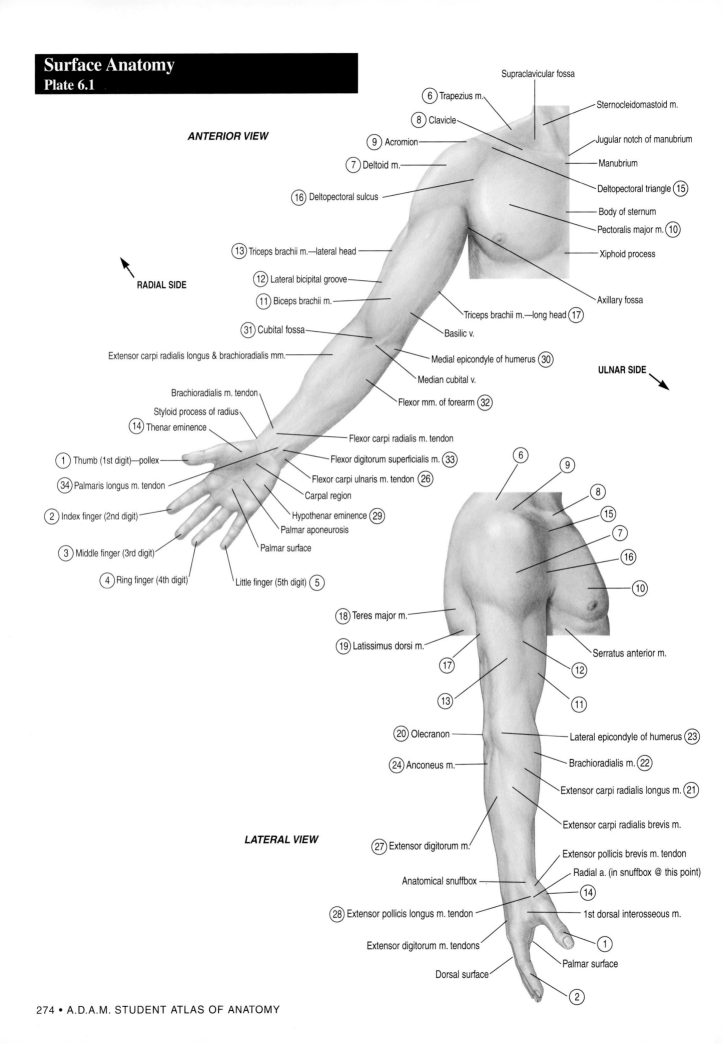

ANTERIOR VIEW

Supraclavicular fossa

⑥ Trapezius m.

⑧ Clavicle

Sternocleidomastoid m.

⑨ Acromion

Jugular notch of manubrium

⑦ Deltoid m.

Manubrium

⑯ Deltopectoral sulcus

Deltopectoral triangle ⑮

Body of sternum

Pectoralis major m. ⑩

⑬ Triceps brachii m.—lateral head

Xiphoid process

⑫ Lateral bicipital groove

⑪ Biceps brachii m.

Triceps brachii m.—long head ⑰

Axillary fossa

㉛ Cubital fossa

Basilic v.

Extensor carpi radialis longus & brachioradialis mm.

Medial epicondyle of humerus ㉚

Median cubital v.

RADIAL SIDE

Brachioradialis m. tendon

Flexor mm. of forearm ㉜

Styloid process of radius

⑭ Thenar eminence

Flexor carpi radialis m. tendon

ULNAR SIDE

① Thumb (1st digit)—pollex

Flexor digitorum superficialis m. ㉝

㉞ Palmaris longus m. tendon

Flexor carpi ulnaris m. tendon ㉖

② Index finger (2nd digit)

Carpal region

Hypothenar eminence ㉙

③ Middle finger (3rd digit)

Palmar aponeurosis

Palmar surface

④ Ring finger (4th digit)

Little finger (5th digit) ⑤

⑥   ⑨

⑧

⑮

⑦

⑯

⑩

⑱ Teres major m.

⑲ Latissimus dorsi m.

Serratus anterior m.

⑰

⑫

⑬

⑪

⑳ Olecranon

Lateral epicondyle of humerus ㉓

㉔ Anconeus m.

Brachioradialis m. ㉒

Extensor carpi radialis longus m. ㉑

Extensor carpi radialis brevis m.

㉗ Extensor digitorum m.

Extensor pollicis brevis m. tendon

Anatomical snuffbox

Radial a. (in snuffbox @ this point)

⑭

㉘ Extensor pollicis longus m. tendon

1st dorsal interosseous m.

①

Palmar surface

Extensor digitorum m. tendons

LATERAL VIEW

Dorsal surface

②

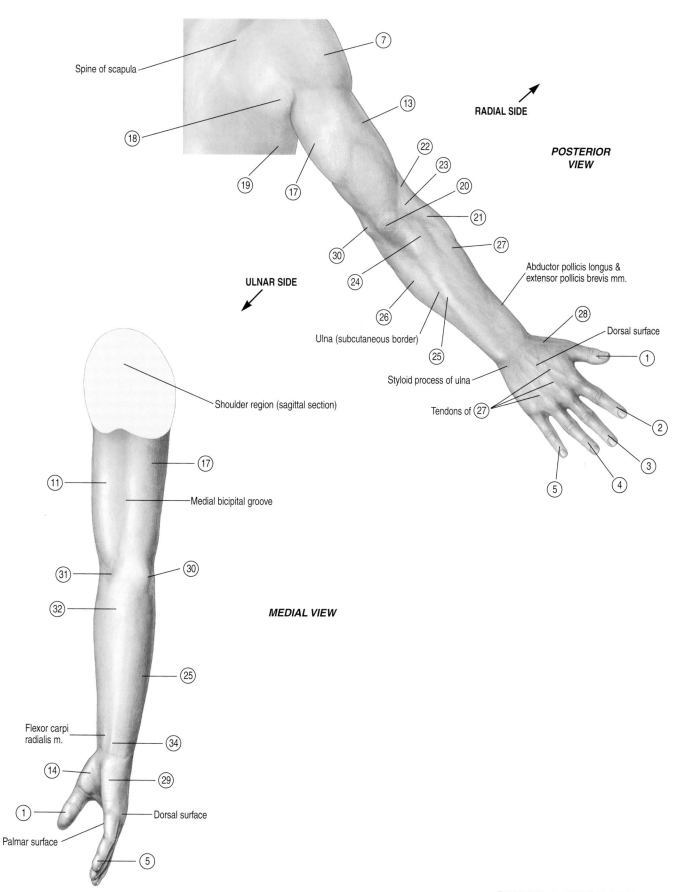

Spine of scapula

RADIAL SIDE

POSTERIOR VIEW

ULNAR SIDE

Abductor pollicis longus & extensor pollicis brevis mm.

Dorsal surface

Ulna (subcutaneous border)

Styloid process of ulna

Tendons of 27

Shoulder region (sagittal section)

Medial bicipital groove

MEDIAL VIEW

Flexor carpi radialis m.

Dorsal surface

Palmar surface

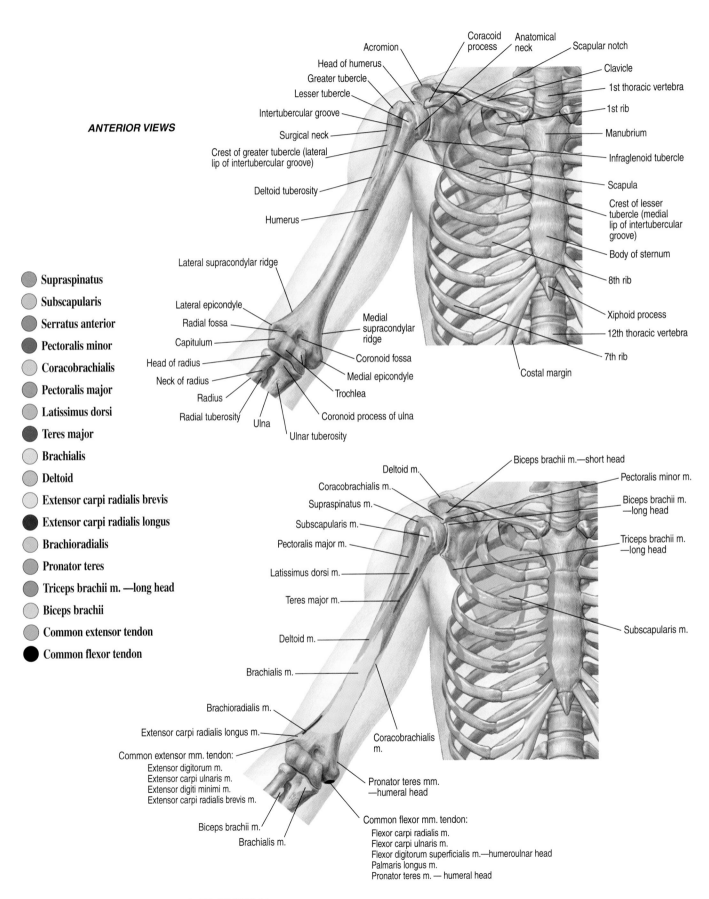

ANTERIOR VIEWS

Acromion
Coracoid process
Anatomical neck
Scapular notch
Head of humerus
Greater tubercle
Clavicle
Lesser tubercle
1st thoracic vertebra
Intertubercular groove
1st rib
Surgical neck
Manubrium
Crest of greater tubercle (lateral lip of intertubercular groove)
Infraglenoid tubercle
Deltoid tuberosity
Scapula
Crest of lesser tubercle (medial lip of intertubercular groove)
Humerus
Body of sternum
Lateral supracondylar ridge
8th rib
Lateral epicondyle
Xiphoid process
Radial fossa
Medial supracondylar ridge
12th thoracic vertebra
Capitulum
7th rib
Head of radius
Coronoid fossa
Neck of radius
Medial epicondyle
Costal margin
Radius
Trochlea
Radial tuberosity
Coronoid process of ulna
Ulna
Ulnar tuberosity

Supraspinatus
Subscapularis
Serratus anterior
Pectoralis minor
Coracobrachialis
Pectoralis major
Latissimus dorsi
Teres major
Brachialis
Deltoid
Extensor carpi radialis brevis
Extensor carpi radialis longus
Brachioradialis
Pronator teres
Triceps brachii m. —long head
Biceps brachii
Common extensor tendon
Common flexor tendon

Deltoid m.
Coracobrachialis m.
Supraspinatus m.
Subscapularis m.
Pectoralis major m.
Latissimus dorsi m.
Teres major m.
Deltoid m.
Brachialis m.
Brachioradialis m.
Extensor carpi radialis longus m.
Common extensor mm. tendon:
   Extensor digitorum m.
   Extensor carpi ulnaris m.
   Extensor digiti minimi m.
   Extensor carpi radialis brevis m.
Biceps brachii m.
Brachialis m.

Biceps brachii m.—short head
Pectoralis minor m.
Biceps brachii m. —long head
Triceps brachii m. —long head
Subscapularis m.
Coracobrachialis m.
Pronator teres mm. —humeral head
Common flexor mm. tendon:
   Flexor carpi radialis m.
   Flexor carpi ulnaris m.
   Flexor digitorum superficialis m.—humeroulnar head
   Palmaris longus m.
   Pronator teres m. — humeral head

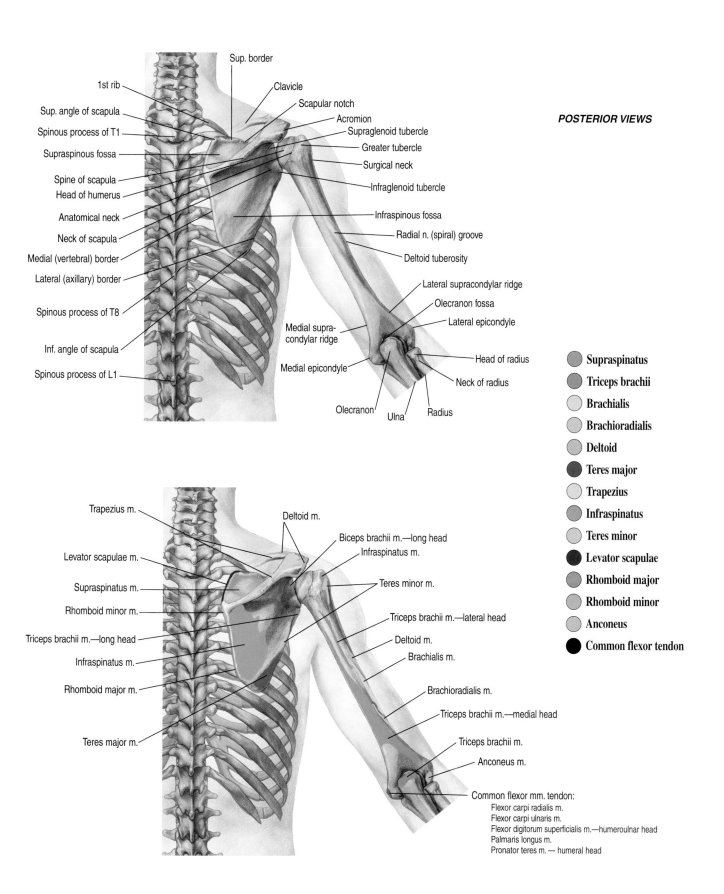

POSTERIOR VIEWS

Sup. border

1st rib

Clavicle

Sup. angle of scapula

Scapular notch

Spinous process of T1

Acromion

Supraspinous fossa

Supraglenoid tubercle

Greater tubercle

Spine of scapula

Surgical neck

Head of humerus

Infraglenoid tubercle

Anatomical neck

Infraspinous fossa

Neck of scapula

Radial n. (spiral) groove

Medial (vertebral) border

Deltoid tuberosity

Lateral (axillary) border

Lateral supracondylar ridge

Spinous process of T8

Olecranon fossa

Lateral epicondyle

Inf. angle of scapula

Medial supra-condylar ridge

Head of radius

Spinous process of L1

Medial epicondyle

Neck of radius

Olecranon   Ulna   Radius

Trapezius m.

Deltoid m.

Levator scapulae m.

Biceps brachii m.—long head

Infraspinatus m.

Supraspinatus m.

Teres minor m.

Rhomboid minor m.

Triceps brachii m.—lateral head

Triceps brachii m.—long head

Deltoid m.

Infraspinatus m.

Brachialis m.

Rhomboid major m.

Brachioradialis m.

Triceps brachii m.—medial head

Teres major m.

Triceps brachii m.

Anconeus m.

Common flexor mm. tendon:
  Flexor carpi radialis m.
  Flexor carpi ulnaris m.
  Flexor digitorum superficialis m.—humeroulnar head
  Palmaris longus m.
  Pronator teres m. — humeral head

Supraspinatus

Triceps brachii

Brachialis

Brachioradialis

Deltoid

Teres major

Trapezius

Infraspinatus

Teres minor

Levator scapulae

Rhomboid major

Rhomboid minor

Anconeus

Common flexor tendon

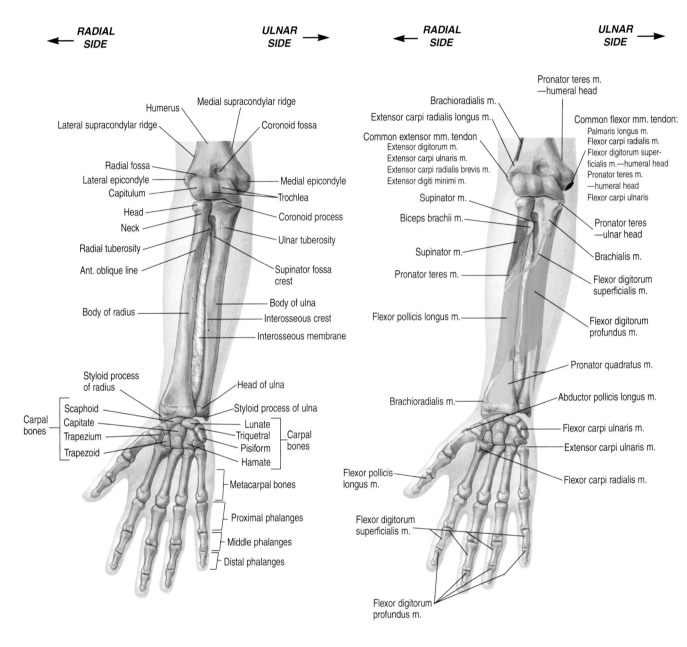

RADIAL SIDE ← ULNAR SIDE → RADIAL SIDE ← ULNAR SIDE →

Humerus
Lateral supracondylar ridge
Medial supracondylar ridge
Coronoid fossa
Radial fossa
Lateral epicondyle
Capitulum
Head
Neck
Radial tuberosity
Ant. oblique line
Medial epicondyle
Trochlea
Coronoid process
Ulnar tuberosity
Supinator fossa crest
Body of radius
Body of ulna
Interosseous crest
Interosseous membrane
Styloid process of radius
Head of ulna
Styloid process of ulna
Carpal bones
Scaphoid
Capitate
Trapezium
Trapezoid
Lunate
Triquetral
Pisiform
Hamate
Carpal bones
Metacarpal bones
Proximal phalanges
Middle phalanges
Distal phalanges

Pronator teres m. —humeral head
Brachioradialis m.
Extensor carpi radialis longus m.
Common extensor mm. tendon
Extensor digitorum m.
Extensor carpi ulnaris m.
Extensor carpi radialis brevis m.
Extensor digiti minimi m.
Common flexor mm. tendon:
Palmaris longus m.
Flexor carpi radialis m.
Flexor digitorum superficialis m.—humeral head
Pronator teres m. —humeral head
Flexor carpi ulnaris
Supinator m.
Biceps brachii m.
Supinator m.
Pronator teres m.
Pronator teres —ulnar head
Brachialis m.
Flexor digitorum superficialis m.
Flexor pollicis longus m.
Flexor digitorum profundus m.
Pronator quadratus m.
Brachioradialis m.
Abductor pollicis longus m.
Flexor carpi ulnaris m.
Extensor carpi ulnaris m.
Flexor carpi radialis m.
Flexor pollicis longus m.
Flexor digitorum superficialis m.
Flexor digitorum profundus m.

ANTERIOR VIEWS

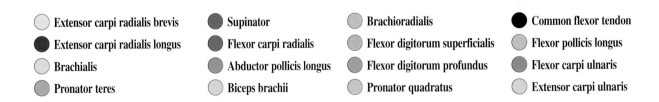

○ Extensor carpi radialis brevis
● Extensor carpi radialis longus
○ Brachialis
○ Pronator teres
● Supinator
● Flexor carpi radialis
○ Abductor pollicis longus
○ Biceps brachii
○ Brachioradialis
○ Flexor digitorum superficialis
○ Flexor digitorum profundus
○ Pronator quadratus
● Common flexor tendon
○ Flexor pollicis longus
○ Flexor carpi ulnaris
○ Extensor carpi ulnaris

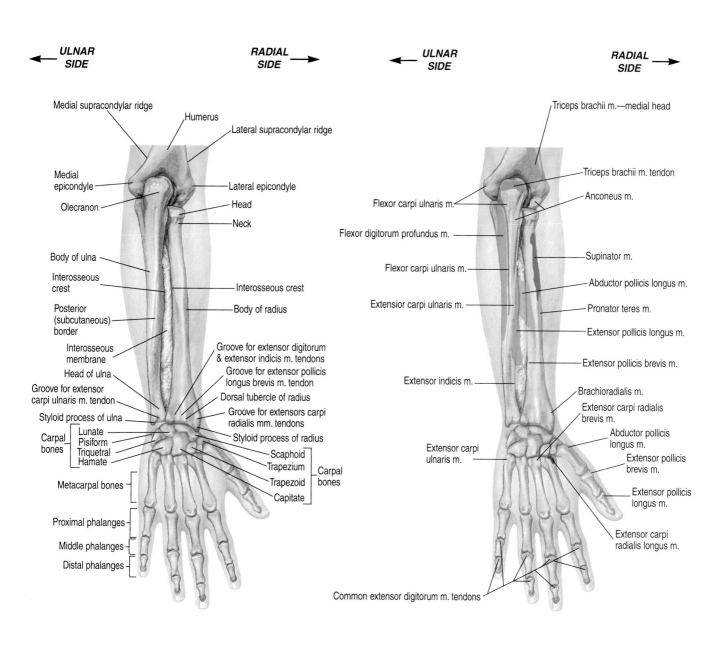

ULNAR SIDE ←   RADIAL SIDE →   ← ULNAR SIDE   RADIAL SIDE →

Medial supracondylar ridge

Humerus

Lateral supracondylar ridge

Medial epicondyle

Olecranon

Lateral epicondyle

Head

Neck

Body of ulna

Interosseous crest

Posterior (subcutaneous) border

Interosseous membrane

Head of ulna

Groove for extensor carpi ulnaris m. tendon

Styloid process of ulna

Carpal bones — Lunate, Pisiform, Triquetral, Hamate

Metacarpal bones

Proximal phalanges

Middle phalanges

Distal phalanges

Interosseous crest

Body of radius

Groove for extensor digitorum & extensor indicis m. tendons

Groove for extensor pollicis longus brevis m. tendon

Dorsal tubercle of radius

Groove for extensors carpi radialis mm. tendons

Styloid process of radius

Scaphoid
Trapezium
Trapezoid
Capitate
— Carpal bones

Triceps brachii m.—medial head

Triceps brachii m. tendon

Anconeus m.

Flexor carpi ulnaris m.

Flexor digitorum profundus m.

Flexor carpi ulnaris m.

Extensior carpi ulnaris m.

Supinator m.

Abductor pollicis longus m.

Pronator teres m.

Extensor pollicis longus m.

Extensor pollicis brevis m.

Extensor indicis m.

Brachioradialis m.

Extensor carpi radialis brevis m.

Abductor pollicis longus m.

Extensor pollicis brevis m.

Extensor pollicis longus m.

Extensor carpi ulnaris m.

Extensor carpi radialis longus m.

Common extensor digitorum m. tendons

POSTERIOR VIEWS

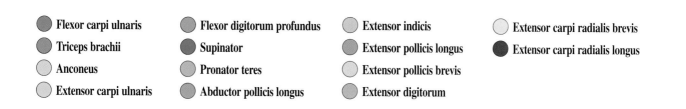

● Flexor carpi ulnaris   ● Flexor digitorum profundus   ● Extensor indicis   ● Extensor carpi radialis brevis
● Triceps brachii   ● Supinator   ● Extensor pollicis longus   ● Extensor carpi radialis longus
● Anconeus   ● Pronator teres   ● Extensor pollicis brevis
● Extensor carpi ulnaris   ● Abductor pollicis longus   ● Extensor digitorum

Pectoral & Scapular Muscles
Table 6.1

Muscles in Pectoral Region

Muscle	Proximal Attachment	Distal Attachment	Innervation[a]	Main Actions
Pectoralis major	*Clavicular head:* ant. surface of the medial half of clavicle *Sternocostal head:* ant. surface of sternum, sup. six costal cartilages & aponeurosis of ext. abdominal oblique muscle	Lateral lip of intertubercular groove of humerus	Lateral & medial pectoral n.: clavicular head (C5 & **C6**) Sternocostal head (**C7**, **C8**, & T1)	Adducts & medially rotates humerus Draws shoulder joint anteriorly & inferiorly *Acting alone:* Clavicular head flexes humerus & sternoclavicular head extends it
Pectoralis minor	Ribs 3–5 near their costal cartilages	Medial border & sup. surface of coracoid process of scapula	Medial pectoral n. (C8 & T1)	Stabilizes scapula by drawing it inferiorly & anteriorly against thoracic wall
Subclavius	Junction of rib 1 & its costal cartilage	Inf. surface of middle third of clavicle	N. to subclavius (**C5** & C6)	(Draws clavicle medially?)
Serratus anterior	Ext. surfaces of lateral parts of ribs 1–8/9	Ant. surface of medial border of scapula	Long thoracic n. (C5, **C6**, & **C7**)	Protracts scapula & holds it against thoracic wall; rotates scapula superiorly

Muscles Connecting Upper Limb to Vertebral Column

Muscle	Medial Attachment	Lateral Attachment	Innervation[a]	Main Actions
Trapezius	Medial third of sup. nuchal line; ext. occipital protuberance, ligamentum nuchae & spinous processes of C7–T12 vertebrae	Lateral thrid of clavicle, acromion & spine of scapula	Spinal root of accessory n. (CN XI) & cervical nn. (C3 & C4)	Elevates, retracts & rotates scapula; *sup. fibers* elevate, *middle fibers* retract, *inf. fibers* depress scapula; sup. & inf. fibers act together in sup. rotation of scapula
Latissimus dorsi	Spinous processes of the inf. six thoracic vertebrae, thoracolumbar fascia, iliac crest & inf. 3 or 4 ribs	Floor of intertubercular groove & crest of lesser tubercle of humerus	Thoracodorsal n. (**C6**, **C7**, & C8)	Extends, adducts & medially rotates humerus; raises body toward arms during climbing
Levator scapulae	Post. tubercles of transverse processes of C1–C4 vertebrae	Sup. part of medial border of scapula	Dorsal scapular (C5) & cervical (C3 & C4) nn.	Elevates scapula & tilts its glenoid cavity inferiorly by rotating scapula
Rhomboid minor & major	*Minor:* Ligamentum nuchae & spinous processes of C7 & T1 vertebrae *Major:* Spinous processes of T2–T5 vertebrae	Medial border of scapula from level of spine to inf. angle	Dorsal scapular n. (C4 & **C5**) rotate	Retracts scapula & rotates it to depress glenoid cavity; fixes scapula to thoracic wall

[a]In this and subsequent tables, the numbers indicate the spinal cord segmental innervation of the nerves (*e.g.,* C5 and C6 indicate that the nerves supplying the clavicular head of the pectoralis major muscle are derived from the 5th and 6th cervical segments of the spinal cord). **Boldface** indicates the main segmental innervation. Damage to these segments of the spinal cord, or to the motor nerve roots arising from them, results in paralysis of the muscles concerned.

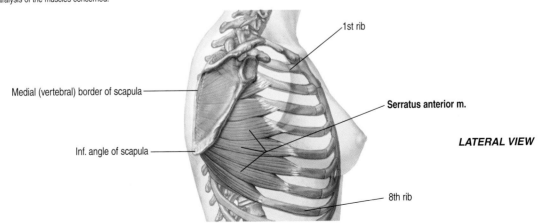

1st rib

Medial (vertebral) border of scapula

Serratus anterior m.

LATERAL VIEW

Inf. angle of scapula

8th rib

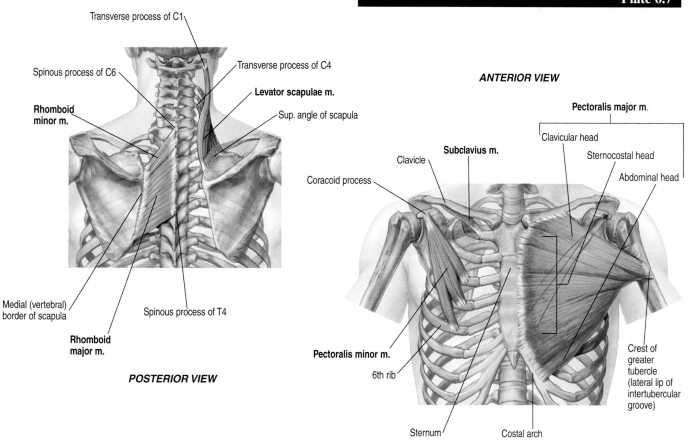

Transverse process of C1

Transverse process of C4

Spinous process of C6

Levator scapulae m.

Rhomboid minor m.

Sup. angle of scapula

ANTERIOR VIEW

Pectoralis major m.

Clavicular head

Subclavius m.

Sternocostal head

Clavicle

Abdominal head

Coracoid process

Medial (vertebral) border of scapula

Spinous process of T4

Rhomboid major m.

POSTERIOR VIEW

Pectoralis minor m.

6th rib

Sternum

Costal arch

Crest of greater tubercle (lateral lip of intertubercular groove)

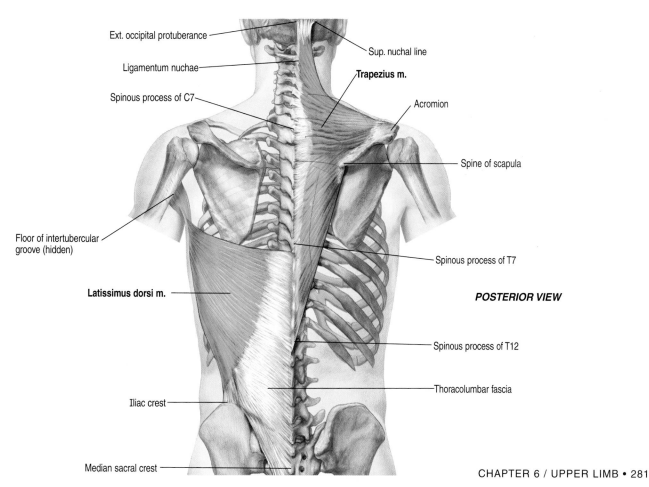

Ext. occipital protuberance

Sup. nuchal line

Ligamentum nuchae

Trapezius m.

Spinous process of C7

Acromion

Spine of scapula

Floor of intertubercular groove (hidden)

Spinous process of T7

Latissimus dorsi m.

POSTERIOR VIEW

Spinous process of T12

Thoracolumbar fascia

Iliac crest

Median sacral crest

Scapular & Posterior Arm Muscles
Table 6.2

Scapular Muscles

Muscle	Proximal/Medial Attachment	Distal/Lateral Attachment	Innervation[a]	Main Actions
Deltoid	Lateral third of clavicle, acromion & spine of scapula	Deltoid tuberosity of humerus	Axillary n. (**C5** & **C6**)	*Anterior part:* flexes & medially rotates arm *Middle part:* abducts arm *Posterior part:* extends & laterally rotates arm
Supraspinatus[a]	Supraspinous fossa of scapula	Sup. facet on greater tubercle of humerus	Suprascapular n. (C4, **C5** & C6)	Helps deltoid to abduct arm & acts with rotator cuff muscles[a]
Infraspinatus[a]	Infraspinous fossa of scapula	Middle facet on greater tubercle of humerus	Suprascapular n. (C4, **C5** & C6)	Laterally rotate arm; help to hold humeral head in glenoid cavity of scapula
Teres minor[a]	Sup. part of lateral border of scapula	Inf. facet on greater tubercle of humerus	Axillary n. (**C5** & C6)	
Teres major	Dorsal surface of inf. angle of scapula	Medial lip of intertubular groove of humerus	Lower subscapular n. (**C6** & C7)	Adducts & medially rotates arm
Subscapularis[a]	Subscapular fossa	Lesser tubercle of humerus	Upper & lower subscapular nn. (C5, **C6** & C7)	Medially rotates arm & adducts it; helps to hold humeral head in glenoid cavity

[a] Collectively, the supraspinatus, infraspinatus, teres minor, and subscapularis muscles are referred to as the **rotator cuff muscles**. Their prime function during all movements of the shoulder joint is to hold the head of the humerus in the glenoid cavity of the scapula.

Posterior Arm Muscles

Muscle	Proximal Attachment	Distal Attachment	Innervation	Main Actions
Triceps brachii	*Long head:* infraglenoid tubercle of scapula *Lateral head:* post. surface of humerus, sup. to radial n. groove *Medial head:* post. surface of humerus, inf. to radial n. groove	Proximal end of olecranon ulna & fascia of forearm	Radial n. (**C6, C7,** & C8)	Extends the forearm; it is *chief extensor of forearm*, long head steadies head of abducted humerus
Anconeus	Lateral epicondyle of humerus	Lateral surface of olecranon & sup. part of post. surface of ulna	Radial n. (C7, C8 & T1)	Assists triceps in extending forearm; stabilizes elbow joint; abducts ulna during pronation

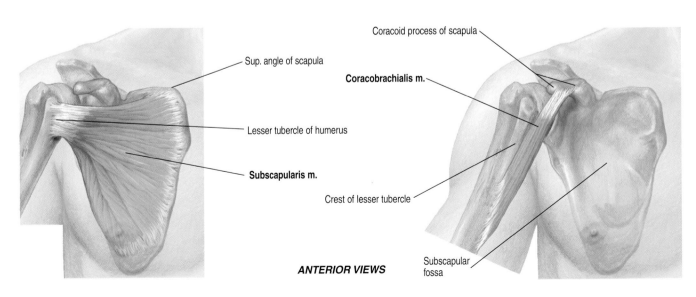

Sup. angle of scapula

Lesser tubercle of humerus

Subscapularis m.

Coracoid process of scapula

Coracobrachialis m.

Crest of lesser tubercle

Subscapular fossa

ANTERIOR VIEWS

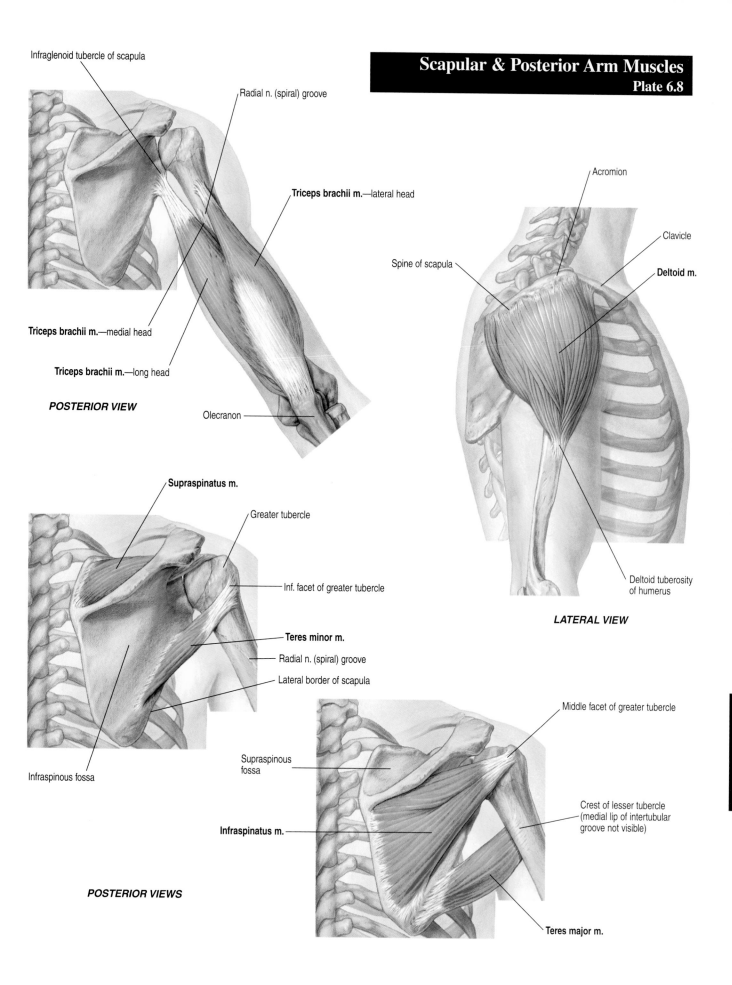

Infraglenoid tubercle of scapula

Radial n. (spiral) groove

Triceps brachii m.—lateral head

Triceps brachii m.—medial head

Triceps brachii m.—long head

POSTERIOR VIEW

Olecranon

Acromion

Clavicle

Deltoid m.

Spine of scapula

Deltoid tuberosity of humerus

LATERAL VIEW

Supraspinatus m.

Greater tubercle

Inf. facet of greater tubercle

Teres minor m.

Radial n. (spiral) groove

Lateral border of scapula

Infraspinous fossa

Supraspinous fossa

Infraspinatus m.

POSTERIOR VIEWS

Middle facet of greater tubercle

Crest of lesser tubercle (medial lip of intertubular groove not visible)

Teres major m.

Anterior Arm & Forearm Muscles
Table 6.3

Muscles of Anterior Arm

Muscle	Proximal Attachment	Distal Attachment	Innervation[a]	Main Actions
Biceps brachii	*Short head:* Tip of coracoid process of scapula *Long head:* Supraglenoid tubercle of scapula	Tuberosity of radius & fascia of forearm via bicipital aponeurosis	Musculocutaneous n. (C5 & **C6**)	Supinates forearm and, when it is supine, flexes forearm
Brachialis	Distal half of ant. surface of humerus	Coronoid process & tuberosity of ulna		Flexes forearm in all positions
Coracobrachialis	Tip of coracoid process of scapula	Middle third of medial surface of humerus	Musculocutaneous n. (C5, **C6** & C7)	Helps to flex & adduct arm

Superficial and Intermediate Layers of Muscles on Anterior Surface of Forearm[a]

Muscle	Proximal Attachment	Distal Attachment	Innervation[b]	Main Actions
Pronator teres	Medial epicondyle of humerus & coronoid process of ulna	Middle of lateral surface of radius	Median n. (C6 & **C7**)	Pronates forearm & flexes it
Flexor carpi radialis	Medial epicondyle of humerus	Base of 2nd metacarpal bone		Flexes hand & abducts it radially
Palmaris longus	Medial epicondyle of humerus	Distal half of flexor retinanculum & palmar aponeurosis	Median n. (C7 & C8)	Flexes hand & tightens palmar aponeurosis
Flexor carpi ulnaris[b]	*Humeral head:* medial epicondyle of humerus *Ulnar head:* olecranon & post. border of ulna	Pisiform bone (hook of hamate bone & 5th metacarpal bone)	Ulnar n. (C7 & **C8**)	Flexes hand & adducts it ulnarly
Flexor digitorum superficialis[c]	*Humeroulnar head:* medial epicondyle of humerus, ulnar collateral lig. & coronoid process of ulna *Radial head:* sup. half of ant. border of radius	Bodies of the middle phalanges of medial four digits	Median n. (C7, **C8** & T1)	Flexes middle phalanges of medial four digits: acting more strongly, it flexes proximal phalanges & hand

[a]The superficial muscles of the *flexor-pronator group* are attached, in whole or in part, to the anterior surface of the medial epicondyle by a *common flexor tendon.*
[b]In contrast to the other superficial flexor muscles, the flexor carpi ulnaris is supplied by the ulnar nerve.
[c]This muscle comprises the *intermediate muscle layer* in the anterior part of the forearm. In some clinical texts, this muscle is referred to by its old name, "flexor digitorum sublimis."

Deep Layer of Muscles on Anterior Surface of Forearm

Muscle	Proximal Attachment	Distal Attachment	Innervation	Main Actions
Pronator quadratus	Distal fourth of ant. surface of ulna	Distal fourth of ant. surface of radius	Ant. interosseous n. from median (**C8** & T1)	Pronates forearm; deep fibers bind radius & ulna together

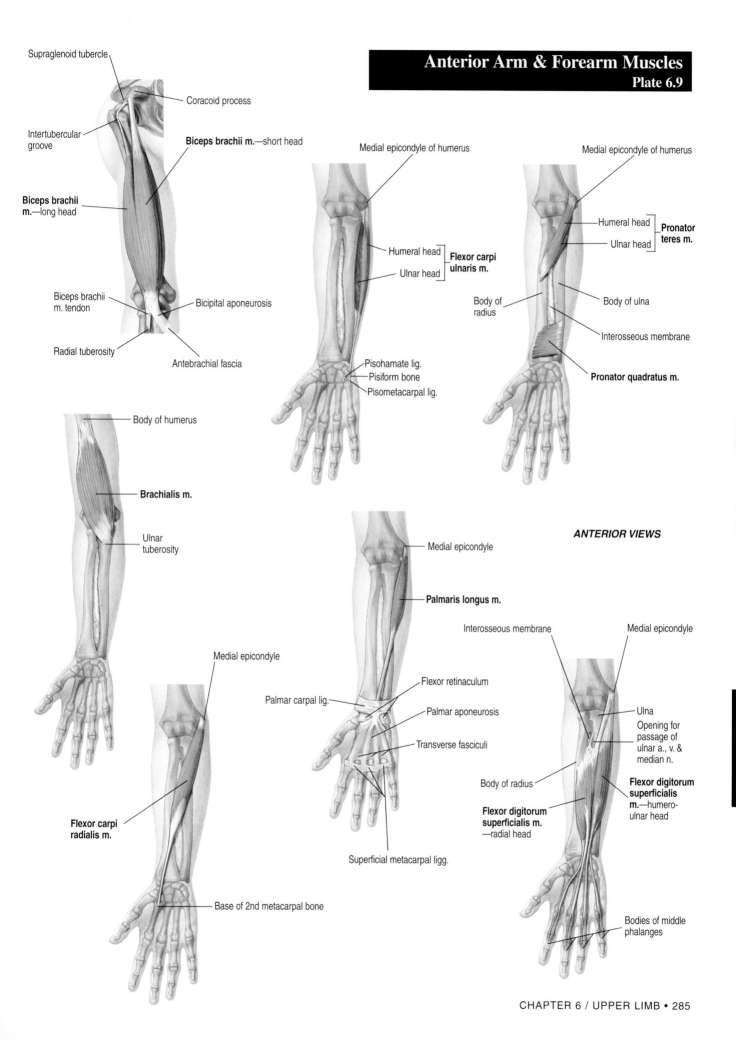

Supraglenoid tubercle

Coracoid process

Intertubercular groove

Biceps brachii m.—short head

Biceps brachii m.—long head

Biceps brachii m. tendon

Bicipital aponeurosis

Radial tuberosity

Antebrachial fascia

Medial epicondyle of humerus

Humeral head
Ulnar head
Flexor carpi ulnaris m.

Pisohamate lig.
Pisiform bone
Pisometacarpal lig.

Medial epicondyle of humerus

Humeral head
Ulnar head
Pronator teres m.

Body of radius

Body of ulna

Interosseous membrane

Pronator quadratus m.

Body of humerus

Brachialis m.

Ulnar tuberosity

ANTERIOR VIEWS

Medial epicondyle

Palmaris longus m.

Palmar carpal lig.

Flexor retinaculum

Palmar aponeurosis

Transverse fasciculi

Superficial metacarpal ligg.

Interosseous membrane

Medial epicondyle

Ulna

Opening for passage of ulnar a., v. & median n.

Flexor digitorum superficialis m.—humero-ulnar head

Body of radius

Flexor digitorum superficialis m. —radial head

Bodies of middle phalanges

Medial epicondyle

Flexor carpi radialis m.

Base of 2nd metacarpal bone

Forearm Muscles
Table 6.4

Deep Layer of Muscles on Anterior Surface of Forearm

Muscle	Proximal Attachment	Distal Attachment	Innervation	Main Actions
Flexor digitorum profundus	Proximal three-fourths of medial & ant. surfaces of ulna & interosseous membrane	Bases of distal phalanges of medial four digits	*Medial part:* Ulnar n. (**C8** & T1) *Lateral part:* Median n. (**C8** & T1)	Flexes distal phalanges of medial four digits (fingers)
Flexor pollicis longus	Ant. surface of the distal radius & adjacent interosseous membrane	Base of distal phalanx of thumb	Ant. interosseous n. from median (**C8** & T1)	Flexes phalanges of first digit (thumb)

Superficial Muscles on Posterior or Extensor Surface of Forearm

Muscle	Proximal Attachment	Distal Attachment	Innervation	Main Actions
Brachioradialis	Proximal two-thirds of lateral supracondylar ridge of humerus, lat. intermuscular septum	Lateral surface of distal end of radius	Radial n. (C5, **C6** & C7)	Flexes forearm
Extensor carpi radialis longus	Lateral supracondylar ridge of humerus, lat. intermuscular septum	Base of 2nd metacarpal bone	Radial n. (C6 & C7)	Extend & abduct hand at wrist joint
Extensor carpi radialis brevis	Lateral epicondyle of humerus	Base of 3rd metacarpal bone	Deep br. of radial n. (**C7** & C8)	Extend & abduct hand at wrist joint
Extensor digitorum	Lateral epicondyle of humerus	Extensor expansions of medial four digits	Post. interosseous n. (**C7** & C8), a br. of the radial n.	Extends medial four digits at metacarpophalangeal joints; extends hand at wrist joint
Extensor carpi ulnaris	Lateral epicondyle of humerus & post. border of ulna	Base of 5th metacarpal bone	Post. interosseous n. (**C7** & C8), a br. of the radial n.	Extends & adducts hand at wrist joint

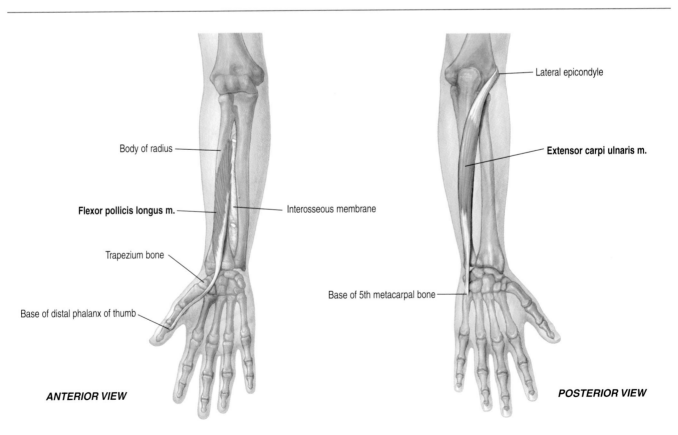

ANTERIOR VIEW

Body of radius

Flexor pollicis longus m.

Trapezium bone

Base of distal phalanx of thumb

Interosseous membrane

Lateral epicondyle

Extensor carpi ulnaris m.

Base of 5th metacarpal bone

POSTERIOR VIEW

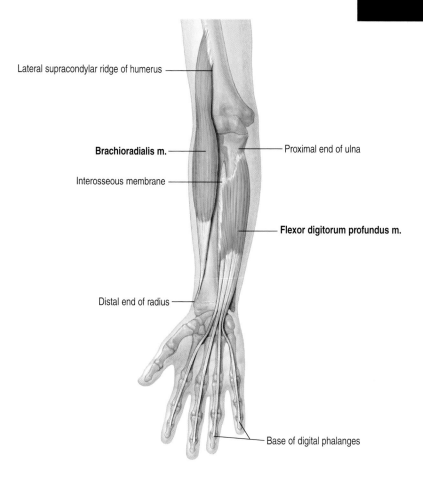

Lateral supracondylar ridge of humerus

Brachioradialis m.

Interosseous membrane

Distal end of radius

Proximal end of ulna

Flexor digitorum profundus m.

Base of digital phalanges

ANTERIOR VIEW

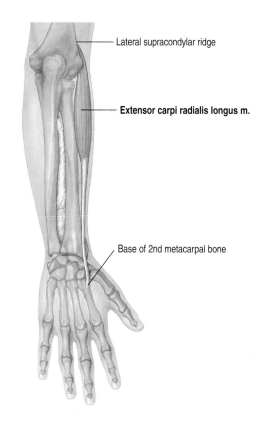

Lateral supracondylar ridge

Extensor carpi radialis longus m.

Base of 2nd metacarpal bone

POSTERIOR VIEW

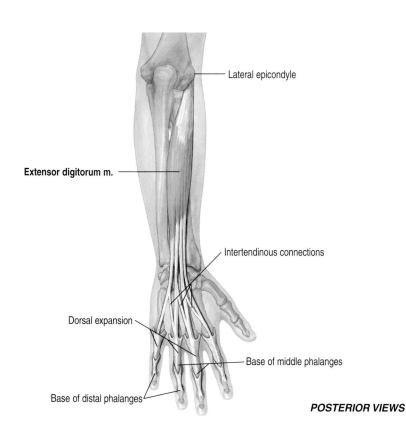

Lateral epicondyle

Extensor digitorum m.

Intertendinous connections

Dorsal expansion

Base of middle phalanges

Base of distal phalanges

POSTERIOR VIEWS

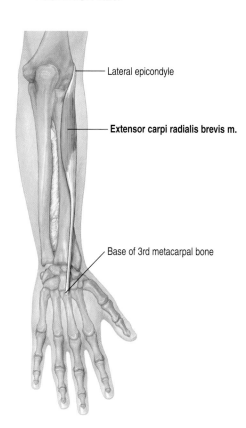

Lateral epicondyle

Extensor carpi radialis brevis m.

Base of 3rd metacarpal bone

Posterior Forearm Muscles
Table 6.5

Deep Muscles on Posterior or Extensor Surface of Forearm

Muscle	Proximal Attachment	Distal Attachment	Innervation	Main Actions
Supinator	Lateral epicondyle of humerus, radial collateral & anular ligaments, supinator fossa & crest of ulna	Lateral, post. & ant. surfaces of proximal third of radius	Deep br. of radial n. (C5 & **C6**)	Supinates forearm, *i.e.,* rotates radius to turn palm anteriorly
Abductor pollicis longus	Post. surfaces of ulna & radius & interosseous membrane	Base of 1st metacarpal bone	Post. interosseous n. (C7 & **C8**)	Abducts thumb & extends it at carpometacarpal joint
Extensor pollicis brevis	Post. surface of radius & interosseous membrane	Base of proximal phalanx of thumb		Extends proximal phalanx of thumb at carpometacarpal joint
Extensor pollicis longus	Post. surface of middle third of ulnar & interosseous membrane	Base of distal phalanx of thumb		Extends distal phalanx of thumb at metacarpophalangeal & interphalangeal joints
Extensor indicis	Post. surface of ulna & interosseous membrane	Extensor expansion of second digit (index finger)		Extends digit 2 & helps to extend wrist
Extensor digiti minimi	Lateral epicondyle of humerus	Extensor expansion of 5th digit	Post. interosseous n. (**C7** & C8), a br. of the radial n.	Extends digit 5 at metacarpophalangeal & interphalangeal joints

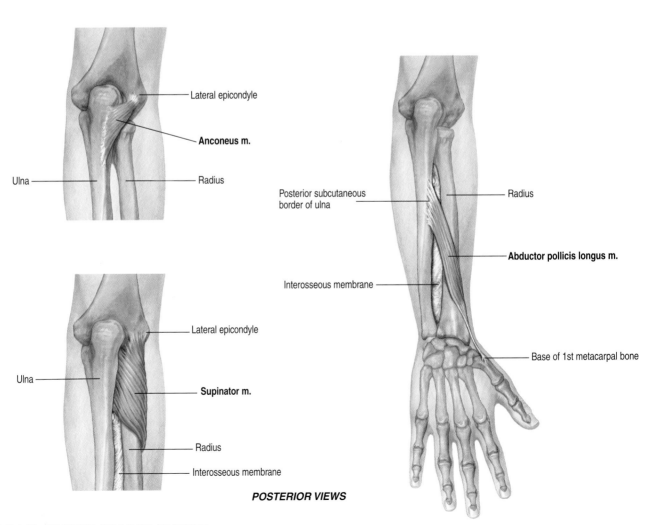

Lateral epicondyle

Anconeus m.

Ulna — Radius

Lateral epicondyle

Ulna

Supinator m.

Radius

Interosseous membrane

Posterior subcutaneous border of ulna

Radius

Abductor pollicis longus m.

Interosseous membrane

Base of 1st metacarpal bone

POSTERIOR VIEWS

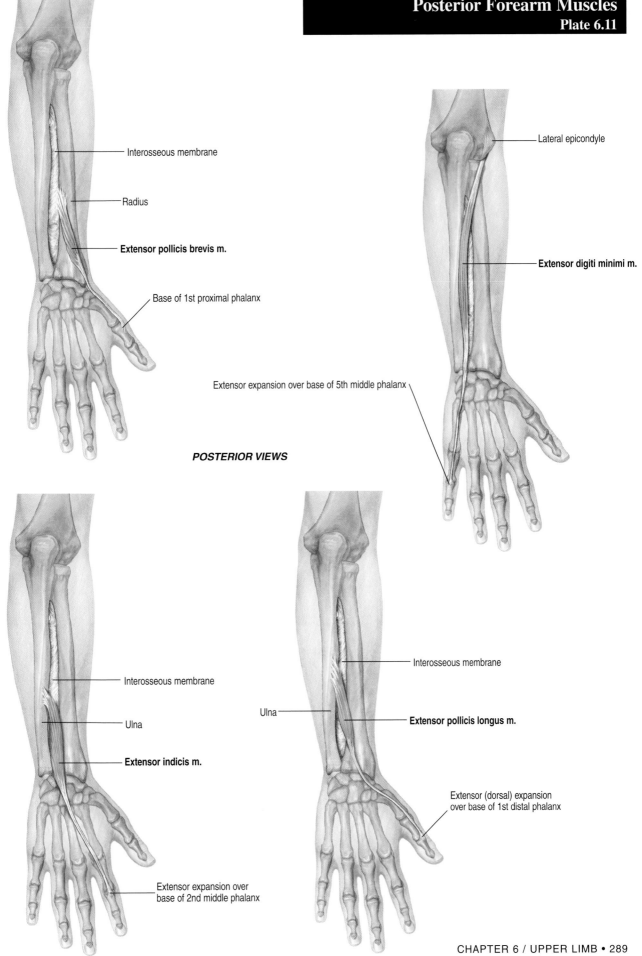

Interosseous membrane

Radius

Extensor pollicis brevis m.

Base of 1st proximal phalanx

Lateral epicondyle

Extensor digiti minimi m.

Extensor expansion over base of 5th middle phalanx

POSTERIOR VIEWS

Interosseous membrane

Ulna

Extensor indicis m.

Extensor expansion over
base of 2nd middle phalanx

Interosseous membrane

Ulna

Extensor pollicis longus m.

Extensor (dorsal) expansion
over base of 1st distal phalanx

Intrinsic Hand Muscles
Table 6.6

Short Muscles of Hand

Muscle	Proximal Attachment	Distal Attachment	Innervation	Main Actions
Lumbricalis 1 & 2	Lateral two tendons of flexor digitorum profundus	Lateral sides of extensor expansions of digits 2 to 5	*Lumbricals 1 & 2,* median n. (C8 & **T1**)	Flex digits at metacarpophalangeal joints & extend interphalangeal joints
Lumbricalis 3 & 4	Medial three tendons of flexor digitorum profundus		*Lumbricals 3 & 4,* deep br. of ulnar n. (C8 & **T1**)	
Dorsal interossei 1–4	Adjacent sides of two metacarpal bones	Extensor expansions & bases of proximal phalanges of digits 2–4	Deep br. of ulnar n. (C8 & **T1**)	Abduct digits 2–4
Palmar interossei 1–3	Palmar surfaces of 1st, 2nd, 4th & 5th metacarpal bones	Extensor expansions of digits and bases of proximal phalanges of digits 1, 2, 4 & 5		Adduct digits 2–4
Abductor digiti minimi	Pisiform bone	Medial side of base of proximal phalanx of digit 5 (little finger)	Deep br. of ulnar n. (C8 & **T1**)	Abducts digit 5 (little finger)
Flexor digiti minimi brevis	Hook of hamate bone & flexor retinaculum			Flexes proximal phalanx of digit 5
Opponens digiti minimi		Medial border of 5th metacarpal bone		Draws 5th metacarpal bone anteriorly & rotates it, bringing digit 5 into opposition with thumb
Abductor pollicis brevis	Flexor retinaculum & tubercles of scaphoid & trapezium bones	Lateral side of base of proximal phalanx of thumb	Recurrent br. of median n. (**C8** & T1)	Abducts thumb & helps oppose it
Flexor pollicis brevis	Flexor retinaculum & tubercle of trapezium bone			Flexes thumb
Opponens pollicis		Lateral side of 1st metacarpal bone		Opposes thumb toward center of palm & rotates it medially
Adductor pollicis	*Oblique head:* Bases of 2nd & 3rd metacarpals, captate & adjacent carpal bones *Transverse head:* Ant. surface of body of 3rd metacarpal bone	Medial side of base of proximal phalanx of thumb	Deep br. of ulnar n. (C8 & **T1**)	Adducts thumb toward middle digit

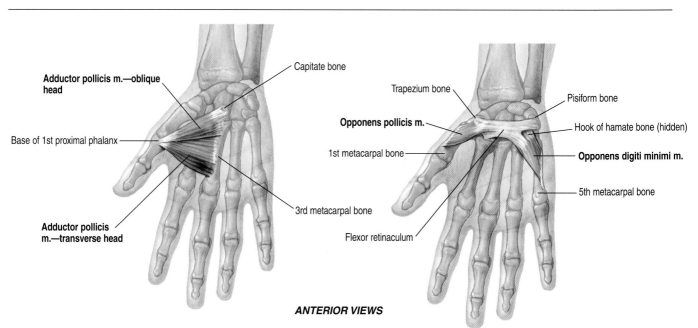

ANTERIOR VIEWS

Adductor pollicis m.—oblique head

Capitate bone

Base of 1st proximal phalanx

Adductor pollicis m.—transverse head

3rd metacarpal bone

Trapezium bone

Pisiform bone

Opponens pollicis m.

Hook of hamate bone (hidden)

1st metacarpal bone

Opponens digiti minimi m.

5th metacarpal bone

Flexor retinaculum

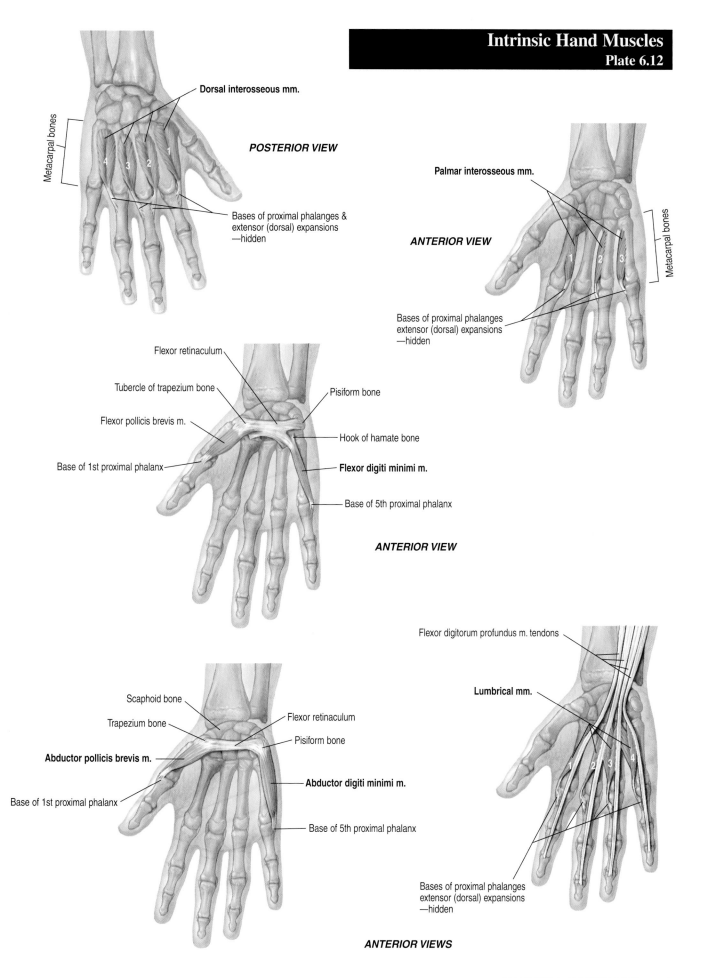

Dorsal interosseous mm.

POSTERIOR VIEW

Metacarpal bones

4 3 2 1

Bases of proximal phalanges &
extensor (dorsal) expansions
—hidden

Palmar interosseous mm.

ANTERIOR VIEW

1 2 3

Metacarpal bones

Bases of proximal phalanges
extensor (dorsal) expansions
—hidden

Flexor retinaculum

Tubercle of trapezium bone

Flexor pollicis brevis m.

Base of 1st proximal phalanx

Pisiform bone

Hook of hamate bone

Flexor digiti minimi m.

Base of 5th proximal phalanx

ANTERIOR VIEW

Flexor digitorum profundus m. tendons

Lumbrical mm.

1 2 3 4

Scaphoid bone

Trapezium bone

Abductor pollicis brevis m.

Base of 1st proximal phalanx

Flexor retinaculum

Pisiform bone

Abductor digiti minimi m.

Base of 5th proximal phalanx

Bases of proximal phalanges
extensor (dorsal) expansions
—hidden

ANTERIOR VIEWS

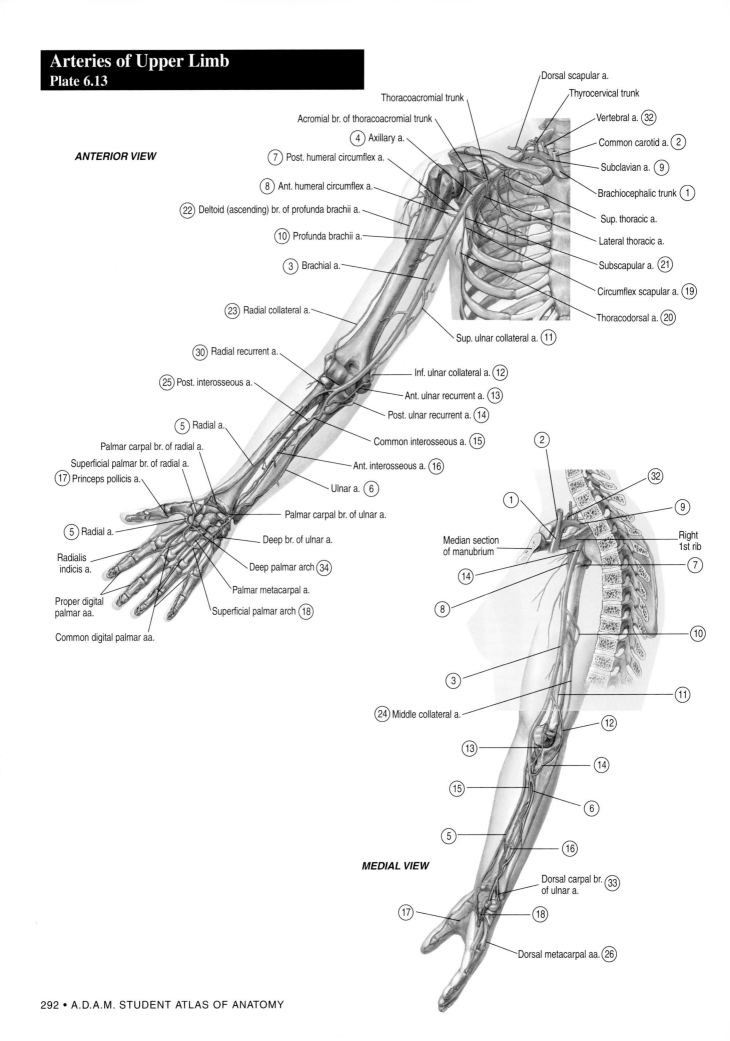

ANTERIOR VIEW

Dorsal scapular a.
Thoracoacromial trunk
Thyrocervical trunk
Acromial br. of thoracoacromial trunk
Vertebral a. (32)
(4) Axillary a.
Common carotid a. (2)
(7) Post. humeral circumflex a.
Subclavian a. (9)
(8) Ant. humeral circumflex a.
Brachiocephalic trunk (1)
(22) Deltoid (ascending) br. of profunda brachii a.
Sup. thoracic a.
(10) Profunda brachii a.
Lateral thoracic a.
(3) Brachial a.
Subscapular a. (21)
Circumflex scapular a. (19)
(23) Radial collateral a.
Thoracodorsal a. (20)
Sup. ulnar collateral a. (11)
(30) Radial recurrent a.
Inf. ulnar collateral a. (12)
(25) Post. interosseous a.
Ant. ulnar recurrent a. (13)
Post. ulnar recurrent a. (14)
(5) Radial a.
Common interosseous a. (15)
Palmar carpal br. of radial a.
Ant. interosseous a. (16)
Superficial palmar br. of radial a.
Ulnar a. (6)
(17) Princeps pollicis a.
Palmar carpal br. of ulnar a.
(5) Radial a.
Deep br. of ulnar a.
Radialis indicis a.
Deep palmar arch (34)
Palmar metacarpal a.
Proper digital palmar aa.
Superficial palmar arch (18)
Common digital palmar aa.

(2)
(32)
(1)
(9)
Median section of manubrium
Right 1st rib
(14)
(7)
(8)
(10)
(3)
(11)
(24) Middle collateral a.
(12)
(13)
(14)
(15)
(6)
(5)
(16)
MEDIAL VIEW
Dorsal carpal br. (33) of ulnar a.
(17)
(18)
Dorsal metacarpal aa. (26)

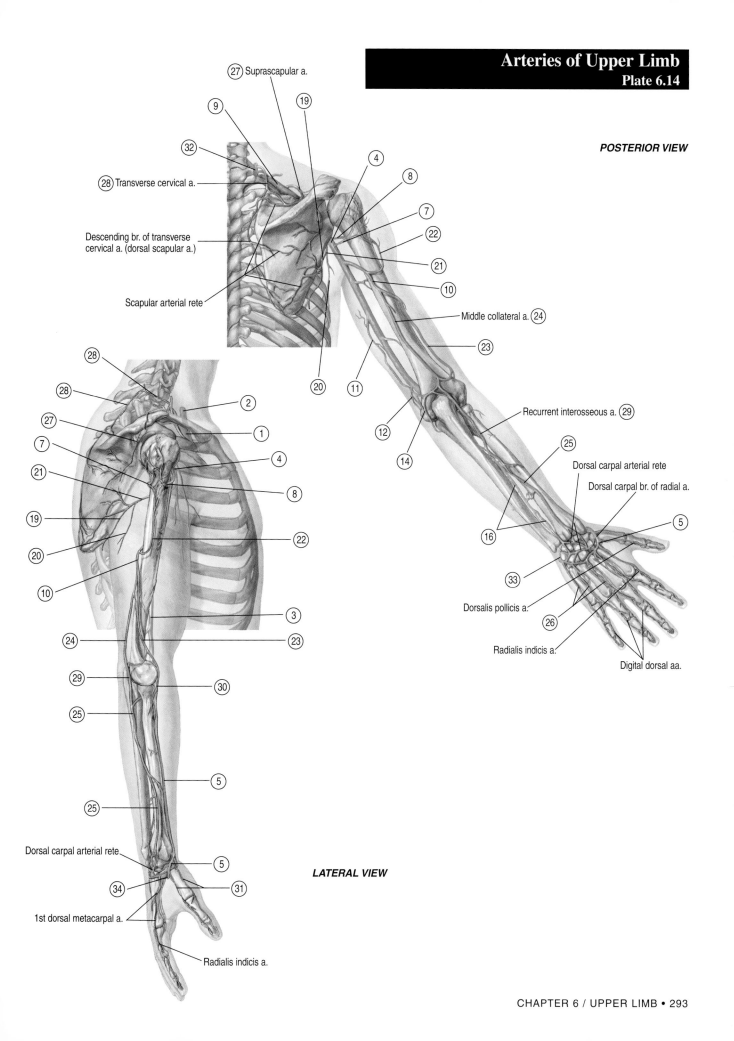

㉗ Suprascapular a.

⑨

⑲

POSTERIOR VIEW

㉜

㉘ Transverse cervical a.

④

⑧

⑦

㉒

㉑

⑩

Descending br. of transverse
cervical a. (dorsal scapular a.)

Scapular arterial rete

Middle collateral a. ㉔

㉓

⑳

⑪

Recurrent interosseous a. ㉙

㉘

㉘

⑫

㉕

②

⑭

Dorsal carpal arterial rete

㉗

①

Dorsal carpal br. of radial a.

⑦

④

㉑

⑧

⑲

⑤

⑳

㉒

⑯

⑩

③

㉝

㉓

Dorsalis pollicis a.

㉔

㉖

㉙

㉚

Radialis indicis a.

㉕

Digital dorsal aa.

⑤

㉕

Dorsal carpal arterial rete

LATERAL VIEW

⑤

㉞

㉛

1st dorsal metacarpal a.

Radialis indicis a.

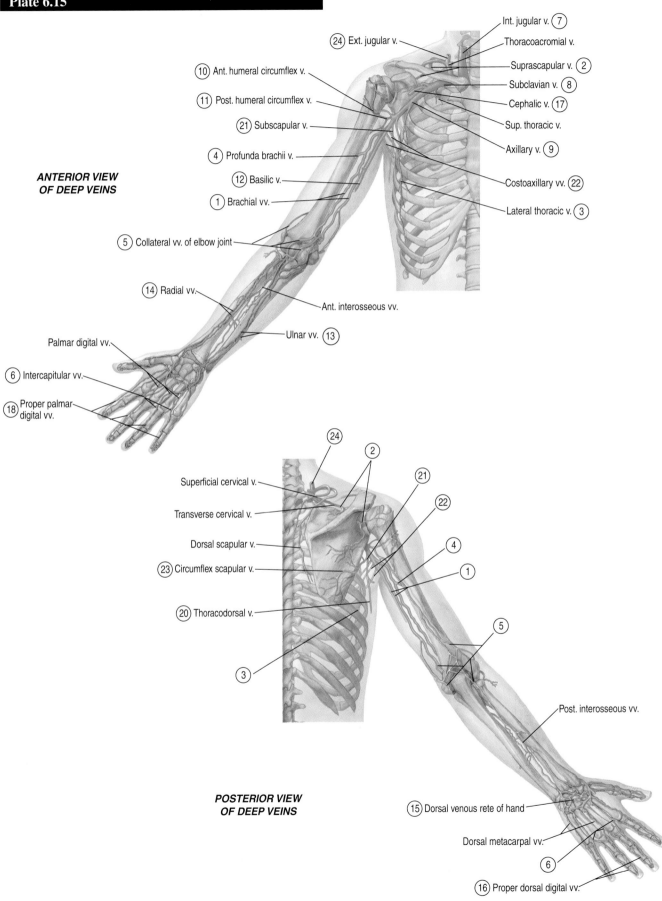

ANTERIOR VIEW OF DEEP VEINS

- (24) Ext. jugular v.
- Int. jugular v. (7)
- Thoracoacromial v.
- (10) Ant. humeral circumflex v.
- Suprascapular v. (2)
- (11) Post. humeral circumflex v.
- Subclavian v. (8)
- Cephalic v. (17)
- (21) Subscapular v.
- Sup. thoracic v.
- (4) Profunda brachii v.
- Axillary v. (9)
- (12) Basilic v.
- (1) Brachial vv.
- Costoaxillary vv. (22)
- Lateral thoracic v. (3)
- (5) Collateral vv. of elbow joint
- (14) Radial vv.
- Ant. interosseous vv.
- Palmar digital vv.
- Ulnar vv. (13)
- (6) Intercapitular vv.
- (18) Proper palmar digital vv.

POSTERIOR VIEW OF DEEP VEINS

- (24)
- (2)
- (21)
- (22)
- Superficial cervical v.
- Transverse cervical v.
- (4)
- Dorsal scapular v.
- (1)
- (23) Circumflex scapular v.
- (5)
- (20) Thoracodorsal v.
- Post. interosseous vv.
- (3)
- (15) Dorsal venous rete of hand
- Dorsal metacarpal vv.
- (6)
- (16) Proper dorsal digital vv.

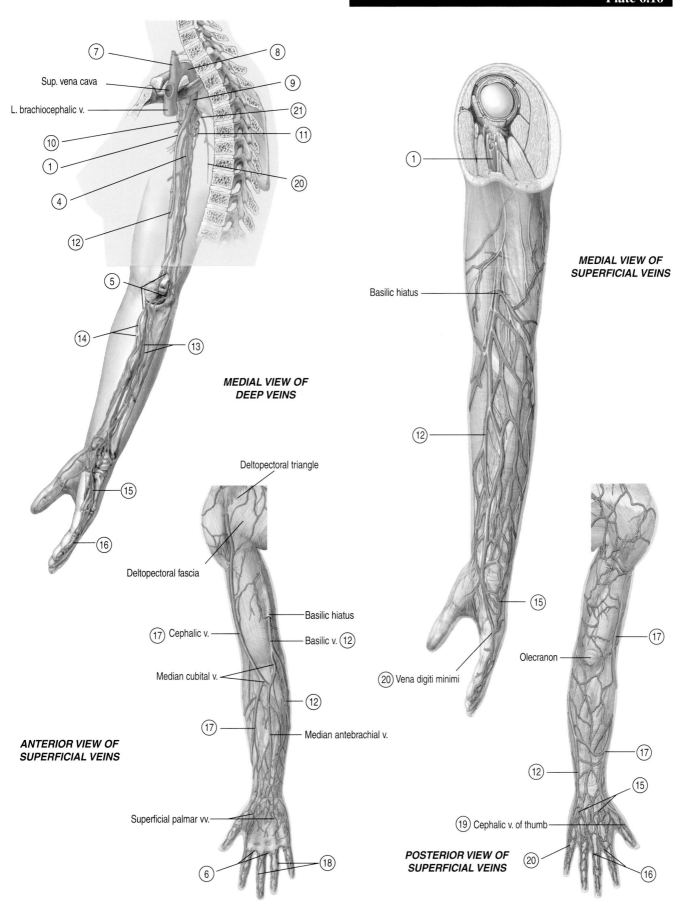

Sup. vena cava

L. brachiocephalic v.

*MEDIAL VIEW OF
DEEP VEINS*

*MEDIAL VIEW OF
SUPERFICIAL VEINS*

Basilic hiatus

Deltopectoral triangle

Deltopectoral fascia

Basilic hiatus

Cephalic v.

Basilic v.

Median cubital v.

Median antebrachial v.

*ANTERIOR VIEW OF
SUPERFICIAL VEINS*

Superficial palmar vv.

Vena digiti minimi

Olecranon

Cephalic v. of thumb

*POSTERIOR VIEW OF
SUPERFICIAL VEINS*

Dermatomes & Cutaneous Nerves
Plate 6.17

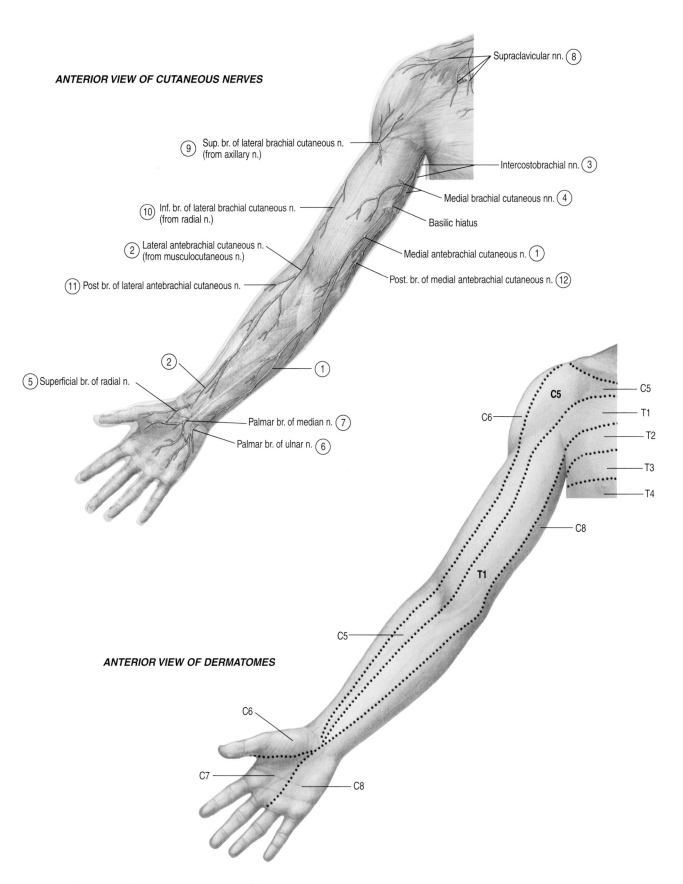

ANTERIOR VIEW OF CUTANEOUS NERVES

Supraclavicular nn. (8)

(9) Sup. br. of lateral brachial cutaneous n. (from axillary n.)

Intercostobrachial nn. (3)

(10) Inf. br. of lateral brachial cutaneous n. (from radial n.)

Medial brachial cutaneous nn. (4)

Basilic hiatus

(2) Lateral antebrachial cutaneous n. (from musculocutaneous n.)

Medial antebrachial cutaneous n. (1)

(11) Post br. of lateral antebrachial cutaneous n.

Post. br. of medial antebrachial cutaneous n. (12)

(2)

(1)

(5) Superficial br. of radial n.

Palmar br. of median n. (7)

Palmar br. of ulnar n. (6)

C5

C6

C5

T1

T2

T3

T4

C8

T1

C5

ANTERIOR VIEW OF DERMATOMES

C6

C7

C8

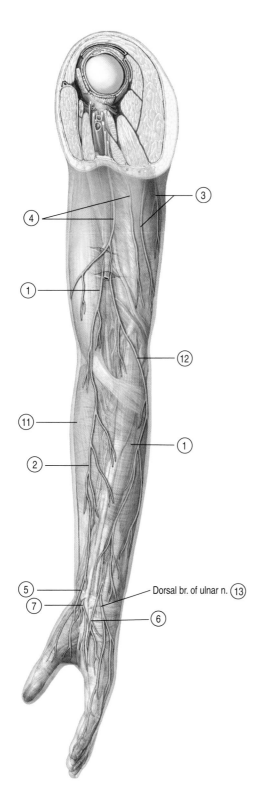

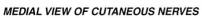

MEDIAL VIEW OF CUTANEOUS NERVES

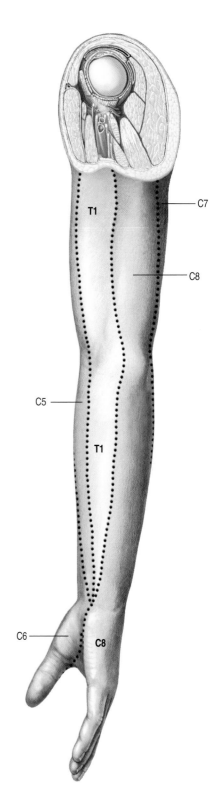

MEDIAL VIEW OF DERMATOMES

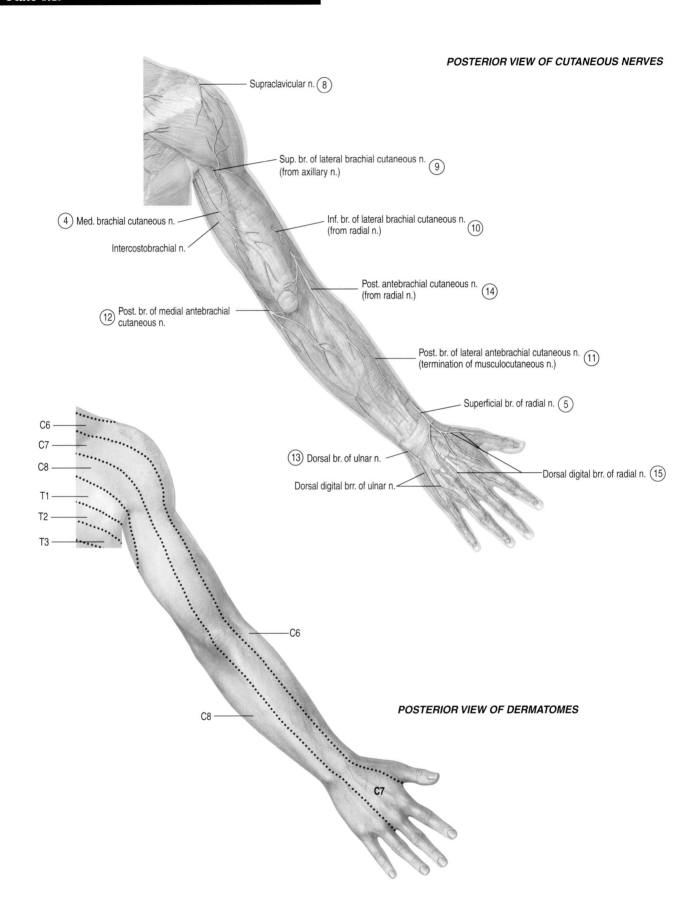

POSTERIOR VIEW OF CUTANEOUS NERVES

Supraclavicular n. (8)

Sup. br. of lateral brachial cutaneous n. (9)
(from axillary n.)

(4) Med. brachial cutaneous n.

Intercostobrachial n.

Inf. br. of lateral brachial cutaneous n. (10)
(from radial n.)

Post. antebrachial cutaneous n. (14)
(from radial n.)

(12) Post. br. of medial antebrachial cutaneous n.

Post. br. of lateral antebrachial cutaneous n. (11)
(termination of musculocutaneous n.)

Superficial br. of radial n. (5)

(13) Dorsal br. of ulnar n.

Dorsal digital brr. of ulnar n.

Dorsal digital brr. of radial n. (15)

C6
C7
C8
T1
T2
T3

C6

C8

POSTERIOR VIEW OF DERMATOMES

C7

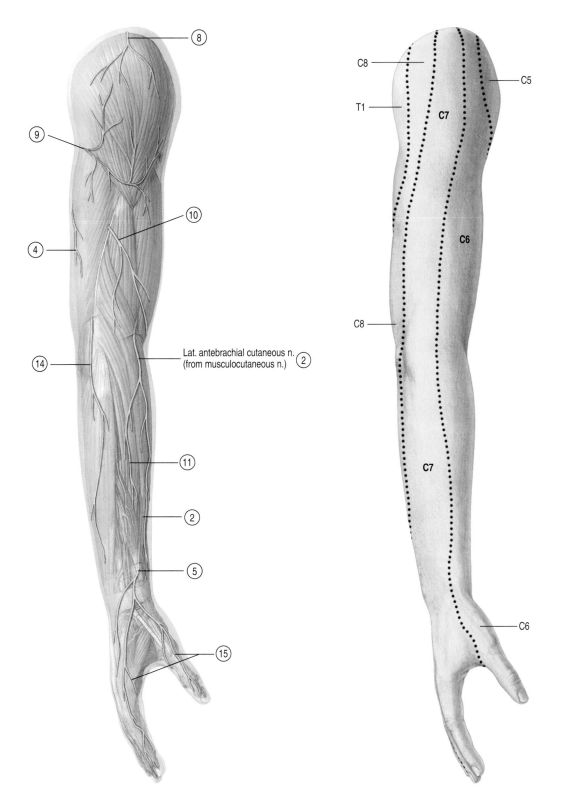

Lat. antebrachial cutaneous n. (from musculocutaneous n.) ②

LATERAL VIEW OF CUTANEOUS NERVES

LATERAL VIEW OF DERMATOMES

Segmental Innervation of Joint Actions
Plate 6.21

GLENOHUMERAL JOINT
C5
External (Lateral) Rotation
C6–C8
Internal (Medial) Rotation
Abduction
C5
C6–C8
Adduction
GLENOHUMERAL JOINT
Extension
C6–C8
Flexion
C5
ELBOW & RADIOULNAR JOINTS
Supination
C6
Pronation
C7,C8
Adduction C8,T1
Flexion
C8,T1
Extension C7,C8
Abduction C7,C8
1st CARPOMETACARPAL JOINT
Reposition
C7–T1
Opposition
C6–T1
ELBOW JOINT
Flexion C5,C6
RADIOCARPAL JOINT
Extension C7,C8
Extension
C6–C8
Flexion
C6,C7
Distal interphalangeal joint
Proximal interphalangeal joint
Metacarpophalangeal joint
Extension
C7,C8
Flexion
C7,C8
2nd–5th METACARPOPHALANGEAL JOINTS
Abduction
C8,T1
Adduction
C8,T1
Median plane of hand

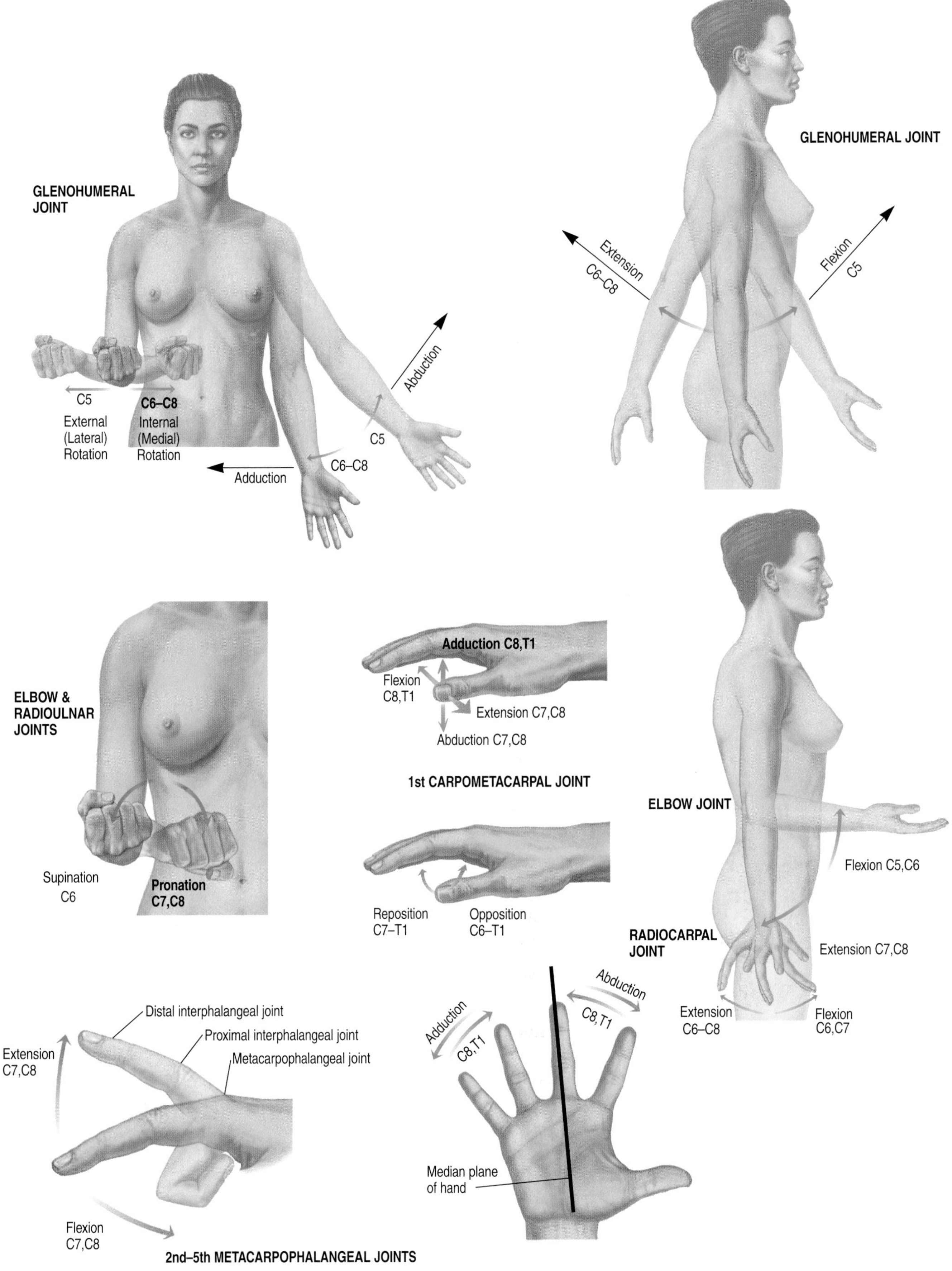

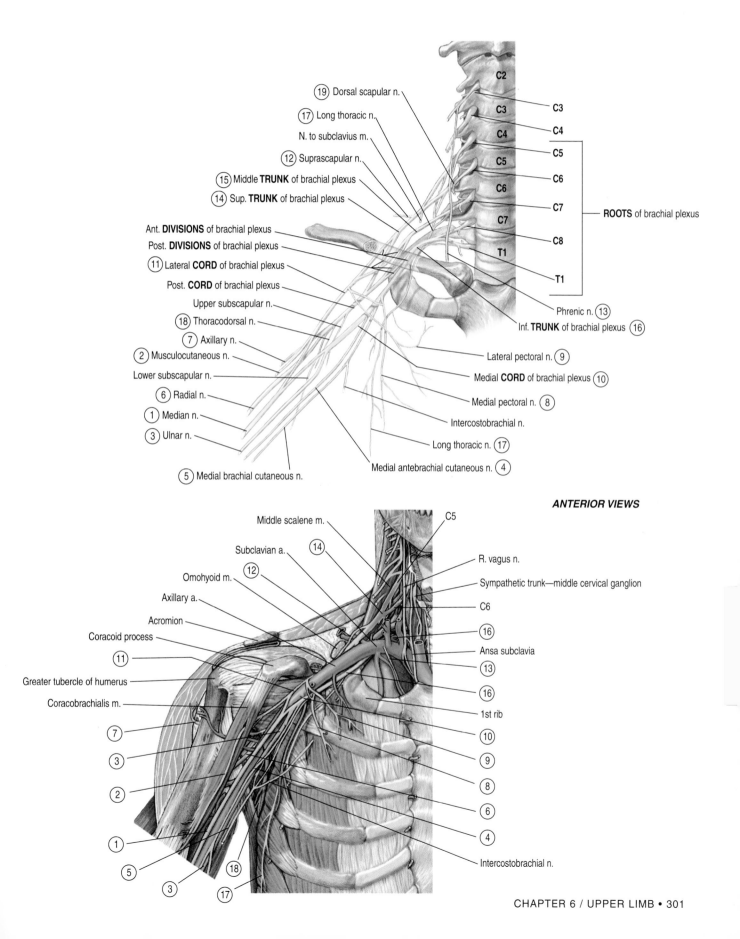

(19) Dorsal scapular n.

(17) Long thoracic n.

N. to subclavius m.

(12) Suprascapular n.

(15) Middle **TRUNK** of brachial plexus

(14) Sup. **TRUNK** of brachial plexus

Ant. **DIVISIONS** of brachial plexus

Post. **DIVISIONS** of brachial plexus

(11) Lateral **CORD** of brachial plexus

Post. **CORD** of brachial plexus

Upper subscapular n.

(18) Thoracodorsal n.

(7) Axillary n.

(2) Musculocutaneous n.

Lower subscapular n.

(6) Radial n.

(1) Median n.

(3) Ulnar n.

(5) Medial brachial cutaneous n.

C2

C3 — C3

C4 — C4

C5 — C5

C5 — C6

C6 — C7

C7 — C8

T1 — T1

ROOTS of brachial plexus

Phrenic n. (13)

Inf. **TRUNK** of brachial plexus (16)

Lateral pectoral n. (9)

Medial **CORD** of brachial plexus (10)

Medial pectoral n. (8)

Intercostobrachial n.

Long thoracic n. (17)

Medial antebrachial cutaneous n. (4)

ANTERIOR VIEWS

Middle scalene m.

Subclavian a.

(14)

Omohyoid m.

(12)

Axillary a.

Acromion

Coracoid process

(11)

Greater tubercle of humerus

Coracobrachialis m.

(7)

(3)

(2)

(1)

(5)

(18)

(3)

(17)

C5

R. vagus n.

Sympathetic trunk—middle cervical ganglion

C6

(16)

Ansa subclavia

(13)

(16)

1st rib

(10)

(9)

(8)

(6)

(4)

Intercostobrachial n.

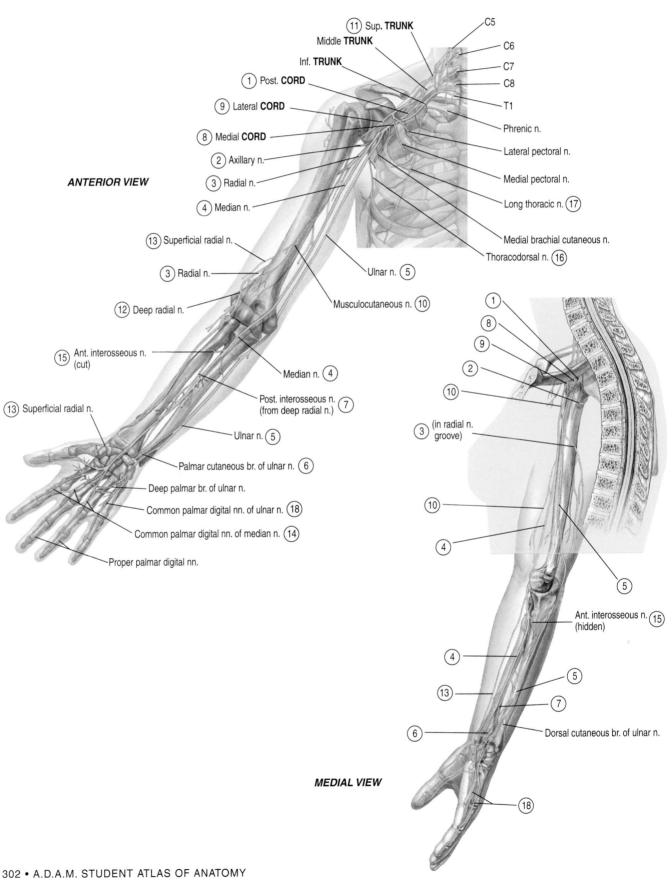

(11) Sup. **TRUNK**

Middle **TRUNK**

Inf. **TRUNK**

(1) Post. **CORD**

(9) Lateral **CORD**

(8) Medial **CORD**

(2) Axillary n.

(3) Radial n.

(4) Median n.

C5

C6

C7

C8

T1

Phrenic n.

Lateral pectoral n.

Medial pectoral n.

Long thoracic n. (17)

Medial brachial cutaneous n.

Thoracodorsal n. (16)

ANTERIOR VIEW

(13) Superficial radial n.

(3) Radial n.

(12) Deep radial n.

(15) Ant. interosseous n. (cut)

(13) Superficial radial n.

Ulnar n. (5)

Musculocutaneous n. (10)

Median n. (4)

Post. interosseous n. (7) (from deep radial n.)

Ulnar n. (5)

Palmar cutaneous br. of ulnar n. (6)

Deep palmar br. of ulnar n.

Common palmar digital nn. of ulnar n. (18)

Common palmar digital nn. of median n. (14)

Proper palmar digital nn.

(1)
(8)
(9)
(2)
(10)

(3) (in radial n. groove)

(10)

(10)

(4)

(5)

Ant. interosseous n. (15) (hidden)

(4)

(5)

(13)

(7)

(6)

Dorsal cutaneous br. of ulnar n.

MEDIAL VIEW

(18)

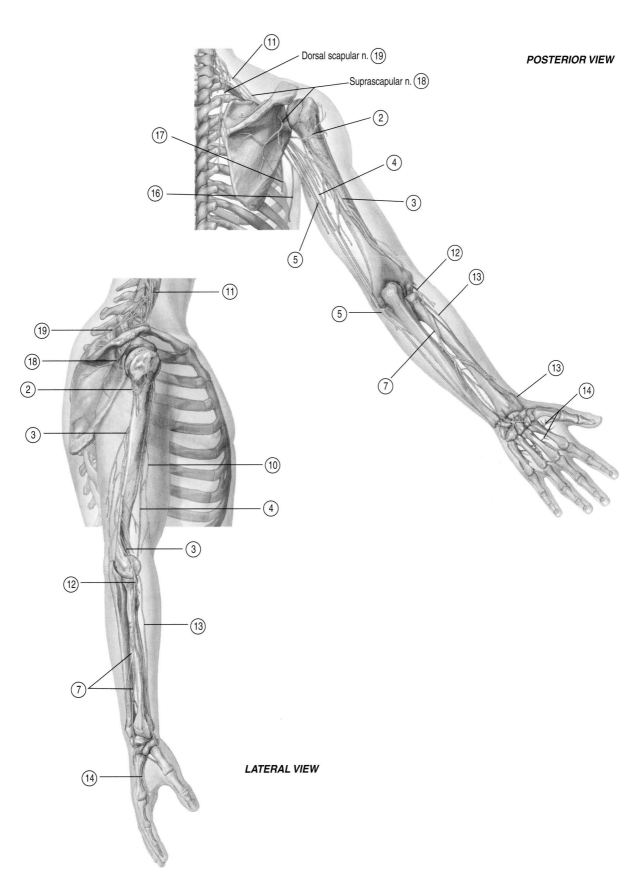

POSTERIOR VIEW

Dorsal scapular n. ⑲

Suprascapular n. ⑱

LATERAL VIEW

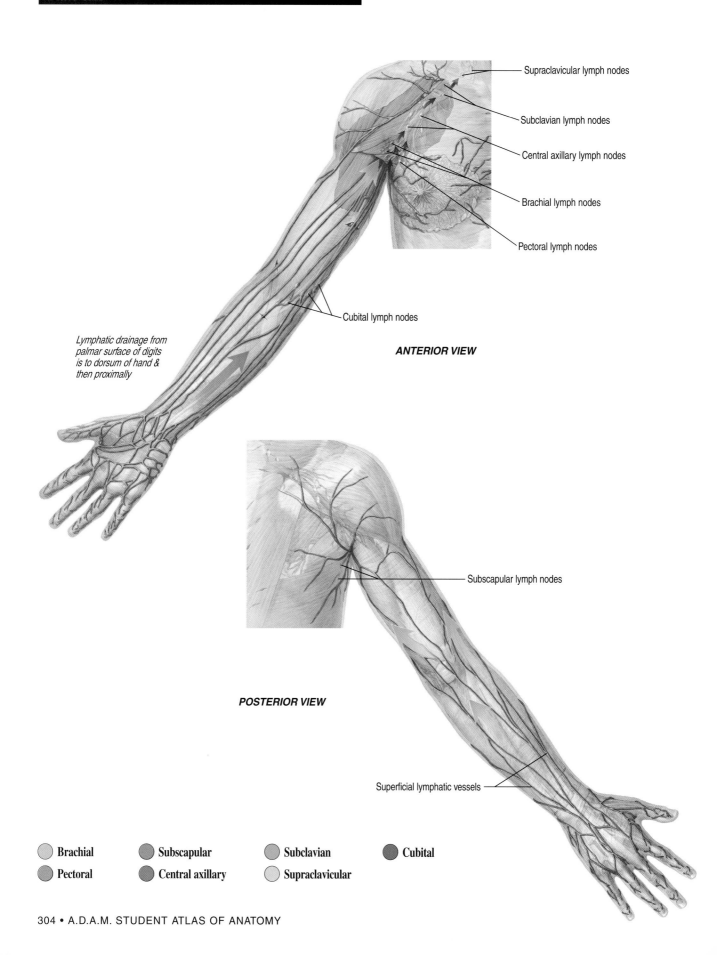

Supraclavicular lymph nodes

Subclavian lymph nodes

Central axillary lymph nodes

Brachial lymph nodes

Pectoral lymph nodes

Cubital lymph nodes

Lymphatic drainage from palmar surface of digits is to dorsum of hand & then proximally

ANTERIOR VIEW

Subscapular lymph nodes

POSTERIOR VIEW

Superficial lymphatic vessels

- ⬤ Brachial
- ⬤ Pectoral
- ⬤ Subscapular
- ⬤ Central axillary
- ⬤ Subclavian
- ⬤ Supraclavicular
- ⬤ Cubital

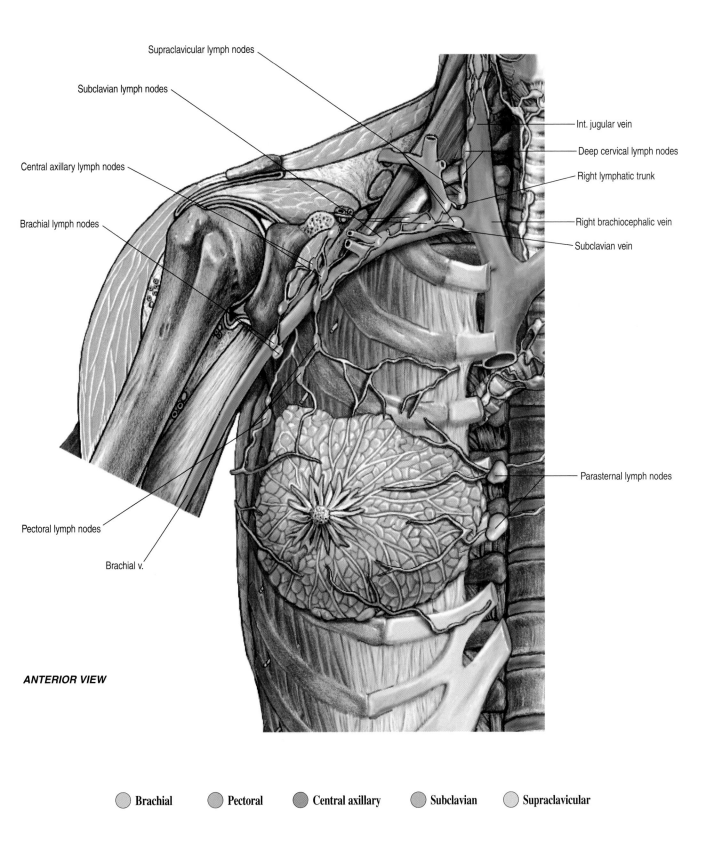

Supraclavicular lymph nodes

Subclavian lymph nodes

Central axillary lymph nodes

Brachial lymph nodes

Pectoral lymph nodes

Brachial v.

Int. jugular vein

Deep cervical lymph nodes

Right lymphatic trunk

Right brachiocephalic vein

Subclavian vein

Parasternal lymph nodes

ANTERIOR VIEW

Brachial   Pectoral   Central axillary   Subclavian   Supraclavicular

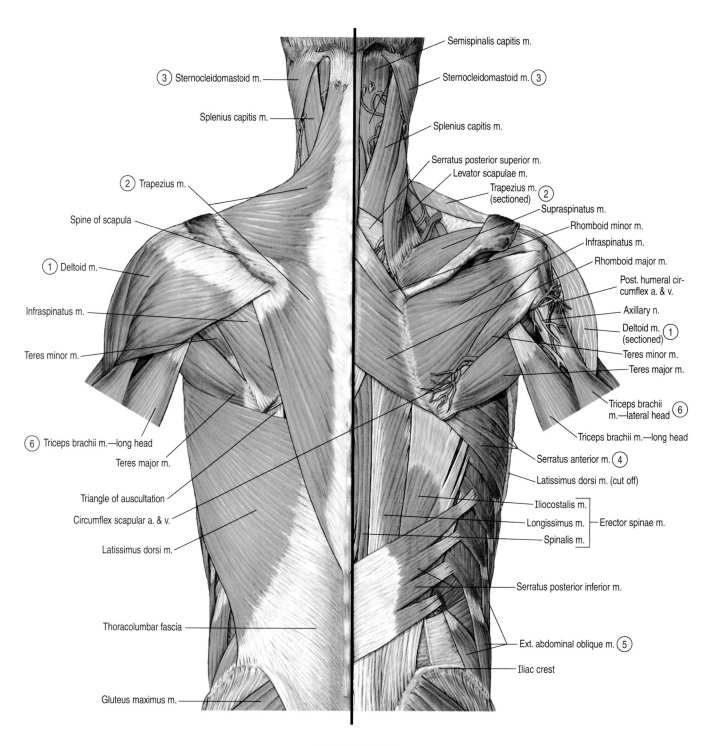

③ Sternocleidomastoid m.

Splenius capitis m.

② Trapezius m.

Spine of scapula

① Deltoid m.

Infraspinatus m.

Teres minor m.

⑥ Triceps brachii m.—long head

Teres major m.

Triangle of auscultation

Circumflex scapular a. & v.

Latissimus dorsi m.

Thoracolumbar fascia

Gluteus maximus m.

Semispinalis capitis m.

Sternocleidomastoid m. ③

Splenius capitis m.

Serratus posterior superior m.

Levator scapulae m.

Trapezius m. (sectioned) ②

Supraspinatus m.

Rhomboid minor m.

Infraspinatus m.

Rhomboid major m.

Post. humeral circumflex a. & v.

Axillary n.

Deltoid m. (sectioned) ①

Teres minor m.

Teres major m.

Triceps brachii m.—lateral head ⑥

Triceps brachii m.—long head

Serratus anterior m. ④

Latissimus dorsi m. (cut off)

Iliocostalis m.

Longissimus m. — Erector spinae m.

Spinalis m.

Serratus posterior inferior m.

Ext. abdominal oblique m. ⑤

Iliac crest

POSTERIOR VIEW

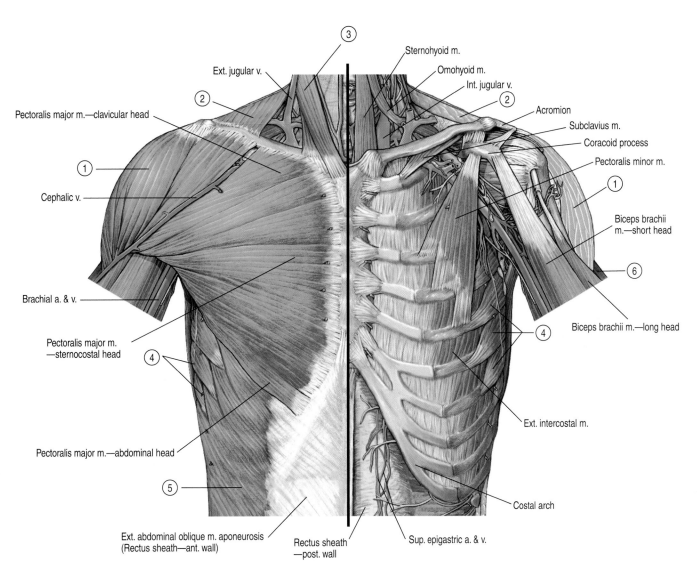

③

Ext. jugular v.

Sternohyoid m.

Omohyoid m.

Int. jugular v.

②

②

Acromion

Subclavius m.

Pectoralis major m.—clavicular head

Coracoid process

Pectoralis minor m.

①

①

Cephalic v.

Biceps brachii
m.—short head

⑥

Brachial a. & v.

Biceps brachii m.—long head

④

Pectoralis major m.
—sternocostal head

④

Ext. intercostal m.

Pectoralis major m.—abdominal head

Costal arch

⑤

Ext. abdominal oblique m. aponeurosis
(Rectus sheath—ant. wall)

Rectus sheath
—post. wall

Sup. epigastric a. & v.

ANTERIOR VIEW

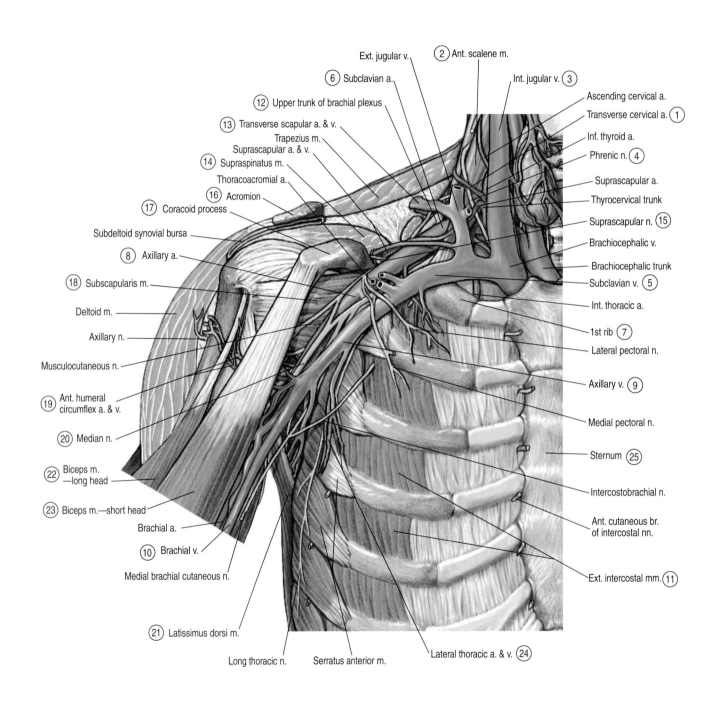

Ext. jugular v.

② Ant. scalene m.

⑥ Subclavian a.

Int. jugular v. ③

⑫ Upper trunk of brachial plexus

Ascending cervical a.

Transverse cervical a. ①

⑬ Transverse scapular a. & v.

Inf. thyroid a.

Trapezius m.

Phrenic n. ④

Suprascapular a. & v.

⑭ Supraspinatus m.

Suprascapular a.

Thoracoacromial a.

Thyrocervical trunk

⑯ Acromion

Suprascapular n. ⑮

⑰ Coracoid process

Brachiocephalic v.

Subdeltoid synovial bursa

Brachiocephalic trunk

⑧ Axillary a.

Subclavian v. ⑤

⑱ Subscapularis m.

Int. thoracic a.

Deltoid m.

1st rib ⑦

Axillary n.

Lateral pectoral n.

Musculocutaneous n.

Axillary v. ⑨

⑲ Ant. humeral circumflex a. & v.

Medial pectoral n.

⑳ Median n.

Sternum ㉕

㉒ Biceps m. —long head

Intercostobrachial n.

㉓ Biceps m.—short head

Ant. cutaneous br. of intercostal nn.

Brachial a.

⑩ Brachial v.

Ext. intercostal mm. ⑪

Medial brachial cutaneous n.

㉑ Latissimus dorsi m.

Lateral thoracic a. & v. ㉔

Long thoracic n.   Serratus anterior m.

ANTERIOR VIEW

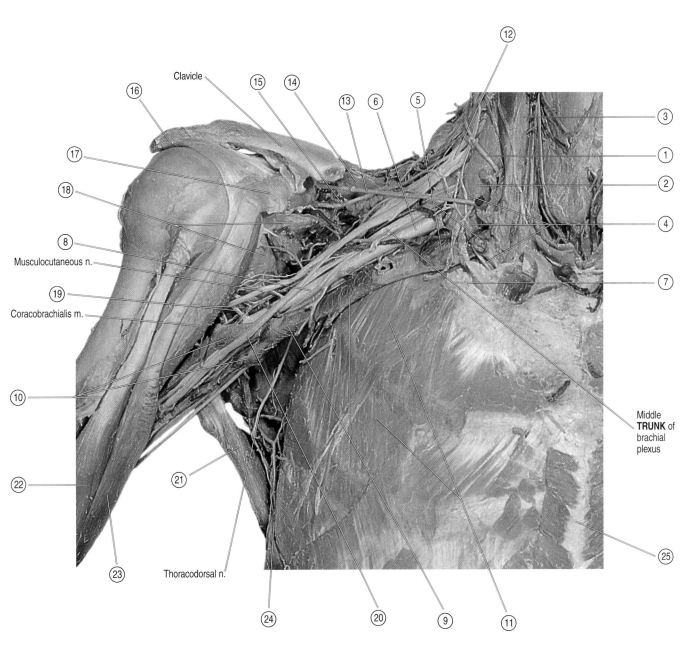

Clavicle

Musculocutaneous n.

Coracobrachialis m.

Middle **TRUNK** of brachial plexus

Thoracodorsal n.

ANTERIOR VIEW

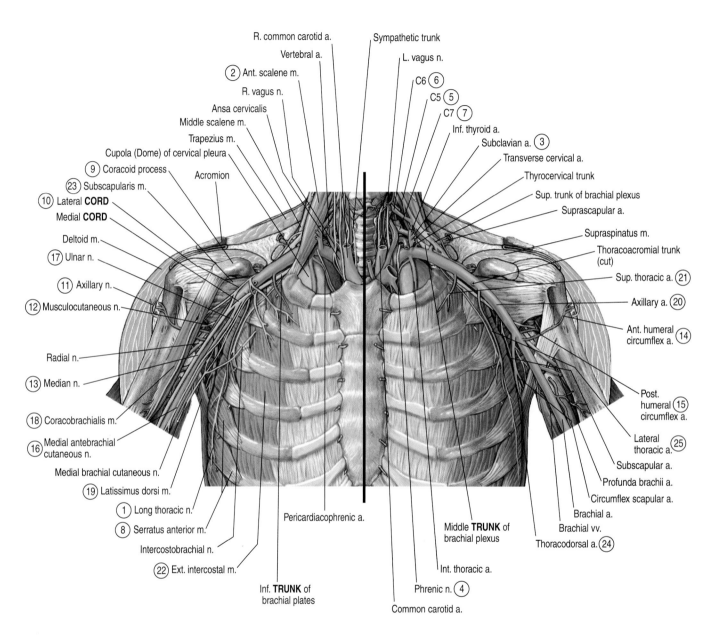

R. common carotid a.
Vertebral a.
② Ant. scalene m.
R. vagus n.
Ansa cervicalis
Middle scalene m.
Trapezius m.
Cupola (Dome) of cervical pleura
⑨ Coracoid process
㉓ Subscapularis m.
⑩ Lateral **CORD**
Medial **CORD**
Deltoid m.
⑰ Ulnar n.
⑪ Axillary n.
⑫ Musculocutaneous n.
Radial n.
⑬ Median n.
⑱ Coracobrachialis m.
⑯ Medial antebrachial cutaneous n.
Medial brachial cutaneous n.
⑲ Latissimus dorsi m.
① Long thoracic n.
⑧ Serratus anterior m.
Intercostobrachial n.
㉒ Ext. intercostal m.
Inf. **TRUNK** of brachial plates

Sympathetic trunk
L. vagus n.
C6 ⑥
C5 ⑤
C7 ⑦
Inf. thyroid a.
Subclavian a. ③
Transverse cervical a.
Thyrocervical trunk
Sup. trunk of brachial plexus
Suprascapular a.
Supraspinatus m.
Thoracoacromial trunk (cut)
Sup. thoracic a. ㉑
Axillary a. ⑳
Ant. humeral circumflex a. ⑭
Post. humeral circumflex a. ⑮
Lateral thoracic a. ㉕
Subscapular a.
Profunda brachii a.
Circumflex scapular a.
Brachial a.
Brachial vv.
Thoracodorsal a. ㉔

Acromion
Pericardiacophrenic a.
Middle **TRUNK** of brachial plexus
Int. thoracic a.
Phrenic n. ④
Common carotid a.

ANTERIOR VIEW

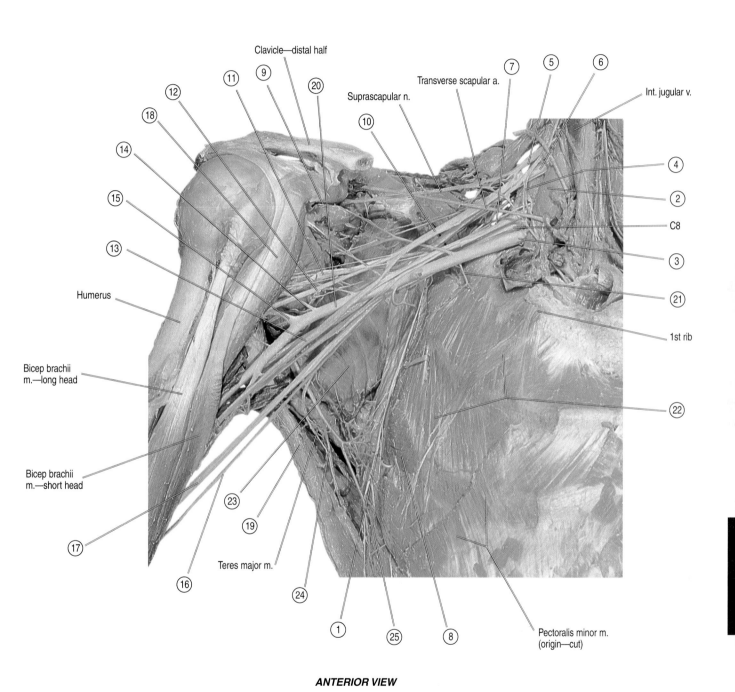

Clavicle—distal half

⑪ ⑨ ⑳

⑫

⑱

Transverse scapular a.

⑦ ⑤ ⑥

Suprascapular n.

Int. jugular v.

⑭

⑩

④

②

⑮

C8

⑬

③

Humerus

㉑

Bicep brachii
m.—long head

1st rib

Bicep brachii
m.—short head

㉒

㉓

⑲

⑰

Teres major m.

⑯

㉔

① ㉕ ⑧

Pectoralis minor m.
(origin—cut)

ANTERIOR VIEW

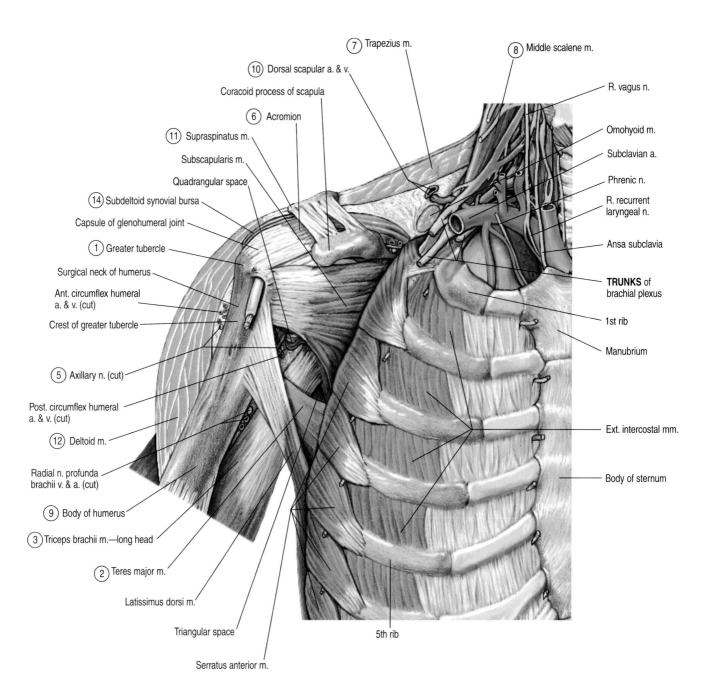

⑦ Trapezius m.

⑧ Middle scalene m.

⑩ Dorsal scapular a. & v.

Coracoid process of scapula

⑥ Acromion

⑪ Supraspinatus m.

Subscapularis m.

Quadrangular space

⑭ Subdeltoid synovial bursa

Capsule of glenohumeral joint

① Greater tubercle

Surgical neck of humerus

Ant. circumflex humeral
a. & v. (cut)

Crest of greater tubercle

⑤ Axillary n. (cut)

Post. circumflex humeral
a. & v. (cut)

⑫ Deltoid m.

Radial n. profunda
brachii v. & a. (cut)

⑨ Body of humerus

③ Triceps brachii m.—long head

② Teres major m.

Latissimus dorsi m.

Triangular space

Serratus anterior m.

5th rib

R. vagus n.

Omohyoid m.

Subclavian a.

Phrenic n.

R. recurrent
laryngeal n.

Ansa subclavia

TRUNKS of
brachial plexus

1st rib

Manubrium

Ext. intercostal mm.

Body of sternum

ANTERIOR VIEW

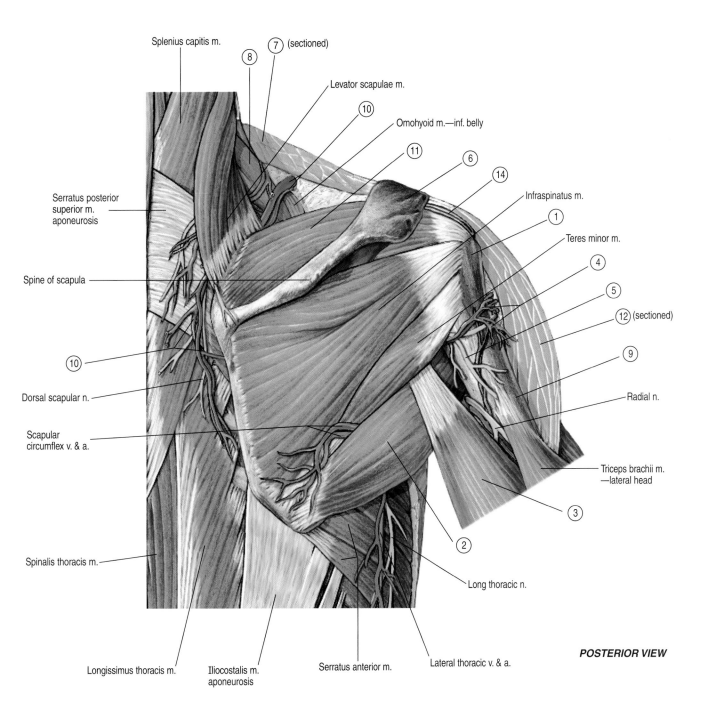

Splenius capitis m.

⑦ (sectioned)

⑧

Levator scapulae m.

⑩

Omohyoid m.—inf. belly

⑪

⑥

⑭

Infraspinatus m.

①

Teres minor m.

④

⑤

⑫ (sectioned)

⑨

Radial n.

Serratus posterior
superior m.
aponeurosis

Spine of scapula

⑩

Dorsal scapular n.

Scapular
circumflex v. & a.

Triceps brachii m.
—lateral head

③

②

Spinalis thoracis m.

Long thoracic n.

Longissimus thoracis m.

Iliocostalis m.
aponeurosis

Serratus anterior m.

Lateral thoracic v. & a.

POSTERIOR VIEW

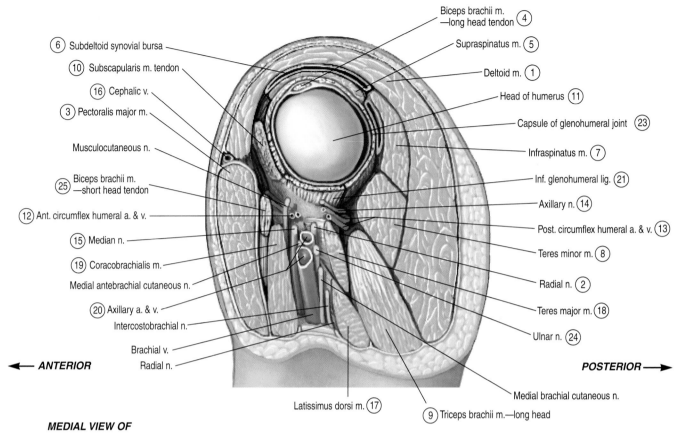

6 Subdeltoid synovial bursa

10 Subscapularis m. tendon

16 Cephalic v.

3 Pectoralis major m.

Musculocutaneous n.

25 Biceps brachii m. —short head tendon

12 Ant. circumflex humeral a. & v.

15 Median n.

19 Coracobrachialis m.

Medial antebrachial cutaneous n.

20 Axillary a. & v.

Intercostobrachial n.

Brachial v.

Radial n.

Biceps brachii m. —long head tendon 4

Supraspinatus m. 5

Deltoid m. 1

Head of humerus 11

Capsule of glenohumeral joint 23

Infraspinatus m. 7

Inf. glenohumeral lig. 21

Axillary n. 14

Post. circumflex humeral a. & v. 13

Teres minor m. 8

Radial n. 2

Teres major m. 18

Ulnar n. 24

Medial brachial cutaneous n.

◄— **ANTERIOR**

POSTERIOR —►

Latissimus dorsi m. 17

9 Triceps brachii m.—long head

**MEDIAL VIEW OF
SAGITTALLY SECTIONED AXILLA**

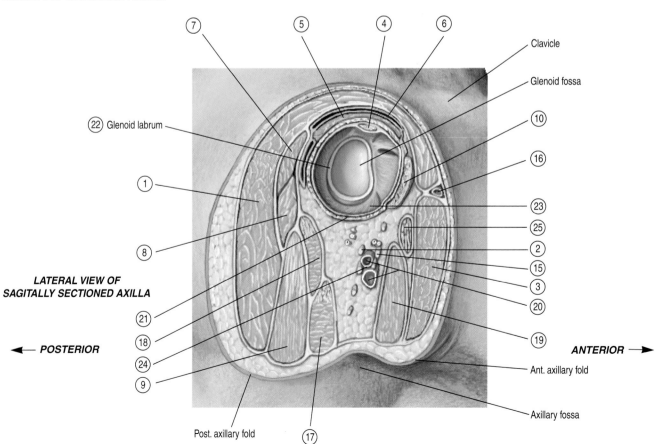

22 Glenoid labrum

1

8

Clavicle

Glenoid fossa

10

16

23

25

2

15

3

20

19

**LATERAL VIEW OF
SAGITALLY SECTIONED AXILLA**

◄— **POSTERIOR**

ANTERIOR —►

21

18

24

9

Ant. axillary fold

Axillary fossa

Post. axillary fold

17

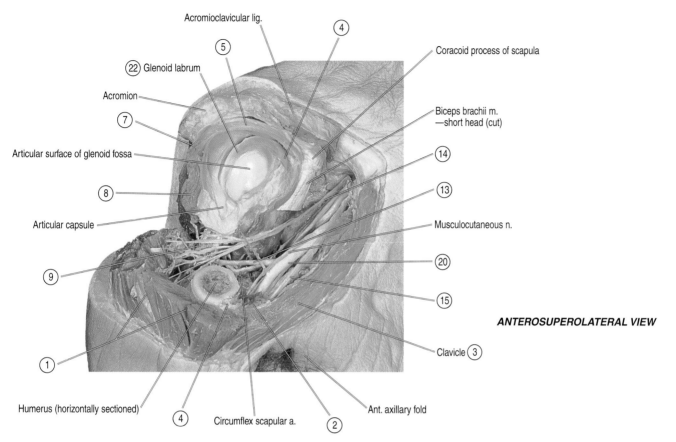

Acromioclavicular lig.

⑤

④

Coracoid process of scapula

㉒ Glenoid labrum

Acromion

⑦

Articular surface of glenoid fossa

⑧

Articular capsule

⑨

①

Humerus (horizontally sectioned)

④

Circumflex scapular a.

②

Ant. axillary fold

Biceps brachii m.
—short head (cut)

⑭

⑬

Musculocutaneous n.

⑳

⑮

Clavicle ③

ANTEROSUPEROLATERAL VIEW

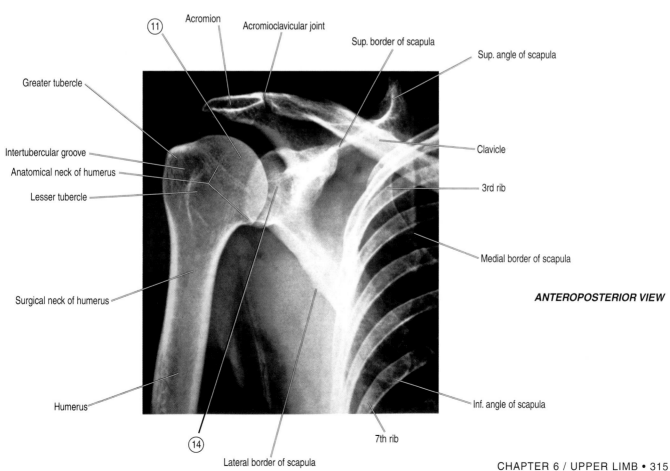

⑪

Acromion

Acromioclavicular joint

Sup. border of scapula

Sup. angle of scapula

Greater tubercle

Intertubercular groove

Anatomical neck of humerus

Lesser tubercle

Surgical neck of humerus

Humerus

⑭

Lateral border of scapula

7th rib

Clavicle

3rd rib

Medial border of scapula

Inf. angle of scapula

ANTEROPOSTERIOR VIEW

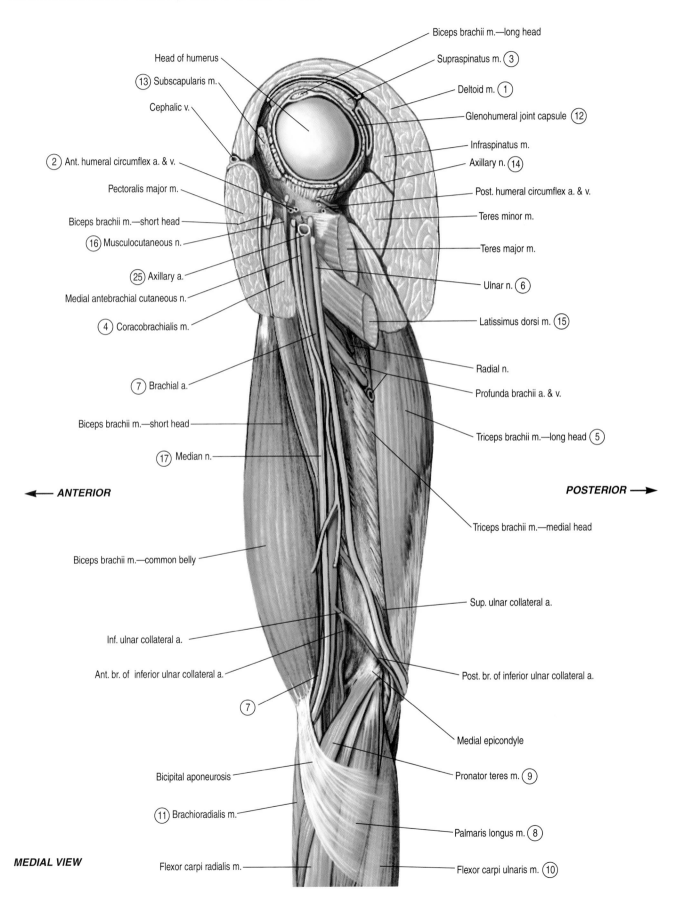

Head of humerus

⑬ Subscapularis m.

Cephalic v.

② Ant. humeral circumflex a. & v.

Pectoralis major m.

Biceps brachii m.—short head

⑯ Musculocutaneous n.

㉕ Axillary a.

Medial antebrachial cutaneous n.

④ Coracobrachialis m.

⑦ Brachial a.

Biceps brachii m.—short head

⑰ Median n.

◄— **ANTERIOR**

Biceps brachii m.—common belly

Inf. ulnar collateral a.

Ant. br. of inferior ulnar collateral a.

⑦

Bicipital aponeurosis

⑪ Brachioradialis m.

MEDIAL VIEW

Flexor carpi radialis m.

Biceps brachii m.—long head

Supraspinatus m. ③

Deltoid m. ①

Glenohumeral joint capsule ⑫

Infraspinatus m.

Axillary n. ⑭

Post. humeral circumflex a. & v.

Teres minor m.

Teres major m.

Ulnar n. ⑥

Latissimus dorsi m. ⑮

Radial n.

Profunda brachii a. & v.

Triceps brachii m.—long head ⑤

Triceps brachii m.—medial head

POSTERIOR —►

Sup. ulnar collateral a.

Post. br. of inferior ulnar collateral a.

Medial epicondyle

Pronator teres m. ⑨

Palmaris longus m. ⑧

Flexor carpi ulnaris m. ⑩

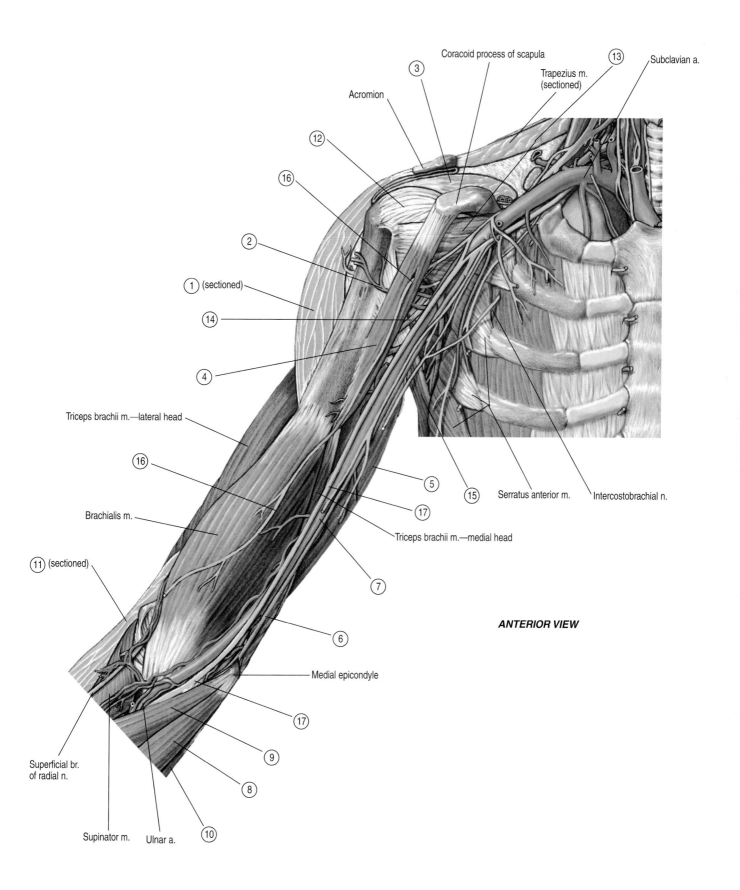

Coracoid process of scapula

③

⑬

Subclavian a.

Trapezius m.
(sectioned)

Acromion

⑫

⑯

②

① (sectioned)

⑭

④

Triceps brachii m.—lateral head

⑯

Brachialis m.

⑪ (sectioned)

⑤

⑮

Serratus anterior m.

Intercostobrachial n.

⑰

Triceps brachii m.—medial head

⑦

ANTERIOR VIEW

⑥

Medial epicondyle

⑰

⑨

Superficial br.
of radial n.

⑧

Supinator m.

Ulnar a.

⑩

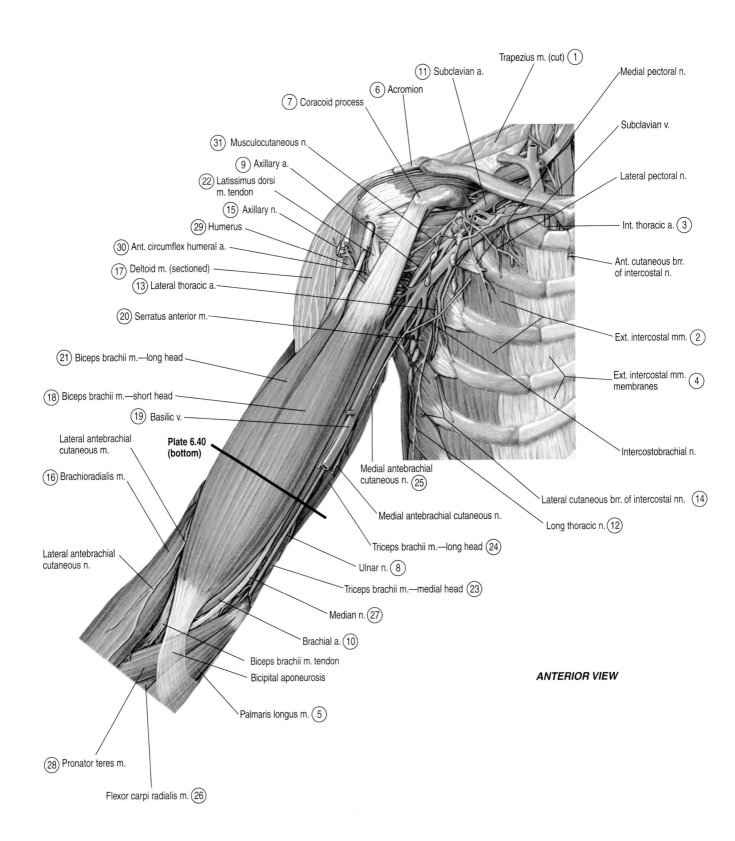

Trapezius m. (cut) ①

⑪ Subclavian a.

⑥ Acromion

⑦ Coracoid process

Medial pectoral n.

Subclavian v.

Lateral pectoral n.

③ Musculocutaneous n.

⑨ Axillary a.

㉒ Latissimus dorsi m. tendon

⑮ Axillary n.

㉙ Humerus

㉚ Ant. circumflex humeral a.

⑰ Deltoid m. (sectioned)

⑬ Lateral thoracic a.

⑳ Serratus anterior m.

㉑ Biceps brachii m.—long head

⑱ Biceps brachii m.—short head

⑲ Basilic v.

Int. thoracic a. ③

Ant. cutaneous brr. of intercostal n.

Ext. intercostal mm. ②

Ext. intercostal mm. membranes ④

Lateral antebrachial cutaneous m.

Plate 6.40 (bottom)

⑯ Brachioradialis m.

Medial antebrachial cutaneous n. ㉕

Intercostobrachial n.

Lateral cutaneous brr. of intercostal nn. ⑭

Lateral antebrachial cutaneous n.

Medial antebrachial cutaneous n.

Long thoracic n. ⑫

Triceps brachii m.—long head ㉔

Ulnar n. ⑧

Triceps brachii m.—medial head ㉓

Median n. ㉗

Brachial a. ⑩

Biceps brachii m. tendon

Bicipital aponeurosis

ANTERIOR VIEW

Palmaris longus m. ⑤

㉘ Pronator teres m.

Flexor carpi radialis m. ㉖

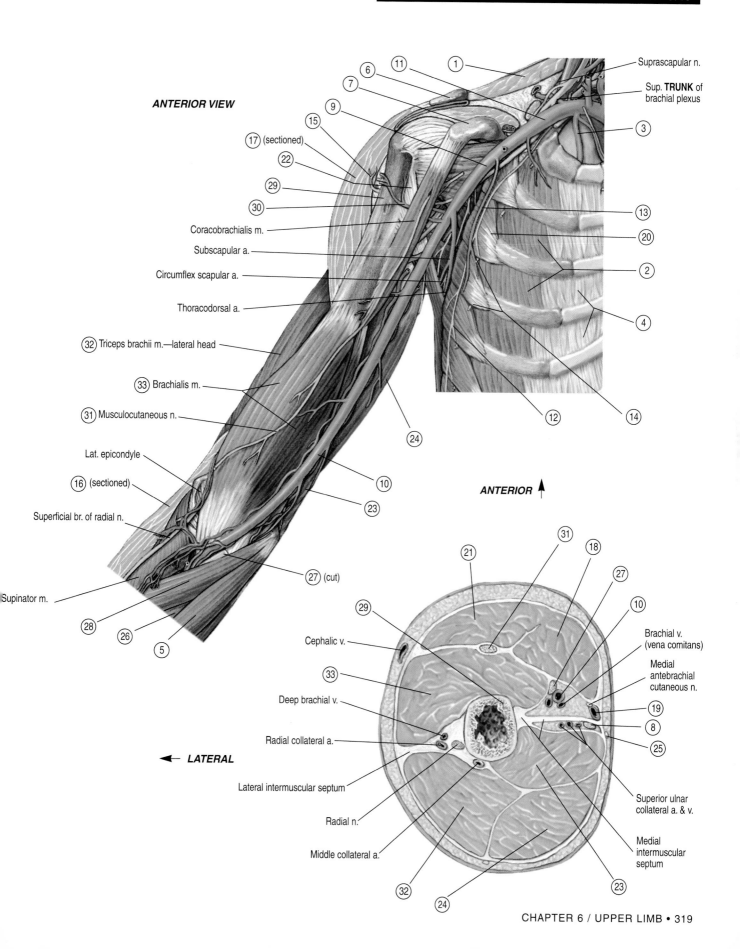

ANTERIOR VIEW

Suprascapular n.

Sup. **TRUNK** of
brachial plexus

(17) (sectioned)

(22)

(29)

(30)

Coracobrachialis m.

Subscapular a.

Circumflex scapular a.

Thoracodorsal a.

(32) Triceps brachii m.—lateral head

(33) Brachialis m.

(31) Musculocutaneous n.

Lat. epicondyle

(16) (sectioned)

Superficial br. of radial n.

Supinator m.

(28)   (26)   (5)

ANTERIOR ↑

Cephalic v.

(33)

Deep brachial v.

Radial collateral a.

◄ LATERAL

Lateral intermuscular septum

Radial n.

Middle collateral a.

Brachial v.
(vena comitans)

Medial
antebrachial
cutaneous n.

(19)

(8)

(25)

Superior ulnar
collateral a. & v.

Medial
intermuscular
septum

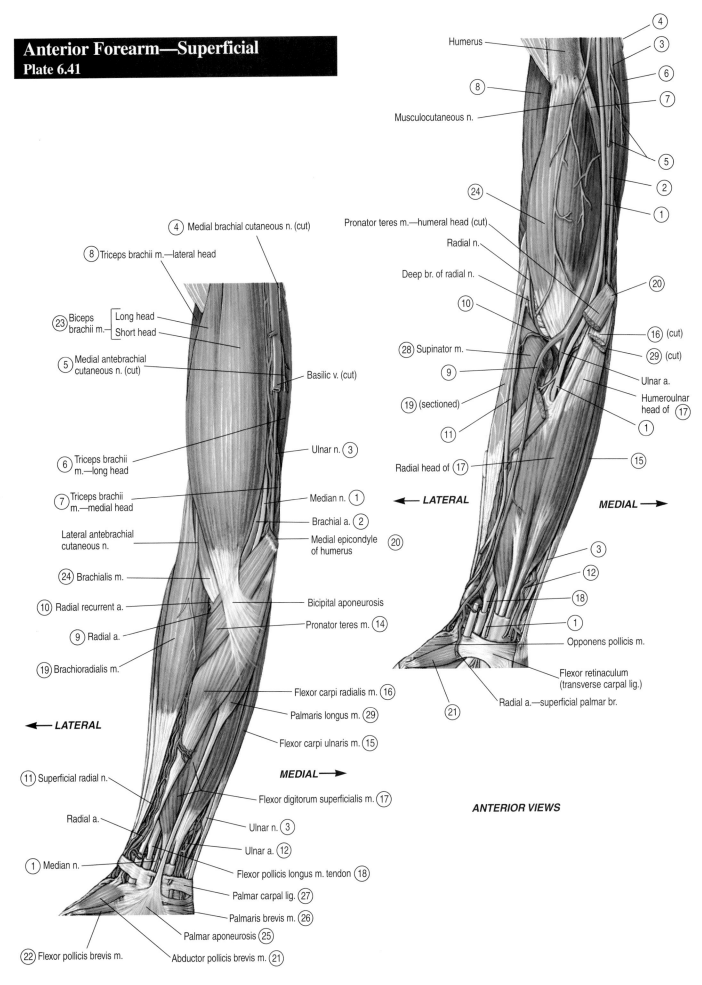

Humerus

(4)

(3)

(6)

(8)

(7)

Musculocutaneous n.

(5)

(2)

(1)

(24)

Pronator teres m.—humeral head (cut)

Radial n.

Deep br. of radial n.

(20)

(10)

(16) (cut)

(28) Supinator m.

(29) (cut)

(9)

Ulnar a.

(19) (sectioned)

Humeroulnar head of (17)

(11)

(1)

Radial head of (17)

(15)

← LATERAL

MEDIAL →

(3)

(12)

(18)

(1)

Opponens pollicis m.

Flexor retinaculum (transverse carpal lig.)

(21)

Radial a.—superficial palmar br.

ANTERIOR VIEWS

(4) Medial brachial cutaneous n. (cut)

(8) Triceps brachii m.—lateral head

(23) Biceps brachii m. [Long head / Short head]

(5) Medial antebrachial cutaneous n. (cut)

Basilic v. (cut)

(6) Triceps brachii m.—long head

(7) Triceps brachii m.—medial head

Ulnar n. (3)

Lateral antebrachial cutaneous n.

Median n. (1)

Brachial a. (2)

Medial epicondyle of humerus (20)

(24) Brachialis m.

(10) Radial recurrent a.

Bicipital aponeurosis

(9) Radial a.

Pronator teres m. (14)

(19) Brachioradialis m.

Flexor carpi radialis m. (16)

Palmaris longus m. (29)

Flexor carpi ulnaris m. (15)

← LATERAL

MEDIAL →

(11) Superficial radial n.

Flexor digitorum superficialis m. (17)

Radial a.

Ulnar n. (3)

(1) Median n.

Ulnar a. (12)

Flexor pollicis longus m. tendon (18)

Palmar carpal lig. (27)

Palmaris brevis m. (26)

Palmar aponeurosis (25)

(22) Flexor pollicis brevis m.

Abductor pollicis brevis m. (21)

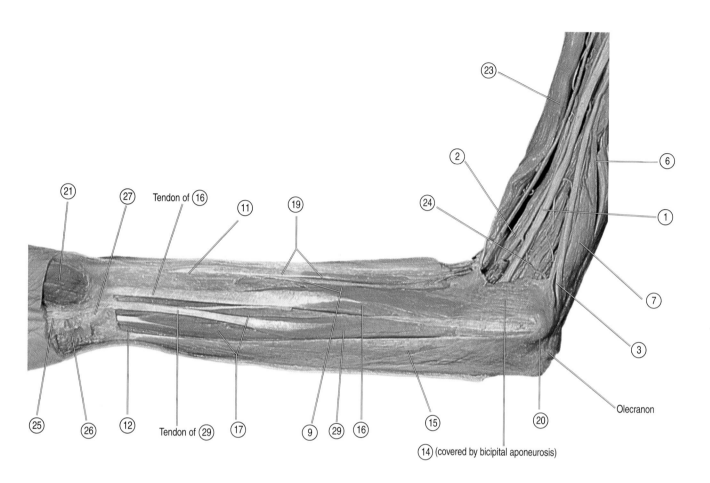

㉑ ㉗ Tendon of ⑯ ⑪ ⑲ ㉔ ② ㉓ ⑥ ① ⑦ ③

㉕ ㉖ ⑫ Tendon of ㉙ ⑰ ⑨ ㉙ ⑯ ⑮ ⑭ (covered by bicipital aponeurosis) ⑳ Olecranon

MEDIAL ARM & ANTERIOR FOREARM & WRIST

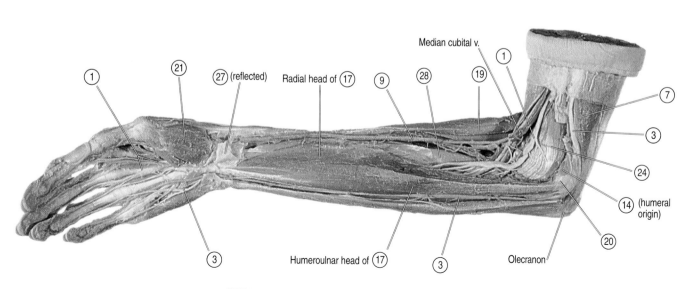

Median cubital v.

① ㉑ ㉗ (reflected) Radial head of ⑰ ⑨ ㉘ ⑲ ① ⑦ ③ ㉔ ⑭ (humeral origin) ⑳

③ Humeroulnar head of ⑰ ③ Olecranon

MEDIAL ELBOW & ANTERIOR FOREARM & HAND

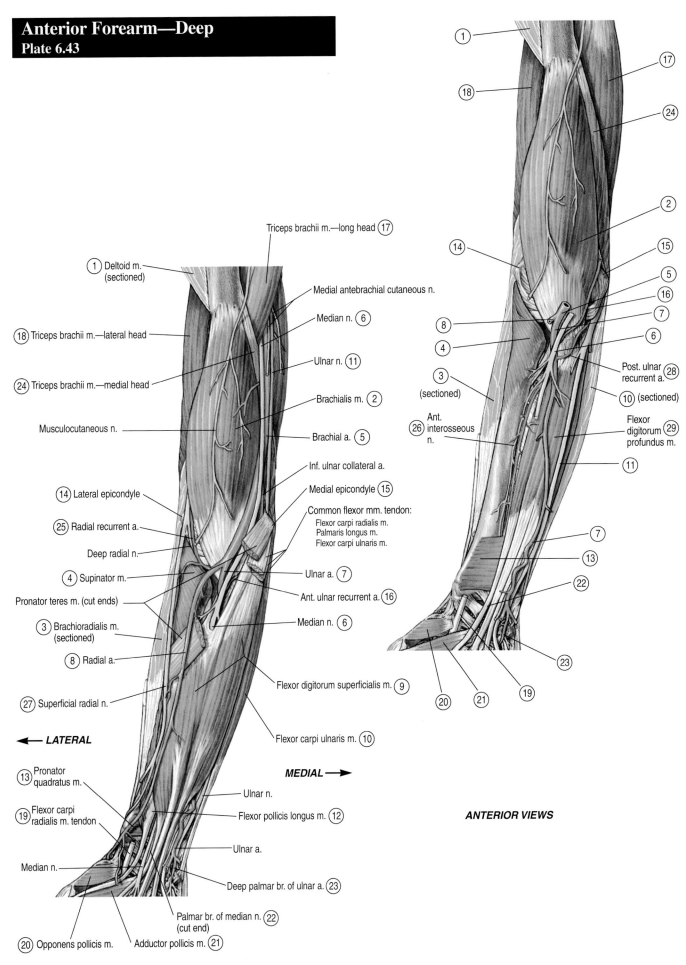

Triceps brachii m.—long head ⑰

① Deltoid m. (sectioned)

Medial antebrachial cutaneous n.

Median n. ⑥

⑱ Triceps brachii m.—lateral head

Ulnar n. ⑪

㉔ Triceps brachii m.—medial head

Brachialis m. ②

Musculocutaneous n.

Brachial a. ⑤

Inf. ulnar collateral a.

⑭ Lateral epicondyle

Medial epicondyle ⑮

㉕ Radial recurrent a.

Common flexor mm. tendon:
Flexor carpi radialis m.
Palmaris longus m.
Flexor carpi ulnaris m.

Deep radial n.

④ Supinator m.

Ulnar a. ⑦

Pronator teres m. (cut ends)

Ant. ulnar recurrent a. ⑯

③ Brachioradialis m. (sectioned)

Median n. ⑥

⑧ Radial a.

⑳ Superficial radial n.

Flexor digitorum superficialis m. ⑨

Flexor carpi ulnaris m. ⑩

← LATERAL

MEDIAL →

⑬ Pronator quadratus m.

Ulnar n.

⑲ Flexor carpi radialis m. tendon

Flexor pollicis longus m. ⑫

Median n.

Ulnar a.

Deep palmar br. of ulnar a. ㉓

Palmar br. of median n. ㉒ (cut end)

⑳ Opponens pollicis m.   Adductor pollicis m. ㉑

①

⑱

⑭

⑧

④

③ (sectioned)

㉖ Ant. interosseous n.

⑳

㉑

⑲

㉓

⑰

㉔

②

⑮

⑤

⑯

⑦

⑥

Post. ulnar recurrent a. ㉘

⑩ (sectioned)

Flexor digitorum profundus m. ㉙

⑪

⑦

⑬

㉒

ANTERIOR VIEWS

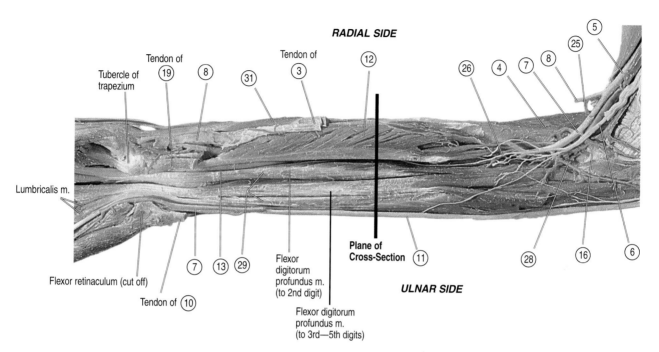

RADIAL SIDE

Tubercle of trapezium

Tendon of ⑲ ⑧ ㉛ Tendon of ③ ⑫ ㉖ ④ ⑦ ⑧ ㉕ ⑤

Lumbricalis m.

⑦ ⑬ ㉙

Flexor retinaculum (cut off)

Tendon of ⑩

Flexor digitorum profundus m. (to 2nd digit)

Flexor digitorum profundus m. (to 3rd—5th digits)

Plane of Cross-Section ⑪

㉘ ⑯ ⑥

ULNAR SIDE

ANTERIOR ↑

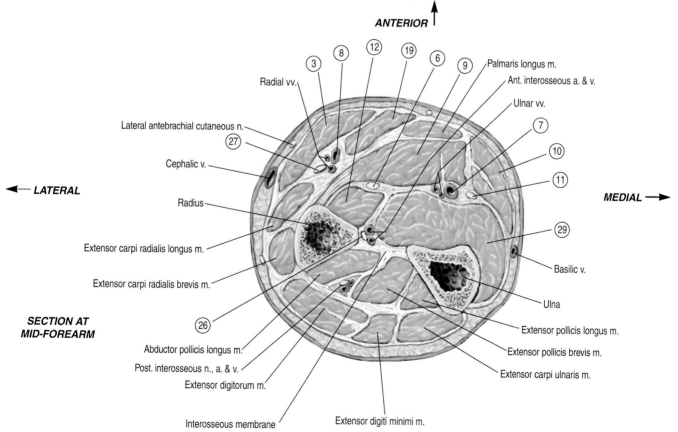

Radial vv.

Lateral antebrachial cutaneous n. ㉗

Cephalic v.

Radius

Extensor carpi radialis longus m.

Extensor carpi radialis brevis m.

SECTION AT MID-FOREARM

㉖

Abductor pollicis longus m.

Post. interosseous n., a. & v.

Extensor digitorum m.

Interosseous membrane

③ ⑧ ⑫ ⑲ ⑥ ⑨

Palmaris longus m.

Ant. interosseous a. & v.

Ulnar vv.

⑦

⑩

⑪

㉙

Basilic v.

Ulna

Extensor pollicis longus m.

Extensor pollicis brevis m.

Extensor carpi ulnaris m.

Extensor digiti minimi m.

← LATERAL

MEDIAL →

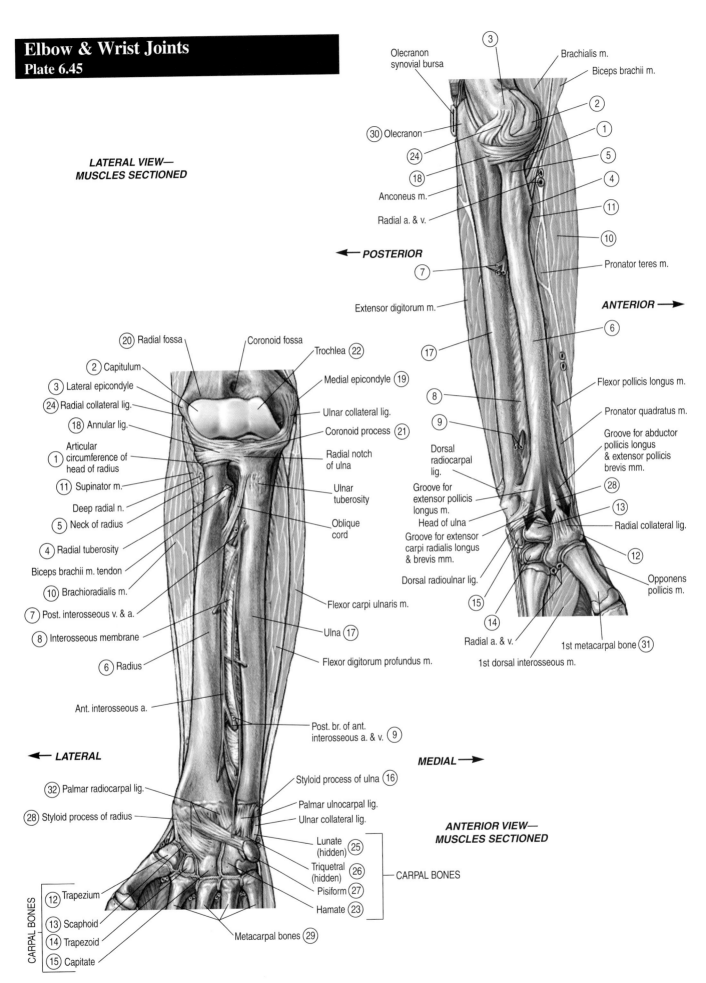

LATERAL VIEW—
MUSCLES SECTIONED

(3) Olecranon synovial bursa

Brachialis m.

Biceps brachii m.

(2)

(1)

(5)

(4)

(11)

(10)

(30) Olecranon

(24)

(18)

Anconeus m.

Radial a. & v.

◄— POSTERIOR

(7)

Extensor digitorum m.

Pronator teres m.

ANTERIOR —►

(6)

(8)

(9)

(17)

Dorsal radiocarpal lig.

Flexor pollicis longus m.

Pronator quadratus m.

Groove for abductor pollicis longus & extensor pollicis brevis mm.

(28)

(13)

Radial collateral lig.

(12)

Opponens pollicis m.

Groove for extensor pollicis longus m.

Head of ulna

Groove for extensor carpi radialis longus & brevis mm.

Dorsal radioulnar lig.

(15)

(14)

Radial a. & v.

1st dorsal interosseous m.

1st metacarpal bone (31)

(20) Radial fossa

Coronoid fossa

Trochlea (22)

Medial epicondyle (19)

(2) Capitulum

(3) Lateral epicondyle

(24) Radial collateral lig.

(18) Annular lig.

Articular circumference of head of radius (1)

(11) Supinator m.

Deep radial n.

(5) Neck of radius

(4) Radial tuberosity

Biceps brachii m. tendon

(10) Brachioradialis m.

(7) Post. interosseous v. & a.

(8) Interosseous membrane

(6) Radius

Ant. interosseous a.

Ulnar collateral lig.

Coronoid process (21)

Radial notch of ulna

Ulnar tuberosity

Oblique cord

Flexor carpi ulnaris m.

Ulna (17)

Flexor digitorum profundus m.

Post. br. of ant. interosseous a. & v. (9)

◄— LATERAL

MEDIAL —►

ANTERIOR VIEW—
MUSCLES SECTIONED

(32) Palmar radiocarpal lig.

(28) Styloid process of radius

Styloid process of ulna (16)

Palmar ulnocarpal lig.

Ulnar collateral lig.

Lunate (hidden) (25)

Triquetral (hidden) (26)

Pisiform (27)

Hamate (23)

CARPAL BONES

Metacarpal bones (29)

CARPAL BONES

(12) Trapezium

(13) Scaphoid

(14) Trapezoid

(15) Capitate

LATERAL VIEW

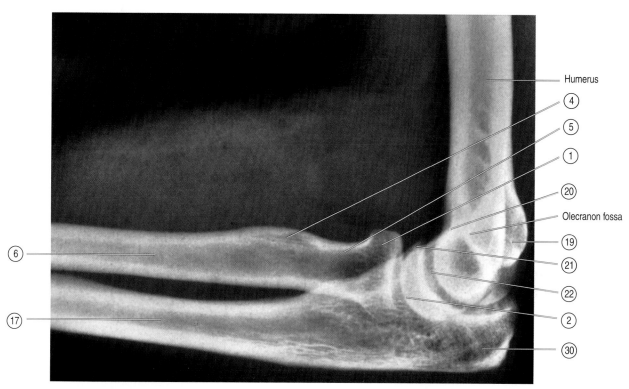

Humerus
4
5
1
20
Olecranon fossa
19
21
22
2
30
6
17

ANTEROPOSTERIOR VIEW

LATERAL VIEW

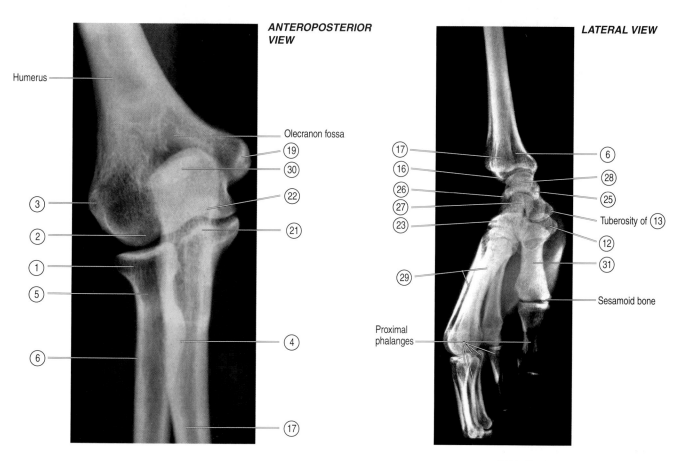

Humerus

Olecranon fossa
19
30
3
22
2
21
1
5
4
6
17

17
16
26
27
23
6
28
25
Tuberosity of 13
12
31
29
Sesamoid bone
Proximal phalanges

Lateral Forearm & Hand
Plate 6.47

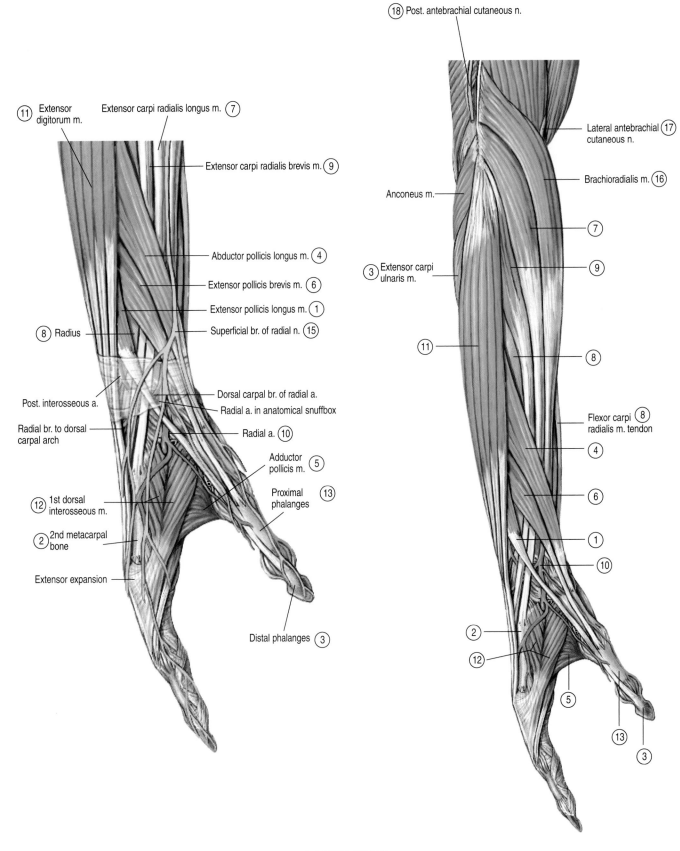

(11) Extensor digitorum m.

Extensor carpi radialis longus m. (7)

Extensor carpi radialis brevis m. (9)

Abductor pollicis longus m. (4)

Extensor pollicis brevis m. (6)

Extensor pollicis longus m. (1)

(8) Radius

Superficial br. of radial n. (15)

Dorsal carpal br. of radial a.

Radial a. in anatomical snuffbox

Post. interosseous a.

Radial br. to dorsal carpal arch

Radial a. (10)

Adductor pollicis m. (5)

Proximal phalanges (13)

(12) 1st dorsal interosseous m.

(2) 2nd metacarpal bone

Extensor expansion

Distal phalanges (3)

(18) Post. antebrachial cutaneous n.

Lateral antebrachial (17) cutaneous n.

Brachioradialis m. (16)

Anconeus m.

(7)

(3) Extensor carpi ulnaris m.

(9)

(11)

(8)

Flexor carpi (8) radialis m. tendon

(4)

(6)

(1)

(10)

(2)

(12)

(5)

(13)

(3)

LATERAL VIEWS

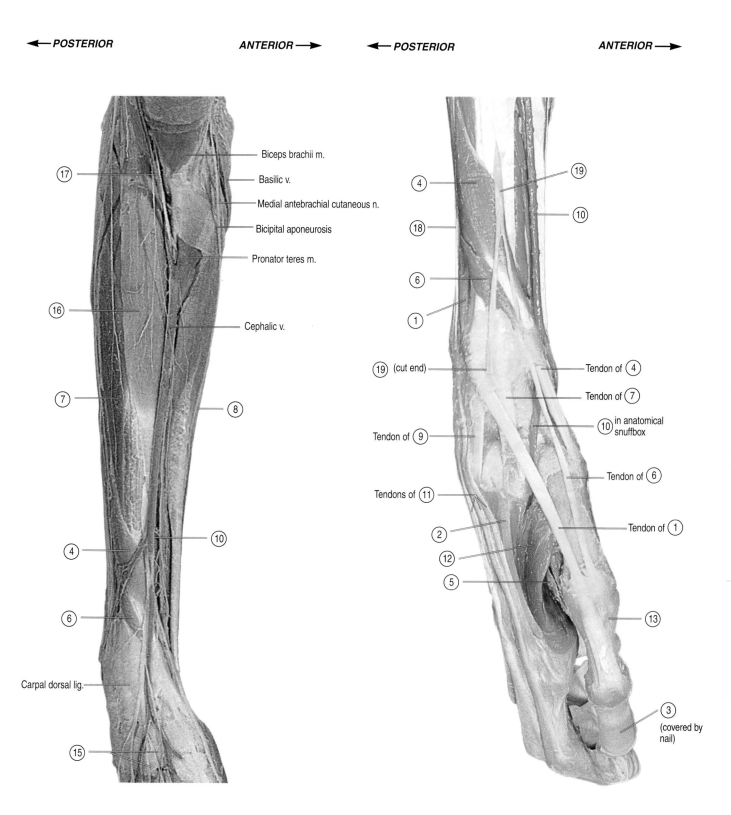

← POSTERIOR

ANTERIOR →

← POSTERIOR

ANTERIOR →

Biceps brachii m.

17

Basilic v.

Medial antebrachial cutaneous n.

Bicipital aponeurosis

Pronator teres m.

16

Cephalic v.

7

8

4

6

Carpal dorsal lig.

15

4

18

6

1

19

10

19 (cut end)

Tendon of 4

Tendon of 7

10 in anatomical snuffbox

Tendon of 9

Tendon of 6

Tendons of 11

2

Tendon of 1

12

5

13

3
(covered by nail)

LATERAL VIEWS

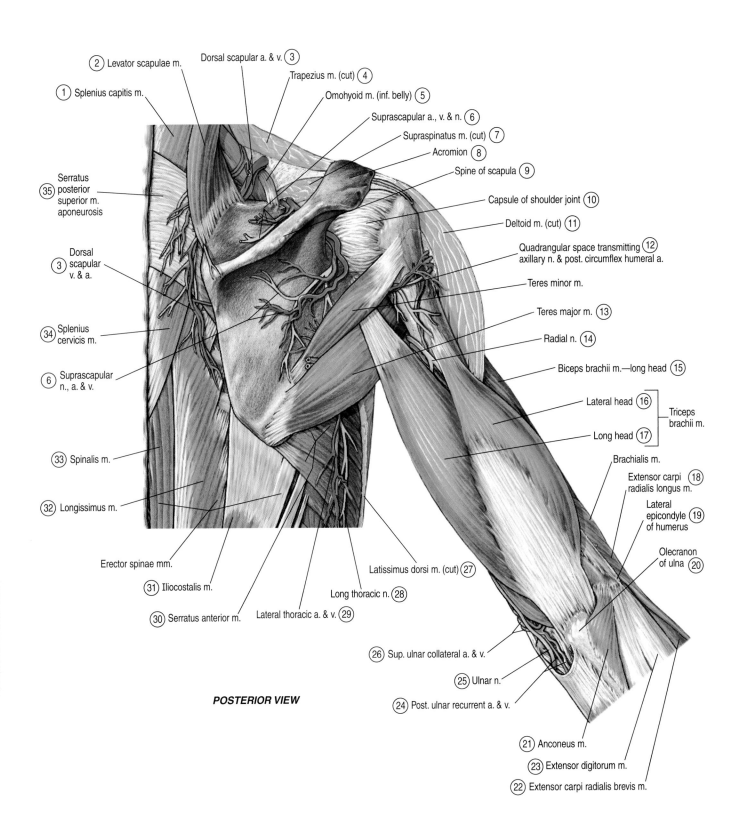

② Levator scapulae m.

Dorsal scapular a. & v. ③

Trapezius m. (cut) ④

① Splenius capitis m.

Omohyoid m. (inf. belly) ⑤

Suprascapular a., v. & n. ⑥

Supraspinatus m. (cut) ⑦

Acromion ⑧

Spine of scapula ⑨

Capsule of shoulder joint ⑩

Deltoid m. (cut) ⑪

Quadrangular space transmitting ⑫
axillary n. & post. circumflex humeral a.

Teres minor m.

Teres major m. ⑬

Radial n. ⑭

Biceps brachii m.—long head ⑮

Lateral head ⑯
                    } Triceps
Long head ⑰   brachii m.

Brachialis m.

Extensor carpi ⑱
radialis longus m.

Lateral
epicondyle ⑲
of humerus

Olecranon
of ulna ⑳

Serratus
㉟ posterior
superior m.
aponeurosis

Dorsal
③ scapular
v. & a.

㉞ Splenius
cervicis m.

⑥ Suprascapular
n., a. & v.

㉝ Spinalis m.

㉜ Longissimus m.

Erector spinae mm.

㉛ Iliocostalis m.

㉚ Serratus anterior m.

Latissimus dorsi m. (cut) ㉗

Long thoracic n. ㉘

Lateral thoracic a. & v. ㉙

POSTERIOR VIEW

㉖ Sup. ulnar collateral a. & v.

㉕ Ulnar n.

㉔ Post. ulnar recurrent a. & v.

㉑ Anconeus m.

㉓ Extensor digitorum m.

㉒ Extensor carpi radialis brevis m.

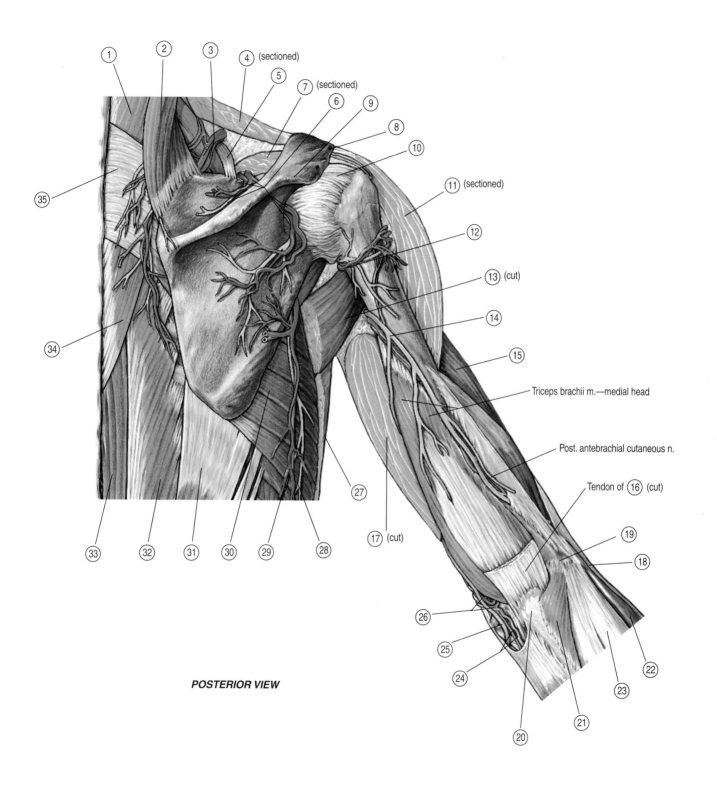

Triceps brachii m.—medial head

Post. antebrachial cutaneous n.

Tendon of ⑯ (cut)

POSTERIOR VIEW

Superficial Dorsum of Hand

Plate • 6.51

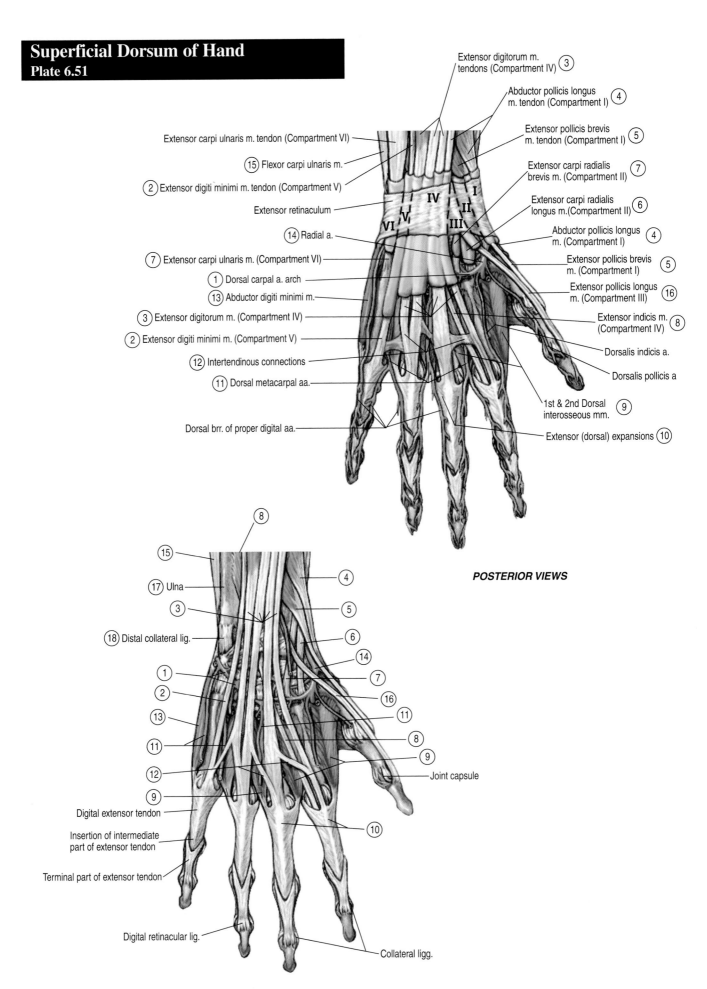

Extensor digitorum m. tendons (Compartment IV) ③

Abductor pollicis longus m. tendon (Compartment I) ④

Extensor pollicis brevis m. tendon (Compartment I) ⑤

Extensor carpi radialis brevis m. (Compartment II) ⑦

Extensor carpi radialis longus m.(Compartment II) ⑥

Abductor pollicis longus m. (Compartment I) ④

Extensor pollicis brevis m. (Compartment I) ⑤

Extensor pollicis longus m. (Compartment III) ⑯

Extensor indicis m. (Compartment IV) ⑧

Dorsalis indicis a.

Dorsalis pollicis a

1st & 2nd Dorsal interosseous mm. ⑨

Extensor (dorsal) expansions ⑩

Extensor carpi ulnaris m. tendon (Compartment VI)

⑮ Flexor carpi ulnaris m.

② Extensor digiti minimi m. tendon (Compartment V)

Extensor retinaculum

⑭ Radial a.

⑦ Extensor carpi ulnaris m. (Compartment VI)

① Dorsal carpal a. arch

⑬ Abductor digiti minimi m.

③ Extensor digitorum m. (Compartment IV)

② Extensor digiti minimi m. (Compartment V)

⑫ Intertendinous connections

⑪ Dorsal metacarpal aa.

Dorsal brr. of proper digital aa.

POSTERIOR VIEWS

⑧

⑮

⑰ Ulna

③

⑱ Distal collateral lig.

①

②

⑬

⑪

⑫

⑨

Digital extensor tendon

Insertion of intermediate part of extensor tendon

Terminal part of extensor tendon

Digital retinacular lig.

④

⑤

⑥

⑭

⑦

⑯

⑪

⑧

⑨

Joint capsule

⑩

Collateral ligg.

③

⑰

⑧

⑳ Post. interosseous a. & v.

⑲ Distal ulnar collateral lig.

㉓ Dorsal carpal br. of ulnar a.

①

㉖ Dorsal carpometacarpal lig.

②

⑬

㉔ 4th dorsal interosseous m.

④

⑤

⑦

⑥

⑭

Dorsal carpal venous arch

Radial a.—dorsal carpal br. ㉗

Dorsal pollicis a. ㉕

⑪

⑨

⑧

⑩

Proximal interphalangeal
joint capsule

Distal interphalangeal
joint capsule

Lateral bands

Insertion of extensor
tendon at base of distal
phalanges

Metacarpophalangeal joint capsule ㉒

Proximal phalanx ㉘

Triangular aponeuroses

Middle phalanx ⑲

Distal phalanx ㉑

POSTERIOR VIEWS

Post. interosseous n.

⑳

Dorsal radioulnar lig.

⑲

㉓

Hamate bone

㉖

①

⑬

⑪

㉔

㉒

㉘

⑲

㉑

Interosseous membrane

Dorsal tubercle of radius

Dorsal radiocarpal lig.

Distal radial collateral lig.

⑭

Scaphoid bone

㉗

㉕

⑨

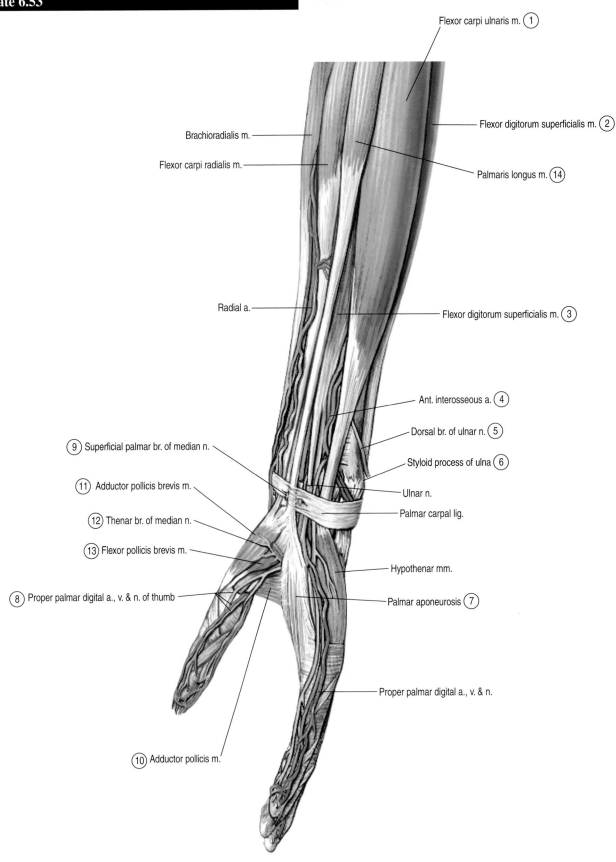

Flexor carpi ulnaris m. (1)

Flexor digitorum superficialis m. (2)

Brachioradialis m.

Flexor carpi radialis m.

Palmaris longus m. (14)

Radial a.

Flexor digitorum superficialis m. (3)

Ant. interosseous a. (4)

Dorsal br. of ulnar n. (5)

(9) Superficial palmar br. of median n.

Styloid process of ulna (6)

(11) Adductor pollicis brevis m.

Ulnar n.

(12) Thenar br. of median n.

Palmar carpal lig.

(13) Flexor pollicis brevis m.

Hypothenar mm.

(8) Proper palmar digital a., v. & n. of thumb

Palmar aponeurosis (7)

Proper palmar digital a., v. & n.

(10) Adductor pollicis m.

MEDIAL VIEW

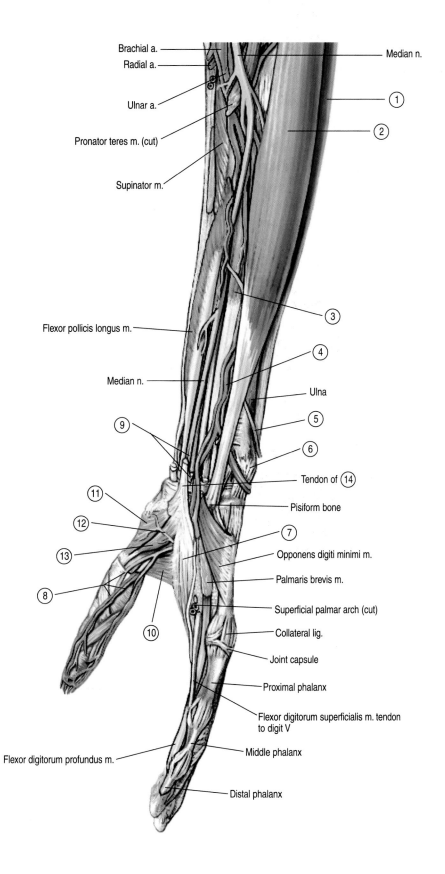

Brachial a.

Radial a.

Ulnar a.

Pronator teres m. (cut)

Supinator m.

Median n.

(1)

(2)

(3)

Flexor pollicis longus m.

(4)

Median n.

Ulna

(5)

(9)

(6)

Tendon of (14)

Pisiform bone

(11)

(12)

(7)

Opponens digiti minimi m.

(13)

Palmaris brevis m.

(8)

Superficial palmar arch (cut)

(10)

Collateral lig.

Joint capsule

Proximal phalanx

Flexor digitorum superficialis m. tendon
to digit V

Flexor digitorum profundus m.

Middle phalanx

Distal phalanx

MEDIAL VIEW

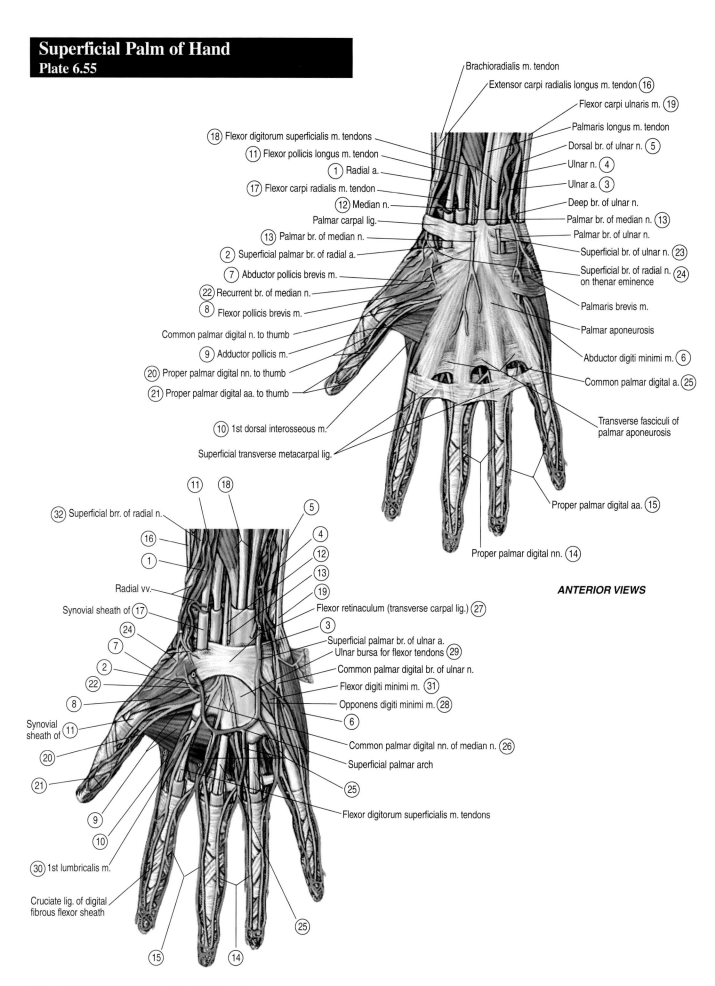

Brachioradialis m. tendon

Extensor carpi radialis longus m. tendon (16)

Flexor carpi ulnaris m. (19)

Palmaris longus m. tendon

Dorsal br. of ulnar n. (5)

Ulnar n. (4)

Ulnar a. (3)

Deep br. of ulnar n.

Palmar br. of median n. (13)

Palmar br. of ulnar n.

Superficial br. of ulnar n. (23)

Superficial br. of radial n. (24) on thenar eminence

Palmaris brevis m.

Palmar aponeurosis

Abductor digiti minimi m. (6)

Common palmar digital a. (25)

Transverse fasciculi of palmar aponeurosis

Proper palmar digital aa. (15)

Proper palmar digital nn. (14)

(18) Flexor digitorum superficialis m. tendons

(11) Flexor pollicis longus m. tendon

(1) Radial a.

(17) Flexor carpi radialis m. tendon

(12) Median n.

Palmar carpal lig.

(13) Palmar br. of median n.

(2) Superficial palmar br. of radial a.

(7) Abductor pollicis brevis m.

(22) Recurrent br. of median n.

(8) Flexor pollicis brevis m.

Common palmar digital n. to thumb

(9) Adductor pollicis m.

(20) Proper palmar digital nn. to thumb

(21) Proper palmar digital aa. to thumb

(10) 1st dorsal interosseous m.

Superficial transverse metacarpal lig.

ANTERIOR VIEWS

(11) (18)

(32) Superficial brr. of radial n.

(16)

(1)

Radial vv.

Synovial sheath of (17)

(24)

(7)

(2)

(22)

(8)

Synovial sheath of (11)

(20)

(21)

(9)

(10)

(30) 1st lumbricalis m.

Cruciate lig. of digital fibrous flexor sheath

(5)

(4)

(12)

(13)

(19)

Flexor retinaculum (transverse carpal lig.) (27)

(3)

Superficial palmar br. of ulnar a.

Ulnar bursa for flexor tendons (29)

Common palmar digital br. of ulnar n.

Flexor digiti minimi m. (31)

Opponens digiti minimi m. (28)

(6)

Common palmar digital nn. of median n. (26)

Superficial palmar arch

(25)

Flexor digitorum superficialis m. tendons

(15) (14)

(25)

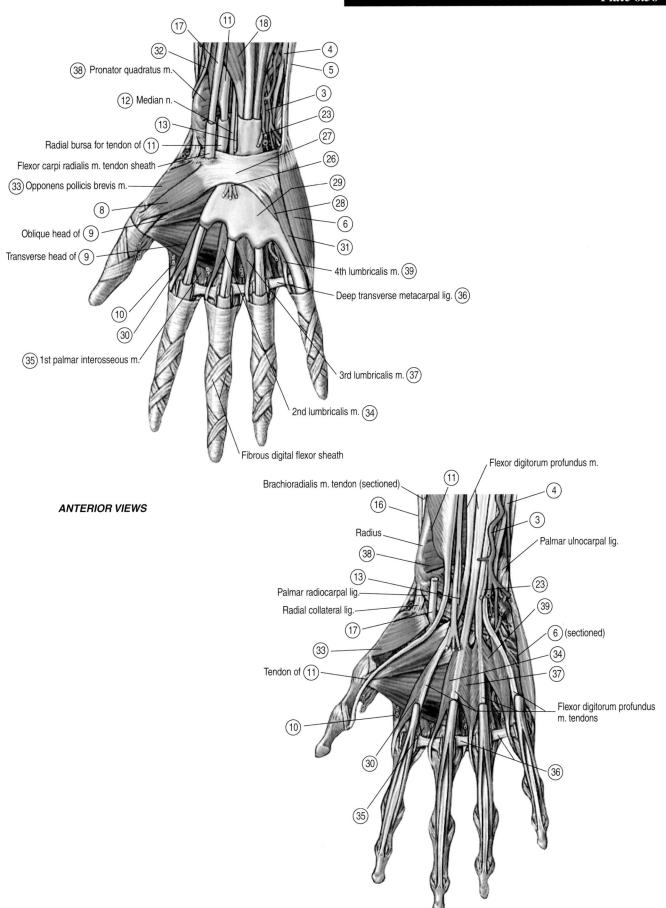

(17) (11) (18)

(32)

(38) Pronator quadratus m.

(12) Median n.

(13)

Radial bursa for tendon of (11)

Flexor carpi radialis m. tendon sheath

(33) Opponens pollicis brevis m.

(8)

Oblique head of (9)

Transverse head of (9)

(10)

(30)

(35) 1st palmar interosseous m.

(4)
(5)

(3)
(23)
(27)
(26)
(29)
(28)
(6)
(31)

4th lumbricalis m. (39)

Deep transverse metacarpal lig. (36)

3rd lumbricalis m. (37)

2nd lumbricalis m. (34)

Fibrous digital flexor sheath

ANTERIOR VIEWS

Flexor digitorum profundus m.

Brachioradialis m. tendon (sectioned)

(16)

Radius

(38)

(13)

Palmar radiocarpal lig.

Radial collateral lig.

(17)

(33)

Tendon of (11)

(10)

(30)

(35)

(11)

(4)
(3)

Palmar ulnocarpal lig.

(23)

(39)

(6) (sectioned)

(34)
(37)

Flexor digitorum profundus
m. tendons

(36)

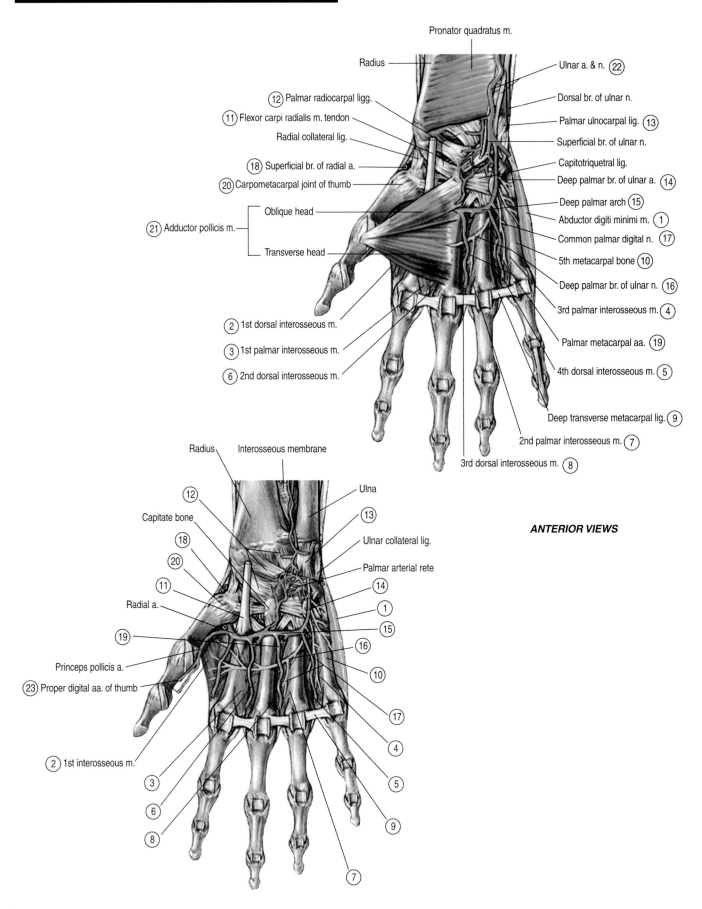

Pronator quadratus m.

Radius

Ulnar a. & n. (22)

Dorsal br. of ulnar n.

(12) Palmar radiocarpal ligg.

(11) Flexor carpi radialis m. tendon

Radial collateral lig.

Palmar ulnocarpal lig. (13)

Superficial br. of ulnar n.

Capitotriquetral lig.

(18) Superficial br. of radial a.

Deep palmar br. of ulnar a. (14)

(20) Carpometacarpal joint of thumb

Deep palmar arch (15)

Oblique head

Abductor digiti minimi m. (1)

(21) Adductor pollicis m.

Common palmar digital n. (17)

5th metacarpal bone (10)

Transverse head

Deep palmar br. of ulnar n. (16)

3rd palmar interosseous m. (4)

(2) 1st dorsal interosseous m.

Palmar metacarpal aa. (19)

(3) 1st palmar interosseous m.

4th dorsal interosseous m. (5)

(6) 2nd dorsal interosseous m.

Deep transverse metacarpal lig. (9)

2nd palmar interosseous m. (7)

3rd dorsal interosseous m. (8)

Radius   Interosseous membrane

ANTERIOR VIEWS

(12)

Ulna

Capitate bone

(13)

(18)

Ulnar collateral lig.

(20)

Palmar arterial rete

(11)

(14)

Radial a.

(1)

(15)

(19)

(16)

Princeps pollicis a.

(10)

(23) Proper digital aa. of thumb

(17)

(4)

(2) 1st interosseous m.

(5)

(3)

(6)

(9)

(8)

(7)

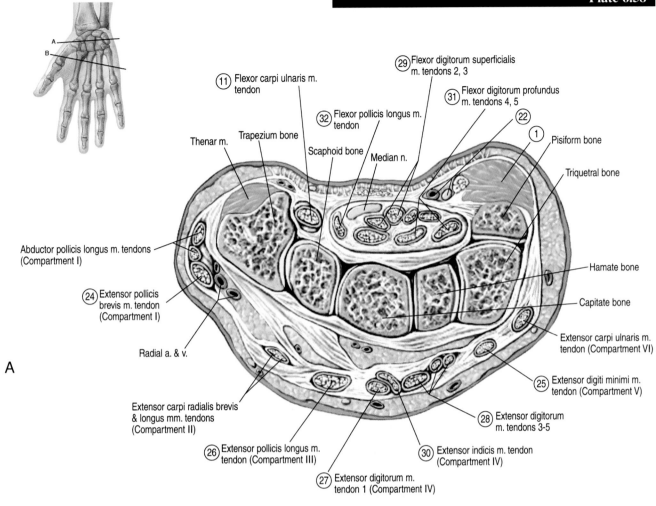

(11) Flexor carpi ulnaris m. tendon

(29) Flexor digitorum superficialis m. tendons 2, 3

(32) Flexor pollicis longus m. tendon

(31) Flexor digitorum profundus m. tendons 4, 5

(22)

(1)

Thenar m.

Trapezium bone

Scaphoid bone

Median n.

Pisiform bone

Triquetral bone

Abductor pollicis longus m. tendons (Compartment I)

(24) Extensor pollicis brevis m. tendon (Compartment I)

Hamate bone

Capitate bone

Radial a. & v.

Extensor carpi ulnaris m. tendon (Compartment VI)

A

Extensor carpi radialis brevis & longus mm. tendons (Compartment II)

(26) Extensor pollicis longus m. tendon (Compartment III)

(27) Extensor digitorum m. tendon 1 (Compartment IV)

(30) Extensor indicis m. tendon (Compartment IV)

(28) Extensor digitorum m. tendons 3-5

(25) Extensor digiti minimi m. tendon (Compartment V)

◄— RADIAL SIDE

DISTAL VIEWS OF SECTIONS THROUGH RIGHT WRIST (TOP) & HAND (BOTTOM)

ULNAR SIDE —►

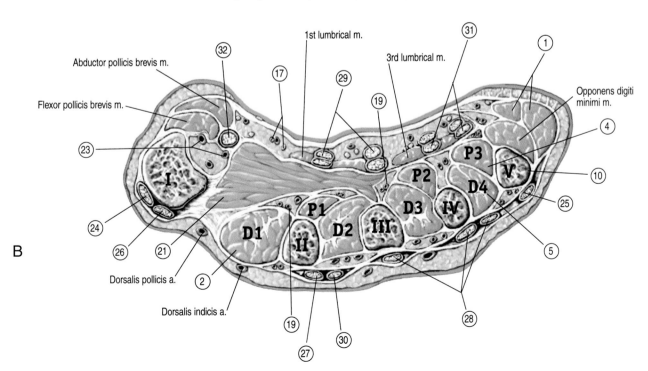

1st lumbrical m.

(31)

(1)

Abductor pollicis brevis m.

(32)

(17)

(29)

3rd lumbrical m.

(19)

Opponens digiti minimi m.

Flexor pollicis brevis m.

(4)

(23)

P3

V

(10)

I

P2

D4

(25)

(24)

P1

D3

IV

(5)

(26) (21)

D1

D2

III

(28)

Dorsalis pollicis a.

(2)

B

Dorsalis indicis a.

(19)

(27)

(30)

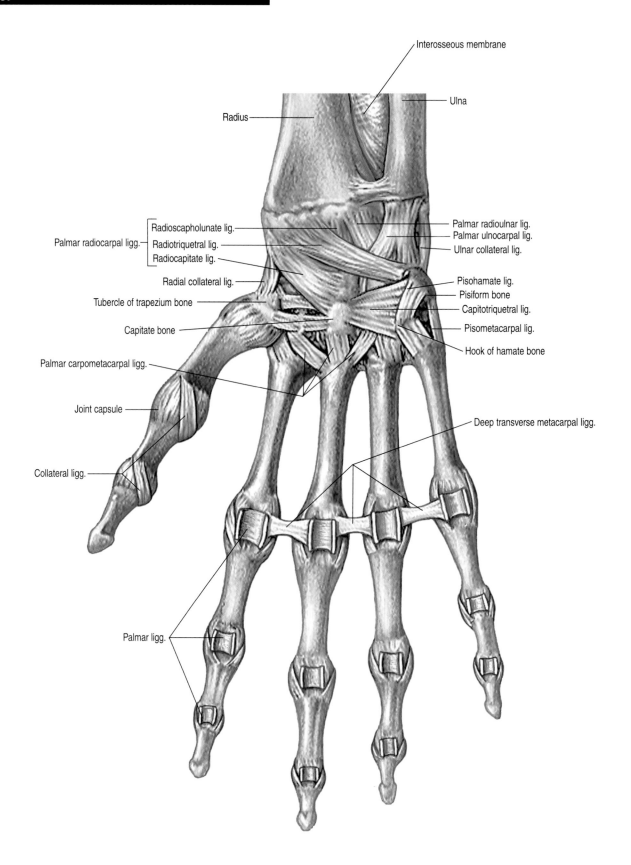

Interosseous membrane

Ulna

Radius

Radioscapholunate lig.

Palmar radiocarpal ligg.

Radiotriquetral lig.

Radiocapitate lig.

Radial collateral lig.

Tubercle of trapezium bone

Capitate bone

Palmar carpometacarpal ligg.

Joint capsule

Collateral ligg.

Palmar radioulnar lig.

Palmar ulnocarpal lig.

Ulnar collateral lig.

Pisohamate lig.

Pisiform bone

Capitotriquetral lig.

Pisometacarpal lig.

Hook of hamate bone

Deep transverse metacarpal ligg.

Palmar ligg.

ANTERIOR VIEW OF PALMAR SURFACE

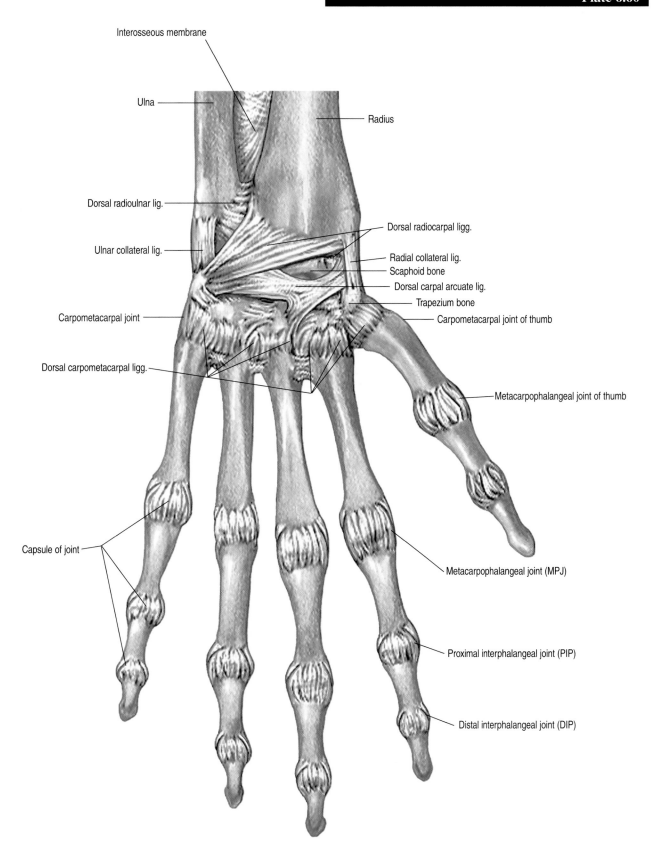

Interosseous membrane

Ulna

Radius

Dorsal radioulnar lig.

Dorsal radiocarpal ligg.

Ulnar collateral lig.

Radial collateral lig.

Scaphoid bone

Dorsal carpal arcuate lig.

Trapezium bone

Carpometacarpal joint

Carpometacarpal joint of thumb

Dorsal carpometacarpal ligg.

Metacarpophalangeal joint of thumb

Capsule of joint

Metacarpophalangeal joint (MPJ)

Proximal interphalangeal joint (PIP)

Distal interphalangeal joint (DIP)

POSTERIOR VIEW OF DORSAL SURFACE

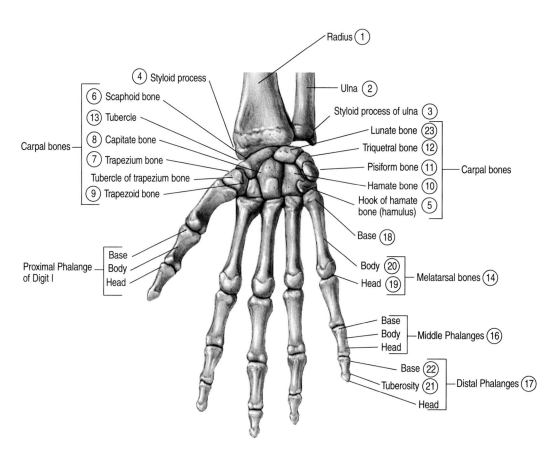

Radius ①

④ Styloid process

⑥ Scaphoid bone

⑬ Tubercle

⑧ Capitate bone

Carpal bones

⑦ Trapezium bone

Tubercle of trapezium bone

⑨ Trapezoid bone

Ulna ②

Styloid process of ulna ③

Lunate bone ㉓

Triquetral bone ⑫

Pisiform bone ⑪

Hamate bone ⑩

Hook of hamate bone (hamulus) ⑤

Carpal bones

Base ⑱

Proximal Phalange of Digit I

Base

Body

Head

Body ⑳

Head ⑲

Melatarsal bones ⑭

Base

Body

Head

Middle Phalanges ⑯

Base ㉒

Tuberosity ㉑

Head

Distal Phalanges ⑰

ANTERIOR VIEW

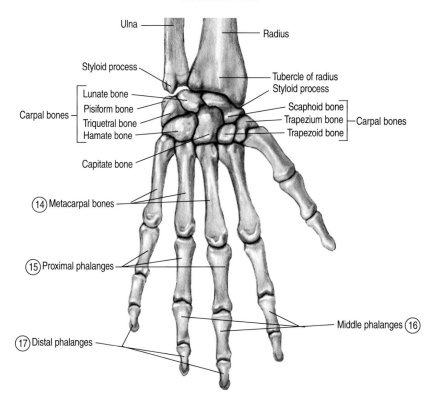

Ulna

Radius

Styloid process

Tubercle of radius

Styloid process

Lunate bone

Pisiform bone

Carpal bones

Triquetral bone

Hamate bone

Scaphoid bone

Trapezium bone

Trapezoid bone

Carpal bones

Capitate bone

⑭ Metacarpal bones

⑮ Proximal phalanges

Middle phalanges ⑯

⑰ Distal phalanges

POSTERIOR VIEW

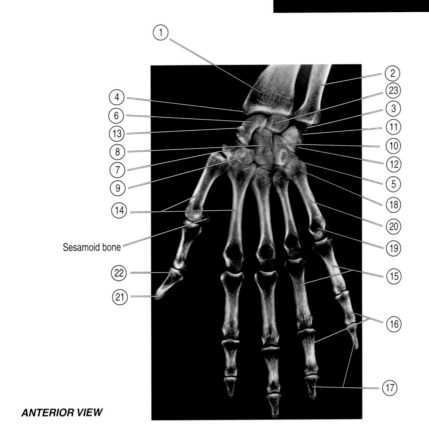

ANTERIOR VIEW

Sesamoid bone

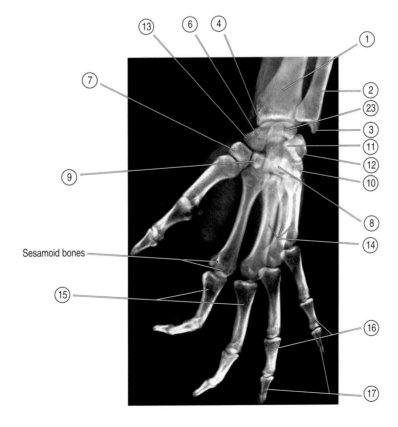

Sesamoid bones

OBLIQUE VIEW

Head and Neck

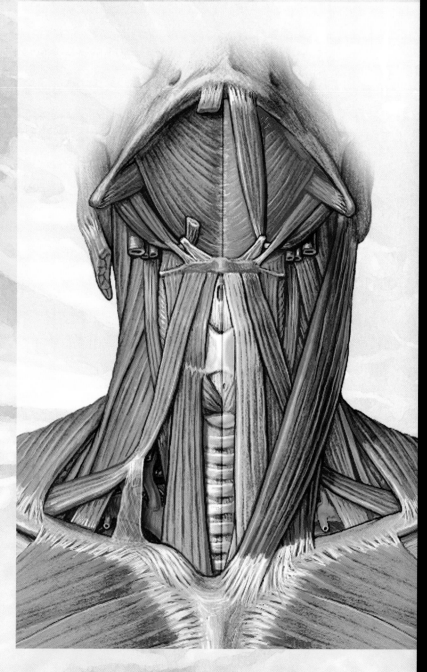

Chapter **7**

Topography
Plate 7.1

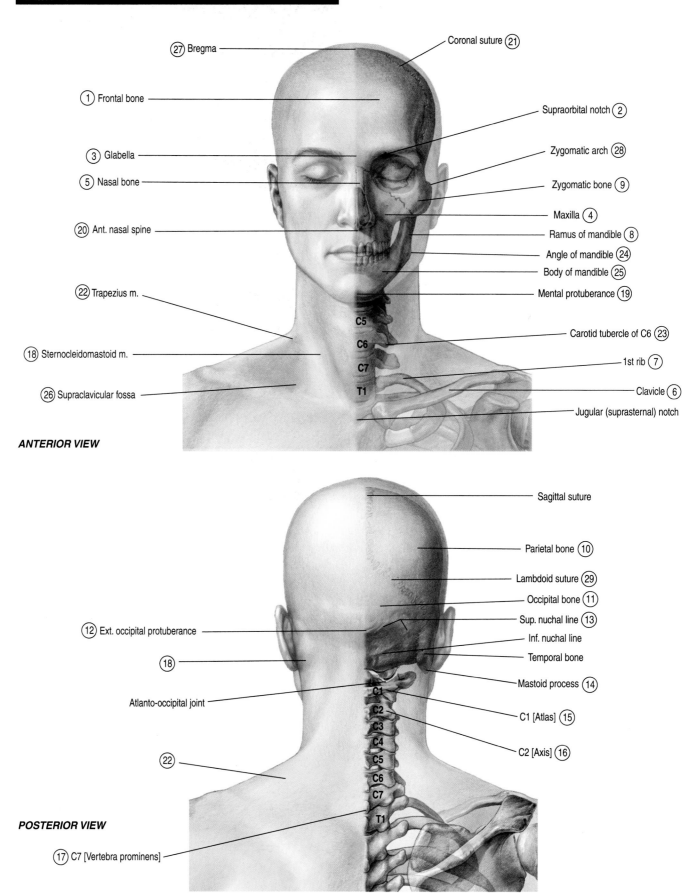

Bregma ㉗

Coronal suture ㉑

① Frontal bone

Supraorbital notch ②

③ Glabella

Zygomatic arch ㉘

⑤ Nasal bone

Zygomatic bone ⑨

Maxilla ④

⑳ Ant. nasal spine

Ramus of mandible ⑧

Angle of mandible ㉔

Body of mandible ㉕

㉒ Trapezius m.

Mental protuberance ⑲

C5

⑱ Sternocleidomastoid m.

C6

Carotid tubercle of C6 ㉓

C7

1st rib ⑦

㉖ Supraclavicular fossa

T1

Clavicle ⑥

Jugular (suprasternal) notch

ANTERIOR VIEW

Sagittal suture

Parietal bone ⑩

Lambdoid suture ㉙

Occipital bone ⑪

Sup. nuchal line ⑬

⑫ Ext. occipital protuberance

Inf. nuchal line

⑱

Temporal bone

Mastoid process ⑭

Atlanto-occipital joint

C1

C2

C1 [Atlas] ⑮

C3

C4

C2 [Axis] ⑯

㉒

C5

C6

C7

T1

POSTERIOR VIEW

⑰ C7 [Vertebra prominens]

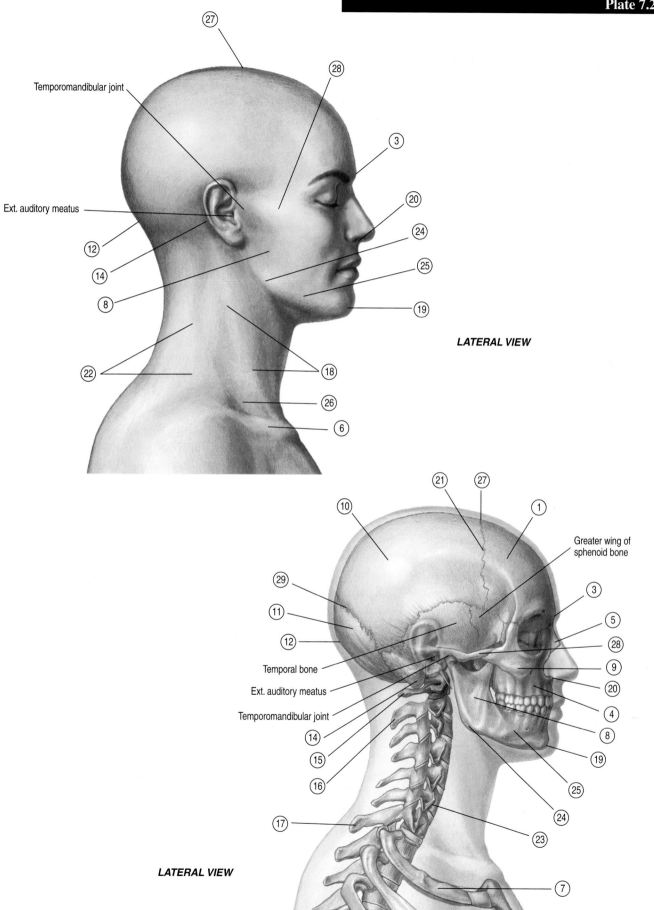

(27)

(28)

(3)

Temporomandibular joint

(20)

Ext. auditory meatus

(24)

(12)

(25)

(14)

(19)

(8)

LATERAL VIEW

(22)

(18)

(26)

(6)

(21) (27)

(10)

(1)

Greater wing of
sphenoid bone

(29)

(3)

(11)

(5)

(12)

(28)

Temporal bone

(9)

Ext. auditory meatus

(20)

Temporomandibular joint

(4)

(14)

(8)

(15)

(19)

(16)

(25)

(24)

LATERAL VIEW

(23)

(17)

(7)

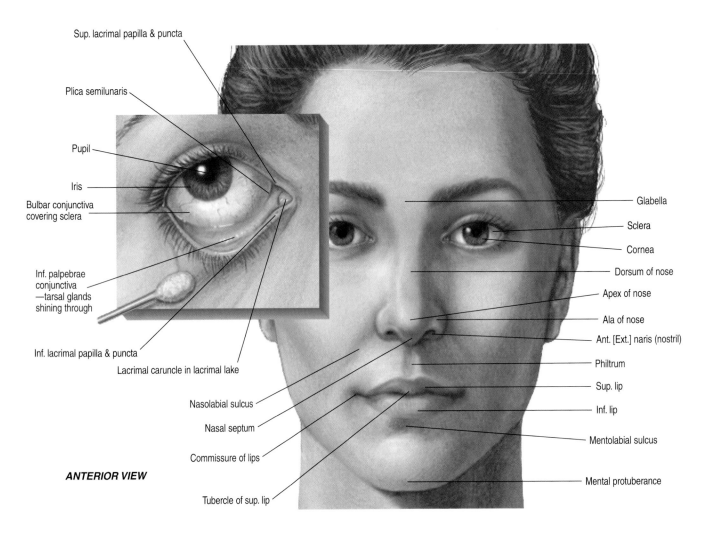

Sup. lacrimal papilla & puncta

Plica semilunaris

Pupil

Iris

Bulbar conjunctiva covering sclera

Inf. palpebrae conjunctiva —tarsal glands shining through

Inf. lacrimal papilla & puncta

Lacrimal caruncle in lacrimal lake

Nasolabial sulcus

Nasal septum

Commissure of lips

ANTERIOR VIEW

Tubercle of sup. lip

Glabella

Sclera

Cornea

Dorsum of nose

Apex of nose

Ala of nose

Ant. [Ext.] naris (nostril)

Philtrum

Sup. lip

Inf. lip

Mentolabial sulcus

Mental protuberance

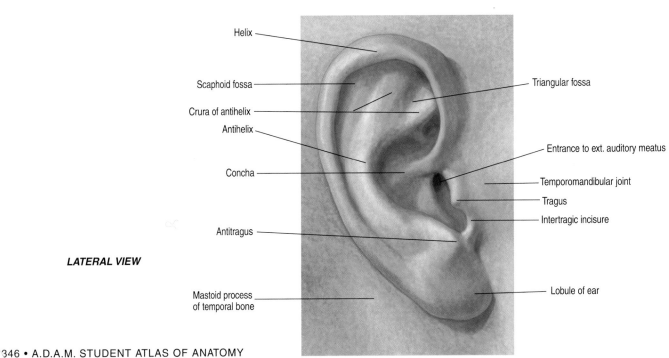

Helix

Scaphoid fossa

Crura of antihelix

Antihelix

Concha

Antitragus

LATERAL VIEW

Mastoid process of temporal bone

Triangular fossa

Entrance to ext. auditory meatus

Temporomandibular joint

Tragus

Intertragic incisure

Lobule of ear

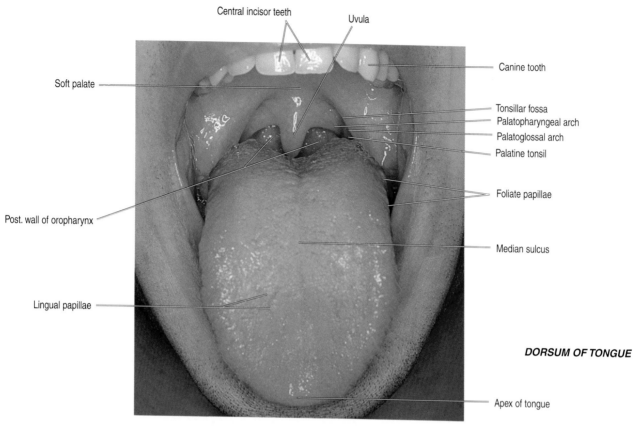

Central incisor teeth

Uvula

Canine tooth

Soft palate

Tonsillar fossa

Palatopharyngeal arch

Palatoglossal arch

Palatine tonsil

Foliate papillae

Post. wall of oropharynx

Median sulcus

Lingual papillae

DORSUM OF TONGUE

Apex of tongue

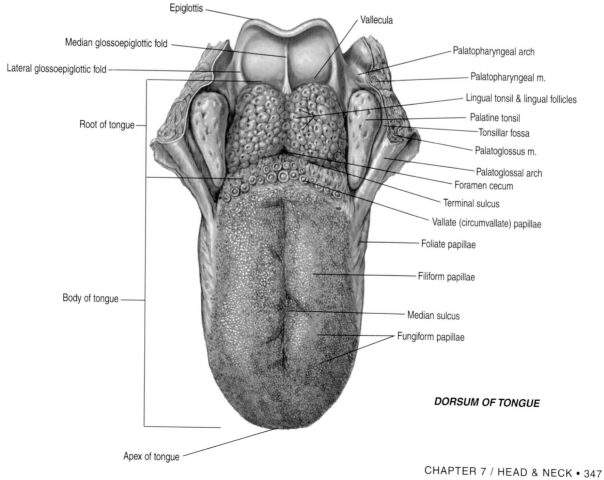

Epiglottis

Vallecula

Median glossoepiglottic fold

Palatopharyngeal arch

Lateral glossoepiglottic fold

Palatopharyngeal m.

Lingual tonsil & lingual follicles

Palatine tonsil

Root of tongue

Tonsillar fossa

Palatoglossus m.

Palatoglossal arch

Foramen cecum

Terminal sulcus

Vallate (circumvallate) papillae

Foliate papillae

Filiform papillae

Body of tongue

Median sulcus

Fungiform papillae

DORSUM OF TONGUE

Apex of tongue

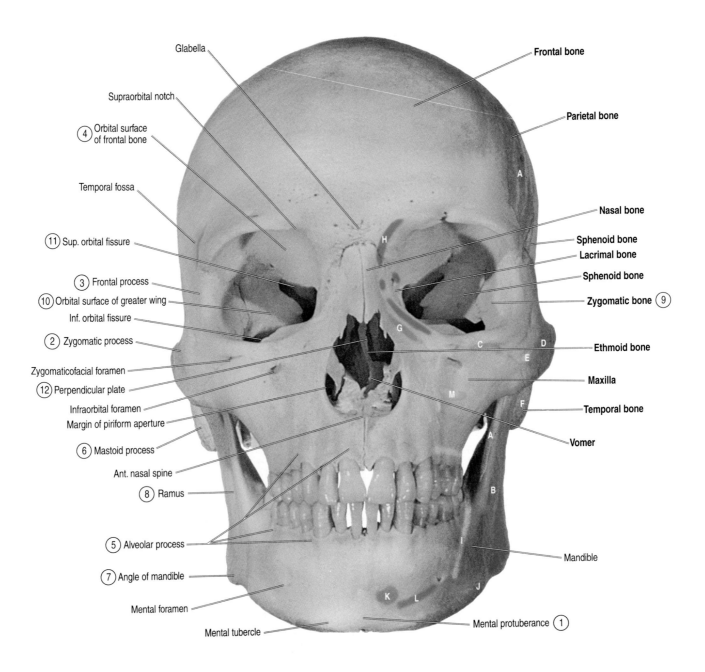

Glabella

Frontal bone

Supraorbital notch

Parietal bone

(4) Orbital surface of frontal bone

Temporal fossa

Nasal bone

(11) Sup. orbital fissure

Sphenoid bone

Lacrimal bone

(3) Frontal process

Sphenoid bone

(10) Orbital surface of greater wing

Zygomatic bone (9)

Inf. orbital fissure

(2) Zygomatic process

Ethmoid bone

Zygomaticofacial foramen

(12) Perpendicular plate

Maxilla

Infraorbital foramen

Temporal bone

Margin of piriform aperture

(6) Mastoid process

Vomer

Ant. nasal spine

(8) Ramus

(5) Alveolar process

Mandible

(7) Angle of mandible

Mental foramen

Mental protuberance (1)

Mental tubercle

ANTERIOR VIEW

(A) Temporalis

(B) Masseter

(C) Levator labii superioris

(D) Zygomaticus major

(E) Zygomaticus minor

(F) Sternocleidomastoid

(G) Levator labii superioris alaeque nasi

(H) Orbicularis oculi

(I) Buccinator

(J) Platysma

(K) Mentalis

(L) Depressor labii inferioris & Depressor anguli oris

(M) Levator anguli oris

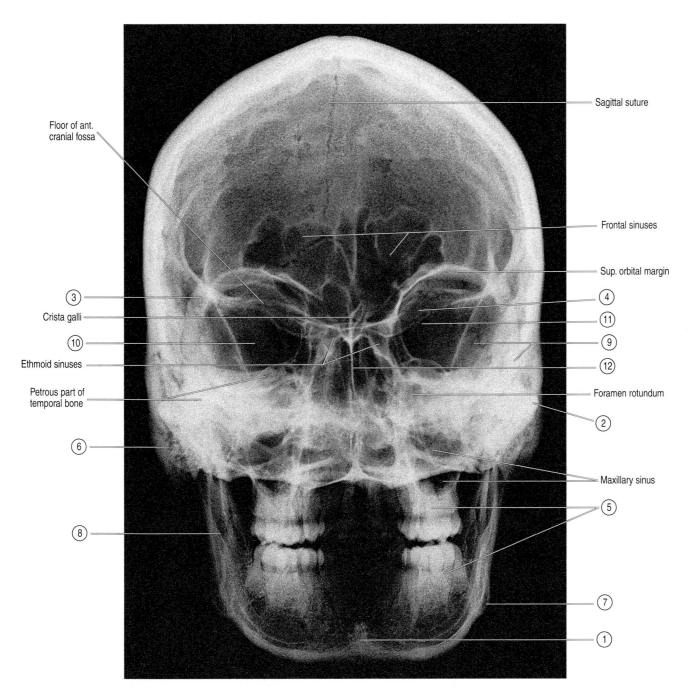

Sagittal suture

Floor of ant.
cranial fossa

Frontal sinuses

Sup. orbital margin

③

Crista galli

④

⑪

⑩

⑨

Ethmoid sinuses

⑫

Petrous part of
temporal bone

Foramen rotundum

②

⑥

Maxillary sinus

⑤

⑧

⑦

①

ANTEROPOSTERIOR VIEW OF SKULL

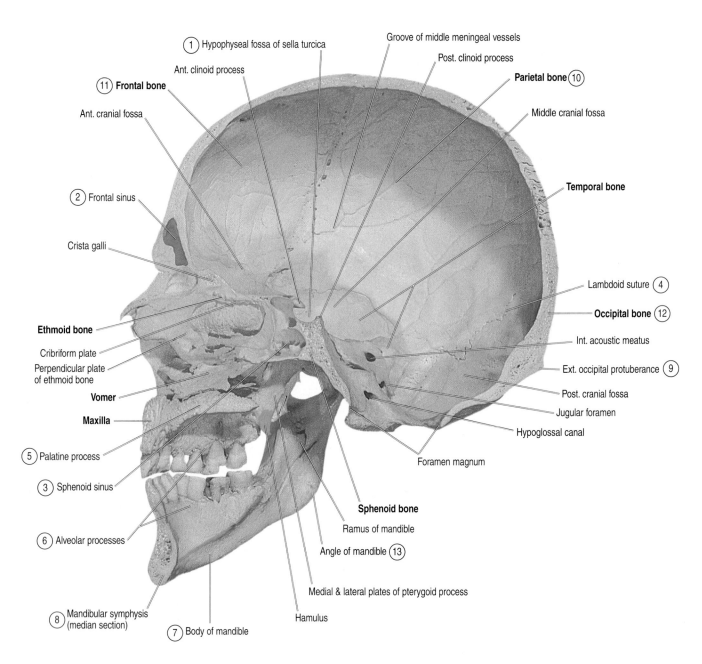

1. Hypophyseal fossa of sella turcica

Ant. clinoid process

Groove of middle meningeal vessels

Post. clinoid process

11 **Frontal bone**

Parietal bone 10

Ant. cranial fossa

Middle cranial fossa

2. Frontal sinus

Temporal bone

Crista galli

Lambdoid suture 4

Ethmoid bone

Occipital bone 12

Cribriform plate

Int. acoustic meatus

Perpendicular plate of ethmoid bone

Ext. occipital protuberance 9

Vomer

Post. cranial fossa

Maxilla

Jugular foramen

Hypoglossal canal

5. Palatine process

3. Sphenoid sinus

Foramen magnum

Sphenoid bone

6. Alveolar processes

Ramus of mandible

Angle of mandible 13

Medial & lateral plates of pterygoid process

8. Mandibular symphysis (median section)

Hamulus

7. Body of mandible

LEFT LATERAL VIEW OF SKULL SECTIONED IN MEDIAN PLANE

| Mylohyoid | Lateral pterygoid | Genioglossus |
| Superior pharyngeal constrictor | Medial pterygoid | Temporalis |

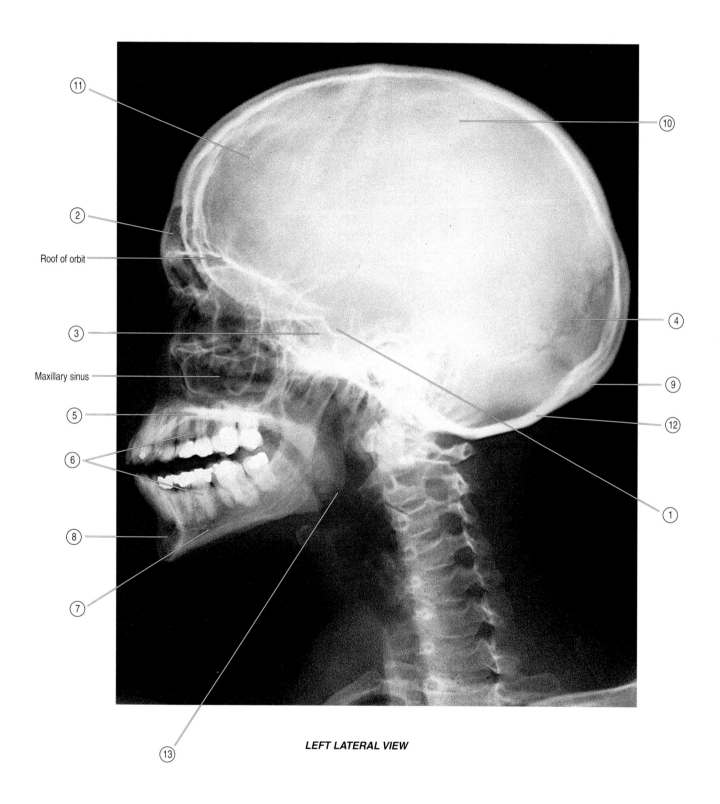

⑪

②

Roof of orbit

③

Maxillary sinus

⑤

⑥

⑧

⑦

⑩

④

⑨

⑫

①

⑬

LEFT LATERAL VIEW

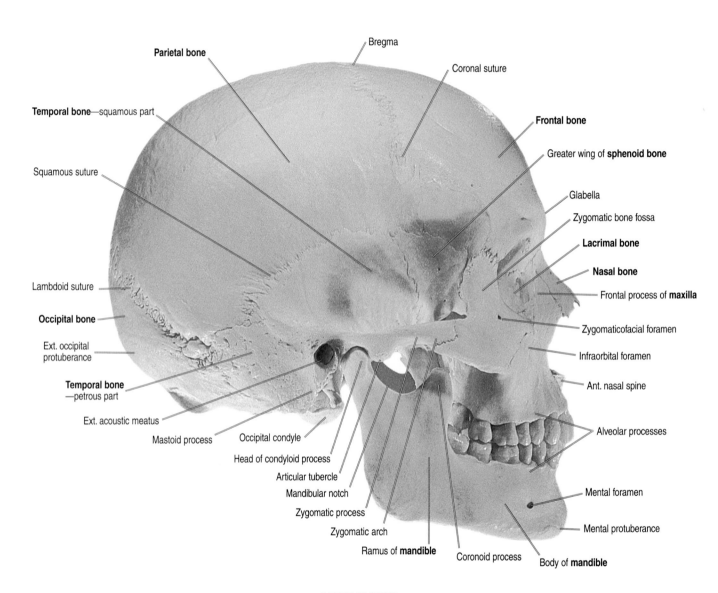

Bregma

Parietal bone

Coronal suture

Temporal bone—squamous part

Frontal bone

Greater wing of **sphenoid bone**

Squamous suture

Glabella

Zygomatic bone fossa

Lacrimal bone

Nasal bone

Lambdoid suture

Frontal process of **maxilla**

Occipital bone

Zygomaticofacial foramen

Ext. occipital protuberance

Infraorbital foramen

Temporal bone —petrous part

Ant. nasal spine

Ext. acoustic meatus

Mastoid process

Head of condyloid process

Occipital condyle

Alveolar processes

Articular tubercle

Mandibular notch

Zygomatic process

Zygomatic arch

Mental foramen

Mental protuberance

Ramus of **mandible**

Coronoid process

Body of **mandible**

LATERAL VIEW

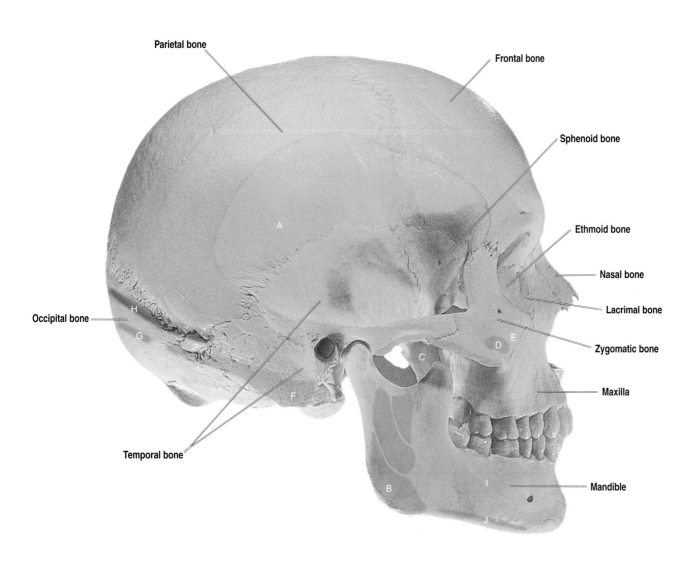

Parietal bone

Frontal bone

Sphenoid bone

Ethmoid bone

Nasal bone

Lacrimal bone

Occipital bone

Zygomatic bone

Maxilla

Temporal bone

Mandible

A Temporalis

B Masseter

C Lateral pterygoid

D Zygomaticus major

E Zygomaticus minor

F Sternocleidomastoid

G Trapezius

H Epicranius-occipital belly

I Buccinator

J Platysma

Cranial Foramina, Fissures & Canals
Table 7.1

Foramina/Openings	Contents
FACE	
Supraorbital notch/foramen	CN V^1 - supraorbital n. & vessels
Infraorbital notch/foramen	CN V^2 - infraorbital n. & vessels
Mental foramen	CN V^3 - mental n. & vessels
Zygomaticofacial foramen	CN V^2 - zygomaticofacial n. & vessels
ORBIT	
Superior orbital fissure	Passage between middle cranial fossa & orbit for CN III, V, VI, V^1 — lacrimal n., V^1 — frontal n., V^1—nasociliary n., postganglionic sympathetic n. fibers, & ophthalmic v.
Optic canal	CN II, & ophthalmic a.
Inferior orbital fissure	Passage between pterygopalatine fossa & orbit for CN V^2 — infraorbital n. & vessels, & nerves from pterygopalatine ganglion
Anterior ethmoidal foramen	CN V^1— ant. ethmoidal br. of nasociliary n. & vessels
Posterior ethmoidal foramen	CN V^1— post. ethmoidal br. of nasociliary n. & vessels
Nasolacrimal canal	Nasolacrimal duct
NASAL CAVITY	
Piriform aperture (anterior nasal aperture)	Anterior opening into nasal cavity
Incisive canals	CN V^1— nasopalatine n. & greater palatine vessels
Foramina in cribriform plates	CN I — Sensory axons from olfactory epithelium that collectively constitute olfactory nn.
Sphenoethmoidal recess	Duct from sphenoid sinuses
Superior meatus	Duct from post. ethmoid sinuses
Middle meatus	Ducts from frontal sinus, ant. & middle ethmoidal sinuses, & duct from maxillary sinus through semilunar hiatus
Anterior meatus	Nasolacrimal duct
Sphenopalatine foramen	CN V^2 — nasopalatine n. & sphenopalatine vessels
Choana (posterior nasal aperture)	Opening between nasal cavity & nasopharynx
LATERAL CRANIAL SURFACE	
Zygomaticofacial foramen	CN V^2 — zygomaticofacial n. & vessels
Pterygomaxillary fissure	Passage between infratemporal & pterygopalatine fossae for CN V^2 — post. sup. alveolar nn. & vessels, & 3rd part of maxillary a.
External acoustic meatus—bony part	Opening in temporal bone leading to tympanic membrane
Mastoid foramen	Mastoid br. of occipital a. & mastoid emissary v. to sigmoid sinus & diploic vv.
CRANIAL BASE	
Incisive fossa & canals	CN V^1 — nasopalatine n., & greater palatine vessels
Greater palatine foramen/canal	Passage between oral cavity & pterygopalatine fossa for CN V^2 — greater palatine n. & vessels
Lesser palatine foramina	Passages between greater palatine canal & oral cavity for CN V^2 — lesser palatine n. & vessels
Mandibular canal	CN V^3 — inf. alveolar n. & vessels
Foramen lacerum	Closed inferoexternally by fibrocartilage plug
Auditory tube - bony portion	Passage between nasopharynx & middle ear, tensor tympani m., & sup. tympanic a.
Pterygoid (vidian) canal	Passage through base of median pterygoid process between foramen lacerum & pterygopalatine fossa for CN VII — n. & vessels of pterygoid (vidian) canal
Foramen ovale	CN V^3 — mandibular n., CN IX — lesser petrosal n. & accessory meningeal a.
Foramen spinosum	CN V^3 — meningeal br. & middle meningeal vessels
Carotid canal	Internal carotid a. & sympathetic n. plexus
Stylomastoid foramen	CN VII — facial n., & stylomastoid vessels
Petrotympanic fissure	CN VII — chorda tympani n., & ant. tympanic a.
Mastoid canaliculus	CN IX — auricular br.
Tympanic canaliculus	CN IX — tympanic br., & inf. tympanic a.
Jugular fossa & foramen	CN IX, X & XI, sup. bulb of internal jugular v., inferior petrosal & sigmoid sinuses, & meningeal brr. of ascending pharyngeal & occipital aa.
Condylar fossa & canal	*Inconsistent* passage for condylar emissary v. between sigmoid sinus & vertebral venous plexi
Hypoglossal canal	CN XII — hypoglossal n., meningeal br. of ascending pharyngeal a.
Foramen magnum	Medulla & meninges of spinal cord, CN XI — spinal roots, vertebral aa., ant. & post. spinal aa., & brr. of internal vertebral venous plexus

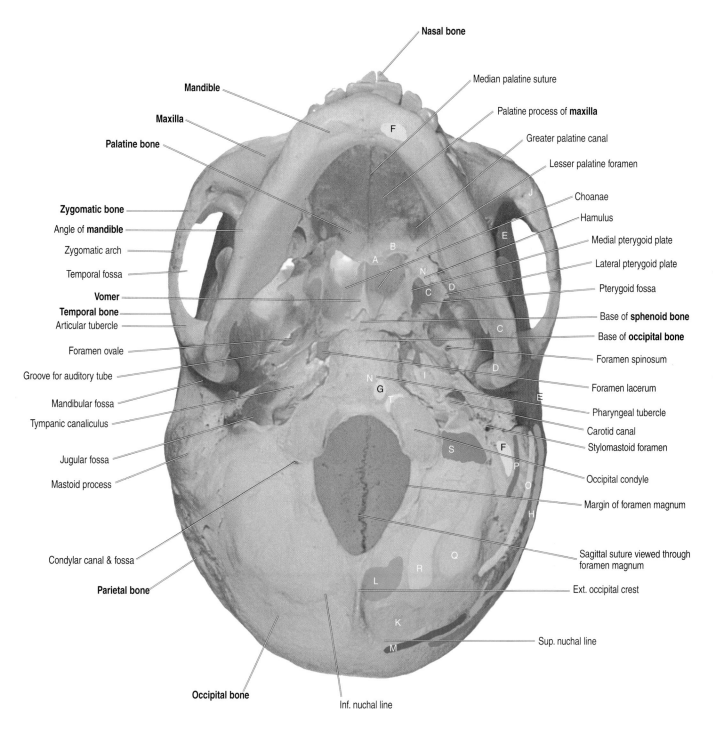

Nasal bone

Mandible

Maxilla

Palatine bone

Zygomatic bone

Angle of **mandible**

Zygomatic arch

Temporal fossa

Vomer

Temporal bone

Articular tubercle

Foramen ovale

Groove for auditory tube

Mandibular fossa

Tympanic canaliculus

Jugular fossa

Mastoid process

Condylar canal & fossa

Parietal bone

Occipital bone

Inf. nuchal line

Median palatine suture

Palatine process of **maxilla**

Greater palatine canal

Lesser palatine foramen

Choanae

Hamulus

Medial pterygoid plate

Lateral pterygoid plate

Pterygoid fossa

Base of **sphenoid bone**

Base of **occipital bone**

Foramen spinosum

Foramen lacerum

Pharyngeal tubercle

Carotid canal

Stylomastoid foramen

Occipital condyle

Margin of foramen magnum

Sagittal suture viewed through foramen magnum

Ext. occipital crest

Sup. nuchal line

INFERIOR VIEW OF CRANIAL BASE

A Musculus uvulae	**F** Digastric	**K** Semispinalis capitis	**P** Longissimus capitis
B Tensor veli palatini	**G** Longus capitis	**L** Rectus capitis posterior minor	**Q** Obliquus capitis superior
C Medial pterygoid	**H** Sternocleidomastoid	**M** Trapezius	**R** Rectus capitis posterior major
D Lateral pterygoid	**I** Levator veli palantini	**N** Superior pharyngeal constrictor	**S** Rectus capitis lateralis
E Temporalis	**J** Masseter	**O** Splenius capitis	**T** Rectus capitis anterior

Internal Neurocranial Foramina, Fissures & Canals
Table 7.2

Foramina/Openings	Contents
ANTERIOR CRANIAL FOSSA	
Foramen cecum	Inconsistent passage for nasal emissary vv. tributaries of superior sagittal sinus
Foramina in cribriform plates	CN I — Sensory axons from olfactory epithelium that collectively constitute the olfactory nn.
Anterior ethmoidal foramen	CN V^1 — anterior ethmoidal br. of nasociliary n. & vessels
Posterior ethmoidal foramen	CN V^1 — posterior ethmoidal br. of nasociliary n. & vessels
MIDDLE CRANIAL FOSSA	
Optic canal	CN II, & ophthalmic a.
Superior orbital fissure	Passage between middle cranial fossa & orbit for CN III, IV, VI, V1 — lacrimal n., V1 — frontal n., V^1 — nasociliary n., postganglionic sympathetic n. fibers, & ophthalmic v.
Foramen rotundum	CN V^2 — maxillary n.
Foramen ovale	CN V^3 — mandibular n., CH IX - lesser petrosal n. & accessory meningeal a.
Foramen spinosum	CN V^3 — meningeal br. & middle meningeal vessels
Foramen lacerum	Internal carotid a., sympathetic nn. & venous plexi from carotid canal, & CN VII — greater petrosal n.. Closed inferoexternally by fibrocartilage plug
Hiatus for greater petrosal n. (Facial hiatus)	CN VII — greater petrosal n., & petrosal br. of middle meningeal a.
Hiatus for lesser petrosal n.	CN IX — lesser petrosal n.
POSTERIOR CRANIAL FOSSA	
Internal acoustic meatus	CN VII & VIII, labyrinthine a.
Jugular fossa & foramen	CN IX, X & XI, superior bulb of internal jugular v., inferior petrosal & sigmoid sinuses, & meningeal brr. of ascendingpharyngeal & occipital aa.
Condylar fossa & canal	*Inconsistent* passage for condylar emissary v. between sigmoid sinus & vertebral venous plexi
Mastoid foramen	Mastoid br. of occipital a. & mastoid emissary v. to sigmoid sinus & diploic vv.
Hypoglossal canal	CN XII — hypoglossal n.
Foramen magnum	Medulla & meninges of spinal cord, CN XI— spinal roots, vertebral aa., ant. & post. spinal aa., & brr. of internal vertebral venous plexus

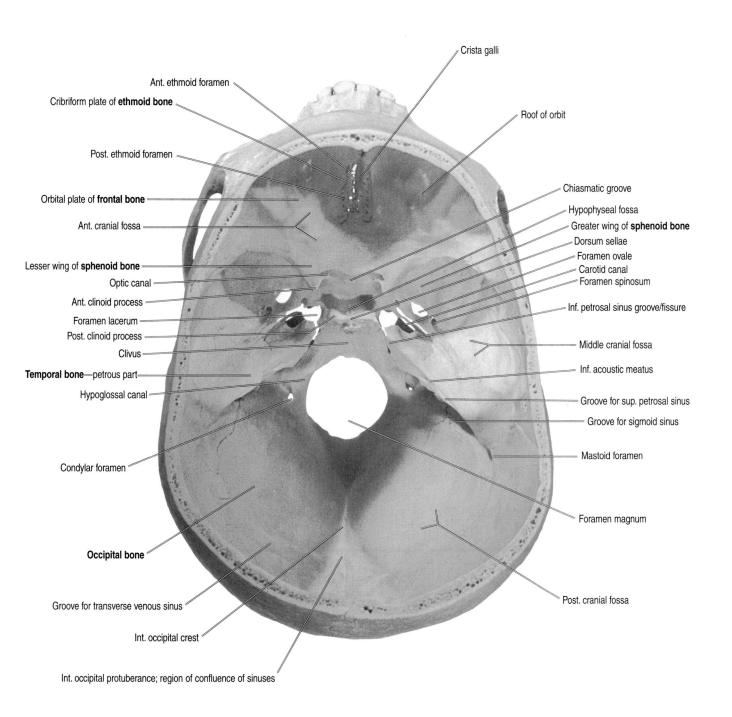

Crista galli

Ant. ethmoid foramen

Cribriform plate of **ethmoid bone**

Roof of orbit

Post. ethmoid foramen

Chiasmatic groove

Orbital plate of **frontal bone**

Hypophyseal fossa

Ant. cranial fossa

Greater wing of **sphenoid bone**

Dorsum sellae

Foramen ovale

Lesser wing of **sphenoid bone**

Carotid canal

Optic canal

Foramen spinosum

Ant. clinoid process

Inf. petrosal sinus groove/fissure

Foramen lacerum

Post. clinoid process

Middle cranial fossa

Clivus

Inf. acoustic meatus

Temporal bone—petrous part

Groove for sup. petrosal sinus

Hypoglossal canal

Groove for sigmoid sinus

Mastoid foramen

Condylar foramen

Foramen magnum

Occipital bone

Post. cranial fossa

Groove for transverse venous sinus

Int. occipital crest

Int. occipital protuberance; region of confluence of sinuses

SUPERIOR VIEW WITH CALVARIA REMOVED

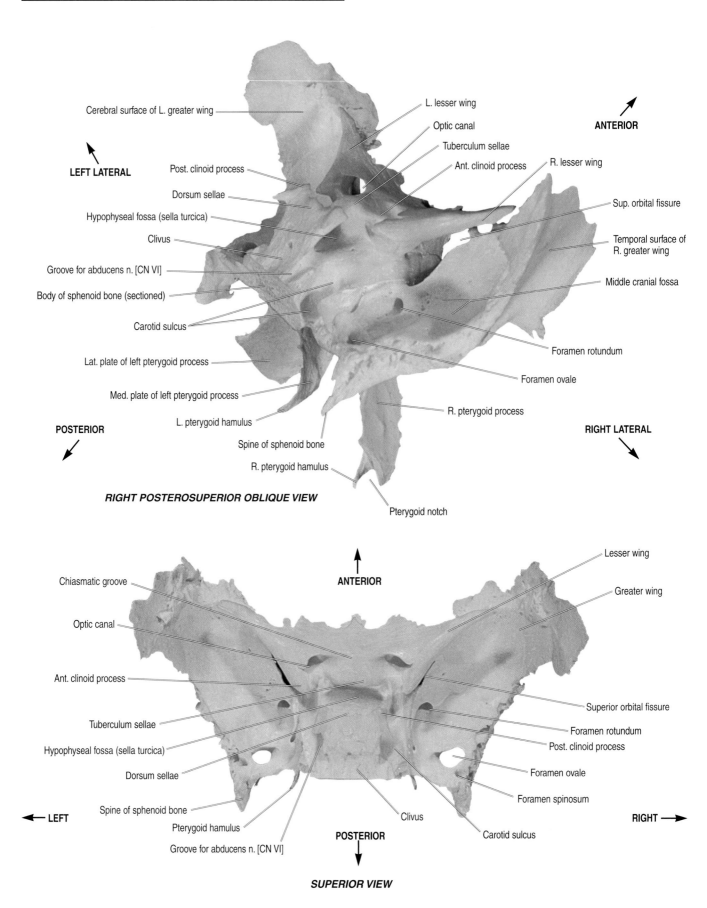

Cerebral surface of L. greater wing

L. lesser wing

Optic canal

Tuberculum sellae

ANTERIOR

Ant. clinoid process

R. lesser wing

LEFT LATERAL

Post. clinoid process

Sup. orbital fissure

Dorsum sellae

Temporal surface of R. greater wing

Hypophyseal fossa (sella turcica)

Clivus

Middle cranial fossa

Groove for abducens n. [CN VI]

Body of sphenoid bone (sectioned)

Carotid sulcus

Foramen rotundum

Lat. plate of left pterygoid process

Foramen ovale

Med. plate of left pterygoid process

R. pterygoid process

L. pterygoid hamulus

POSTERIOR

RIGHT LATERAL

Spine of sphenoid bone

R. pterygoid hamulus

RIGHT POSTEROSUPERIOR OBLIQUE VIEW

Pterygoid notch

Chiasmatic groove

ANTERIOR

Lesser wing

Optic canal

Greater wing

Ant. clinoid process

Tuberculum sellae

Superior orbital fissure

Hypophyseal fossa (sella turcica)

Foramen rotundum

Post. clinoid process

Dorsum sellae

Foramen ovale

Spine of sphenoid bone

Foramen spinosum

LEFT

Pterygoid hamulus

Clivus

RIGHT

Groove for abducens n. [CN VI]

POSTERIOR

Carotid sulcus

SUPERIOR VIEW

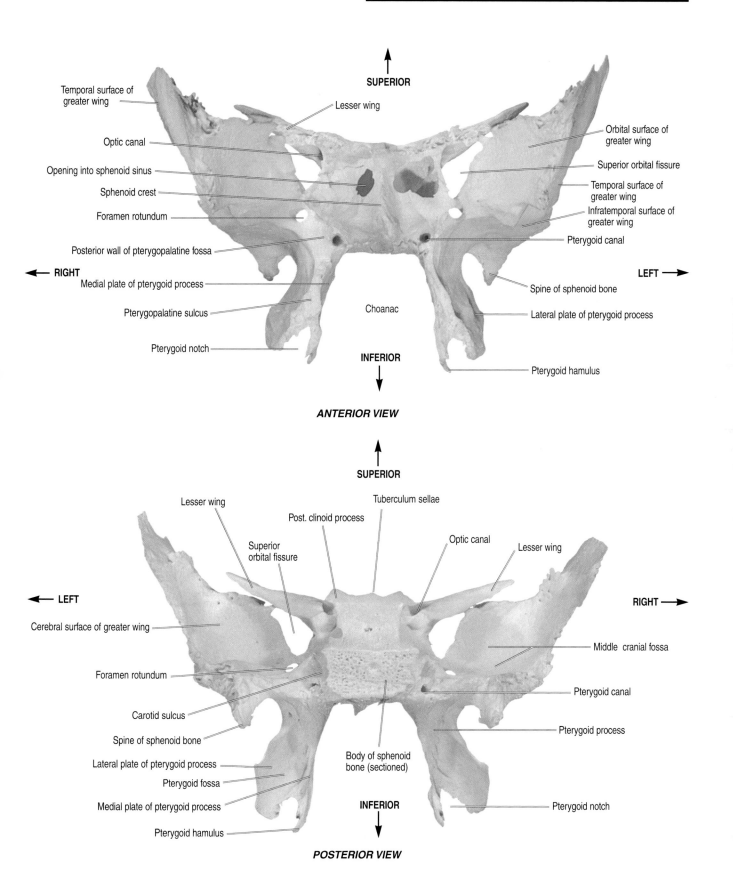

ANTERIOR VIEW

SUPERIOR

Temporal surface of greater wing

Lesser wing

Optic canal

Orbital surface of greater wing

Opening into sphenoid sinus

Superior orbital fissure

Sphenoid crest

Temporal surface of greater wing

Foramen rotundum

Infratemporal surface of greater wing

Posterior wall of pterygopalatine fossa

Pterygoid canal

← RIGHT

LEFT →

Medial plate of pterygoid process

Spine of sphenoid bone

Pterygopalatine sulcus

Choanac

Lateral plate of pterygoid process

Pterygoid notch

INFERIOR

Pterygoid hamulus

POSTERIOR VIEW

SUPERIOR

Lesser wing

Tuberculum sellae

Post. clinoid process

Superior orbital fissure

Optic canal

Lesser wing

← LEFT

RIGHT →

Cerebral surface of greater wing

Middle cranial fossa

Foramen rotundum

Pterygoid canal

Carotid sulcus

Pterygoid process

Spine of sphenoid bone

Lateral plate of pterygoid process

Pterygoid fossa

Body of sphenoid bone (sectioned)

Medial plate of pterygoid process

Pterygoid notch

Pterygoid hamulus

INFERIOR

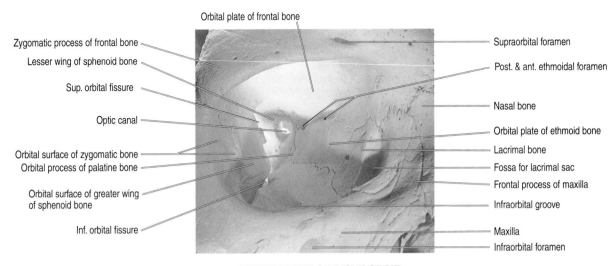

Orbital plate of frontal bone

Zygomatic process of frontal bone
Lesser wing of sphenoid bone
Sup. orbital fissure
Optic canal
Orbital surface of zygomatic bone
Orbital process of palatine bone
Orbital surface of greater wing of sphenoid bone
Inf. orbital fissure

Supraorbital foramen
Post. & ant. ethmoidal foramen
Nasal bone
Orbital plate of ethmoid bone
Lacrimal bone
Fossa for lacrimal sac
Frontal process of maxilla
Infraorbital groove
Maxilla
Infraorbital foramen

ANTERIOR VIEW OF RIGHT ORBIT

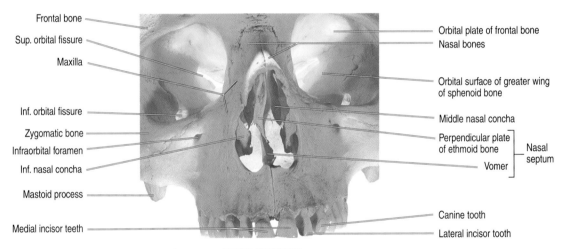

Frontal bone
Sup. orbital fissure
Maxilla
Inf. orbital fissure
Zygomatic bone
Infraorbital foramen
Inf. nasal concha
Mastoid process
Medial incisor teeth

Orbital plate of frontal bone
Nasal bones
Orbital surface of greater wing of sphenoid bone
Middle nasal concha
Perpendicular plate of ethmoid bone
Vomer
} Nasal septum
Canine tooth
Lateral incisor tooth

ANTERIOR VIEW

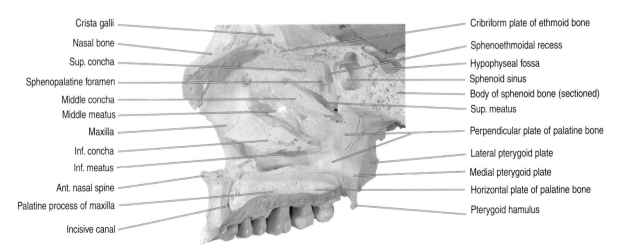

Crista galli
Nasal bone
Sup. concha
Sphenopalatine foramen
Middle concha
Middle meatus
Maxilla
Inf. concha
Inf. meatus
Ant. nasal spine
Palatine process of maxilla
Incisive canal

Cribriform plate of ethmoid bone
Sphenoethmoidal recess
Hypophyseal fossa
Sphenoid sinus
Body of sphenoid bone (sectioned)
Sup. meatus
Perpendicular plate of palatine bone
Lateral pterygoid plate
Medial pterygoid plate
Horizontal plate of palatine bone
Pterygoid hamulus

MEDIAL VIEW OF RIGHT NASAL CAVITY

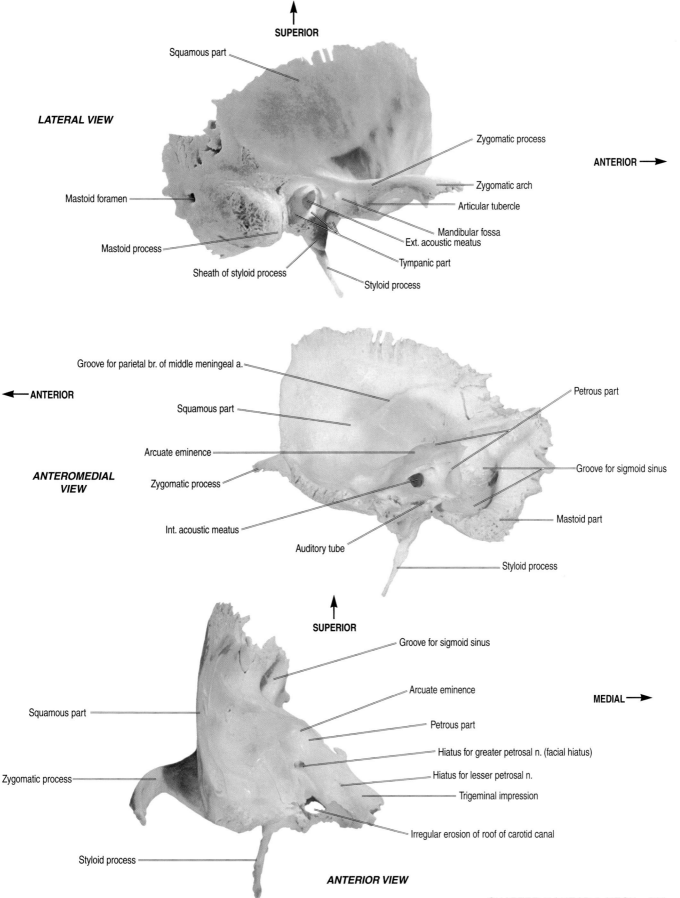

SUPERIOR

Squamous part

LATERAL VIEW

ANTERIOR →

Zygomatic process

Zygomatic arch

Mastoid foramen

Articular tubercle

Mandibular fossa

Ext. acoustic meatus

Mastoid process

Tympanic part

Sheath of styloid process

Styloid process

Groove for parietal br. of middle meningeal a.

← ANTERIOR

Petrous part

Squamous part

**ANTEROMEDIAL
VIEW**

Arcuate eminence

Groove for sigmoid sinus

Zygomatic process

Int. acoustic meatus

Mastoid part

Auditory tube

Styloid process

SUPERIOR

Groove for sigmoid sinus

Arcuate eminence

MEDIAL →

Squamous part

Petrous part

Hiatus for greater petrosal n. (facial hiatus)

Zygomatic process

Hiatus for lesser petrosal n.

Trigeminal impression

Irregular erosion of roof of carotid canal

Styloid process

ANTERIOR VIEW

← RIGHT   ↑ ANTERIOR   LEFT →

OBLIQUE BASAL VIEW OF CHOANAE

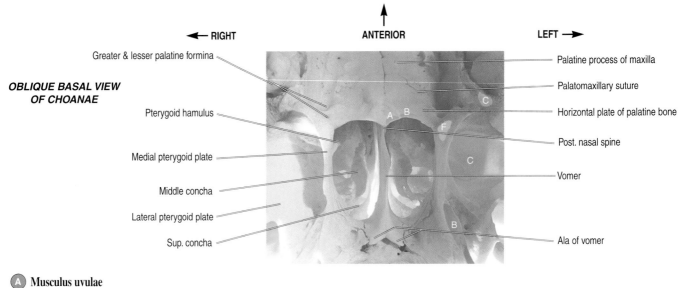

Greater & lesser palatine formina
Pterygoid hamulus
Medial pterygoid plate
Middle concha
Lateral pterygoid plate
Sup. concha

Palatine process of maxilla
Palatomaxillary suture
Horizontal plate of palatine bone
Post. nasal spine
Vomer
Ala of vomer

A Musculus uvulae
B Tensor veli palatini
C Medial pterygoid
D Lateral pterygoid
E Temporalis
F Superior pharyngeal constrictor
G Tensor tympani
H Levator veli palatini

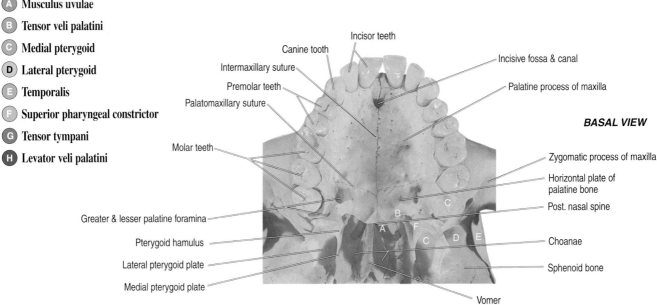

Incisor teeth
Canine tooth
Intermaxillary suture
Premolar teeth
Palatomaxillary suture
Molar teeth
Greater & lesser palatine foramina
Pterygoid hamulus
Lateral pterygoid plate
Medial pterygoid plate

Incisive fossa & canal
Palatine process of maxilla

BASAL VIEW

Zygomatic process of maxilla
Horizontal plate of palatine bone
Post. nasal spine
Choanae
Sphenoid bone
Vomer

BASAL VIEW OF LEFT MANDIBULAR FOSSA

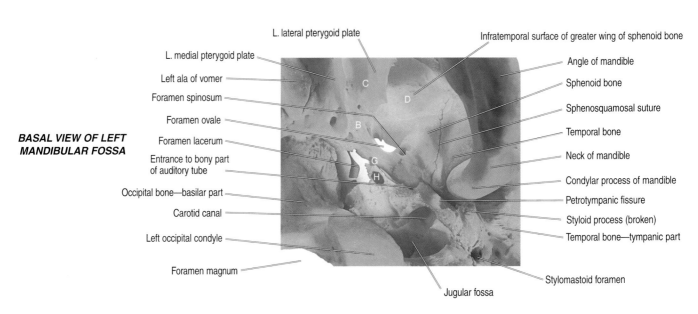

L. lateral pterygoid plate
L. medial pterygoid plate
Left ala of vomer
Foramen spinosum
Foramen ovale
Foramen lacerum
Entrance to bony part of auditory tube
Occipital bone—basilar part
Carotid canal
Left occipital condyle
Foramen magnum

Infratemporal surface of greater wing of sphenoid bone
Angle of mandible
Sphenoid bone
Sphenosquamosal suture
Temporal bone
Neck of mandible
Condylar process of mandible
Petrotympanic fissure
Styloid process (broken)
Temporal bone—tympanic part
Stylomastoid foramen
Jugular fossa

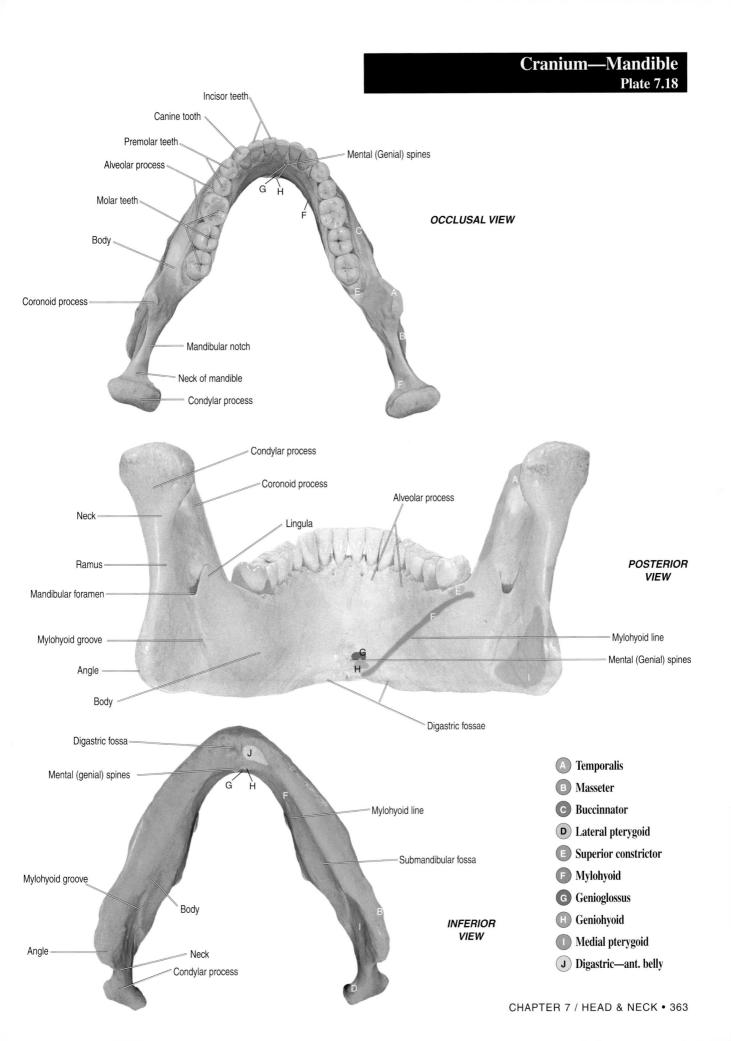

Incisor teeth

Canine tooth

Premolar teeth

Alveolar process

Molar teeth

Body

Coronoid process

Mental (Genial) spines

G H

F

C

E A

B

F

OCCLUSAL VIEW

Mandibular notch

Neck of mandible

Condylar process

Condylar process

Coronoid process

Alveolar process

Neck

Lingula

Ramus

Mandibular foramen

Mylohyoid groove

Angle

Body

A

E

F

G

H

I

POSTERIOR VIEW

Mylohyoid line

Mental (Genial) spines

Digastric fossae

Digastric fossa

Mental (genial) spines

J

G H

F

Mylohyoid line

Submandibular fossa

Mylohyoid groove

Body

B

I

Angle

Neck

Condylar process

D

INFERIOR VIEW

A	**Temporalis**
B	**Masseter**
C	**Buccinnator**
D	**Lateral pterygoid**
E	**Superior constrictor**
F	**Mylohyoid**
G	**Genioglossus**
H	**Geniohyoid**
I	**Medial pterygoid**
J	**Digastric—ant. belly**

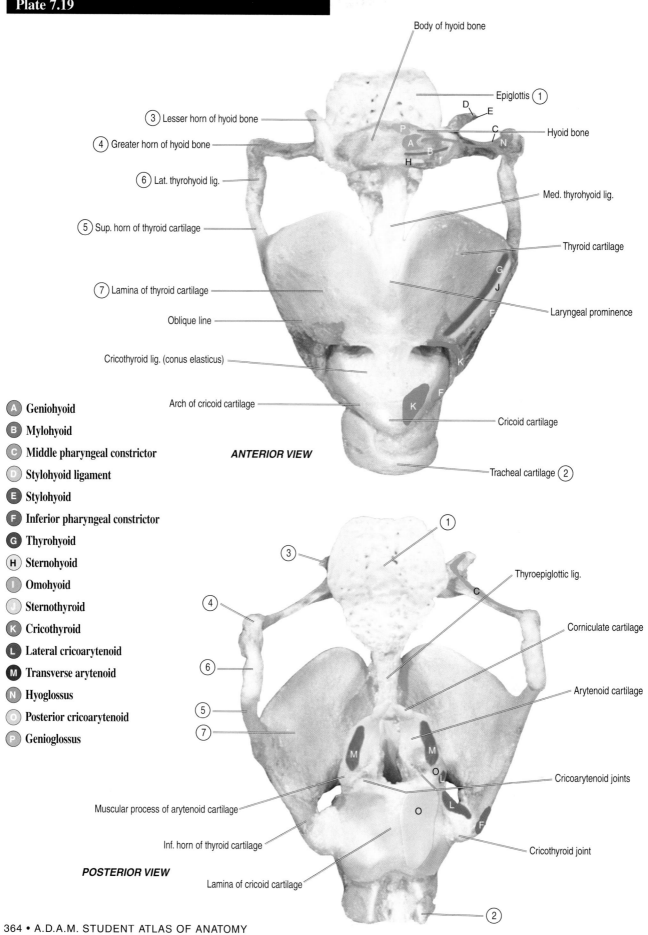

Body of hyoid bone

Epiglottis ①

③ Lesser horn of hyoid bone

④ Greater horn of hyoid bone

Hyoid bone

⑥ Lat. thyrohyoid lig.

Med. thyrohyoid lig.

⑤ Sup. horn of thyroid cartilage

Thyroid cartilage

⑦ Lamina of thyroid cartilage

Laryngeal prominence

Oblique line

Cricothyroid lig. (conus elasticus)

Arch of cricoid cartilage

Cricoid cartilage

ANTERIOR VIEW

Tracheal cartilage ②

Ⓐ Geniohyoid

Ⓑ Mylohyoid

Ⓒ Middle pharyngeal constrictor

Ⓓ Stylohyoid ligament

Ⓔ Stylohyoid

Ⓕ Inferior pharyngeal constrictor

Ⓖ Thyrohyoid

Ⓗ Sternohyoid

Ⓘ Omohyoid

Ⓙ Sternothyroid

Ⓚ Cricothyroid

Ⓛ Lateral cricoarytenoid

Ⓜ Transverse arytenoid

Ⓝ Hyoglossus

Ⓞ Posterior cricoarytenoid

Ⓟ Genioglossus

Thyroepiglottic lig.

Corniculate cartilage

Arytenoid cartilage

Muscular process of arytenoid cartilage

Cricoarytenoid joints

Inf. horn of thyroid cartilage

Cricothyroid joint

POSTERIOR VIEW

Lamina of cricoid cartilage

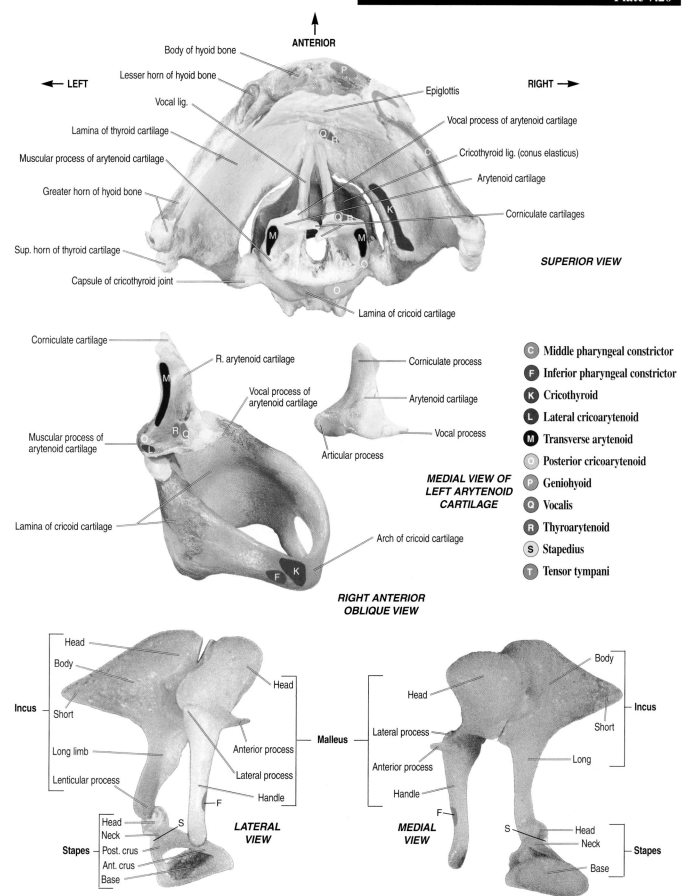

ANTERIOR

LEFT

RIGHT

Body of hyoid bone

Lesser horn of hyoid bone

Vocal lig.

Lamina of thyroid cartilage

Muscular process of arytenoid cartilage

Greater horn of hyoid bone

Sup. horn of thyroid cartilage

Capsule of cricothyroid joint

Epiglottis

Vocal process of arytenoid cartilage

Cricothyroid lig. (conus elasticus)

Arytenoid cartilage

Corniculate cartilages

SUPERIOR VIEW

Lamina of cricoid cartilage

Corniculate cartilage

R. arytenoid cartilage

Vocal process of arytenoid cartilage

Muscular process of arytenoid cartilage

Lamina of cricoid cartilage

Arch of cricoid cartilage

Corniculate process

Arytenoid cartilage

Vocal process

Articular process

MEDIAL VIEW OF LEFT ARYTENOID CARTILAGE

RIGHT ANTERIOR OBLIQUE VIEW

- **C** Middle pharyngeal constrictor
- **F** Inferior pharyngeal constrictor
- **K** Cricothyroid
- **L** Lateral cricoarytenoid
- **M** Transverse arytenoid
- **O** Posterior cricoarytenoid
- **P** Geniohyoid
- **Q** Vocalis
- **R** Thyroarytenoid
- **S** Stapedius
- **T** Tensor tympani

Head

Body

Incus

Short

Long limb

Lenticular process

Head

Head

Anterior process

Lateral process

Handle

F

Malleus

Head

Neck

Stapes Post. crus

Ant. crus

Base

S

LATERAL VIEW

Body

Incus

Short

Long

Head

Lateral process

Anterior process

Handle

F

MEDIAL VIEW

S

Head

Neck

Base

Stapes

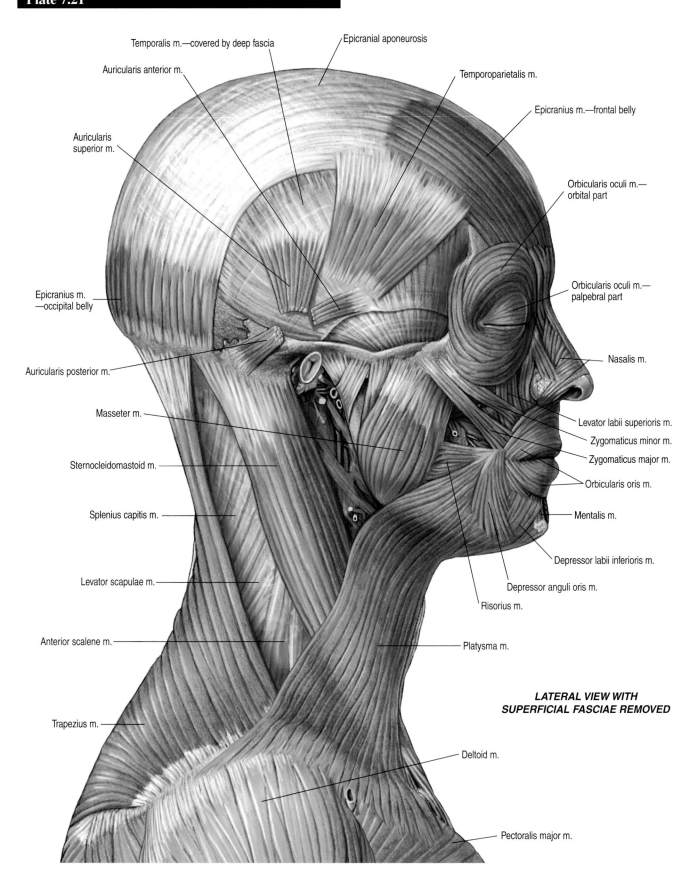

Temporalis m.—covered by deep fascia

Epicranial aponeurosis

Auricularis anterior m.

Temporoparietalis m.

Epicranius m.—frontal belly

Auricularis superior m.

Orbicularis oculi m.—orbital part

Orbicularis oculi m.—palpebral part

Epicranius m.—occipital belly

Nasalis m.

Auricularis posterior m.

Masseter m.

Levator labii superioris m.

Zygomaticus minor m.

Zygomaticus major m.

Sternocleidomastoid m.

Orbicularis oris m.

Splenius capitis m.

Mentalis m.

Depressor labii inferioris m.

Levator scapulae m.

Depressor anguli oris m.

Risorius m.

Anterior scalene m.

Platysma m.

LATERAL VIEW WITH SUPERFICIAL FASCIAE REMOVED

Trapezius m.

Deltoid m.

Pectoralis major m.

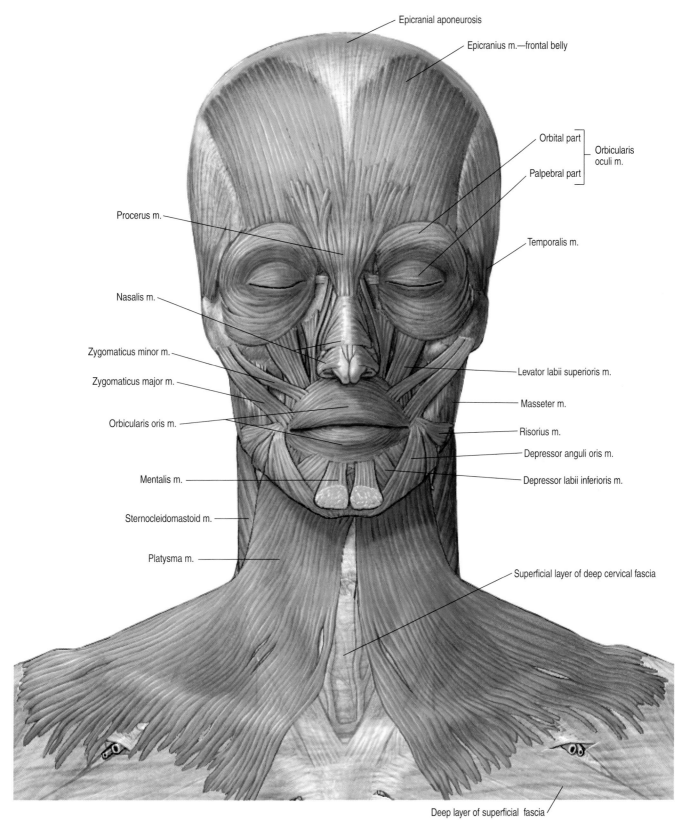

Epicranial aponeurosis

Epicranius m.—frontal belly

Orbital part

Orbicularis oculi m.

Palpebral part

Procerus m.

Temporalis m.

Nasalis m.

Zygomaticus minor m.

Levator labii superioris m.

Zygomaticus major m.

Masseter m.

Orbicularis oris m.

Risorius m.

Depressor anguli oris m.

Mentalis m.

Depressor labii inferioris m.

Sternocleidomastoid m.

Platysma m.

Superficial layer of deep cervical fascia

Deep layer of superficial fascia

ANTERIOR VIEW

Muscles Acting on the Temporomandibular Joint

Muscle	Stable Attachment	Mobile Attachment	Innervation	Main Actions
Temporalis	Floor of temporal fossa & deep surface of temporal fascia	Tip & medial surface of coronoid process & ant. border of ramus of mandible	Deep temporal br. of mandibular n. (CN V^3)	Elevates mandible, closing jaws; its posterior fibers retrude mandible after protrusion
Masseter	Inf. border & medial surface of zygomatic arch	Lateral surface of ramus of mandible & its coronoid process	Mandibular n. (CN V^3) via masseteric nerve that enters its deep surface	Elevates & protrudes mandible, thus closing jaws;
Lateral pterygoid	*Superior head:* Infratemporal surface & infratemporal crest of greater wing of sphenoid bone	Articular disc & capsule of temporomandibular joint	Mandibular n. (CN V^3) via lateral pterygoid n. from ant. trunk, which enters it unilaterally deep surface	*Acting bilaterally,* they protrude mandible & depress chin *Acting unilaterally* & alternately, they produce side-to-side movements of mandible
	Inferior head: Lateral surface of lateral pterygoid plate	Neck of mandible		
Medial pterygoid	*Deep head:* Medial surface of lateral pterygoid plate & pyramidal process of palatine bone	Medial surface of ramus of mandible, inf. to mandibular foramen	Mandibular n. (CN V^3) via medial pterygoid n.	Helps to elevate mandible, closing jaws *Acting bilaterally,* they help to protrude mandible *Acting unilaterally,* it protrudes side of jaw *Acting alternately,* they produce a grinding motion
	Superficial head: Tuberosity of maxilla			

Actions and Nerve Supply of the Ocular Muscles

Muscle	Action(s) on the Eyeball	Nerve Supply
Medial rectus[a]	Adducts	CN III
Lateral rectus[a]	Abducts	CN VI[b]
Superior rectus	Elevates, adducts & rotate medially	CN III
Inferior rectus	Depresses, adducts & rotates laterally	CN III
Superior oblique[c]	Abducts, depresses & rotates eye medially (intorsion), depresses adducted eye	CN IV[b]
Inferior oblique[c]	Abducts, elevates & rotates eye laterally (extorsion), elevates adducted eye	CN III

[a]The medial and lateral rectus muscles move the eyeball in one axis only, whereas each of the other four muscles moves it in all three axes.
[b]CN IV and VI each supply one muscle, whereas CN III supplies the other four muscles.
[c]The superior and inferior oblique muscles are used with the medial rectus muscle in adducting both eyes medially for near vision. This movement, accompanied by pupillary construction, is known as accommodation.

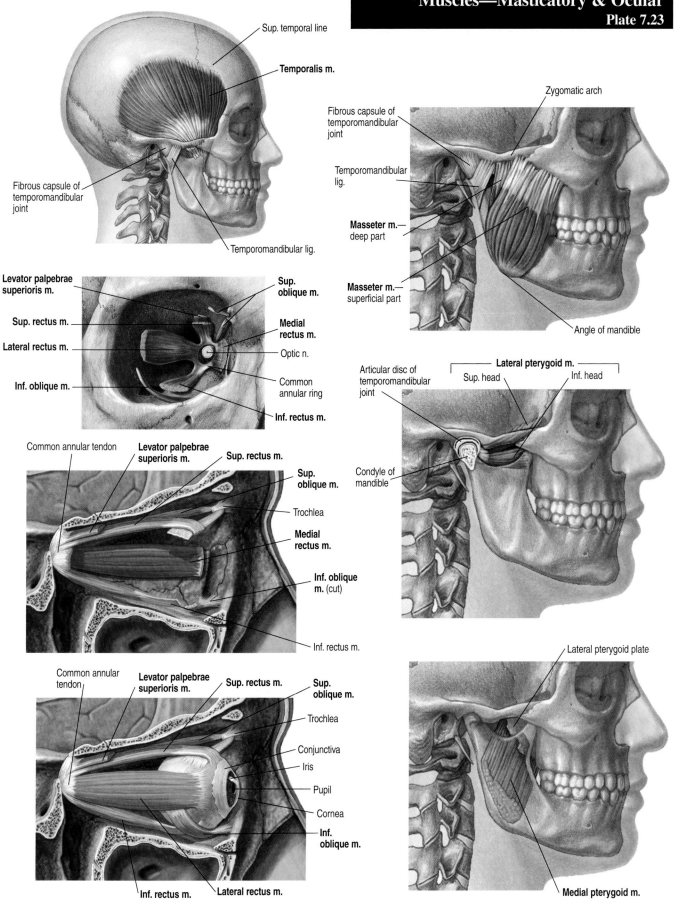

Sup. temporal line

Temporalis m.

Fibrous capsule of temporomandibular joint

Temporomandibular lig.

Zygomatic arch

Fibrous capsule of temporomandibular joint

Temporomandibular lig.

Masseter m.— deep part

Masseter m.— superficial part

Angle of mandible

Levator palpebrae superioris m.

Sup. rectus m.

Lateral rectus m.

Inf. oblique m.

Sup. oblique m.

Medial rectus m.

Optic n.

Common annular ring

Inf. rectus m.

Common annular tendon

Levator palpebrae superioris m.

Sup. rectus m.

Sup. oblique m.

Trochlea

Medial rectus m.

Inf. oblique m. (cut)

Inf. rectus m.

Articular disc of temporomandibular joint

Lateral pterygoid m.
Sup. head   Inf. head

Condyle of mandible

Common annular tendon

Levator palpebrae superioris m.

Sup. rectus m.

Sup. oblique m.

Trochlea

Conjunctiva

Iris

Pupil

Cornea

Inf. oblique m.

Inf. rectus m.   Lateral rectus m.

Lateral pterygoid plate

Medial pterygoid m.

Muscles—Soft Palate & Tongue
Table 7.4

Muscles of the Soft Palate

Muscle	Superior Attachment	Inferior Attachment	Innervation	Main Actions
Levator veli palatini	Cartilage of auditory tube & petrous part of temporal bone		Pharyngeal br. of vagus n. via pharyngeal plexus (CN X)	Elevates soft palate during swallowing & yawning
		Palatine aponeurosis		
Tensor veli palatini	Scaphoid fossa of medial pterygoid plate, spine of sphenoid bone & cartilage of auditory tube		Medial pterygoid n. (a br. of the mandibular n.) via otic ganglion (CN V^3)	Tenses soft palate & opens cartilagenous part of auditory tube during swallowing & yawning
Palatoglossus	Palatine aponeurosis	Side of tongue		Elevates posterior part of tongue & draws soft palate onto tongue
Palatopharyngeus	Hard palate & palatine aponeurosis	Lateral wall of pharynx	Cranial part of CN XI through pharyngeal br. of vagus n. (CN X) via pharyngeal plexus	Tenses soft palate & pulls walls of pharynx superiorly, anteriorly, and medially during swallowing
Musculus uvulae	Posterior nasal spine & palatine aponeurosis	Mucosa of uvula		Shortens uvula & pulls it superiorly

Extrinsic Muscles of the Tongue

Muscle	Stable Attachment	Mobile Attachment	Innervation	Actions
Genioglossus	Sup. part of mental spine of mandible	Dorsum of tongue & body of hyoid bone		Protrudes, retracts & depresses tongue; its post. part protrudes tongue
Hyoglossus	Body & greater horn of hyoid bone	Side of tongue	Hypoglossal n. CN XII	Depresses & retracts tongue
Styloglossus	Styloid process & stylohyoid lig.	Side & inf. aspect of tongue		Retracts tongue & draws it up to create a trough for swallowing
Palatoglossus	Palatine aponeurosis of soft palate	Side of tongue	Cranial root of CN XI via pharyngeal br. CN X & pharyngeal plexus	Elevates post. part of tongue

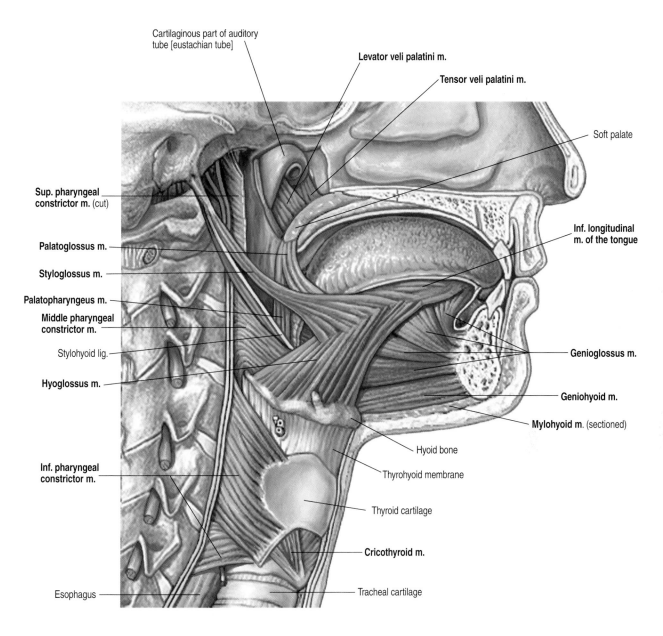

Cartilaginous part of auditory tube [eustachian tube]

Levator veli palatini m.

Tensor veli palatini m.

Soft palate

Sup. pharyngeal constrictor m. (cut)

Inf. longitudinal m. of the tongue

Palatoglossus m.

Styloglossus m.

Palatopharyngeus m.

Middle pharyngeal constrictor m.

Stylohyoid lig.

Hyoglossus m.

Genioglossus m.

Geniohyoid m.

Mylohyoid m. (sectioned)

Hyoid bone

Thyrohyoid membrane

Inf. pharyngeal constrictor m.

Thyroid cartilage

Cricothyroid m.

Esophagus

Tracheal cartilage

LATERAL VIEW OF TONGUE & PHARYNGEAL MUSCLES

Muscles—Hyoid
Table 7.5

Suprahyoid Muscles[a]

Muscle	Superior Attachment	Inferior Attachment	Innervation	Main Actions
Mylohyoid	Mylohyoid line of mandible	Oral raphe & body of hyoid bone	Mylohyoid n., a br. of inf. alveolar n. (CN V^3)	Elevates hyoid bone, floor of mouth & tongue during swallowing & speaking
Geniohyoid	Inf. mental spine of mandible	Body of hyoid bone	C1 via the hypoglossal n. (CN XII)	Pulls hyoid bone anterosuperiorly, shortens floor of mouth & widens pharynx
Stylohyoid	Styloid process of temporal bone	Body of hyoid bone	Cervical br. of facial n. (CN VII)	Elevates & retracts hyoid bone, thereby elongating floor of mouth
Digastric	*Anterior belly:* Digastric fossa of mandible *Posterior belly:* Mastoid notch of temporal bone	Intermediate tendon to body & greater horn of hyoid bone	*Anterior belly:* Mylohyoid n., a br. of inf. alveolar n. (CN V^3) *Posterior belly:* Facial n. (CN VII)	Depresses mandible, raises hyoid bone & steadies it during swallowing & speaking

[a]These muscles connect the hyoid bone to the skull.

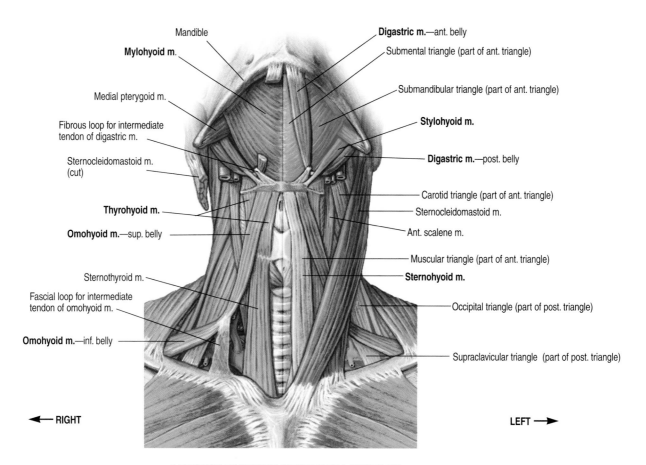

ANTERIOR VIEW WITH SUPERFICIAL MUSCLES
ON LEFT & DEEPER MUSCLES ON RIGHT

Infrahyoid Muscles[a]

Muscle	Origin	Insertion	Innervation	Actions
Sternohyoid	Manubrium of sternum & medial end of clavicle	Body of hyoid bone	C1, C2 & C3 from ansa cervicalis	Depresses hyoid bone after it has been elevated during swallowing
Sternothyroid	Post. surface of manubrium of sternum	Oblique line of thyroid cartilage	C2 & C3 by a br. of ansa cervicalis	Depresses hyoid bone & larynx
Thyrohyoid	Oblique line of thyroid cartilage	Inf. border of body & greater horn of hyoid bone	C1 via hypoglossal n. (CN XII)	Depresses hyoid bone & elevates larynx
Omohyoid	Sup. border of scapula near suprascapular notch	Inf. border of hyoid bone	C1, C2 & C3 by a br. of ansa cervicalis	Depresses, retracts & steadies hyoid bone

[a]These four step-like muscles anchor the hyoid bone (*i.e.,* they fix and steady it). They are concerned with the suprahyoid muscles in movements of the tongue, hyoid bone, and larynx in both swallowing and speaking.

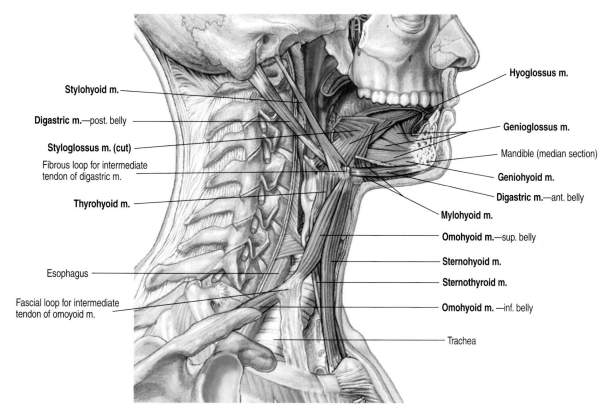

Stylohyoid m.

Digastric m.—post. belly

Styloglossus m. (cut)

Fibrous loop for intermediate tendon of digastric m.

Thyrohyoid m.

Esophagus

Fascial loop for intermediate tendon of omoyoid m.

Hyoglossus m.

Geniolossus m.

Mandible (median section)

Geniohyoid m.

Digastric m.—ant. belly

Mylohyoid m.

Omohyoid m.—sup. belly

Sternohyoid m.

Sternothyroid m.

Omohyoid m. —inf. belly

Trachea

LATERAL VIEW WITH RIGHT HALF OF MANDIBLE REMOVED

Muscle	Lateral Attachments	Medial Attachments	Innervation	Main Actions
CIRCULAR PHARYNGEAL MUSCLES				
Superior constrictor	Pterygoid hamulus, ptergomandibular raphe, post. end of mylohyoid line of mandible & side of tongue	Median raphe of pharynx & pharyngeal tubercle	Pharyngeal & sup. laryngeal brr. of vagus n. [CN X] through pharyngeal plexus	Constrict wall of pharynx during swallowing
Middle constrictor	Stylohyoid lig. and greater & lesser horns of hyoid bone	Median raphe of pharynx		
Inferior constrictor	Oblique line of thyroid cartilage & side of cricoid cartilage			
LONGITUDINAL PHARYNGEAL MUSCLES				
Palatopharyngeus	Hard palate & palatine aponeurosis	Post. border of lamina of thyroid cartilage & side of pharynx & esophagus		Elevate pharynx & larynx during swallowing & speaking[a]
Salpingopharynegeus	Cartilaginous part of auditory tube	Blends with palatopharynegeus		
Stylopharyngeus	Styloid process of temporal bone	Post. & sup. borders of thyroid cartilage with palatopharynegus m.	Glossopharyngeal n.[CN IX]	

[a]The salpingopharyngeus muscle also opens the auditory tube.

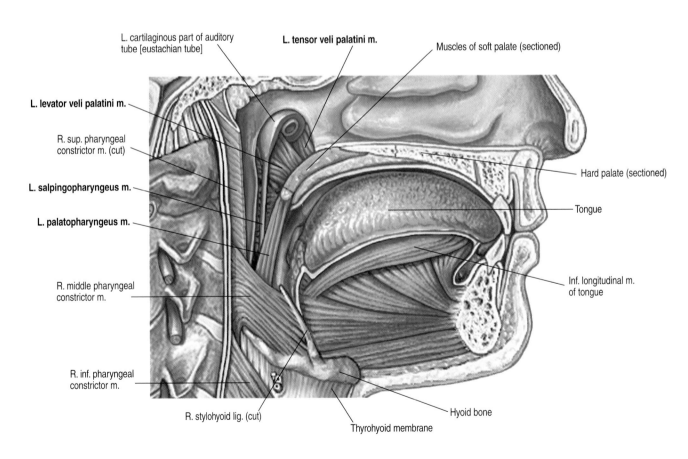

L. cartilaginous part of auditory tube [eustachian tube]

L. tensor veli palatini m.

Muscles of soft palate (sectioned)

L. levator veli palatini m.

R. sup. pharyngeal constrictor m. (cut)

L. salpingopharyngeus m.

L. palatopharyngeus m.

R. middle pharyngeal constrictor m.

R. inf. pharyngeal constrictor m.

R. stylohyoid lig. (cut)

Thyrohyoid membrane

Hyoid bone

Hard palate (sectioned)

Tongue

Inf. longitudinal m. of tongue

LATERAL VIEW OF NECK & MEDIAN SECTIONED SKULL

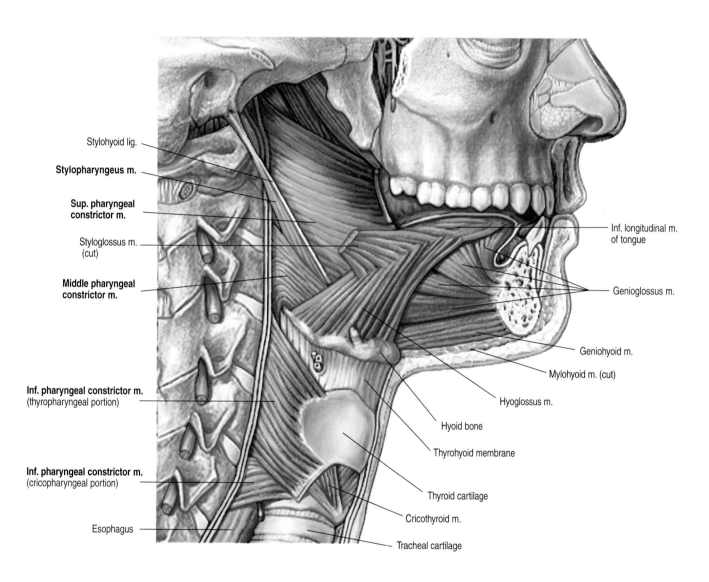

Stylohyoid lig.

Stylopharyngeus m.

**Sup. pharyngeal
constrictor m.**

Styloglossus m.
(cut)

**Middle pharyngeal
constrictor m.**

Inf. pharyngeal constrictor m.
(thyropharyngeal portion)

Inf. pharyngeal constrictor m.
(cricopharyngeal portion)

Esophagus

Inf. longitudinal m.
of tongue

Genioglossus m.

Geniohyoid m.

Mylohyoid m. (cut)

Hyoglossus m.

Hyoid bone

Thyrohyoid membrane

Thyroid cartilage

Cricothyroid m.

Tracheal cartilage

LATERAL VIEW WITH RIGHT HALF OF MANDIBLE REMOVED

Muscles—Laryngeal
Table 7.8

Muscles of the Larynx

Muscle	Origin	Insertion	Innervation	Main Actions
Cricothyroid	Anterolateral part of cricoid cartilage	Inf. margin & inf. horn of thyroid cartilage	Ext. laryngeal n. (CN X)	Stretches & tenses the vocal fold
Posterior cricoarytenoid	Post. surface of laminae of cricoid cartilage	Muscular process of arytenoid cartilage	Recurrent laryngeal n. (CN X)	Abducts vocal fold
Lateral cricoarytenoid	Arch of cricoid cartilage			Adducts vocal fold
Thyroarytenoid[a]	Post. surface of thyroid cartilage	Muscular process of arytenoid process		Relaxes vocal fold
Transverse & oblique arytenoids	One arytenoid cartilage	Opposition arytenoid cartilage		Close laryngeal aditus by approximating arytenoid cartilages
Vocalis[b]	Angle between laminae of thyroid cartilage	Vocal process of arytenoid cartilage		Alters vocal fold during phonation

[a]The superior fibers of the thyroarytenoid muscle pass into the aryepiglottic fold, and some of them reach the epiglottic cartilage. These fibers constitute the *thyroepiglottic muscle,* which widens the inlet of the larynx.
[b]These short fine muscular slips are derived from the most medial fibers of the thyroarytenoid muscle.

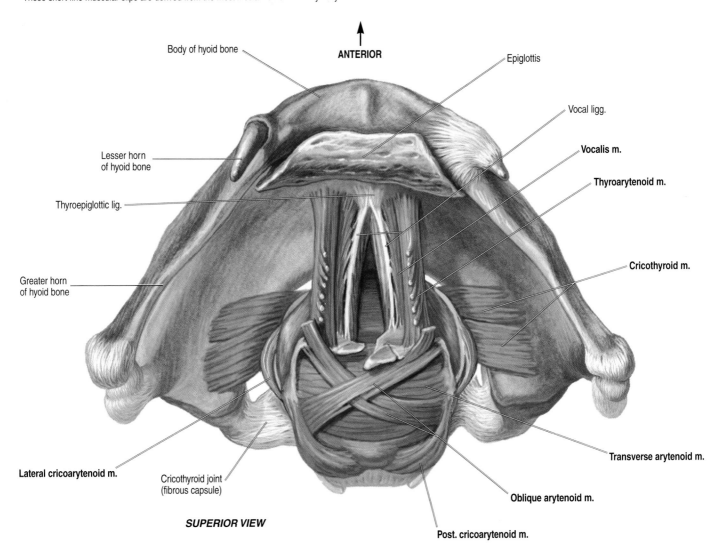

SUPERIOR VIEW

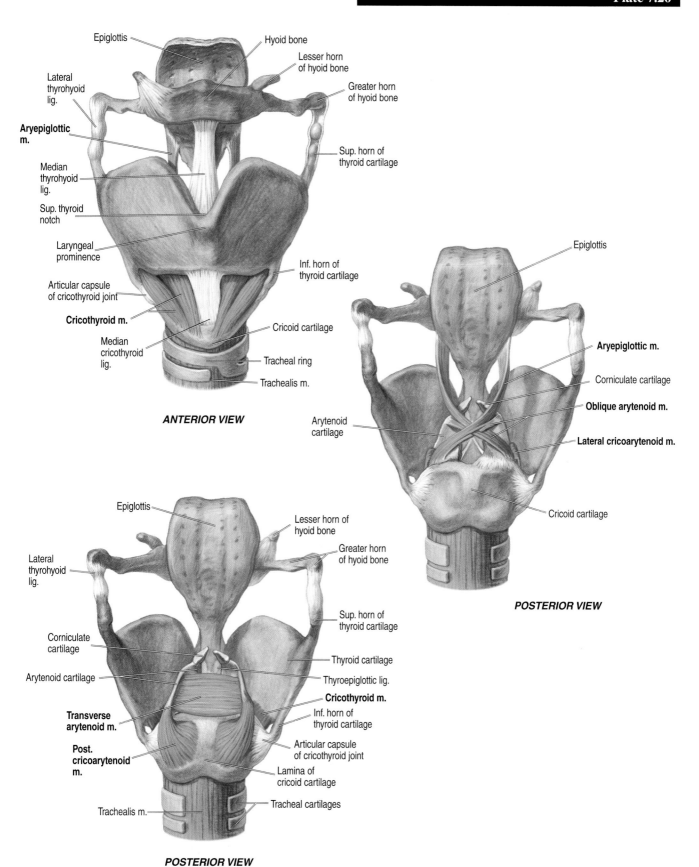

ANTERIOR VIEW

Epiglottis

Hyoid bone

Lesser horn of hyoid bone

Greater horn of hyoid bone

Lateral thyrohyoid lig.

Aryepiglottic m.

Sup. horn of thyroid cartilage

Median thyrohyoid lig.

Sup. thyroid notch

Laryngeal prominence

Inf. horn of thyroid cartilage

Articular capsule of cricothyroid joint

Cricothyroid m.

Median cricothyroid lig.

Cricoid cartilage

Tracheal ring

Trachealis m.

Epiglottis

Aryepiglottic m.

Corniculate cartilage

Oblique arytenoid m.

Lateral cricoarytenoid m.

Arytenoid cartilage

Cricoid cartilage

POSTERIOR VIEW

Epiglottis

Lesser horn of hyoid bone

Greater horn of hyoid bone

Lateral thyrohyoid lig.

Sup. horn of thyroid cartilage

Corniculate cartilage

Arytenoid cartilage

Thyroid cartilage

Thyroepiglottic lig.

Transverse arytenoid m.

Cricothyroid m.

Inf. horn of thyroid cartilage

Articular capsule of cricothyroid joint

Post. cricoarytenoid m.

Lamina of cricoid cartilage

Trachealis m.

Tracheal cartilages

POSTERIOR VIEW

Muscles—Lateral & Prevertebral
Table 7.9

Muscle	Inferior Attachment	Superior Attachment	Innervation	Main Actions
Sternocleidomastoid				
Sternal head	Ventral surface of the manubrium sterni	Lateral surface of mastoid process; sup. nuchal line of occipital bone	Spinal accessory n. (motor); sensory fibers of C2 n.	Various: both sides together support head, move chin upward, and pull back of head down. One side alone turns chin upward and to opposite side.
Clavicular head	Cranial surface of medial third of clavicle			
Splenius capitis	Inf. half of ligamentum nuchae & spinous process of sup. six thoracic vertebrae	Lateral aspect of mastoid process & lateral third of sup. nuchal line	Dorsal rami of middle cervical spinal nn.	Laterally flexes & rotates head & neck to same side; acting bilaterally, they extend head & neck
Splenius cervicis	Spines of 3rd (or 4th) to 6th thoracic vertebrae	Posterior tubercles of the transverse process of the upper three cervical vertebrae	Dorsal rami of nerves C2-C5, lateral brr. (same as splenius capitis m.)	
Posterior scalene	Post. tubercles of transverse processes of C4-C6	Ext. border of second rib	Ventral rami of cervical spinal nn. (C7 & C8)	Flexes neck laterally; elevates second rib during forced inspiration
Middle scalene	Posterior tubercles of transverse processes of C2 & C7	Sup. surface of first rib, posterior to groove for subclavian a.	Ventral rami of cervical spinal nn. (C3-C8)	Flexes neck laterally; elevates first rib during forced inspiration
Anterior scalene	Ant. tubercles of transverse processes of C3-C6	Scalene tubercle of 1st rib	Long thoracic n. (C5-C7)	
Longus colli				
Vertical portion	Body of first three thoracic & last three cervical vertebrae	Bodies of C2-C4	Ventral rami of C2-C6	Bilaterally acting to flex neck and head anteriorly, unilaterally to flex head and neck laterally and to rotate the head toward the same side
Superior oblique	Ant. tubercles of transverse process of C3-C5	Tubercle on ant. arch of the atlas & body axis	Ventral rami of C1 to C4	
Inferior oblique	Ant. surface of bodies of first two or three thoracic vertebrae	Ant. tubercles of the transverse processes of C5 & C6		
Longus capitis	Ant. tubercle of transverse processes of C3-C6	Inf. border of basilar part of occipital		

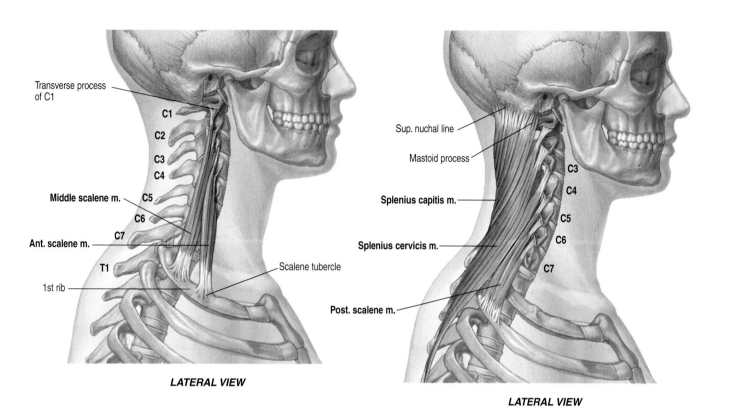

Transverse process of C1

C1
C2
C3
C4

Middle scalene m. C5

C6

Ant. scalene m. C7

T1

1st rib

Scalene tubercle

LATERAL VIEW

Sup. nuchal line

Mastoid process

C3
C4

Splenius capitis m. C5

C6

Splenius cervicis m.

C7

Post. scalene m.

LATERAL VIEW

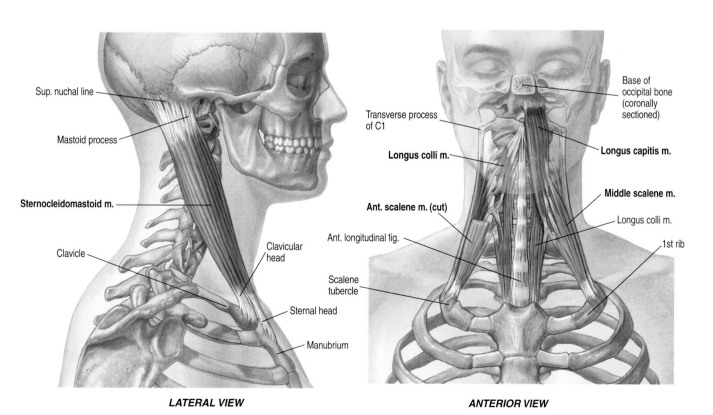

Sup. nuchal line

Mastoid process

Sternocleidomastoid m.

Clavicle

Clavicular head

Sternal head

Manubrium

LATERAL VIEW

Transverse process of C1

Longus colli m.

Ant. scalene m. (cut)

Ant. longitudinal lig.

Scalene tubercle

Base of occipital bone (coronally sectioned)

Longus capitis m.

Middle scalene m.

Longus colli m.

1st rib

ANTERIOR VIEW

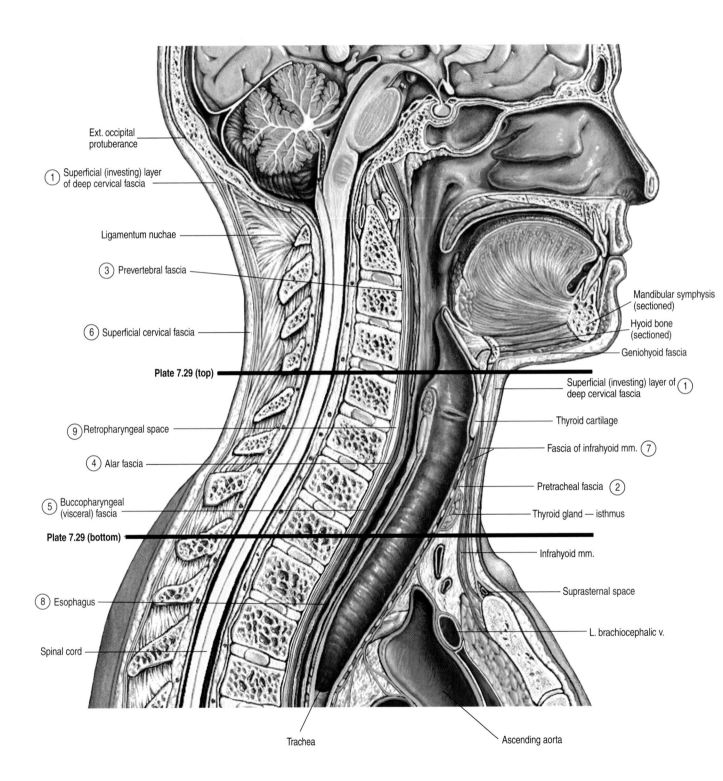

Ext. occipital protuberance

1 Superficial (investing) layer of deep cervical fascia

Ligamentum nuchae

3 Prevertebral fascia

6 Superficial cervical fascia

Plate 7.29 (top)

9 Retropharyngeal space

4 Alar fascia

5 Buccopharyngeal (visceral) fascia

Plate 7.29 (bottom)

8 Esophagus

Spinal cord

Mandibular symphysis (sectioned)

Hyoid bone (sectioned)

Geniohyoid fascia

Superficial (investing) layer of 1 deep cervical fascia

Thyroid cartilage

Fascia of infrahyoid mm. 7

Pretracheal fascia 2

Thyroid gland — isthmus

Infrahyoid mm.

Suprasternal space

L. brachiocephalic v.

Trachea

Ascending aorta

LATERAL VIEW OF MEDIAN SECTION

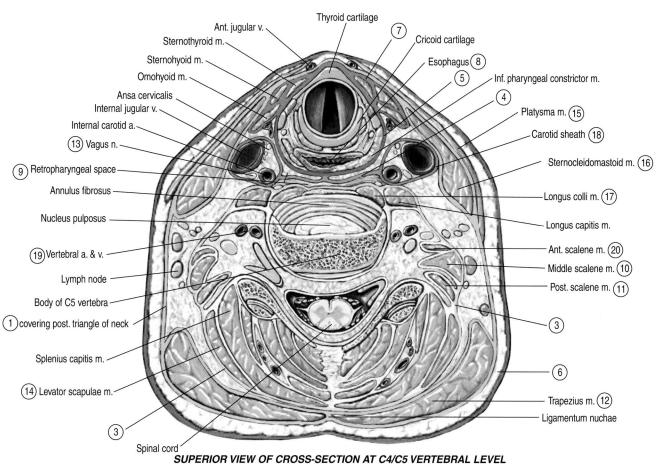

Thyroid cartilage

Ant. jugular v.

Sternothyroid m.

Sternohyoid m.

Omohyoid m.

Ansa cervicalis

Internal jugular v.

Internal carotid a.

⑬ Vagus n.

⑨ Retropharyngeal space

Annulus fibrosus

Nucleus pulposus

⑲ Vertebral a. & v.

Lymph node

Body of C5 vertebra

① covering post. triangle of neck

Splenius capitis m.

⑭ Levator scapulae m.

③

Spinal cord

⑦

Cricoid cartilage

Esophagus ⑧

⑤

Inf. pharyngeal constrictor m.

④

Platysma m. ⑮

Carotid sheath ⑱

Sternocleidomastoid m. ⑯

Longus colli m. ⑰

Longus capitis m.

Ant. scalene m. ⑳

Middle scalene m. ⑩

Post. scalene m. ⑪

③

⑥

Trapezius m. ⑫

Ligamentum nuchae

SUPERIOR VIEW OF CROSS-SECTION AT C4/C5 VERTEBRAL LEVEL

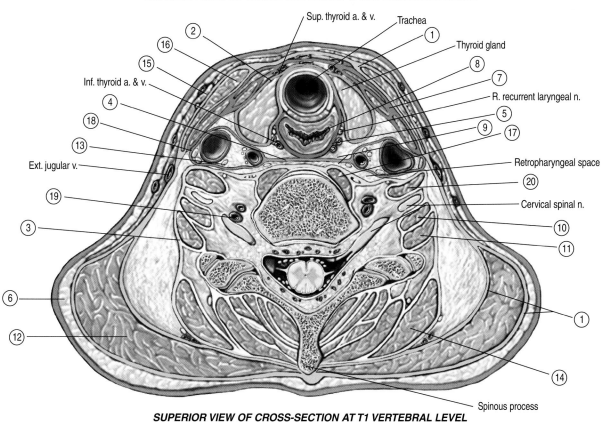

Sup. thyroid a. & v.

Trachea

②

⑯

⑮

Inf. thyroid a. & v.

④

⑱

⑬

Ext. jugular v.

⑲

③

⑥

⑫

①

Thyroid gland

⑧

⑦

R. recurrent laryngeal n.

⑤

⑨ ⑰

Retropharyngeal space

⑳

Cervical spinal n.

⑩

⑪

①

⑭

Spinous process

SUPERIOR VIEW OF CROSS-SECTION AT T1 VERTEBRAL LEVEL

Parietal br. of superficial temporal a.

Frontal br. of superficial temporal a.

LATERAL VIEW

Supraorbital a.

Supratrochlear a.

Superficial temporal a.

Zygomatico-orbital a.

Ophthalmic a.

Transverse facial a.

Post. auricular a.

Infraorbital a.

Occipital a.

Sternocleidomastoid br.of occipital a.

Maxillary a.

Buccal a.

Int. alveolar a.

Facial a.

Sup. labial a.

Lingual a.

Inf. labial a.

Superficial cervical a.

Facial a.

Mental a.

Deep cervical a.

Ext. carotid a.

Int. carotid a.

Sup. thyroid a.

Ascending cervical a.

Transverse cervical a.

Common carotid a.

Highest intercostal a.

Inf. thyroid a.

Dorsal scapular a.

Vertebral a.

Costocervical trunk

Thyrocervical trunk

R. subclavian a.

Inf. thoracic a.

Brachiocephalic a.

1st post. intercostal a.

Suprascapular a.

Axillary a.

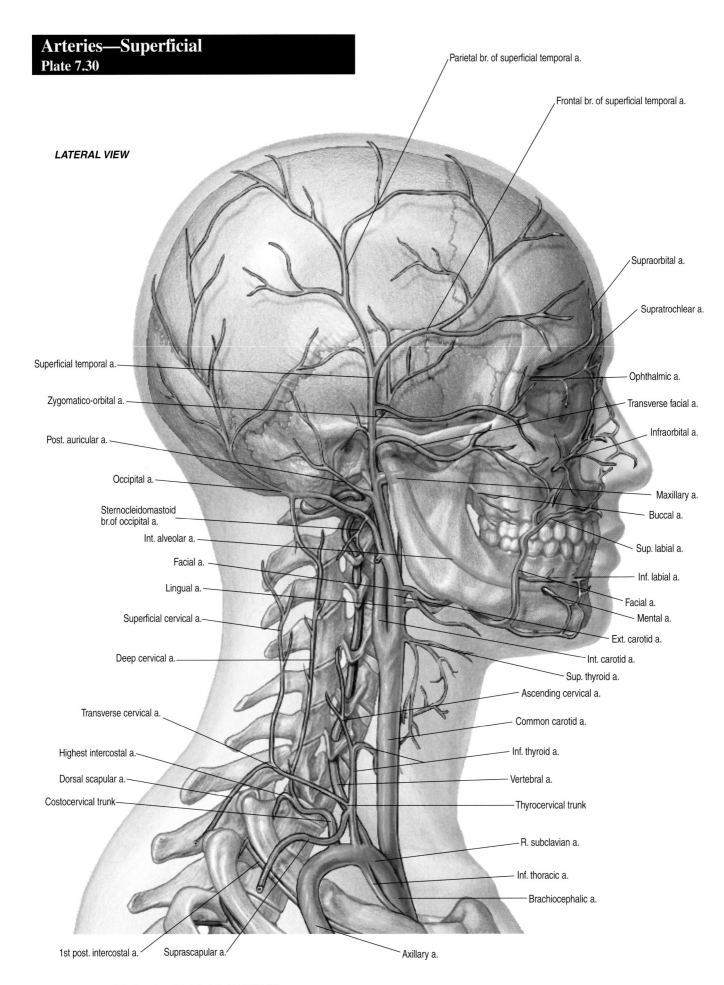

LATERAL VIEW

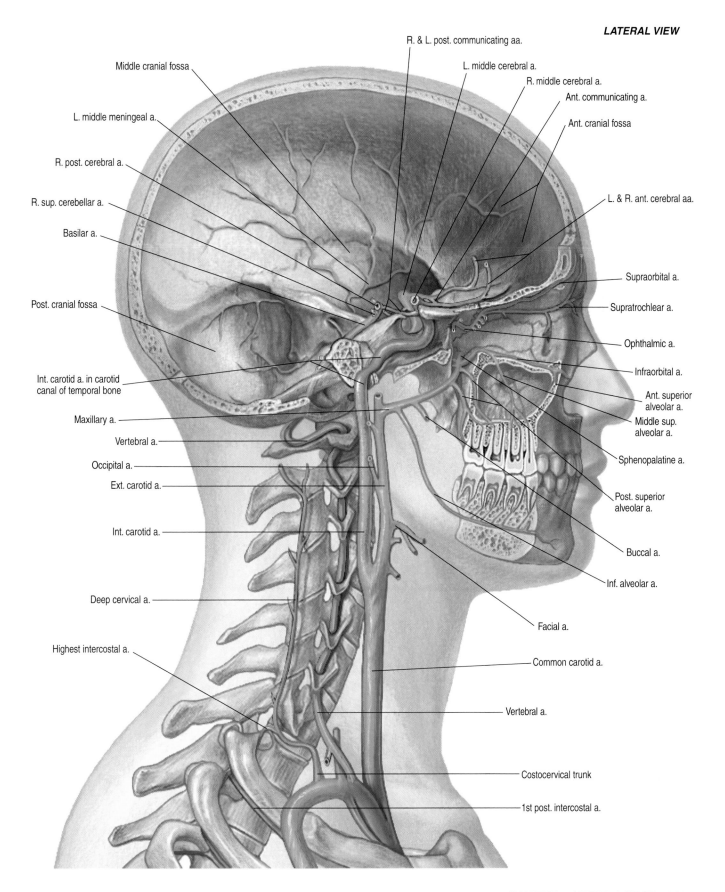

R. & L. post. communicating aa.

Middle cranial fossa

L. middle cerebral a.

R. middle cerebral a.

Ant. communicating a.

L. middle meningeal a.

Ant. cranial fossa

R. post. cerebral a.

L. & R. ant. cerebral aa.

R. sup. cerebellar a.

Basilar a.

Supraorbital a.

Supratrochlear a.

Post. cranial fossa

Ophthalmic a.

Infraorbital a.

Int. carotid a. in carotid
canal of temporal bone

Ant. superior
alveolar a.

Maxillary a.

Middle sup.
alveolar a.

Vertebral a.

Sphenopalatine a.

Occipital a.

Ext. carotid a.

Post. superior
alveolar a.

Int. carotid a.

Buccal a.

Inf. alveolar a.

Deep cervical a.

Facial a.

Highest intercostal a.

Common carotid a.

Vertebral a.

Costocervical trunk

1st post. intercostal a.

LATERAL VIEW

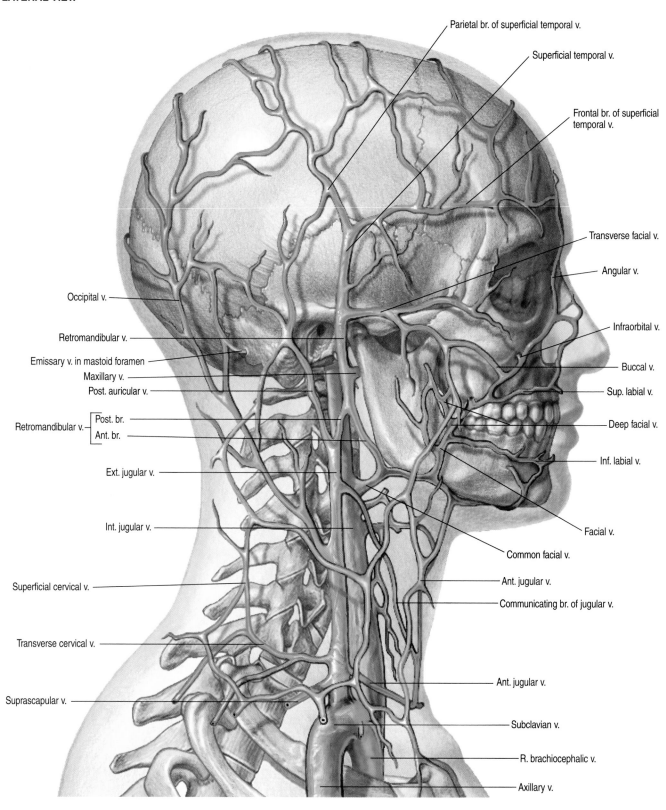

Parietal br. of superficial temporal v.

Superficial temporal v.

Frontal br. of superficial temporal v.

Transverse facial v.

Angular v.

Infraorbital v.

Occipital v.

Retromandibular v.

Emissary v. in mastoid foramen

Maxillary v.

Post. auricular v.

Buccal v.

Sup. labial v.

Deep facial v.

Retromandibular v. — Post. br.
Ant. br.

Inf. labial v.

Ext. jugular v.

Int. jugular v.

Facial v.

Common facial v.

Superficial cervical v.

Ant. jugular v.

Communicating br. of jugular v.

Transverse cervical v.

Suprascapular v.

Ant. jugular v.

Subclavian v.

R. brachiocephalic v.

Axillary v.

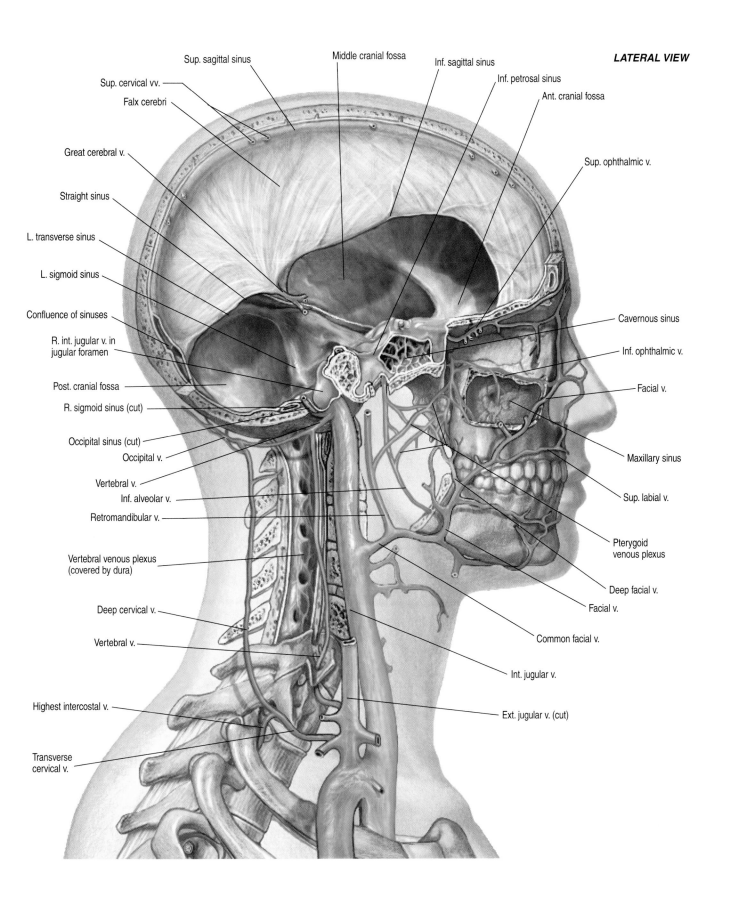

Sup. sagittal sinus

Middle cranial fossa

Inf. sagittal sinus

Inf. petrosal sinus

Ant. cranial fossa

LATERAL VIEW

Sup. cervical vv.

Falx cerebri

Great cerebral v.

Straight sinus

L. transverse sinus

L. sigmoid sinus

Confluence of sinuses

R. int. jugular v. in jugular foramen

Post. cranial fossa

R. sigmoid sinus (cut)

Occipital sinus (cut)

Occipital v.

Vertebral v.

Inf. alveolar v.

Retromandibular v.

Vertebral venous plexus (covered by dura)

Deep cervical v.

Vertebral v.

Highest intercostal v.

Transverse cervical v.

Sup. ophthalmic v.

Cavernous sinus

Inf. ophthalmic v.

Facial v.

Maxillary sinus

Sup. labial v.

Pterygoid venous plexus

Deep facial v.

Facial v.

Common facial v.

Int. jugular v.

Ext. jugular v. (cut)

Dermatomes & Cutaneous Innervation
Plate 7.34

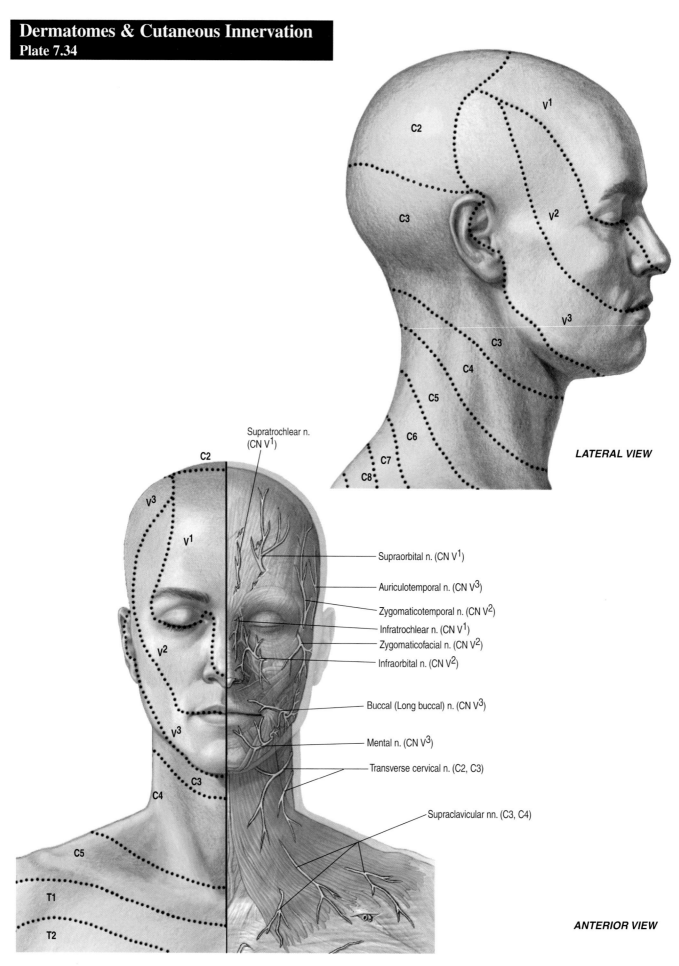

C2

V1

C3

V2

V3

C3

C4

C5

C6

C7

C8

LATERAL VIEW

C2

V3

V1

Supratrochlear n. (CN V1)

Supraorbital n. (CN V1)

Auriculotemporal n. (CN V3)

Zygomaticotemporal n. (CN V2)

Infratrochlear n. (CN V1)

Zygomaticofacial n. (CN V2)

Infraorbital n. (CN V2)

V2

Buccal (Long buccal) n. (CN V3)

V3

Mental n. (CN V3)

Transverse cervical n. (C2, C3)

C3

C4

Supraclavicular nn. (C3, C4)

C5

T1

T2

ANTERIOR VIEW

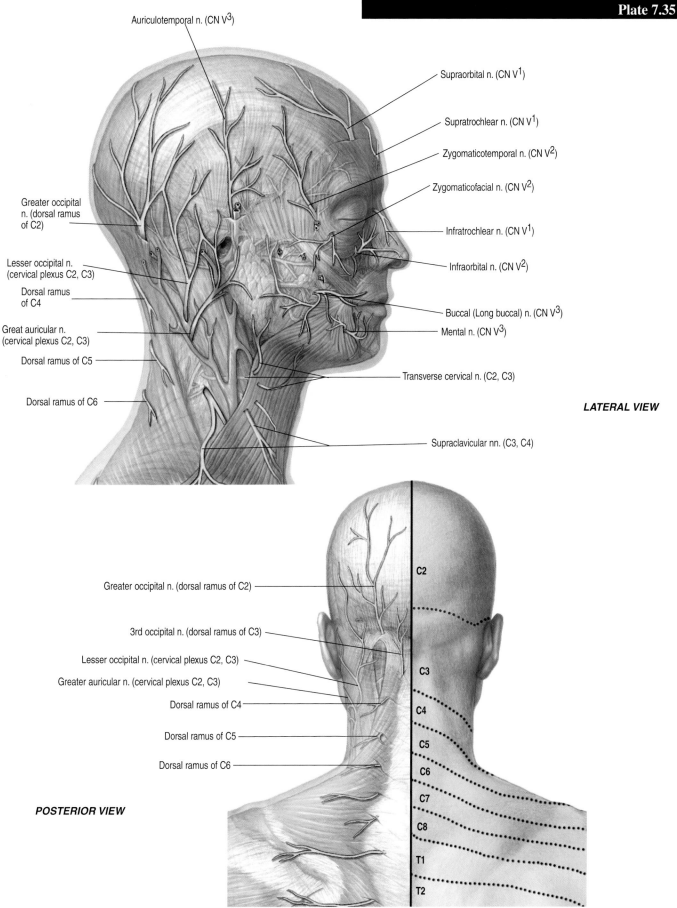

Auriculotemporal n. (CN V³)

Supraorbital n. (CN V¹)

Supratrochlear n. (CN V¹)

Zygomaticotemporal n. (CN V²)

Zygomaticofacial n. (CN V²)

Greater occipital n. (dorsal ramus of C2)

Infratrochlear n. (CN V¹)

Lesser occipital n. (cervical plexus C2, C3)

Infraorbital n. (CN V²)

Dorsal ramus of C4

Buccal (Long buccal) n. (CN V³)

Great auricular n. (cervical plexus C2, C3)

Mental n. (CN V³)

Dorsal ramus of C5

Dorsal ramus of C6

Transverse cervical n. (C2, C3)

LATERAL VIEW

Supraclavicular nn. (C3, C4)

Greater occipital n. (dorsal ramus of C2)

C2

3rd occipital n. (dorsal ramus of C3)

C3

Lesser occipital n. (cervical plexus C2, C3)

Greater auricular n. (cervical plexus C2, C3)

Dorsal ramus of C4

C4

Dorsal ramus of C5

C5

Dorsal ramus of C6

C6

C7

C8

POSTERIOR VIEW

T1

T2

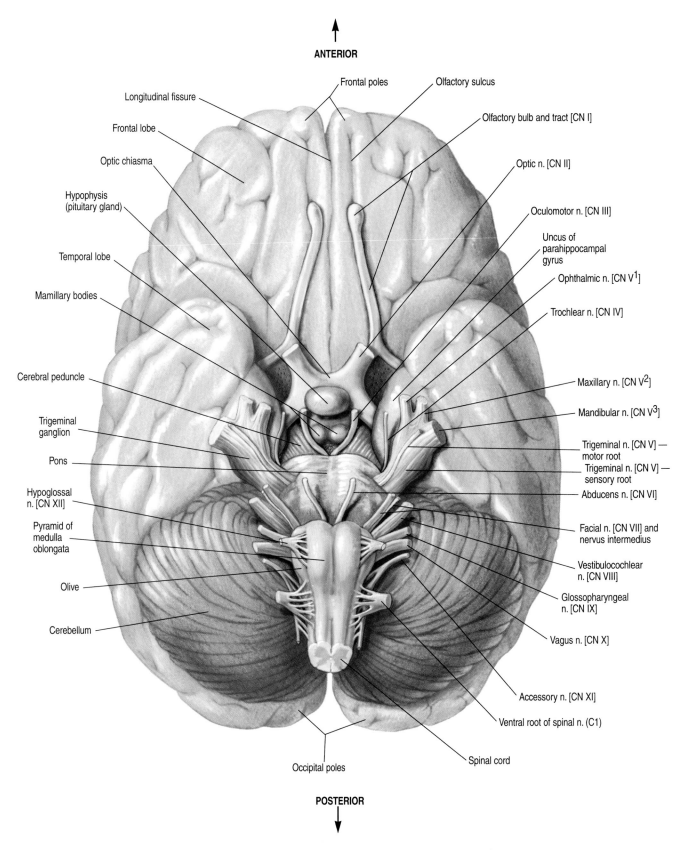

ANTERIOR

Longitudinal fissure

Frontal poles

Olfactory sulcus

Frontal lobe

Olfactory bulb and tract [CN I]

Optic chiasma

Optic n. [CN II]

Hypophysis
(pituitary gland)

Oculomotor n. [CN III]

Uncus of
parahippocampal
gyrus

Temporal lobe

Ophthalmic n. [CN V¹]

Mamillary bodies

Trochlear n. [CN IV]

Cerebral peduncle

Maxillary n. [CN V²]

Mandibular n. [CN V³]

Trigeminal
ganglion

Trigeminal n. [CN V] —
motor root

Pons

Trigeminal n. [CN V] —
sensory root

Hypoglossal
n. [CN XII]

Abducens n. [CN VI]

Pyramid of
medulla
oblongata

Facial n. [CN VII] and
nervus intermedius

Vestibulocochlear
n. [CN VIII]

Olive

Glossopharyngeal
n. [CN IX]

Cerebellum

Vagus n. [CN X]

Accessory n. [CN XI]

Ventral root of spinal n. (C1)

Occipital poles

Spinal cord

POSTERIOR

INFERIOR SURFACE OF BRAIN, BRAINSTEM & SPINAL CORD

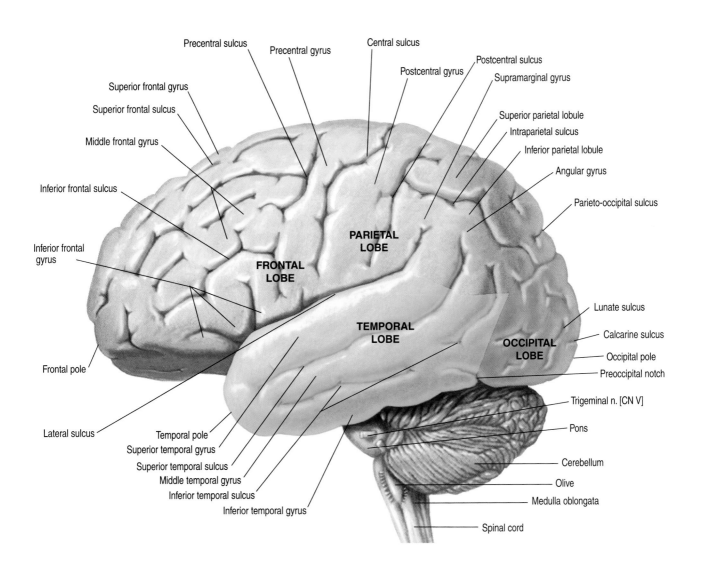

Precentral sulcus

Precentral gyrus

Central sulcus

Postcentral sulcus

Postcentral gyrus

Supramarginal gyrus

Superior frontal gyrus

Superior frontal sulcus

Superior parietal lobule

Middle frontal gyrus

Intraparietal sulcus

Inferior parietal lobule

Angular gyrus

Inferior frontal sulcus

Parieto-occipital sulcus

Inferior frontal gyrus

PARIETAL LOBE

FRONTAL LOBE

Lunate sulcus

TEMPORAL LOBE

Calcarine sulcus

OCCIPITAL LOBE

Occipital pole

Preoccipital notch

Frontal pole

Trigeminal n. [CN V]

Lateral sulcus

Pons

Temporal pole

Superior temporal gyrus

Cerebellum

Superior temporal sulcus

Olive

Middle temporal gyrus

Medulla oblongata

Inferior temporal sulcus

Inferior temporal gyrus

Spinal cord

LEFT LATERAL VIEW OF BRAIN & BRAINSTEM

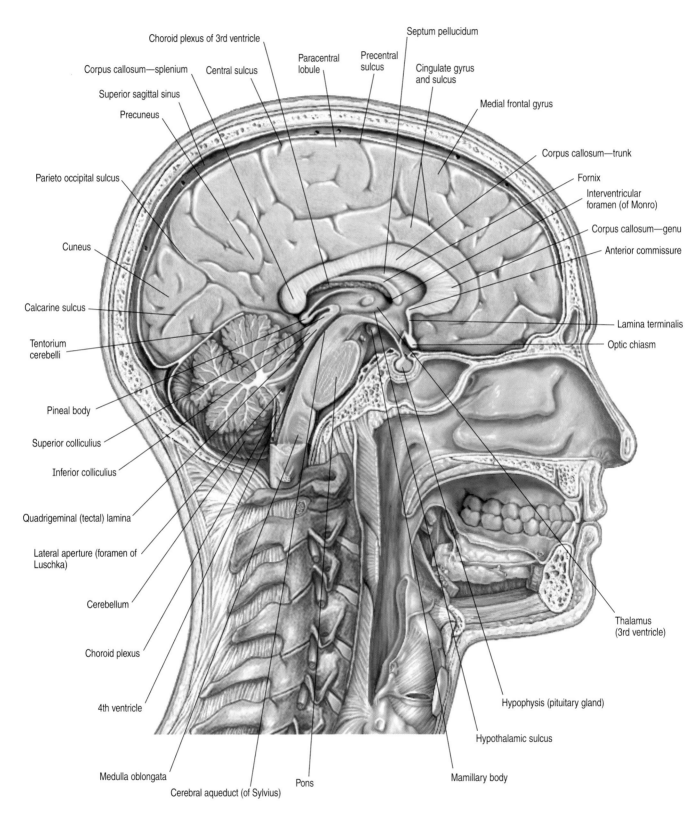

Choroid plexus of 3rd ventricle

Corpus callosum—splenium

Central sulcus

Paracentral lobule

Precentral sulcus

Septum pellucidum

Cingulate gyrus and sulcus

Superior sagittal sinus

Precuneus

Medial frontal gyrus

Parieto occipital sulcus

Corpus callosum—trunk

Fornix

Interventricular foramen (of Monro)

Cuneus

Corpus callosum—genu

Anterior commissure

Calcarine sulcus

Lamina terminalis

Optic chiasm

Tentorium cerebelli

Pineal body

Superior colliculus

Inferior colliculus

Quadrigeminal (tectal) lamina

Lateral aperture (foramen of Luschka)

Cerebellum

Choroid plexus

Thalamus (3rd ventricle)

4th ventricle

Hypophysis (pituitary gland)

Hypothalamic sulcus

Medulla oblongata

Pons

Mamillary body

Cerebral aqueduct (of Sylvius)

LATERAL VIEW WITH BRAIN & BRAINSTEM MEDIAN SECTIONED

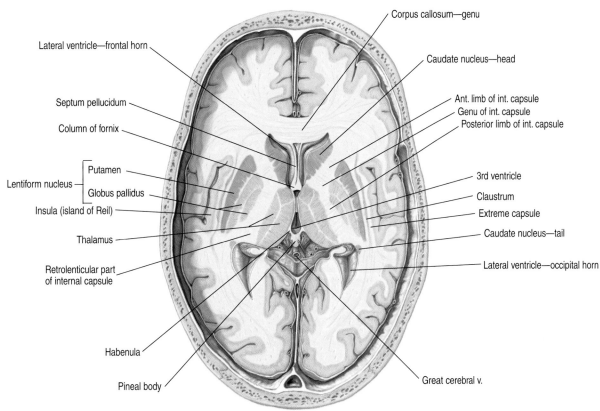

Corpus callosum—genu

Lateral ventricle—frontal horn

Caudate nucleus—head

Septum pellucidum

Ant. limb of int. capsule
Genu of int. capsule
Posterior limb of int. capsule

Column of fornix

Putamen

Lentiform nucleus

Globus pallidus

3rd ventricle

Claustrum

Extreme capsule

Insula (island of Reil)

Thalamus

Caudate nucleus—tail

Retrolenticular part
of internal capsule

Lateral ventricle—occipital horn

Habenula

Pineal body

Great cerebral v.

HORIZONTAL SECTIONS OF BRAIN

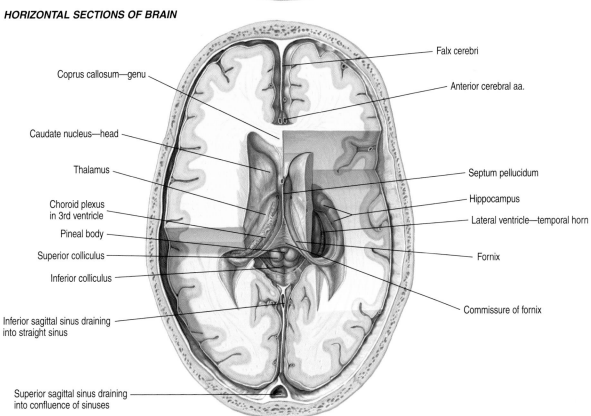

Falx cerebri

Coprus callosum—genu

Anterior cerebral aa.

Caudate nucleus—head

Thalamus

Septum pellucidum

Hippocampus

Choroid plexus
in 3rd ventricle

Lateral ventricle—temporal horn

Pineal body

Superior colliculus

Fornix

Inferior colliculus

Inferior sagittal sinus draining
into straight sinus

Commissure of fornix

Superior sagittal sinus draining
into confluence of sinuses

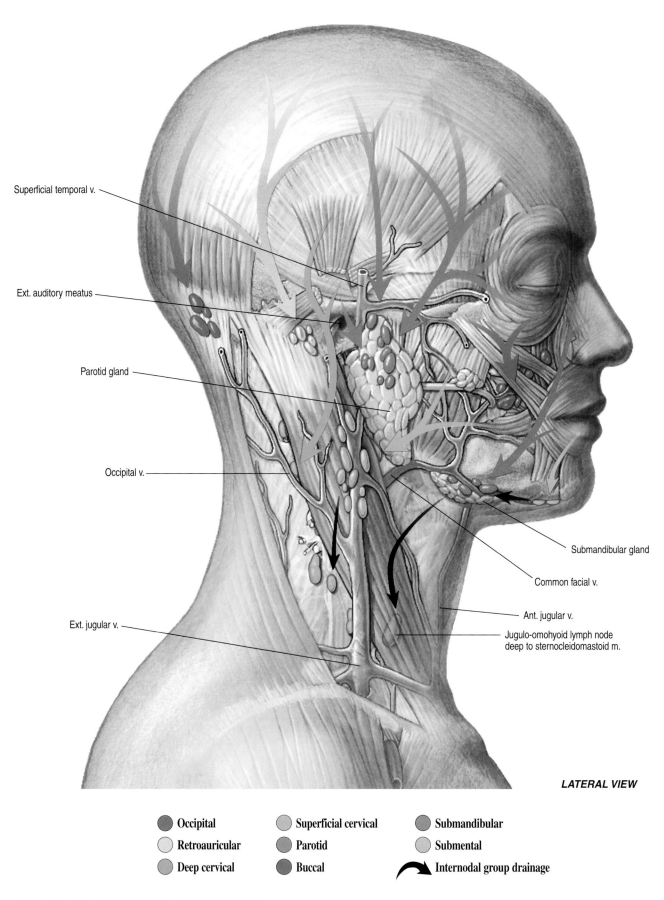

Superficial temporal v.

Ext. auditory meatus

Parotid gland

Occipital v.

Ext. jugular v.

Submandibular gland

Common facial v.

Ant. jugular v.

Jugulo-omohyoid lymph node
deep to sternocleidomastoid m.

LATERAL VIEW

- ⬤ **Occipital**
- ◯ **Retroauricular**
- ◯ **Deep cervical**
- ◯ **Superficial cervical**
- ◯ **Parotid**
- ⬤ **Buccal**
- ⬤ **Submandibular**
- ◯ **Submental**
- ➤ **Internodal group drainage**

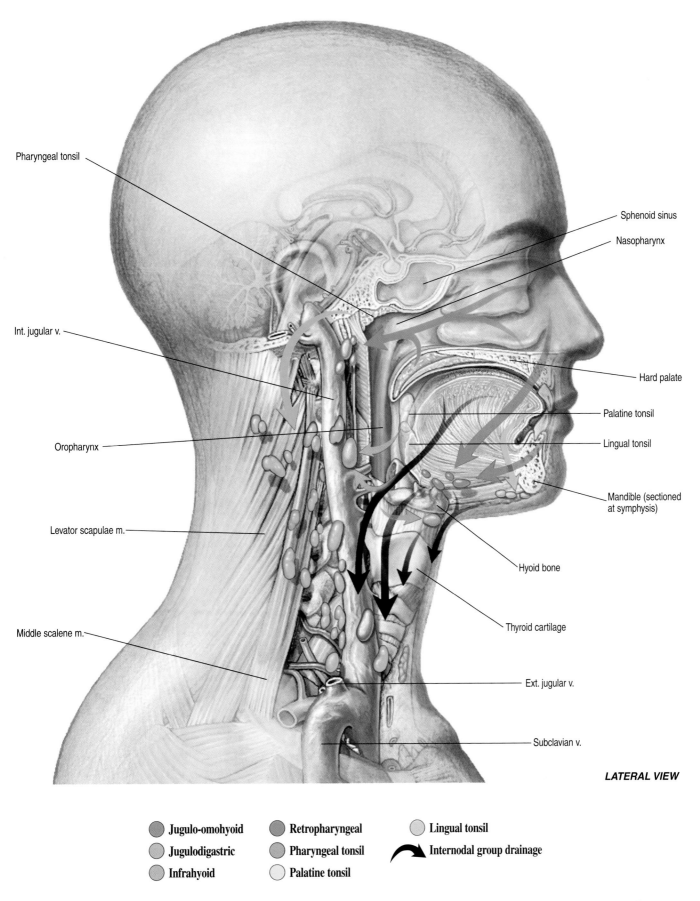

Pharyngeal tonsil

Sphenoid sinus

Nasopharynx

Int. jugular v.

Hard palate

Palatine tonsil

Oropharynx

Lingual tonsil

Mandible (sectioned at symphysis)

Levator scapulae m.

Hyoid bone

Middle scalene m.

Thyroid cartilage

Ext. jugular v.

Subclavian v.

LATERAL VIEW

⬤ **Jugulo-omohyoid**   ⬤ **Retropharyngeal**   ◯ **Lingual tonsil**

⬤ **Jugulodigastric**   ⬤ **Pharyngeal tonsil**   ➥ **Internodal group drainage**

⬤ **Infrahyoid**   ◯ **Palatine tonsil**

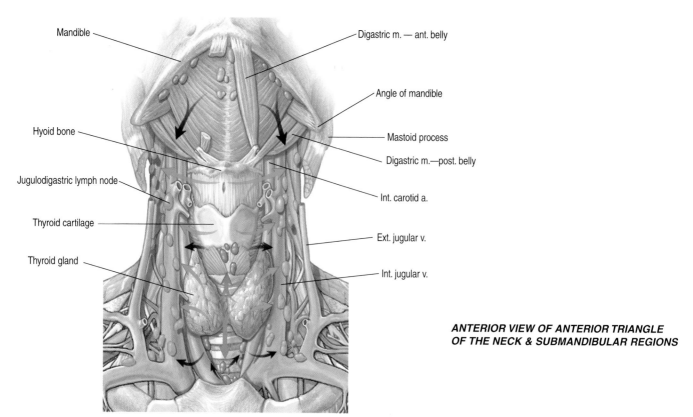

Mandible

Digastric m. — ant. belly

Angle of mandible

Hyoid bone

Mastoid process

Digastric m.—post. belly

Jugulodigastric lymph node

Int. carotid a.

Thyroid cartilage

Ext. jugular v.

Thyroid gland

Int. jugular v.

**ANTERIOR VIEW OF ANTERIOR TRIANGLE
OF THE NECK & SUBMANDIBULAR REGIONS**

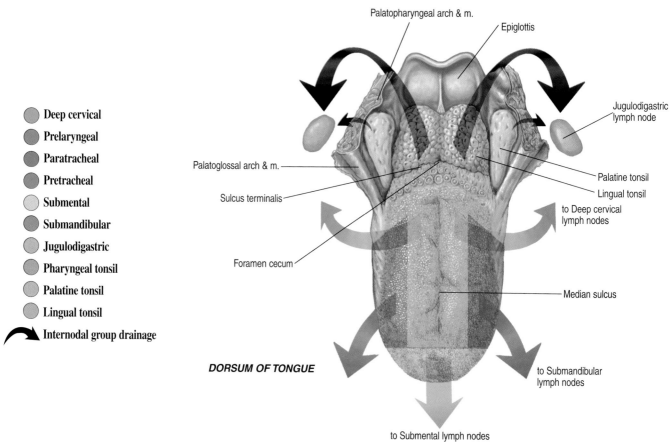

Palatopharyngeal arch & m.

Epiglottis

Jugulodigastric
lymph node

Palatoglossal arch & m.

Palatine tonsil

Sulcus terminalis

Lingual tonsil

to Deep cervical
lymph nodes

Foramen cecum

Median sulcus

● Deep cervical
● Prelaryngeal
● Paratracheal
● Pretracheal
○ Submental
● Submandibular
○ Jugulodigastric
○ Pharyngeal tonsil
○ Palatine tonsil
○ Lingual tonsil
➤ Internodal group drainage

DORSUM OF TONGUE

to Submandibular
lymph nodes

to Submental lymph nodes

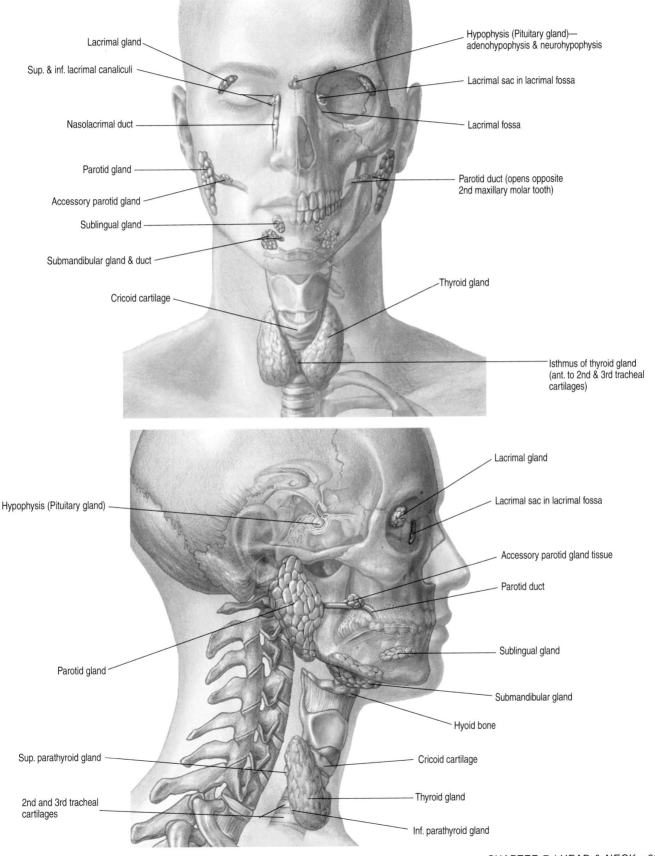

Lacrimal gland

Sup. & inf. lacrimal canaliculi

Nasolacrimal duct

Parotid gland

Accessory parotid gland

Sublingual gland

Submandibular gland & duct

Cricoid cartilage

Hypophysis (Pituitary gland)—
adenohypophysis & neurohypophysis

Lacrimal sac in lacrimal fossa

Lacrimal fossa

Parotid duct (opens opposite
2nd maxillary molar tooth)

Thyroid gland

Isthmus of thyroid gland
(ant. to 2nd & 3rd tracheal
cartilages)

Hypophysis (Pituitary gland)

Parotid gland

Sup. parathyroid gland

2nd and 3rd tracheal
cartilages

Lacrimal gland

Lacrimal sac in lacrimal fossa

Accessory parotid gland tissue

Parotid duct

Sublingual gland

Submandibular gland

Hyoid bone

Cricoid cartilage

Thyroid gland

Inf. parathyroid gland

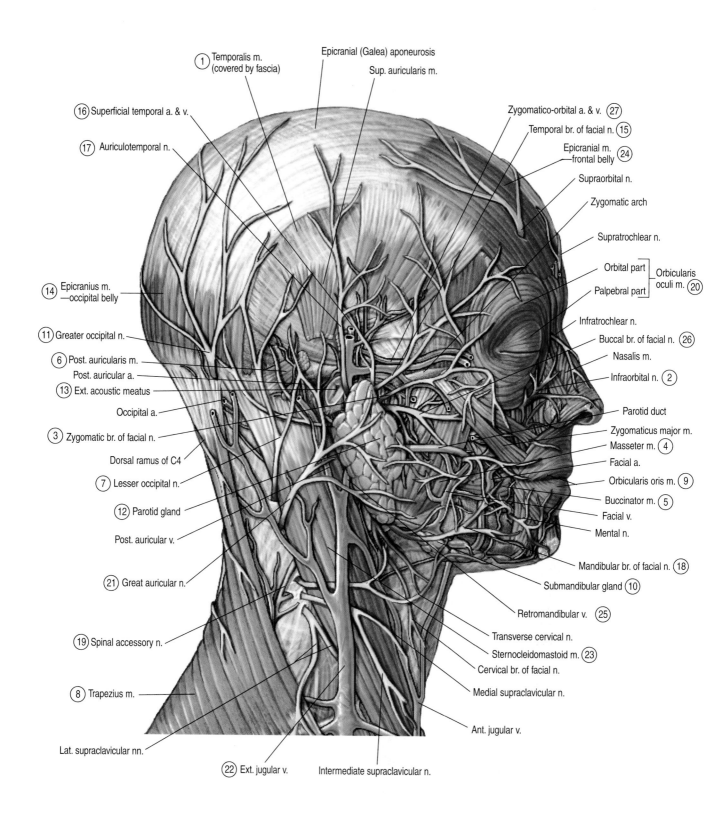

1 Temporalis m. (covered by fascia)

Epicranial (Galea) aponeurosis

Sup. auricularis m.

16 Superficial temporal a. & v.

17 Auriculotemporal n.

Zygomatico-orbital a. & v. 27

Temporal br. of facial n. 15

Epicranial m. —frontal belly 24

Supraorbital n.

Zygomatic arch

Supratrochlear n.

14 Epicranius m. —occipital belly

Orbital part

Palpebral part

Orbicularis oculi m. 20

11 Greater occipital n.

Infratrochlear n.

6 Post. auricularis m.

Post. auricular a.

13 Ext. acoustic meatus

Buccal br. of facial n. 26

Nasalis m.

Infraorbital n. 2

Occipital a.

Parotid duct

3 Zygomatic br. of facial n.

Zygomaticus major m.

Masseter m. 4

Dorsal ramus of C4

Facial a.

7 Lesser occipital n.

Orbicularis oris m. 9

12 Parotid gland

Buccinator m. 5

Facial v.

Post. auricular v.

Mental n.

21 Great auricular n.

Mandibular br. of facial n. 18

Submandibular gland 10

Retromandibular v. 25

19 Spinal accessory n.

Transverse cervical n.

Sternocleidomastoid m. 23

Cervical br. of facial n.

8 Trapezius m.

Medial supraclavicular n.

Ant. jugular v.

Lat. supraclavicular nn.

22 Ext. jugular v.

Intermediate supraclavicular n.

LATERAL VIEW

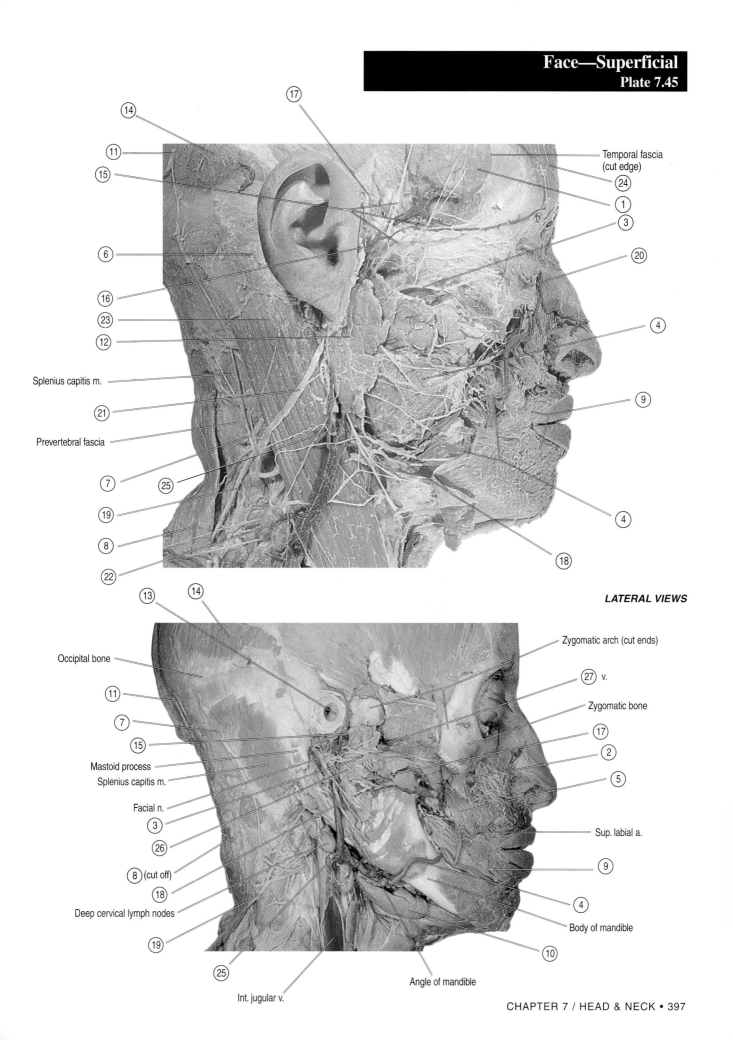

Temporal fascia (cut edge)

Splenius capitis m.

Prevertebral fascia

LATERAL VIEWS

Occipital bone

Zygomatic arch (cut ends)

v.

Zygomatic bone

Mastoid process

Splenius capitis m.

Facial n.

Sup. labial a.

Deep cervical lymph nodes

Body of mandible

Int. jugular v.

Angle of mandible

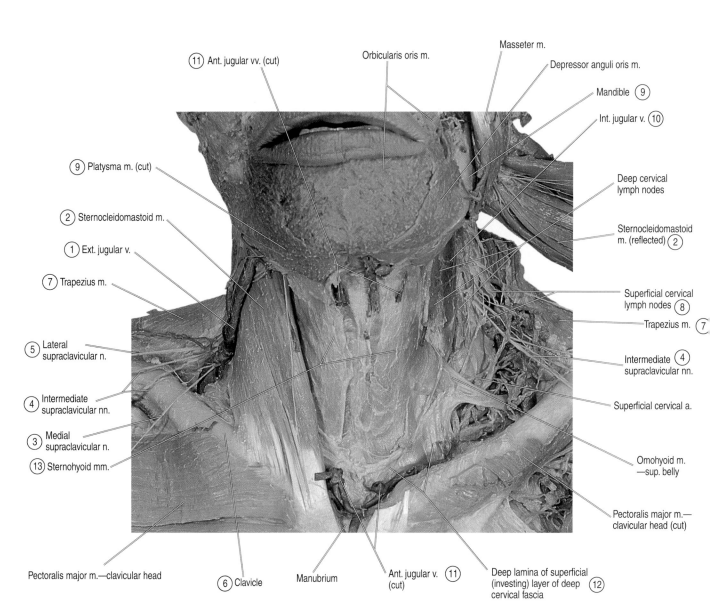

11 Ant. jugular vv. (cut)

Orbicularis oris m.

Masseter m.

Depressor anguli oris m.

Mandible 9

Int. jugular v. 10

9 Platysma m. (cut)

Deep cervical lymph nodes

2 Sternocleidomastoid m.

Sternocleidomastoid m. (reflected) 2

1 Ext. jugular v.

7 Trapezius m.

Superficial cervical lymph nodes 8

Trapezius m. 7

5 Lateral supraclavicular n.

Intermediate 4 supraclavicular nn.

4 Intermediate supraclavicular nn.

Superficial cervical a.

3 Medial supraclavicular n.

Omohyoid m. —sup. belly

13 Sternohyoid mm.

Pectoralis major m.— clavicular head (cut)

Pectoralis major m.—clavicular head

6 Clavicle

Manubrium

Ant. jugular v. 11 (cut)

Deep lamina of superficial (investing) layer of deep cervical fascia 12

ANTERIOR VIEW OF NECK WITH DEEPER STRUCTURES EXPOSED ON LEFT SIDE

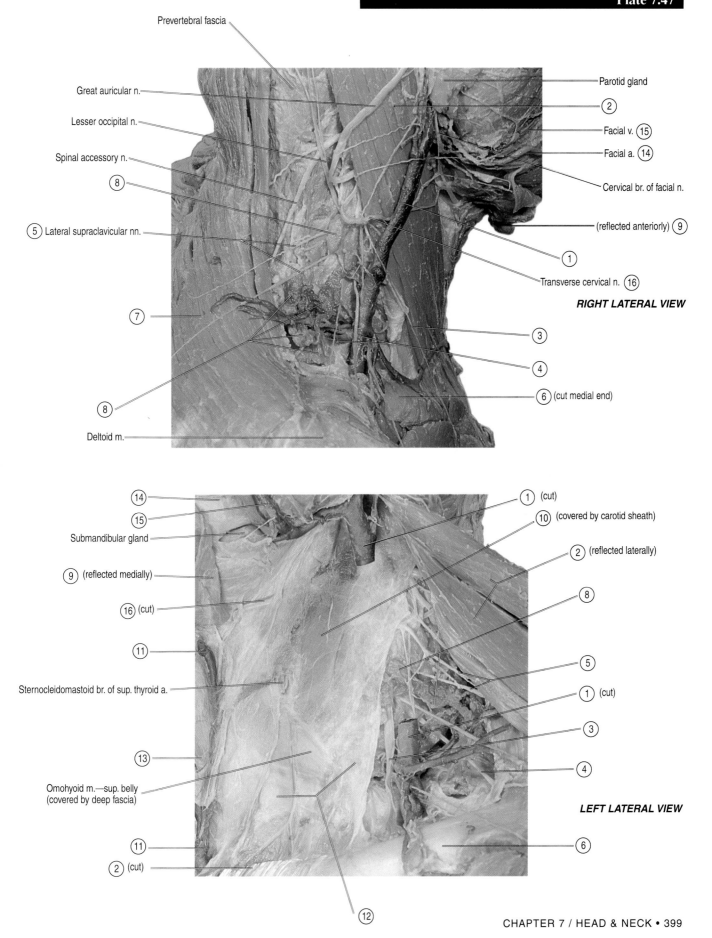

Prevertebral fascia

Great auricular n.

Lesser occipital n.

Spinal accessory n.

⑧

⑤ Lateral supraclavicular nn.

⑦

⑧

Deltoid m.

Parotid gland

②

Facial v. ⑮

Facial a. ⑭

Cervical br. of facial n.

(reflected anteriorly) ⑨

①

Transverse cervical n. ⑯

RIGHT LATERAL VIEW

③

④

⑥ (cut medial end)

⑭

⑮

Submandibular gland

⑨ (reflected medially)

⑯ (cut)

⑪

Sternocleidomastoid br. of sup. thyroid a.

⑬

Omohyoid m.—sup. belly
(covered by deep fascia)

⑪

② (cut)

① (cut)

⑩ (covered by carotid sheath)

② (reflected laterally)

⑧

⑤

① (cut)

③

④

LEFT LATERAL VIEW

⑥

⑫

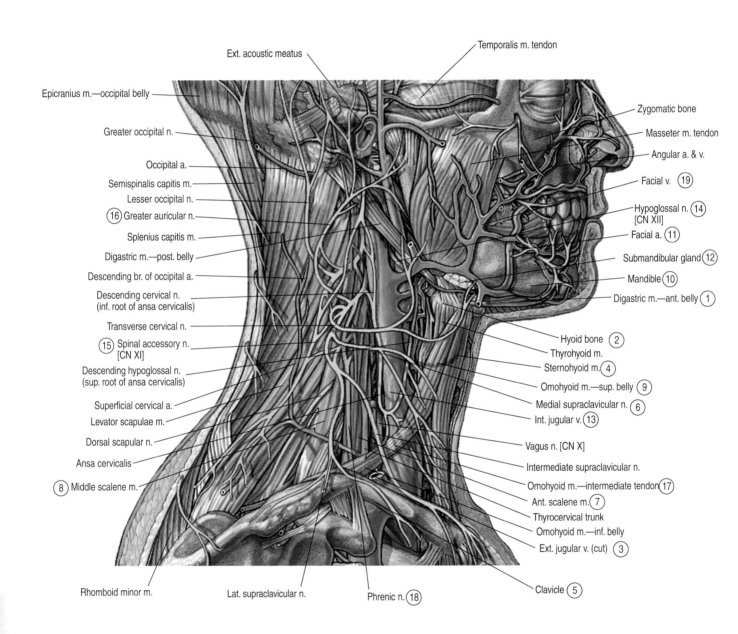

Ext. acoustic meatus

Temporalis m. tendon

Epicranius m.—occipital belly

Greater occipital n.

Occipital a.

Semispinalis capitis m.

Lesser occipital n.

(16) Greater auricular n.

Splenius capitis m.

Digastric m.—post. belly

Descending br. of occipital a.

Descending cervical n.
(inf. root of ansa cervicalis)

Transverse cervical n.

(15) Spinal accessory n.
[CN XI]

Descending hypoglossal n.
(sup. root of ansa cervicalis)

Superficial cervical a.

Levator scapulae m.

Dorsal scapular n.

Ansa cervicalis

(8) Middle scalene m.

Zygomatic bone

Masseter m. tendon

Angular a. & v.

Facial v. (19)

Hypoglossal n. (14)
[CN XII]

Facial a. (11)

Submandibular gland (12)

Mandible (10)

Digastric m.—ant. belly (1)

Hyoid bone (2)

Thyrohyoid m.

Sternohyoid m. (4)

Omohyoid m.—sup. belly (9)

Medial supraclavicular n. (6)

Int. jugular v. (13)

Vagus n. [CN X]

Intermediate supraclavicular n.

Omohyoid m.—intermediate tendon (17)

Ant. scalene m. (7)

Thyrocervical trunk

Omohyoid m.—inf. belly

Ext. jugular v. (cut) (3)

Rhomboid minor m.

Lat. supraclavicular n.

Phrenic n. (18)

Clavicle (5)

LATERAL VIEW

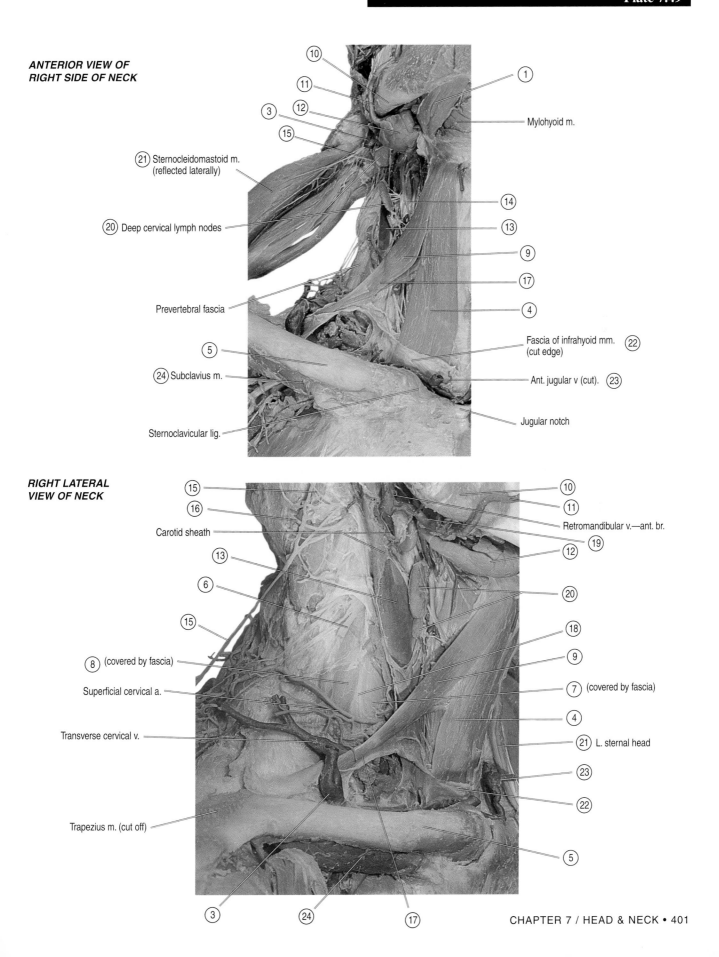

ANTERIOR VIEW OF
RIGHT SIDE OF NECK

⑩
⑪
① — Mylohyoid m.
③ ⑫
⑮

㉑ Sternocleidomastoid m.
(reflected laterally)

⑳ Deep cervical lymph nodes

⑭
⑬
⑨
⑰
④

Prevertebral fascia

Fascia of infrahyoid mm. ㉒
(cut edge)

⑤

㉔ Subclavius m.

Ant. jugular v (cut). ㉓

Sternoclavicular lig.

Jugular notch

RIGHT LATERAL
VIEW OF NECK

⑮
⑯

Carotid sheath

⑩
⑪
Retromandibular v.—ant. br.
⑫ ⑲

⑬

⑥

⑳

⑮

⑱
⑨

⑧ (covered by fascia)

Superficial cervical a.

⑦ (covered by fascia)

④

Transverse cervical v.

㉑ L. sternal head

㉓
㉒

Trapezius m. (cut off)

⑤

③ ㉔ ⑰

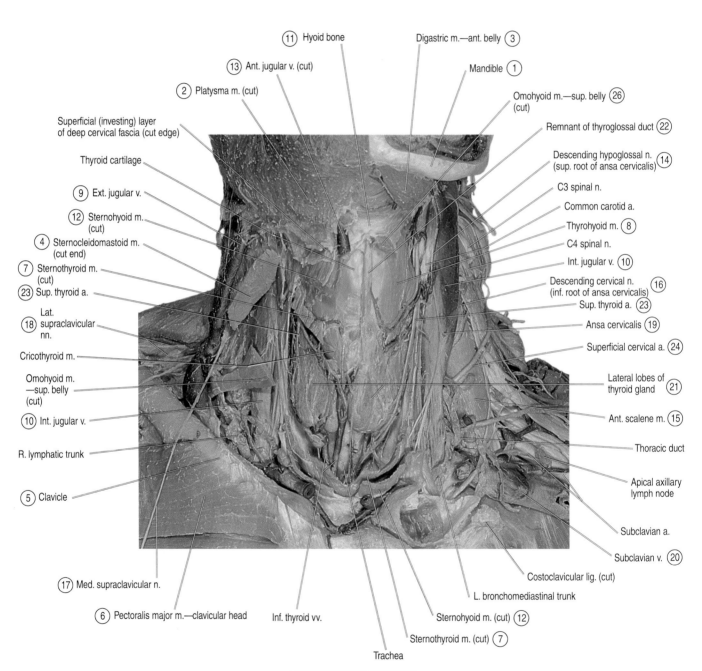

⑪ Hyoid bone

⑬ Ant. jugular v. (cut)

② Platysma m. (cut)

Superficial (investing) layer
of deep cervical fascia (cut edge)

Thyroid cartilage

⑨ Ext. jugular v.

⑫ Sternohyoid m.
(cut)

④ Sternocleidomastoid m.
(cut end)

⑦ Sternothyroid m.
(cut)

㉓ Sup. thyroid a.

⑱ Lat.
supraclavicular
nn.

Cricothyroid m.

Omohyoid m.
—sup. belly
(cut)

⑩ Int. jugular v.

R. lymphatic trunk

⑤ Clavicle

Digastric m.—ant. belly ③

Mandible ①

Omohyoid m.—sup. belly ㉖
(cut)

Remnant of thyroglossal duct ㉒

Descending hypoglossal n. ⑭
(sup. root of ansa cervicalis)

C3 spinal n.

Common carotid a.

Thyrohyoid m. ⑧

C4 spinal n.

Int. jugular v. ⑩

Descending cervical n. ⑯
(inf. root of ansa cervicalis)

Sup. thyroid a. ㉓

Ansa cervicalis ⑲

Superficial cervical a. ㉔

Lateral lobes of ㉑
thyroid gland

Ant. scalene m. ⑮

Thoracic duct

Apical axillary
lymph node

Subclavian a.

Subclavian v. ⑳

Costoclavicular lig. (cut)

L. bronchomediastinal trunk

Sternohyoid m. (cut) ⑫

Sternothyroid m. (cut) ⑦

⑰ Med. supraclavicular n.

⑥ Pectoralis major m.—clavicular head

Inf. thyroid vv.

Trachea

**ANTERIOR VIEW OF NECK
WITH DEEP STRUCTURES ON RIGHT SIDE**

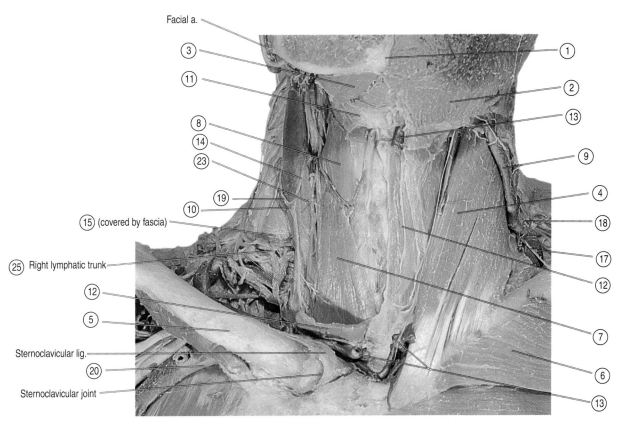

Facial a.

③

⑪

⑧

⑭

㉓

⑲

⑩

⑮ (covered by fascia)

㉕ Right lymphatic trunk

⑫

⑤

Sternoclavicular lig.

⑳

Sternoclavicular joint

①

②

⑬

⑨

④

⑱

⑰

⑫

⑦

⑥

⑬

**ANTERIOR VIEW OF NECK WITH DEEPER STRUCTURES
ON RIGHT SIDE**

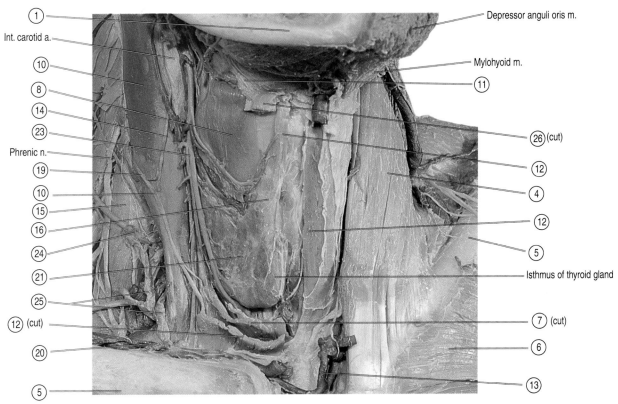

①

Int. carotid a.

⑩

⑧

⑭

㉓

Phrenic n.

⑲

⑩

⑮

⑯

㉔

㉑

㉕

⑫ (cut)

⑳

⑤

Depressor anguli oris m.

Mylohyoid m.

⑪

㉖ (cut)

⑫

④

⑫

⑤

Isthmus of thyroid gland

⑦ (cut)

⑥

⑬

ANTEROLATERAL VIEW OF RIGHT SIDE OF NECK

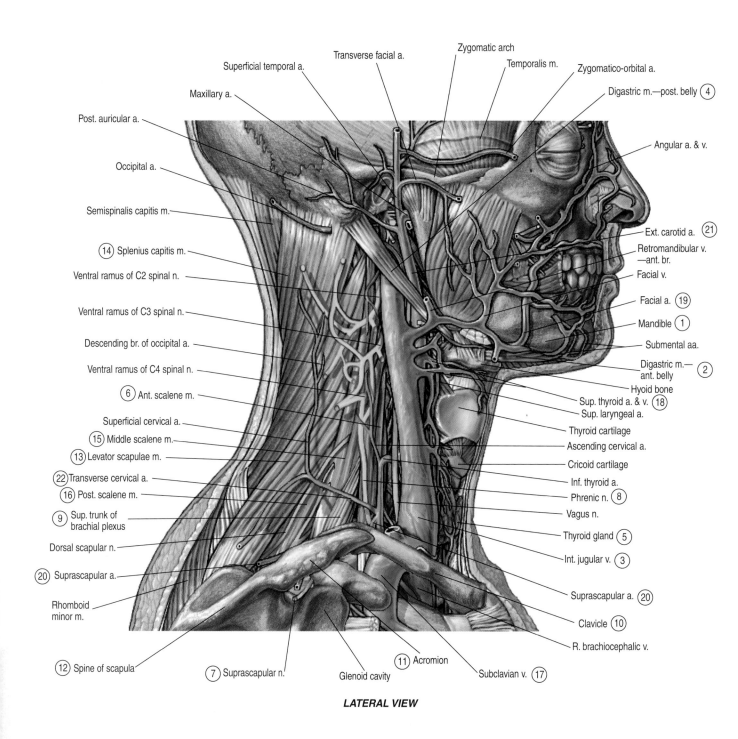

Superficial temporal a.

Transverse facial a.

Zygomatic arch

Temporalis m.

Zygomatico-orbital a.

Maxillary a.

Digastric m.—post. belly ④

Post. auricular a.

Angular a. & v.

Occipital a.

Semispinalis capitis m.

Ext. carotid a. ㉑

⑭ Splenius capitis m.

Retromandibular v.
—ant. br.

Ventral ramus of C2 spinal n.

Facial v.

Facial a. ⑲

Ventral ramus of C3 spinal n.

Mandible ①

Descending br. of occipital a.

Submental aa.

Ventral ramus of C4 spinal n.

Digastric m.—
ant. belly ②

⑥ Ant. scalene m.

Hyoid bone

Sup. thyroid a. & v. ⑱

Superficial cervical a.

Sup. laryngeal a.

⑮ Middle scalene m.

Thyroid cartilage

⑬ Levator scapulae m.

Ascending cervical a.

Cricoid cartilage

㉒ Transverse cervical a.

Inf. thyroid a.

⑯ Post. scalene m.

Phrenic n. ⑧

⑨ Sup. trunk of
brachial plexus

Vagus n.

Dorsal scapular n.

Thyroid gland ⑤

⑳ Suprascapular a.

Int. jugular v. ③

Rhomboid
minor m.

Suprascapular a. ⑳

Clavicle ⑩

R. brachiocephalic v.

⑫ Spine of scapula

⑦ Suprascapular n.

Glenoid cavity

⑪ Acromion

Subclavian v. ⑰

LATERAL VIEW

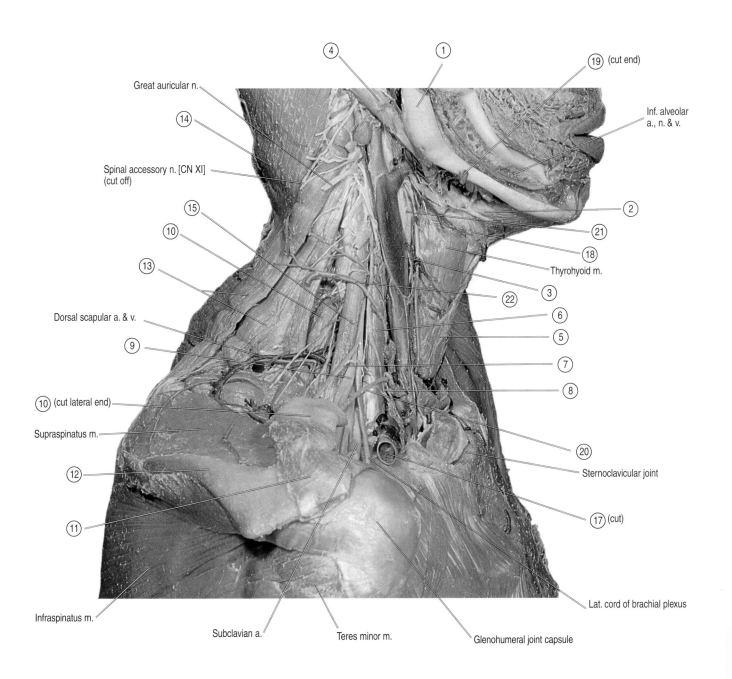

Great auricular n.

④

①

⑲ (cut end)

Inf. alveolar
a., n. & v.

⑭

Spinal accessory n. [CN XI]
(cut off)

②

⑮

㉑

⑱

⑩

Thyrohyoid m.

⑬

㉒

③

Dorsal scapular a. & v.

⑥

⑤

⑨

⑦

⑧

⑩ (cut lateral end)

Supraspinatus m.

⑳

Sternoclavicular joint

⑫

⑪

⑰ (cut)

Lat. cord of brachial plexus

Infraspinatus m.

Subclavian a.

Teres minor m.

Glenohumeral joint capsule

LATERAL VIEW

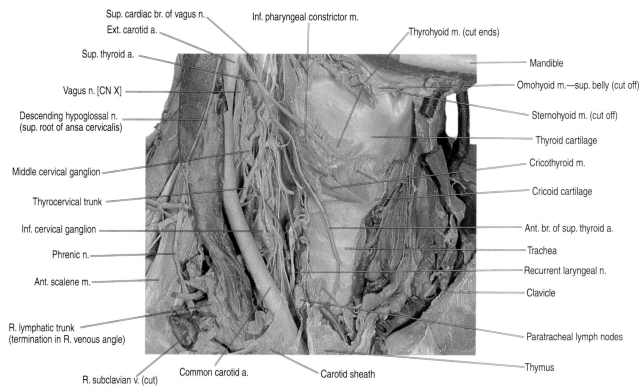

Sup. cardiac br. of vagus n.

Ext. carotid a.

Sup. thyroid a.

Vagus n. [CN X]

Descending hypoglossal n.
(sup. root of ansa cervicalis)

Middle cervical ganglion

Thyrocervical trunk

Inf. cervical ganglion

Phrenic n.

Ant. scalene m.

R. lymphatic trunk
(termination in R. venous angle)

R. subclavian v. (cut)

Common carotid a.

Carotid sheath

Inf. pharyngeal constrictor m.

Thyrohyoid m. (cut ends)

Mandible

Omohyoid m.—sup. belly (cut off)

Sternohyoid m. (cut off)

Thyroid cartilage

Cricothyroid m.

Cricoid cartilage

Ant. br. of sup. thyroid a.

Trachea

Recurrent laryngeal n.

Clavicle

Paratracheal lymph nodes

Thymus

ANTEROLATERAL VIEW OF RELATIONSHIPS OF LARYNX

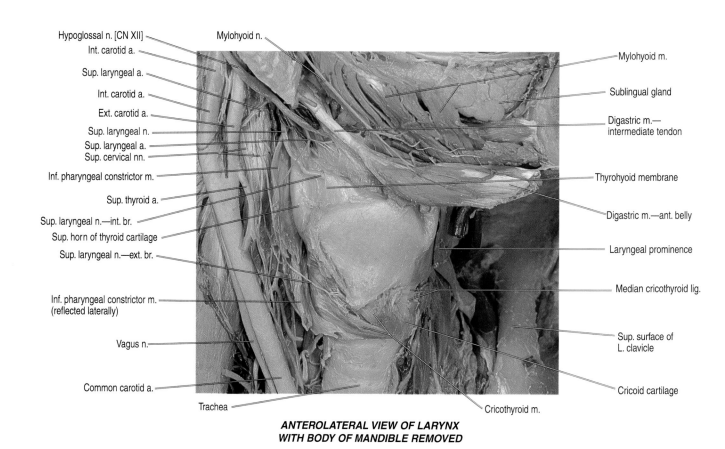

Hypoglossal n. [CN XII]

Int. carotid a.

Sup. laryngeal a.

Int. carotid a.

Ext. carotid a.

Sup. laryngeal n.

Sup. laryngeal a.

Sup. cervical nn.

Inf. pharyngeal constrictor m.

Sup. thyroid a.

Sup. laryngeal n.—int. br.

Sup. horn of thyroid cartilage

Sup. laryngeal n.—ext. br.

Inf. pharyngeal constrictor m.
(reflected laterally)

Vagus n.

Common carotid a.

Trachea

Mylohyoid n.

Mylohyoid m.

Sublingual gland

Digastric m.—
intermediate tendon

Thyrohyoid membrane

Digastric m.—ant. belly

Laryngeal prominence

Median cricothyroid lig.

Sup. surface of
L. clavicle

Cricoid cartilage

Cricothyroid m.

**ANTEROLATERAL VIEW OF LARYNX
WITH BODY OF MANDIBLE REMOVED**

ANTEROLATERAL VIEW
OF LARYNX

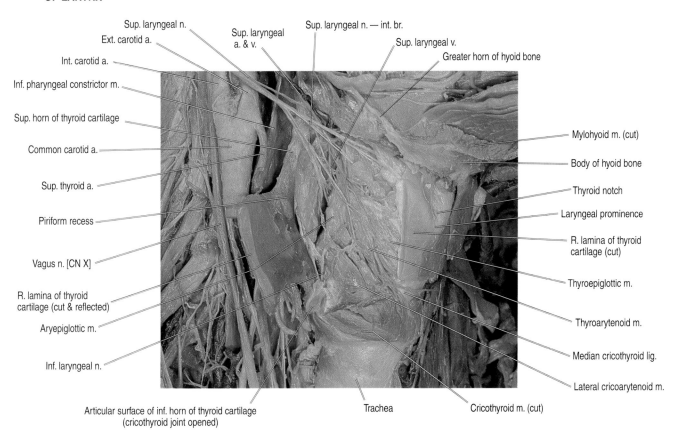

Sup. laryngeal n.

Ext. carotid a.

Int. carotid a.

Inf. pharyngeal constrictor m.

Sup. horn of thyroid cartilage

Common carotid a.

Sup. thyroid a.

Piriform recess

Vagus n. [CN X]

R. lamina of thyroid
cartilage (cut & reflected)

Aryepiglottic m.

Inf. laryngeal n.

Sup. laryngeal
a. & v.

Sup. laryngeal n. — int. br.

Sup. laryngeal v.

Greater horn of hyoid bone

Mylohyoid m. (cut)

Body of hyoid bone

Thyroid notch

Laryngeal prominence

R. lamina of thyroid
cartilage (cut)

Thyroepiglottic m.

Thyroarytenoid m.

Median cricothyroid lig.

Lateral cricoarytenoid m.

Articular surface of inf. horn of thyroid cartilage
(cricothyroid joint opened)

Trachea

Cricothyroid m. (cut)

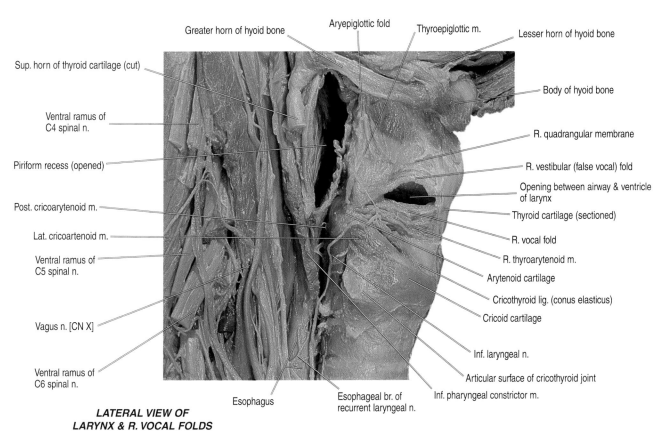

Greater horn of hyoid bone

Aryepiglottic fold

Thyroepiglottic m.

Lesser horn of hyoid bone

Sup. horn of thyroid cartilage (cut)

Ventral ramus of
C4 spinal n.

Piriform recess (opened)

Post. cricoarytenoid m.

Lat. cricoartenoid m.

Ventral ramus of
C5 spinal n.

Vagus n. [CN X]

Ventral ramus of
C6 spinal n.

Body of hyoid bone

R. quadrangular membrane

R. vestibular (false vocal) fold

Opening between airway & ventricle
of larynx

Thyroid cartilage (sectioned)

R. vocal fold

R. thyroarytenoid m.

Arytenoid cartilage

Cricothyroid lig. (conus elasticus)

Cricoid cartilage

Inf. laryngeal n.

Articular surface of cricothyroid joint

Esophagus

Esophageal br. of
recurrent laryngeal n.

Inf. pharyngeal constrictor m.

LATERAL VIEW OF
LARYNX & R. VOCAL FOLDS

POSTERIOR VIEW OF LARYNX

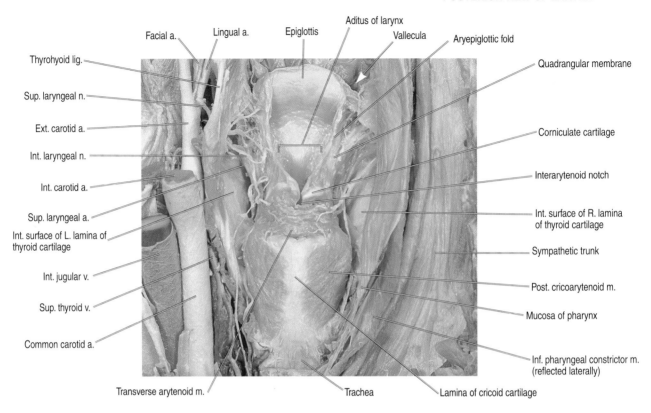

Facial a.
Lingual a.
Epiglottis
Aditus of larynx
Vallecula
Aryepiglottic fold

Thyrohyoid lig.
Quadrangular membrane

Sup. laryngeal n.

Ext. carotid a.
Corniculate cartilage

Int. laryngeal n.

Int. carotid a.
Interarytenoid notch

Sup. laryngeal a.
Int. surface of R. lamina of thyroid cartilage

Int. surface of L. lamina of thyroid cartilage

Int. jugular v.
Sympathetic trunk

Sup. thyroid v.
Post. cricoarytenoid m.

Mucosa of pharynx

Common carotid a.
Inf. pharyngeal constrictor m. (reflected laterally)

Transverse arytenoid m.
Trachea
Lamina of cricoid cartilage

↑
ANTERIOR

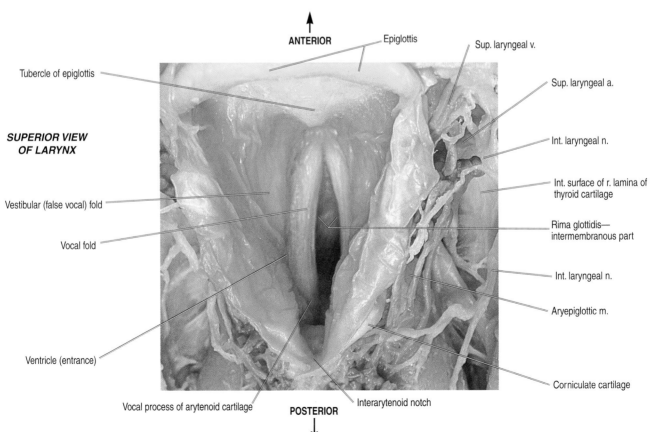

Epiglottis
Sup. laryngeal v.

Tubercle of epiglottis

Sup. laryngeal a.

SUPERIOR VIEW OF LARYNX

Int. laryngeal n.

Int. surface of r. lamina of thyroid cartilage

Vestibular (false vocal) fold

Rima glottidis— intermembranous part

Vocal fold

Int. laryngeal n.

Aryepiglottic m.

Ventricle (entrance)

Corniculate cartilage

Vocal process of arytenoid cartilage
Interarytenoid notch

POSTERIOR
↓

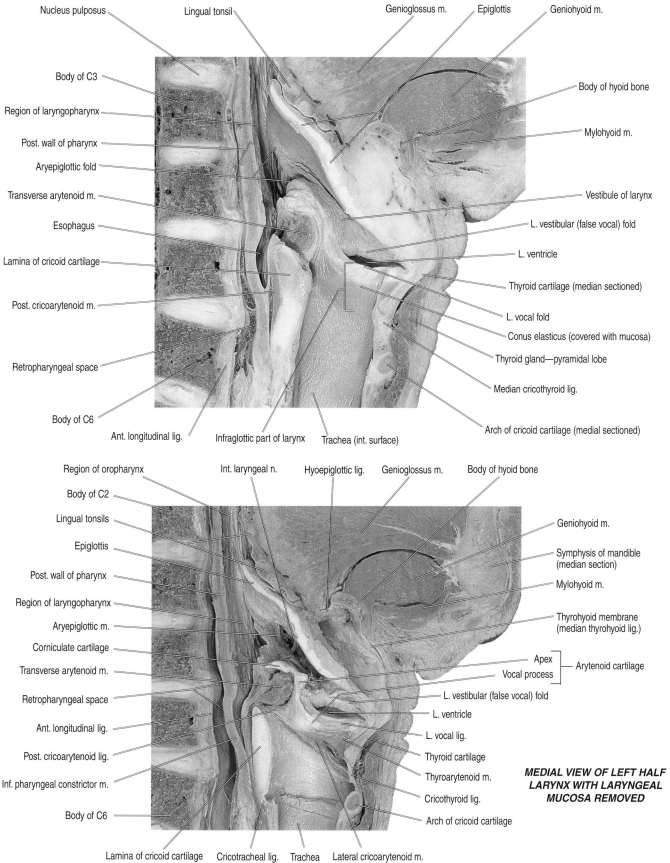

MEDIAL VIEW OF LEFT HALF OF LARYNX

Nucleus pulposus

Lingual tonsil

Genioglossus m.

Epiglottis

Geniohyoid m.

Body of C3

Body of hyoid bone

Region of laryngopharynx

Mylohyoid m.

Post. wall of pharynx

Aryepiglottic fold

Vestibule of larynx

Transverse arytenoid m.

L. vestibular (false vocal) fold

Esophagus

L. ventricle

Lamina of cricoid cartilage

Thyroid cartilage (median sectioned)

Post. cricoarytenoid m.

L. vocal fold

Conus elasticus (covered with mucosa)

Retropharyngeal space

Thyroid gland—pyramidal lobe

Median cricothyroid lig.

Body of C6

Arch of cricoid cartilage (medial sectioned)

Ant. longitudinal lig.

Infraglottic part of larynx

Trachea (int. surface)

Region of oropharynx

Int. laryngeal n.

Hyoepiglottic lig.

Genioglossus m.

Body of hyoid bone

Body of C2

Geniohyoid m.

Lingual tonsils

Symphysis of mandible (median section)

Epiglottis

Mylohyoid m.

Post. wall of pharynx

Region of laryngopharynx

Thyrohyoid membrane (median thyrohyoid lig.)

Aryepiglottic m.

Apex

Corniculate cartilage

Arytenoid cartilage

Vocal process

Transverse arytenoid m.

L. vestibular (false vocal) fold

Retropharyngeal space

L. ventricle

Ant. longitudinal lig.

L. vocal lig.

Post. cricoarytenoid lig.

Thyroid cartilage

Inf. pharyngeal constrictor m.

Thyroarytenoid m.

Cricothyroid lig.

Body of C6

Arch of cricoid cartilage

Lamina of cricoid cartilage

Cricotracheal lig.

Trachea

Lateral cricoarytenoid m.

MEDIAL VIEW OF LEFT HALF LARYNX WITH LARYNGEAL MUCOSA REMOVED

**POSTERIOR VIEW OF POST. WALL
OF PHARYNX & ESOPHAGUS**

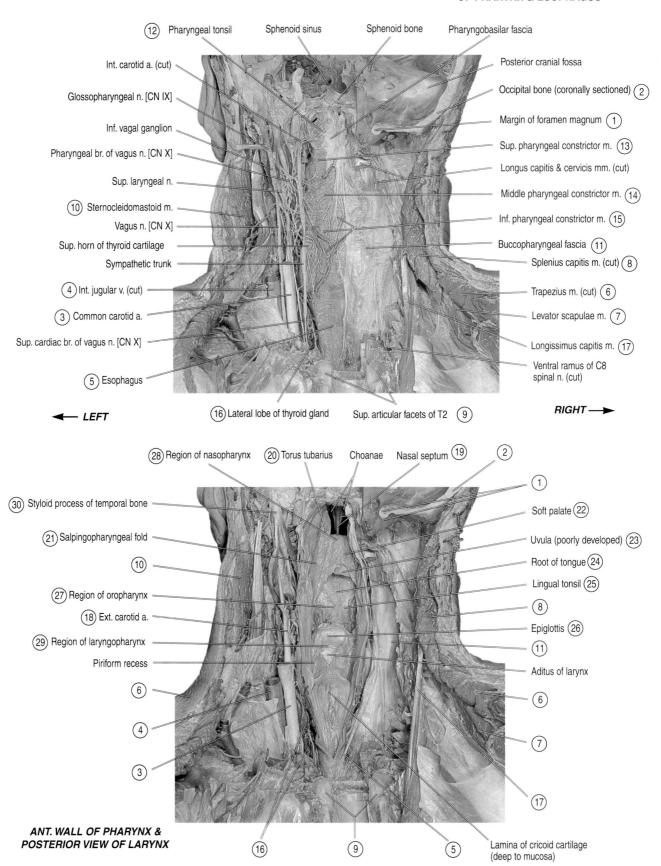

(12) Pharyngeal tonsil

Sphenoid sinus

Sphenoid bone

Pharyngobasilar fascia

Int. carotid a. (cut)

Glossopharyngeal n. [CN IX]

Inf. vagal ganglion

Pharyngeal br. of vagus n. [CN X]

Sup. laryngeal n.

(10) Sternocleidomastoid m.

Vagus n. [CN X]

Sup. horn of thyroid cartilage

Sympathetic trunk

(4) Int. jugular v. (cut)

(3) Common carotid a.

Sup. cardiac br. of vagus n. [CN X]

(5) Esophagus

Posterior cranial fossa

Occipital bone (coronally sectioned) (2)

Margin of foramen magnum (1)

Sup. pharyngeal constrictor m. (13)

Longus capitis & cervicis mm. (cut)

Middle pharyngeal constrictor m. (14)

Inf. pharyngeal constrictor m. (15)

Buccopharyngeal fascia (11)

Splenius capitis m. (cut) (8)

Trapezius m. (cut) (6)

Levator scapulae m. (7)

Longissimus capitis m. (17)

Ventral ramus of C8
spinal n. (cut)

← LEFT

(16) Lateral lobe of thyroid gland

Sup. articular facets of T2 (9)

RIGHT →

(28) Region of nasopharynx

(20) Torus tubarius

Choanae

Nasal septum (19)

(2)

(30) Styloid process of temporal bone

(21) Salpingopharyngeal fold

(10)

(27) Region of oropharynx

(18) Ext. carotid a.

(29) Region of laryngopharynx

Piriform recess

(6)

(4)

(3)

(1)

Soft palate (22)

Uvula (poorly developed) (23)

Root of tongue (24)

Lingual tonsil (25)

(8)

Epiglottis (26)

(11)

Aditus of larynx

(6)

(7)

(17)

**ANT. WALL OF PHARYNX &
POSTERIOR VIEW OF LARYNX**

(16)

(9)

(5)

Lamina of cricoid cartilage
(deep to mucosa)

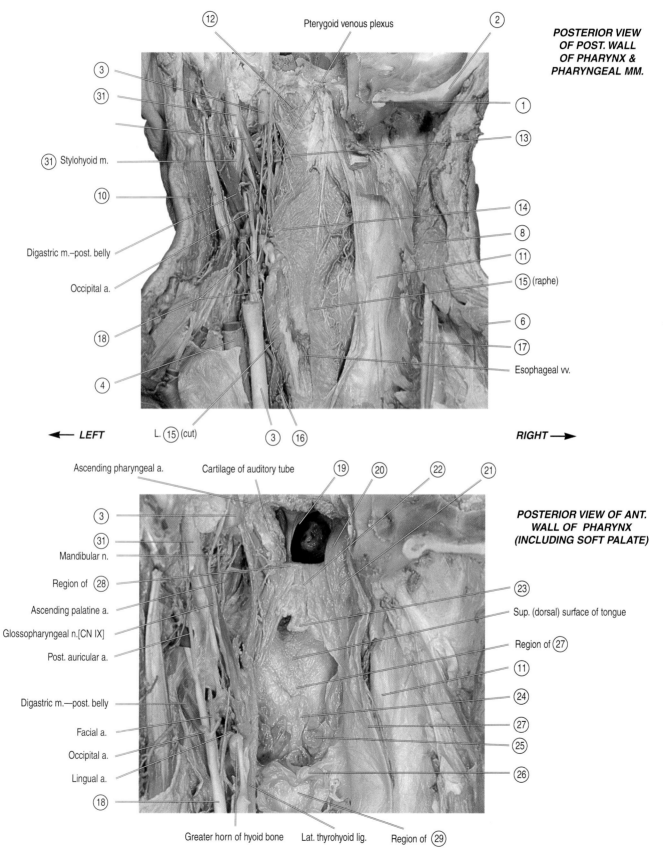

⑫ Pterygoid venous plexus ②

③

㉛

㉛ Stylohyoid m.

⑩

Digastric m.–post. belly

Occipital a.

⑱

④

①

⑬

⑭

⑧

⑪

⑮ (raphe)

⑥

⑰

Esophageal vv.

◄— *LEFT*   L. ⑮ (cut)   ③   ⑯   *RIGHT* —►

Ascending pharyngeal a.   Cartilage of auditory tube   ⑲   ⑳   ㉒   ㉑

③

㉛

Mandibular n.

Region of ㉘

Ascending palatine a.

Glossopharyngeal n.[CN IX]

Post. auricular a.

Digastric m.—post. belly

Facial a.

Occipital a.

Lingual a.

⑱

㉓

Sup. (dorsal) surface of tongue

Region of ㉗

⑪

㉔

㉗

㉕

㉖

Greater horn of hyoid bone   Lat. thyrohyoid lig.   Region of ㉙

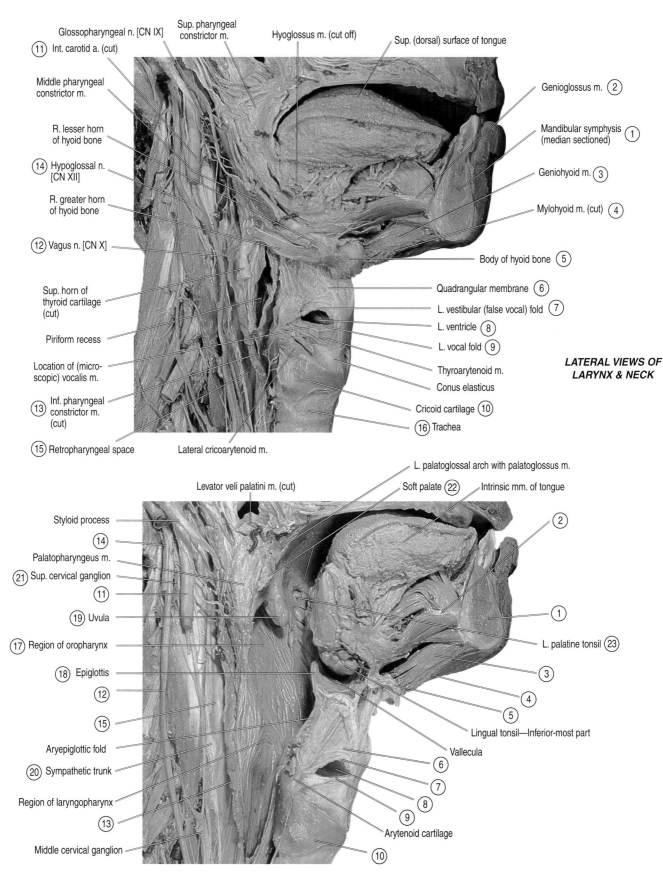

Glossopharyngeal n. [CN IX]

Sup. pharyngeal constrictor m.

Hyoglossus m. (cut off)

Sup. (dorsal) surface of tongue

(11) Int. carotid a. (cut)

Middle pharyngeal constrictor m.

Genioglossus m. (2)

R. lesser horn of hyoid bone

Mandibular symphysis (1) (median sectioned)

(14) Hypoglossal n. [CN XII]

Geniohyoid m. (3)

R. greater horn of hyoid bone

Mylohyoid m. (cut) (4)

(12) Vagus n. [CN X]

Body of hyoid bone (5)

Sup. horn of thyroid cartilage (cut)

Quadrangular membrane (6)

L. vestibular (false vocal) fold (7)

Piriform recess

L. ventricle (8)

L. vocal fold (9)

Location of (micro-scopic) vocalis m.

Thyroarytenoid m.

Conus elasticus

(13) Inf. pharyngeal constrictor m. (cut)

Cricoid cartilage (10)

(16) Trachea

(15) Retropharyngeal space

Lateral cricoarytenoid m.

LATERAL VIEWS OF LARYNX & NECK

L. palatoglossal arch with palatoglossus m.

Levator veli palatini m. (cut)

Soft palate (22)

Intrinsic mm. of tongue

Styloid process

(2)

(14)

Palatopharyngeus m.

(1)

(21) Sup. cervical ganglion

(11)

(19) Uvula

L. palatine tonsil (23)

(17) Region of oropharynx

(3)

(18) Epiglottis

(4)

(12)

(5)

(15)

Lingual tonsil—Inferior-most part

Aryepiglottic fold

Vallecula

(20) Sympathetic trunk

(6)

Region of laryngopharynx

(7)

(8)

(13)

(9)

Arytenoid cartilage

Middle cervical ganglion

(10)

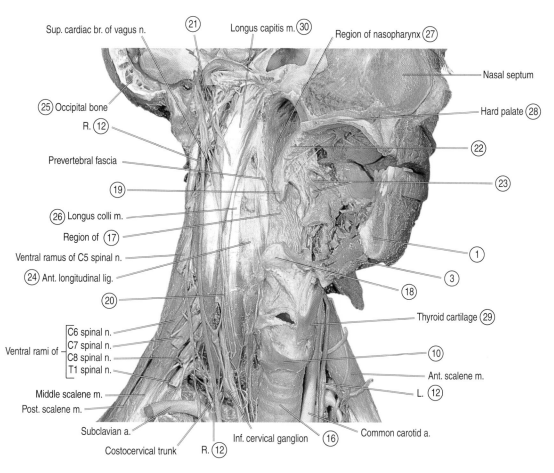

Sup. cardiac br. of vagus n.
(21)
Longus capitis m. (30)
Region of nasopharynx (27)
Nasal septum

(25) Occipital bone
Hard palate (28)

R. (12)
(22)

Prevertebral fascia
(23)

(19)

(26) Longus colli m.
(1)

Region of (17)
(3)

Ventral ramus of C5 spinal n.
(18)

(24) Ant. longitudinal lig.

(20)
Thyroid cartilage (29)

C6 spinal n.
C7 spinal n.
Ventral rami of — C8 spinal n.
T1 spinal n.
(10)

Ant. scalene m.
L. (12)

Middle scalene m.
Post. scalene m.

Subclavian a.
Inf. cervical ganglion (16)
Common carotid a.

Costocervical trunk
R. (12)

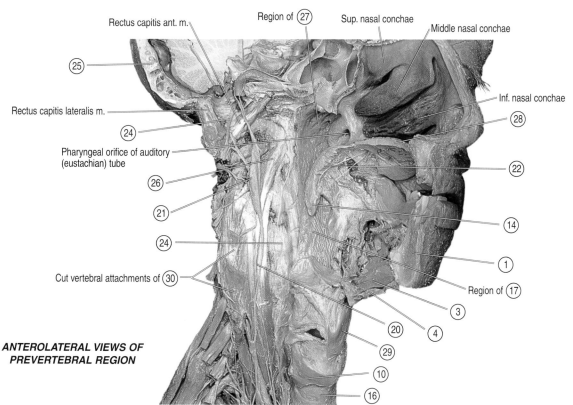

Rectus capitis ant. m.
Region of (27)
Sup. nasal conchae
Middle nasal conchae

(25)

Rectus capitis lateralis m.
Inf. nasal conchae

(24)
(28)

Pharyngeal orifice of auditory
(eustachian) tube
(22)

(26)

(21)
(14)

(24)
(1)

Cut vertebral attachments of (30)
Region of (17)

(3)

(20)
(4)

**ANTEROLATERAL VIEWS OF
PREVERTEBRAL REGION**
(29)

(10)

(16)

Oral Cavity
Plate • 7.62

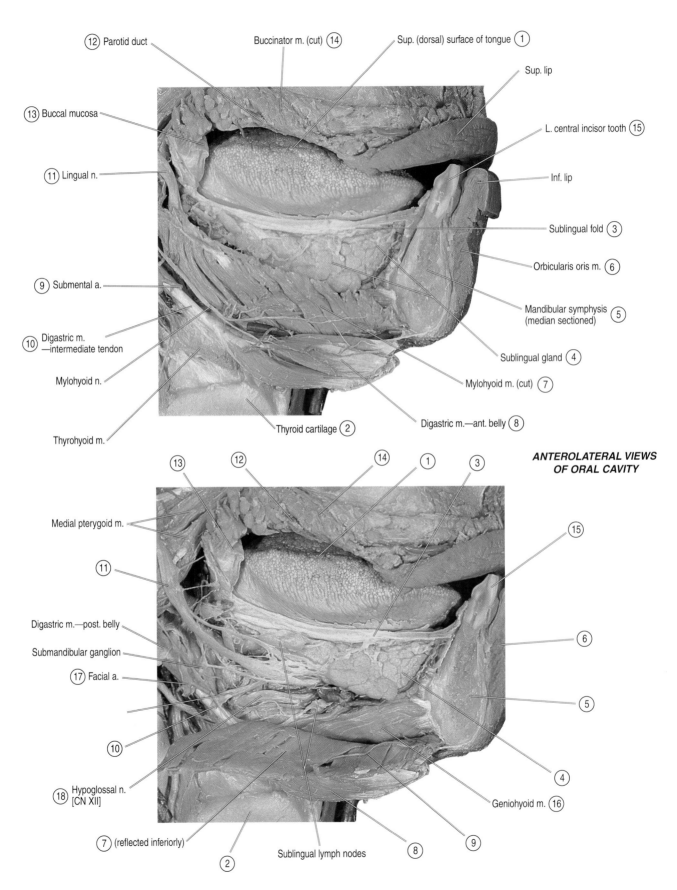

⑫ Parotid duct

Buccinator m. (cut) ⑭

Sup. (dorsal) surface of tongue ①

Sup. lip

⑬ Buccal mucosa

L. central incisor tooth ⑮

⑪ Lingual n.

Inf. lip

Sublingual fold ③

Orbicularis oris m. ⑥

⑨ Submental a.

Mandibular symphysis ⑤
(median sectioned)

⑩ Digastric m.
—intermediate tendon

Sublingual gland ④

Mylohyoid n.

Mylohyoid m. (cut) ⑦

Digastric m.—ant. belly ⑧

Thyrohyoid m.

Thyroid cartilage ②

*ANTEROLATERAL VIEWS
OF ORAL CAVITY*

⑬   ⑫   ⑭   ①   ③

Medial pterygoid m.

⑮

⑪

⑥

Digastric m.—post. belly

Submandibular ganglion

⑰ Facial a.

⑤

⑩

④

⑱ Hypoglossal n.
[CN XII]

Geniohyoid m. ⑯

⑦ (reflected inferiorly)

②

Sublingual lymph nodes

⑧

⑨

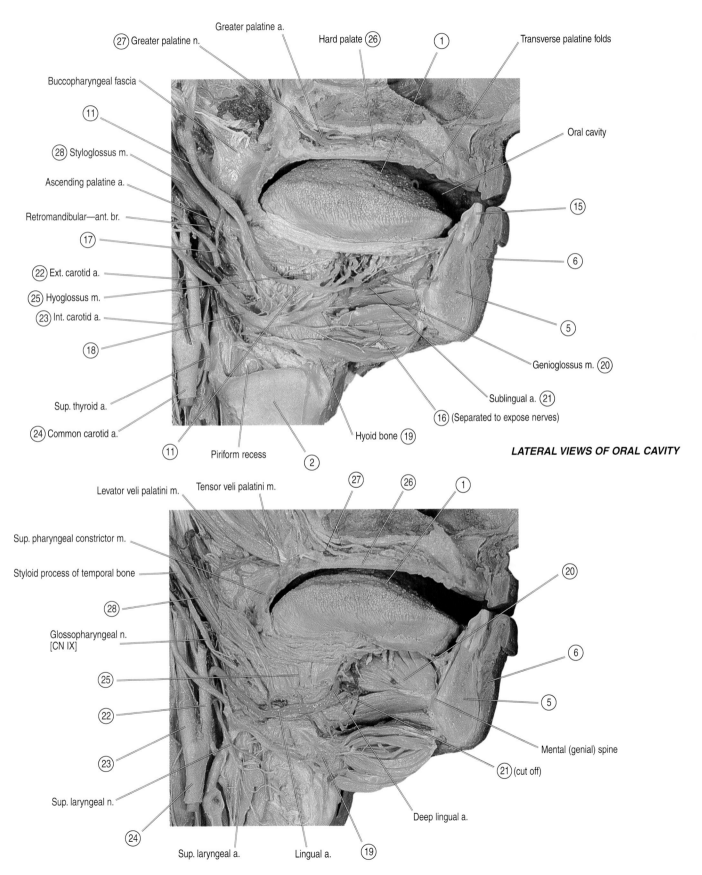

Greater palatine a.

27 Greater palatine n.

Hard palate 26

1

Transverse palatine folds

Buccopharyngeal fascia

11

Oral cavity

28 Styloglossus m.

Ascending palatine a.

Retromandibular—ant. br.

17

15

22 Ext. carotid a.

6

25 Hyoglossus m.

23 Int. carotid a.

5

18

Genioglossus m. 20

Sup. thyroid a.

Sublingual a. 21

24 Common carotid a.

16 (Separated to expose nerves)

11   Piriform recess   2   Hyoid bone 19

LATERAL VIEWS OF ORAL CAVITY

Levator veli palatini m.   Tensor veli palatini m.

27   26   1

Sup. pharyngeal constrictor m.

Styloid process of temporal bone

20

28

6

Glossopharyngeal n.
[CN IX]

5

25

22

Mental (genial) spine

23

21 (cut off)

Sup. laryngeal n.

Deep lingual a.

24

Sup. laryngeal a.   Lingual a.   19

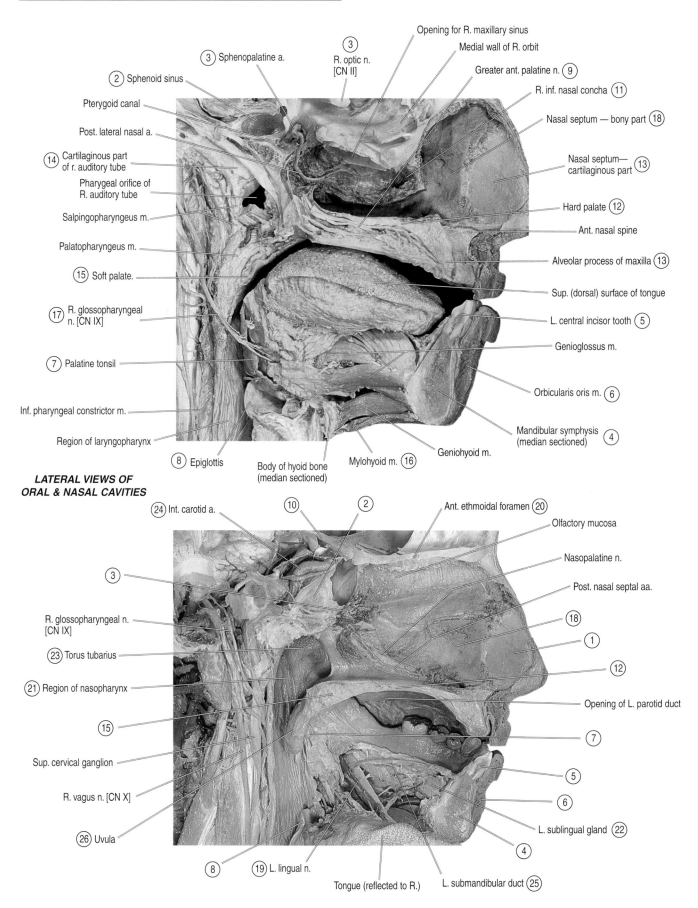

Opening for R. maxillary sinus

R. optic n. ③ [CN II]

Medial wall of R. orbit

③ Sphenopalatine a.

Greater ant. palatine n. ⑨

② Sphenoid sinus

R. inf. nasal concha ⑪

Pterygoid canal

Nasal septum — bony part ⑱

Post. lateral nasal a.

⑭ Cartilaginous part of r. auditory tube

Nasal septum— cartilaginous part ⑬

Pharygeal orifice of R. auditory tube

Hard palate ⑫

Salpingopharyngeus m.

Ant. nasal spine

Palatopharyngeus m.

Alveolar process of maxilla ⑬

⑮ Soft palate.

Sup. (dorsal) surface of tongue

⑰ R. glossopharyngeal n. [CN IX]

L. central incisor tooth ⑤

Genioglossus m.

⑦ Palatine tonsil

Orbicularis oris m. ⑥

Inf. pharyngeal constrictor m.

Mandibular symphysis ④ (median sectioned)

Region of laryngopharynx

⑧ Epiglottis

Body of hyoid bone (median sectioned)

Mylohyoid m. ⑯

Geniohyoid m.

LATERAL VIEWS OF ORAL & NASAL CAVITIES

㉔ Int. carotid a.

⑩   ②

Ant. ethmoidal foramen ⑳

Olfactory mucosa

③

Nasopalatine n.

R. glossopharyngeal n. [CN IX]

Post. nasal septal aa.

⑱

㉓ Torus tubarius

①

⑫

㉑ Region of nasopharynx

Opening of L. parotid duct

⑮

⑦

Sup. cervical ganglion

⑤

R. vagus n. [CN X]

⑥

L. sublingual gland ㉒

㉖ Uvula

④

⑧   ⑲ L. lingual n.

Tongue (reflected to R.)

L. submandibular duct ㉕

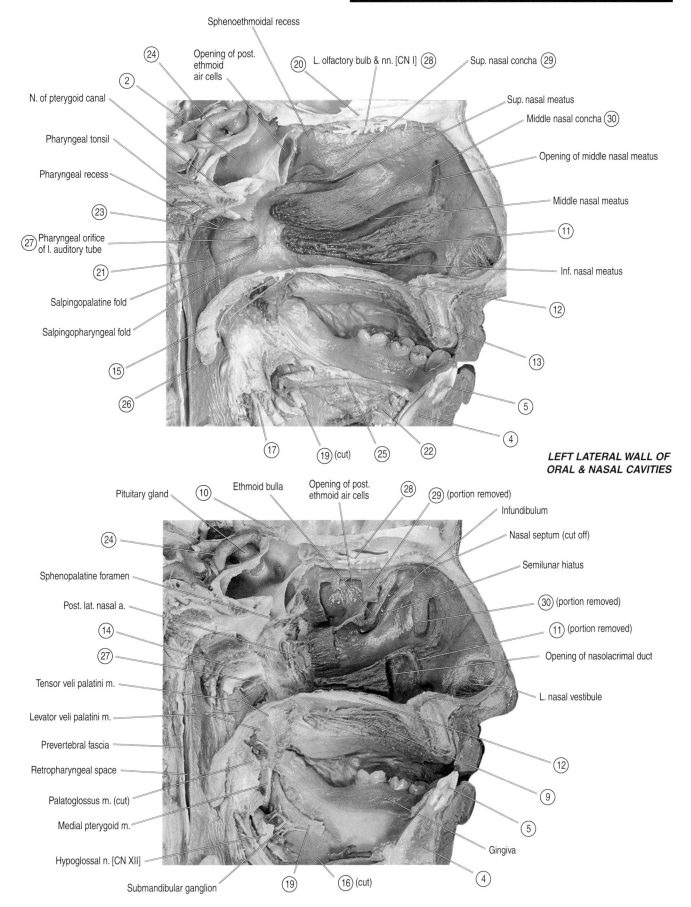

Sphenoethmoidal recess

Opening of post. ethmoid air cells

(24)

(2)

N. of pterygoid canal

Pharyngeal tonsil

Pharyngeal recess

(23)

(27) Pharyngeal orifice of l. auditory tube

(21)

Salpingopalatine fold

Salpingopharyngeal fold

(15)

(26)

(20) L. olfactory bulb & nn. [CN I] (28)

(17)   (19) (cut)   (25)   (22)

Sup. nasal concha (29)

Sup. nasal meatus

Middle nasal concha (30)

Opening of middle nasal meatus

Middle nasal meatus

(11)

Inf. nasal meatus

(12)

(13)

(5)

(4)

**LEFT LATERAL WALL OF
ORAL & NASAL CAVITIES**

Pituitary gland

(10)

Ethmoid bulla

Opening of post. ethmoid air cells

(28)

(29) (portion removed)

(24)

Sphenopalatine foramen

Post. lat. nasal a.

(14)

(27)

Tensor veli palatini m.

Levator veli palatini m.

Prevertebral fascia

Retropharyngeal space

Palatoglossus m. (cut)

Medial pterygoid m.

Hypoglossal n. [CN XII]

Submandibular ganglion

(19)   (16) (cut)

Infundibulum

Nasal septum (cut off)

Semilunar hiatus

(30) (portion removed)

(11) (portion removed)

Opening of nasolacrimal duct

L. nasal vestibule

(12)

(9)

(5)

Gingiva

(4)

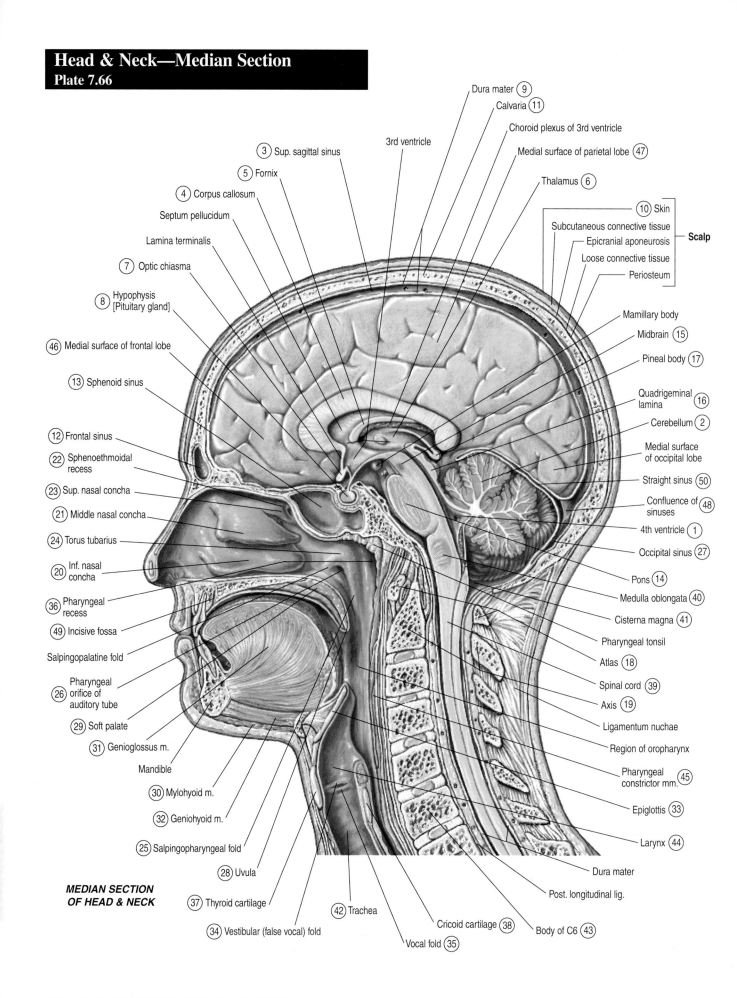

Dura mater (9)
Calvaria (11)
Choroid plexus of 3rd ventricle
Medial surface of parietal lobe (47)
Thalamus (6)

3rd ventricle

(3) Sup. sagittal sinus
(5) Fornix
(4) Corpus callosum
Septum pellucidum
Lamina terminalis
(7) Optic chiasma
(8) Hypophysis [Pituitary gland]
(46) Medial surface of frontal lobe
(13) Sphenoid sinus
(12) Frontal sinus
(22) Sphenoethmoidal recess
(23) Sup. nasal concha
(21) Middle nasal concha
(24) Torus tubarius
(20) Inf. nasal concha
(36) Pharyngeal recess
(49) Incisive fossa
Salpingopalatine fold
(26) Pharyngeal orifice of auditory tube
(29) Soft palate
(31) Genioglossus m.
Mandible
(30) Mylohyoid m.
(32) Geniohyoid m.
(25) Salpingopharyngeal fold
(28) Uvula

(10) Skin
Subcutaneous connective tissue
Epicranial aponeurosis } Scalp
Loose connective tissue
Periosteum

Mamillary body
Midbrain (15)
Pineal body (17)
Quadrigeminal lamina (16)
Cerebellum (2)
Medial surface of occipital lobe
Straight sinus (50)
Confluence of sinuses (48)
4th ventricle (1)
Occipital sinus (27)
Pons (14)
Medulla oblongata (40)
Cisterna magna (41)
Pharyngeal tonsil
Atlas (18)
Spinal cord (39)
Axis (19)
Ligamentum nuchae
Region of oropharynx
Pharyngeal constrictor mm. (45)
Epiglottis (33)
Larynx (44)
Dura mater
Post. longitudinal lig.
Body of C6 (43)

MEDIAN SECTION OF HEAD & NECK

(37) Thyroid cartilage
(42) Trachea
Cricoid cartilage (38)
(34) Vestibular (false vocal) fold
Vocal fold (35)

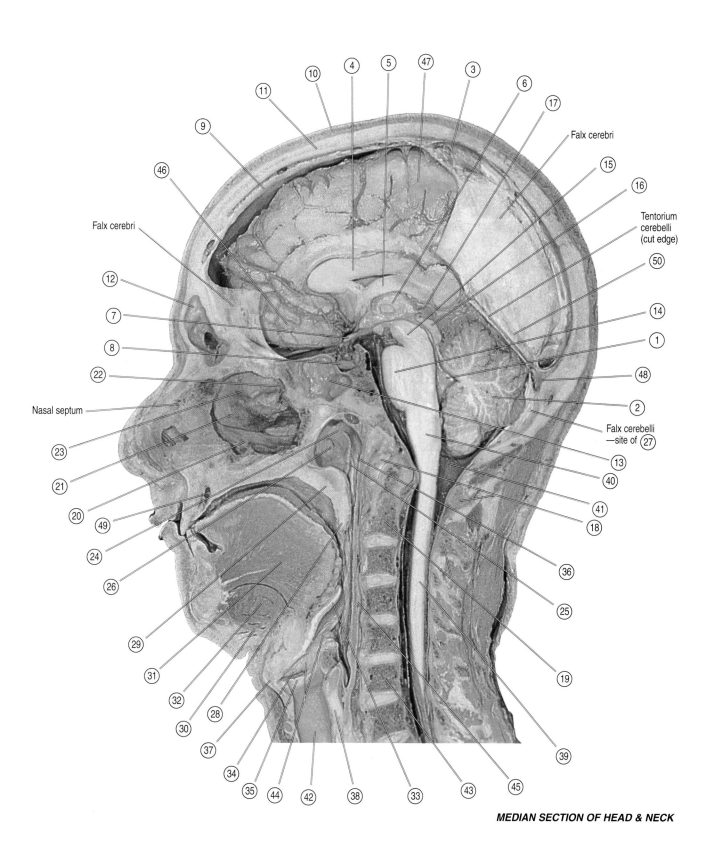

Falx cerebri

Falx cerebri

Tentorium
cerebelli
(cut edge)

Nasal septum

Falx cerebelli
—site of ㉗

MEDIAN SECTION OF HEAD & NECK

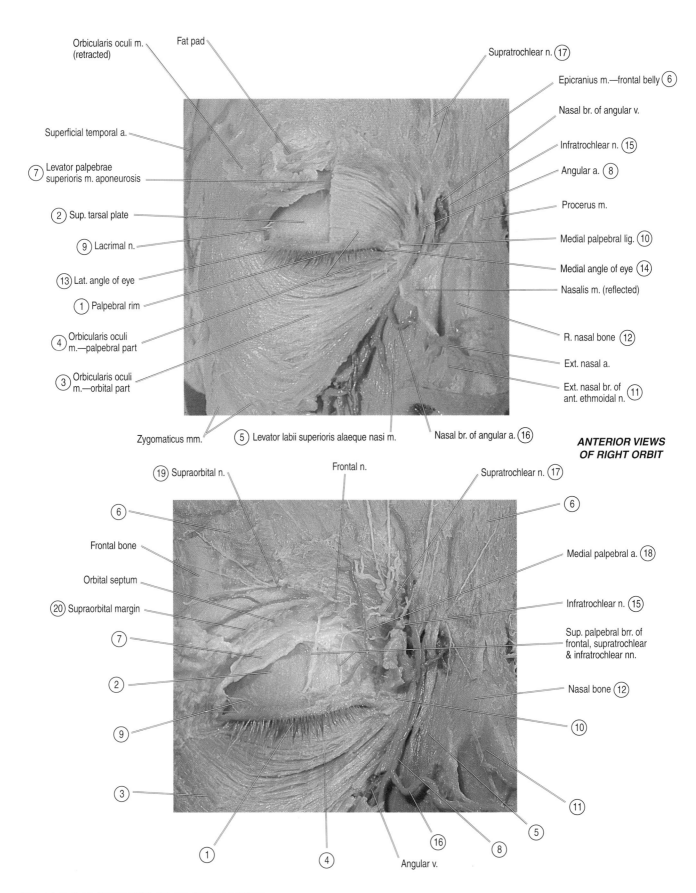

Orbicularis oculi m. (retracted)

Fat pad

Supratrochlear n. (17)

Epicranius m.—frontal belly (6)

Nasal br. of angular v.

Superficial temporal a.

Infratrochlear n. (15)

(7) Levator palpebrae superioris m. aponeurosis

Angular a. (8)

Procerus m.

(2) Sup. tarsal plate

Medial palpebral lig. (10)

(9) Lacrimal n.

Medial angle of eye (14)

(13) Lat. angle of eye

Nasalis m. (reflected)

(1) Palpebral rim

R. nasal bone (12)

(4) Orbicularis oculi m.—palpebral part

Ext. nasal a.

(3) Orbicularis oculi m.—orbital part

Ext. nasal br. of ant. ethmoidal n. (11)

Zygomaticus mm.

(5) Levator labii superioris alaeque nasi m.

Nasal br. of angular a. (16)

ANTERIOR VIEWS OF RIGHT ORBIT

(19) Supraorbital n.

Frontal n.

Supratrochlear n. (17)

(6)

(6)

Frontal bone

Medial palpebral a. (18)

Orbital septum

Infratrochlear n. (15)

(20) Supraorbital margin

(7)

Sup. palpebral brr. of frontal, supratrochlear & infratrochlear nn.

(2)

Nasal bone (12)

(9)

(10)

(3)

(11)

(1)

(4)

(16)

(8)

(5)

Angular v.

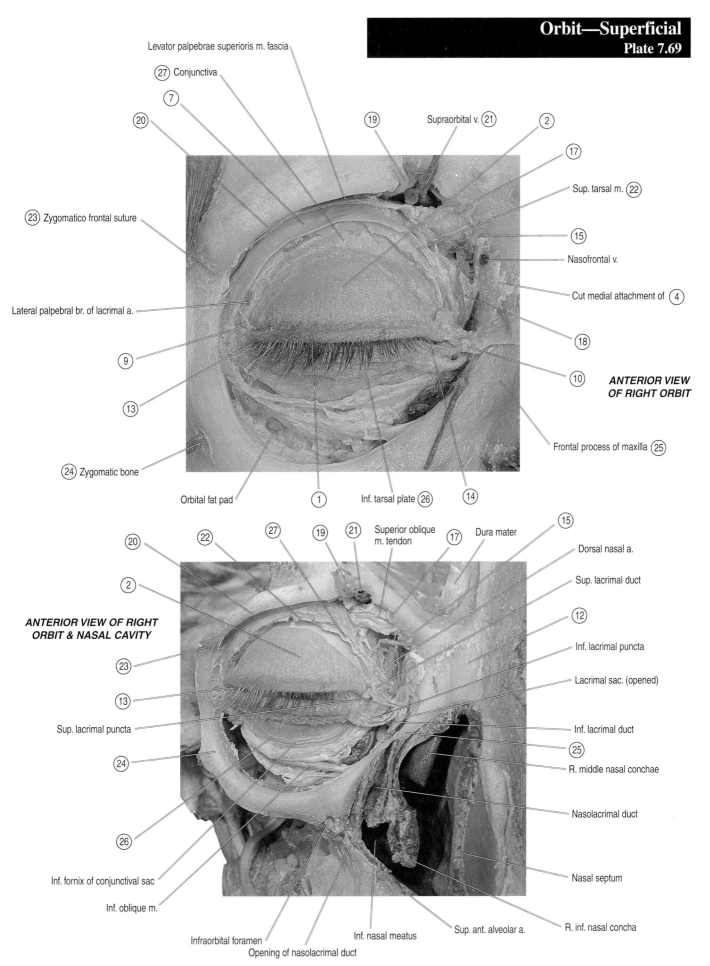

Levator palpebrae superioris m. fascia

㉗ Conjunctiva

⑦

⑳

⑲   Supraorbital v. ㉑   ②

⑰

㉓ Zygomatico frontal suture

Sup. tarsal m. ㉒

⑮

Nasofrontal v.

Lateral palpebral br. of lacrimal a.

Cut medial attachment of ④

⑨

⑱

⑬

⑩   **ANTERIOR VIEW OF RIGHT ORBIT**

㉔ Zygomatic bone

Frontal process of maxilla ㉕

Orbital fat pad   ①   Inf. tarsal plate ㉖   ⑭

⑳   ㉒   ㉗   ⑲   ㉑   Superior oblique m. tendon   ⑰   Dura mater   ⑮

Dorsal nasal a.

②   Sup. lacrimal duct

ANTERIOR VIEW OF RIGHT ORBIT & NASAL CAVITY   ⑫

㉓   Inf. lacrimal puncta

Lacrimal sac. (opened)

⑬

Sup. lacrimal puncta   Inf. lacrimal duct

㉔   ㉕

R. middle nasal conchae

㉖   Nasolacrimal duct

Inf. fornix of conjunctival sac   Nasal septum

Inf. oblique m.

Infraorbital foramen   Inf. nasal meatus   Sup. ant. alveolar a.   R. inf. nasal concha

Opening of nasolacrimal duct

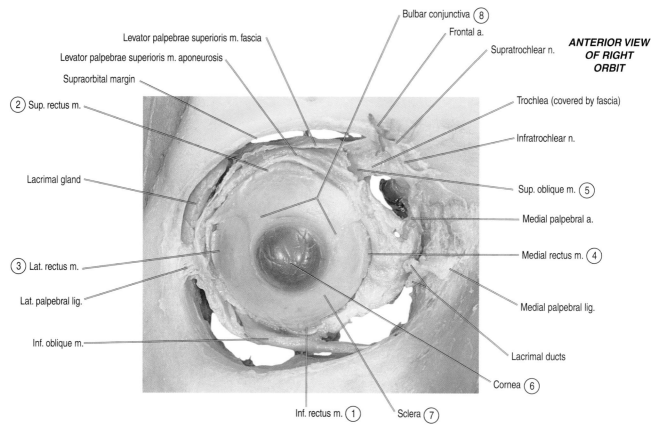

ANTERIOR VIEW OF RIGHT ORBIT

Bulbar conjunctiva ⑧
Frontal a.
Supratrochlear n.
Levator palpebrae superioris m. fascia
Levator palpebrae superioris m. aponeurosis
Supraorbital margin
② Sup. rectus m.
Trochlea (covered by fascia)
Infratrochlear n.
Lacrimal gland
Sup. oblique m. ⑤
Medial palpebral a.
③ Lat. rectus m.
Medial rectus m. ④
Lat. palpebral lig.
Medial palpebral lig.
Inf. oblique m.
Lacrimal ducts
Cornea ⑥
Inf. rectus m. ①   Sclera ⑦

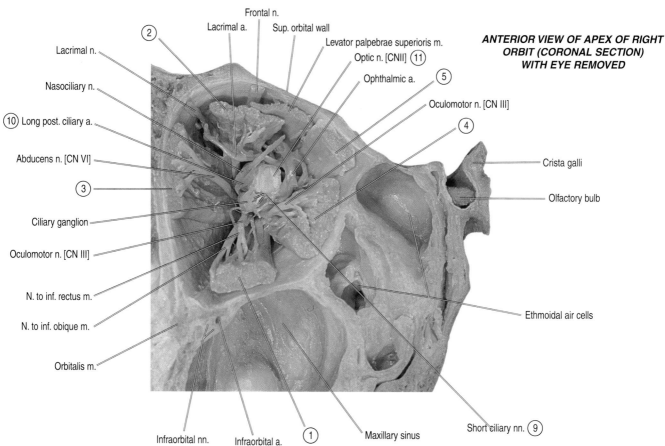

ANTERIOR VIEW OF APEX OF RIGHT ORBIT (CORONAL SECTION) WITH EYE REMOVED

Frontal n.
Lacrimal a.
②
Sup. orbital wall
Lacrimal n.
Levator palpebrae superioris m.
Nasociliary n.
Optic n. [CNII] ⑪
⑩ Long post. ciliary a.
Ophthalmic a.
⑤
Abducens n. [CN VI]
Oculomotor n. [CN III]
③
④
Ciliary ganglion
Crista galli
Oculomotor n. [CN III]
Olfactory bulb
N. to inf. rectus m.
N. to inf. obique m.
Ethmoidal air cells
Orbitalis m.
Infraorbital nn.   Infraorbital a.   ①   Maxillary sinus   Short ciliary nn. ⑨

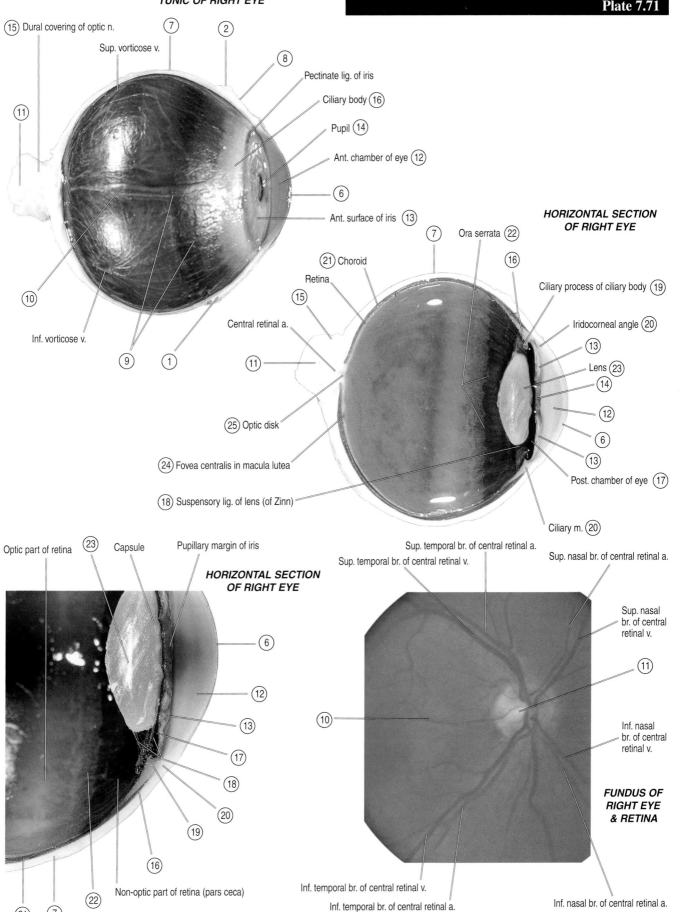

LATERAL VIEW OF VASCULAR TUNIC OF RIGHT EYE

(15) Dural covering of optic n.

(7)

(2)

Sup. vorticose v.

(8)

Pectinate lig. of iris

Ciliary body (16)

Pupil (14)

Ant. chamber of eye (12)

(11)

(6)

Ant. surface of iris (13)

HORIZONTAL SECTION OF RIGHT EYE

(7) Ora serrata (22)

(21) Choroid

(16)

Retina

Ciliary process of ciliary body (19)

(15)

Iridocorneal angle (20)

(13)

Central retinal a.

Lens (23)

(10)

(11)

(14)

(12)

(6)

Inf. vorticose v.

(9)

(1)

(25) Optic disk

(13)

Post. chamber of eye (17)

(24) Fovea centralis in macula lutea

(18) Suspensory lig. of lens (of Zinn)

Ciliary m. (20)

Optic part of retina   (23)   Capsule   Pupillary margin of iris

HORIZONTAL SECTION OF RIGHT EYE

Sup. temporal br. of central retinal a.

Sup. temporal br. of central retinal v.

Sup. nasal br. of central retinal a.

(6)

Sup. nasal br. of central retinal v.

(12)

(11)

(13)

(10)

(17)

(18)

Inf. nasal br. of central retinal v.

(20)

(19)

FUNDUS OF RIGHT EYE & RETINA

(16)

Non-optic part of retina (pars ceca)

(21)   (7)   (22)

Inf. temporal br. of central retinal v.

Inf. temporal br. of central retinal a.

Inf. nasal br. of central retinal a.

LATERAL VIEW OF RIGHT ORBIT

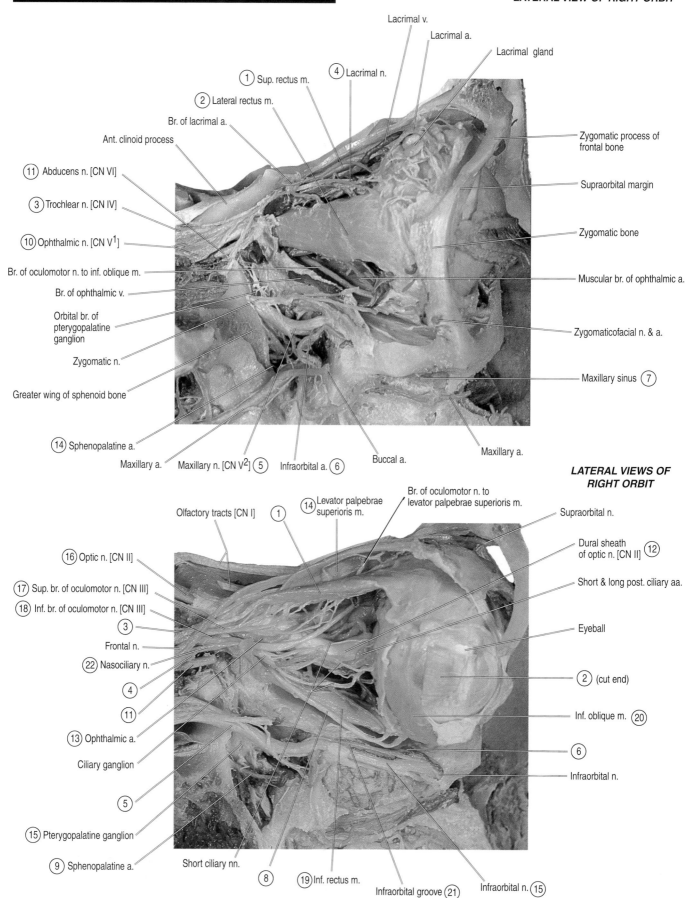

Lacrimal v.

Lacrimal a.

Lacrimal gland

(1) Sup. rectus m.

(4) Lacrimal n.

(2) Lateral rectus m.

Br. of lacrimal a.

Ant. clinoid process

Zygomatic process of frontal bone

Supraorbital margin

(11) Abducens n. [CN VI]

(3) Trochlear n. [CN IV]

Zygomatic bone

(10) Ophthalmic n. [CN V^1]

Br. of oculomotor n. to inf. oblique m.

Muscular br. of ophthalmic a.

Br. of ophthalmic v.

Orbital br. of pterygopalatine ganglion

Zygomaticofacial n. & a.

Zygomatic n.

Greater wing of sphenoid bone

Maxillary sinus (7)

(14) Sphenopalatine a.

Maxillary a.   Maxillary n. [CN V^2] (5)   Infraorbital a. (6)   Buccal a.   Maxillary a.

LATERAL VIEWS OF RIGHT ORBIT

Br. of oculomotor n. to levator palpebrae superioris m.

Olfactory tracts [CN I]   (1)   (14) Levator palpebrae superioris m.

Supraorbital n.

(16) Optic n. [CN II]

Dural sheath of optic n. [CN II] (12)

(17) Sup. br. of oculomotor n. [CN III]

Short & long post. ciliary aa.

(18) Inf. br. of oculomotor n. [CN III]

(3)

Eyeball

Frontal n.

(22) Nasociliary n.

(2) (cut end)

(4)

(11)

Inf. oblique m. (20)

(13) Ophthalmic a.

Ciliary ganglion

(6)

(5)

Infraorbital n.

(15) Pterygopalatine ganglion

(9) Sphenopalatine a.   Short ciliary nn.   (8)   (19) Inf. rectus m.   Infraorbital groove (21)   Infraorbital n. (15)

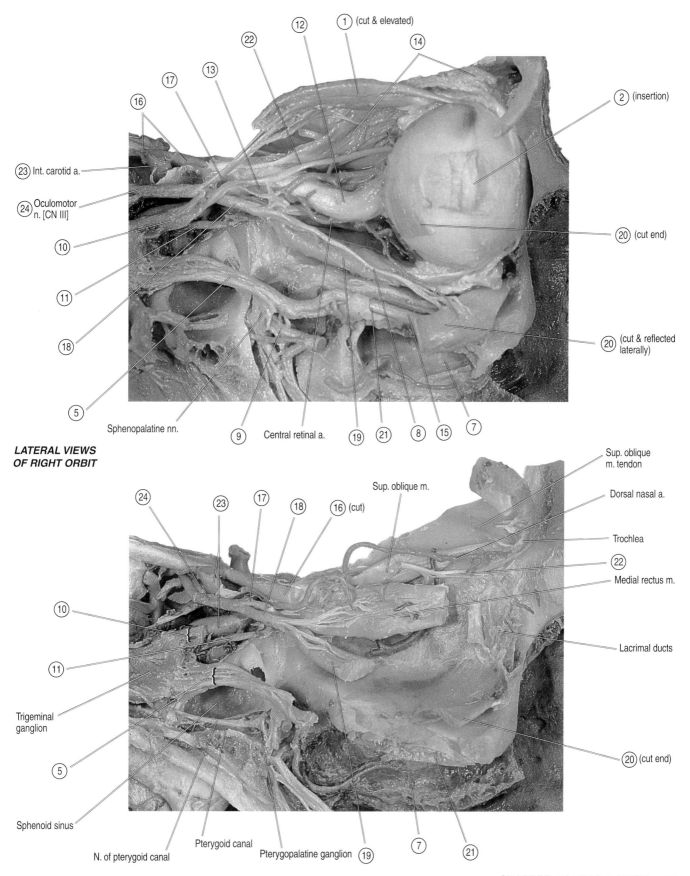

(12) (1) (cut & elevated)

(22) (14)

(17) (13)

(16)

(2) (insertion)

(23) Int. carotid a.

(24) Oculomotor n. [CN III]

(10)

(11)

(18)

(5)

(20) (cut end)

(20) (cut & reflected laterally)

Sphenopalatine nn.

(9) Central retinal a. (19) (21) (8) (15) (7)

LATERAL VIEWS OF RIGHT ORBIT

Sup. oblique m. tendon

Sup. oblique m.

Dorsal nasal a.

(24) (23) (17) (18) (16) (cut)

Trochlea

(22)

(10)

Medial rectus m.

(11)

Lacrimal ducts

Trigeminal ganglion

(5)

(20) (cut end)

Sphenoid sinus

N. of pterygoid canal

Pterygoid canal

Pterygopalatine ganglion (19) (7) (21)

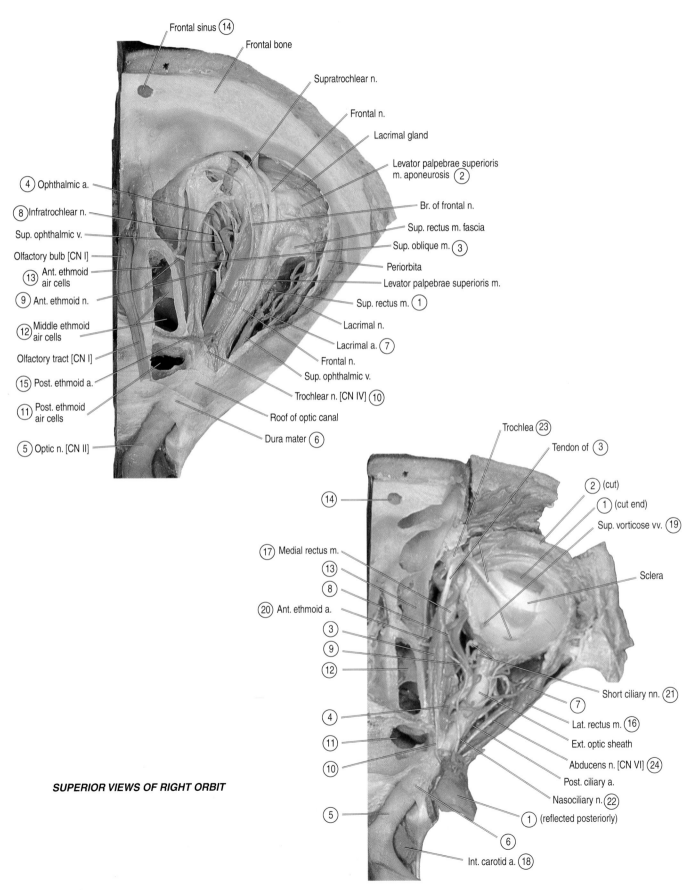

Frontal sinus (14)

Frontal bone

Supratrochlear n.

Frontal n.

Lacrimal gland

Levator palpebrae superioris
m. aponeurosis (2)

(4) Ophthalmic a.

(8) Infratrochlear n.

Br. of frontal n.

Sup. ophthalmic v.

Sup. rectus m. fascia

Olfactory bulb [CN I]

Sup. oblique m. (3)

(13) Ant. ethmoid
air cells

Periorbita

Levator palpebrae superioris m.

(9) Ant. ethmoid n.

Sup. rectus m. (1)

(12) Middle ethmoid
air cells

Lacrimal n.

Olfactory tract [CN I]

Lacrimal a. (7)

Frontal n.

(15) Post. ethmoid a.

Sup. ophthalmic v.

(11) Post. ethmoid
air cells

Trochlear n. [CN IV] (10)

Roof of optic canal

(5) Optic n. [CN II]

Dura mater (6)

Trochlea (23)

Tendon of (3)

(14)

(2) (cut)

(1) (cut end)

Sup. vorticose vv. (19)

(17) Medial rectus m.

(13)

(8)

Sclera

(20) Ant. ethmoid a.

(3)

(9)

(12)

Short ciliary nn. (21)

(4)

(7)

Lat. rectus m. (16)

(11)

Ext. optic sheath

(10)

Abducens n. [CN VI] (24)

Post. ciliary a.

Nasociliary n. (22)

(1) (reflected posteriorly)

(5)

(6)

Int. carotid a. (18)

SUPERIOR VIEWS OF RIGHT ORBIT

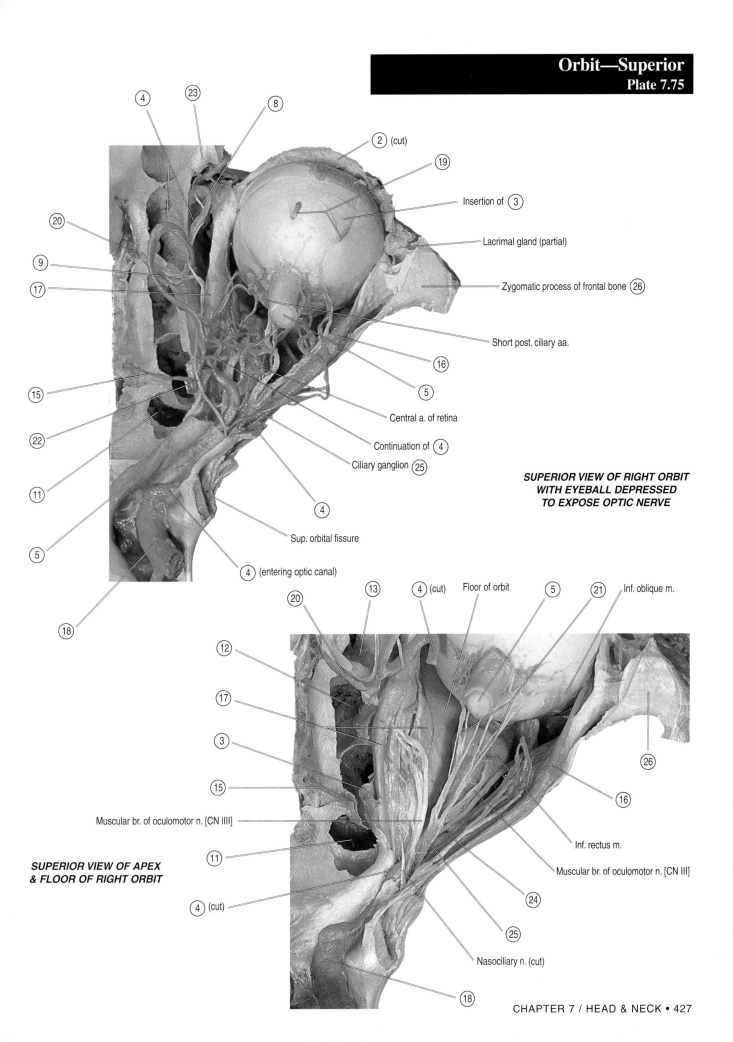

④ ㉓ ⑧

② (cut)

⑲

Insertion of ③

Lacrimal gland (partial)

⑳

⑨

⑰

Zygomatic process of frontal bone ㉖

Short post. ciliary aa.

⑯

⑤

Central a. of retina

⑮

Continuation of ④

㉒

Ciliary ganglion ㉕

⑪

*SUPERIOR VIEW OF RIGHT ORBIT
WITH EYEBALL DEPRESSED
TO EXPOSE OPTIC NERVE*

⑤

Sup. orbital fissure

④ (entering optic canal)

⑱

⑬ ④ (cut) Floor of orbit ⑤ ㉑ Inf. oblique m.

⑳

⑫

⑰

③

㉖

⑮

⑯

Muscular br. of oculomotor n. [CN IIII]

Inf. rectus m.

⑪

Muscular br. of oculomotor n. [CN III]

*SUPERIOR VIEW OF APEX
& FLOOR OF RIGHT ORBIT*

④ (cut)

㉔

㉕

Nasociliary n. (cut)

⑱

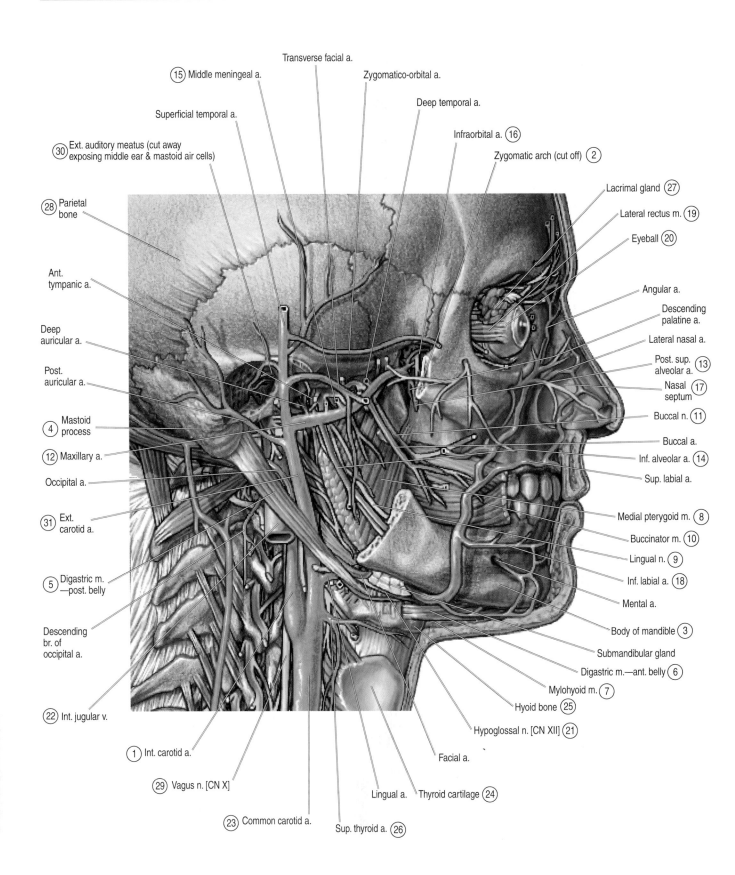

Transverse facial a.

(15) Middle meningeal a.

Zygomatico-orbital a.

Deep temporal a.

Superficial temporal a.

Infraorbital a. (16)

(30) Ext. auditory meatus (cut away exposing middle ear & mastoid air cells)

Zygomatic arch (cut off) (2)

Lacrimal gland (27)

(28) Parietal bone

Lateral rectus m. (19)

Eyeball (20)

Ant. tympanic a.

Angular a.

Descending palatine a.

Deep auricular a.

Lateral nasal a.

Post. auricular a.

Post. sup. alveolar a. (13)

Nasal (17) septum

(4) Mastoid process

Buccal n. (11)

(12) Maxillary a.

Buccal a.

Occipital a.

Inf. alveolar a. (14)

Sup. labial a.

(31) Ext. carotid a.

Medial pterygoid m. (8)

Buccinator m. (10)

Lingual n. (9)

(5) Digastric m. —post. belly

Inf. labial a. (18)

Mental a.

Descending br. of occipital a.

Body of mandible (3)

Submandibular gland

Digastric m.—ant. belly (6)

Mylohyoid m. (7)

(22) Int. jugular v.

Hyoid bone (25)

Hypoglossal n. [CN XII] (21)

(1) Int. carotid a.

(29) Vagus n. [CN X]

Facial a.

Lingual a.   Thyroid cartilage (24)

(23) Common carotid a.

Sup. thyroid a. (26)

LATERAL VIEW

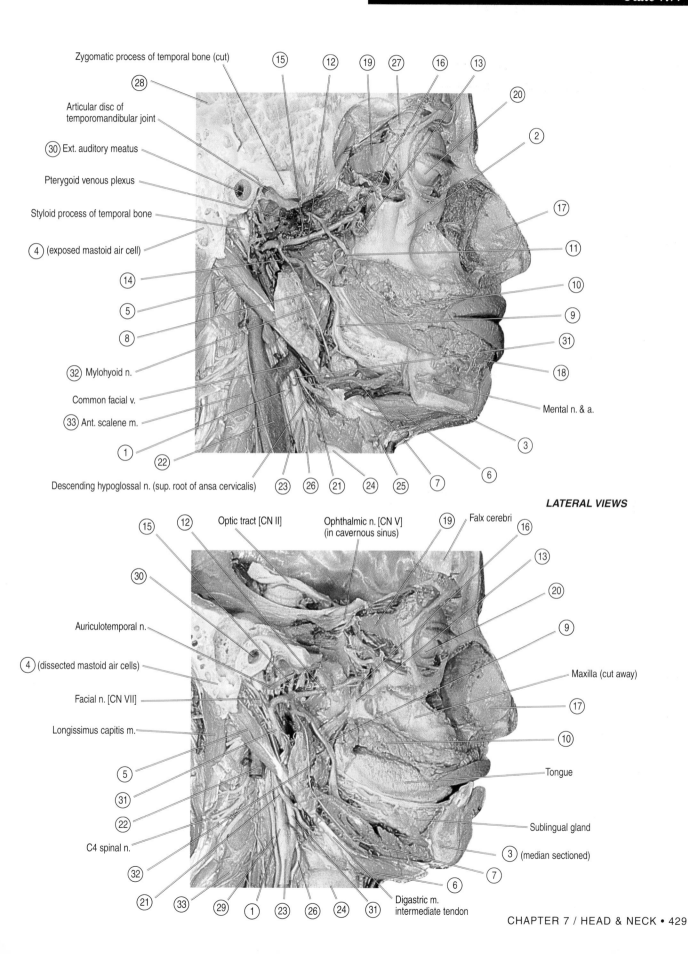

Zygomatic process of temporal bone (cut)

㉘

Articular disc of
temporomandibular joint

㉚ Ext. auditory meatus

Pterygoid venous plexus

Styloid process of temporal bone

④ (exposed mastoid air cell)

⑭

⑤

⑧

㉜ Mylohyoid n.

Common facial v.

㉝ Ant. scalene m.

①

㉒

Descending hypoglossal n. (sup. root of ansa cervicalis) ㉓ ㉖ ㉑ ㉔ ㉕ ⑦ ⑥

⑮ ⑫ ⑲ ㉗ ⑯ ⑬

⑳

②

⑰

⑪

⑩

⑨

㉛

⑱

Mental n. & a.

③

LATERAL VIEWS

⑮ ⑫ Optic tract [CN II] Ophthalmic n. [CN V]
(in cavernous sinus) ⑲ Falx cerebri ⑯

㉚ ⑬

⑳

Auriculotemporal n. ⑨

④ (dissected mastoid air cells) Maxilla (cut away)

Facial n. [CN VII] ⑰

Longissimus capitis m. ⑩

⑤ Tongue

㉛

㉒ Sublingual gland

C4 spinal n. ③ (median sectioned)

㉜ ⑦

㉑ ㉝ ㉙ ① ㉓ ㉖ ㉔ ㉛ ⑥
Digastric m.
intermediate tendon

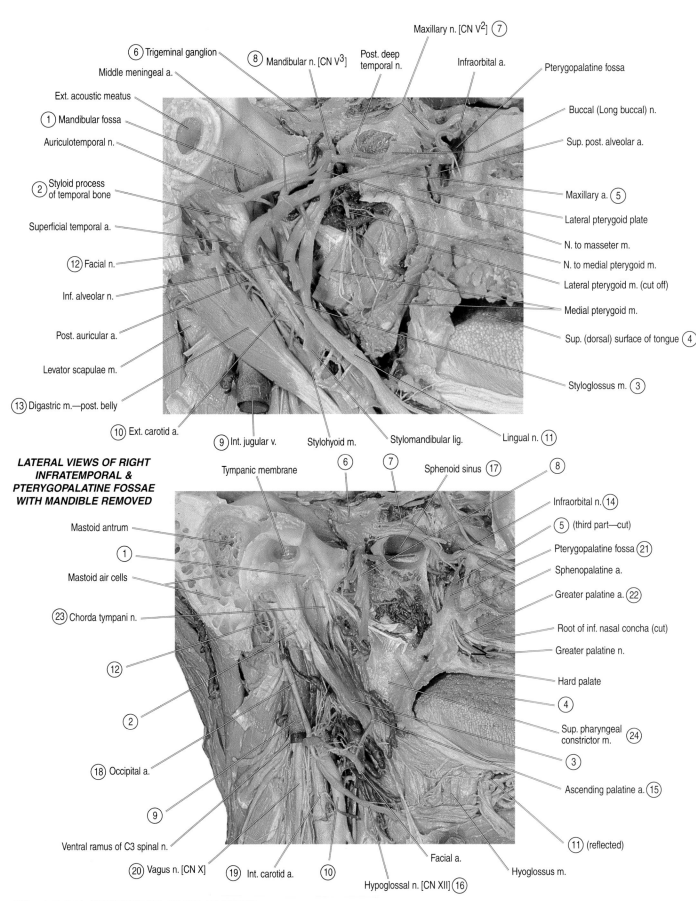

Maxillary n. [CN V²] ⑦

⑥ Trigeminal ganglion
⑧ Mandibular n. [CN V³]
Post. deep temporal n.
Infraorbital a.
Pterygopalatine fossa

Middle meningeal a.

Ext. acoustic meatus

① Mandibular fossa
Buccal (Long buccal) n.

Auriculotemporal n.
Sup. post. alveolar a.

②Styloid process of temporal bone

Maxillary a. ⑤

Superficial temporal a.
Lateral pterygoid plate

N. to masseter m.

⑫ Facial n.
N. to medial pterygoid m.

Inf. alveolar n.
Lateral pterygoid m. (cut off)

Medial pterygoid m.

Post. auricular a.
Sup. (dorsal) surface of tongue ④

Levator scapulae m.

⑬ Digastric m.—post. belly
Styloglossus m. ③

⑩ Ext. carotid a.
⑨ Int. jugular v.   Stylohyoid m.   Stylomandibular lig.   Lingual n. ⑪

LATERAL VIEWS OF RIGHT INFRATEMPORAL & PTERYGOPALATINE FOSSAE WITH MANDIBLE REMOVED

Tympanic membrane   ⑥   ⑦   Sphenoid sinus ⑰   ⑧

Mastoid antrum
Infraorbital n. ⑭

①
⑤ (third part—cut)

Mastoid air cells
Pterygopalatine fossa ㉑

Sphenopalatine a.

㉓ Chorda tympani n.
Greater palatine a. ㉒

⑫
Root of inf. nasal concha (cut)

Greater palatine n.

②
Hard palate

④

Sup. pharyngeal constrictor m. ㉔

⑱ Occipital a.
③

Ascending palatine a. ⑮

⑨

⑪ (reflected)

Ventral ramus of C3 spinal n.
Facial a.

⑳ Vagus n. [CN X]   ⑲ Int. carotid a.   ⑩   Hyoglossus m.

Hypoglossal n. [CN XII] ⑯

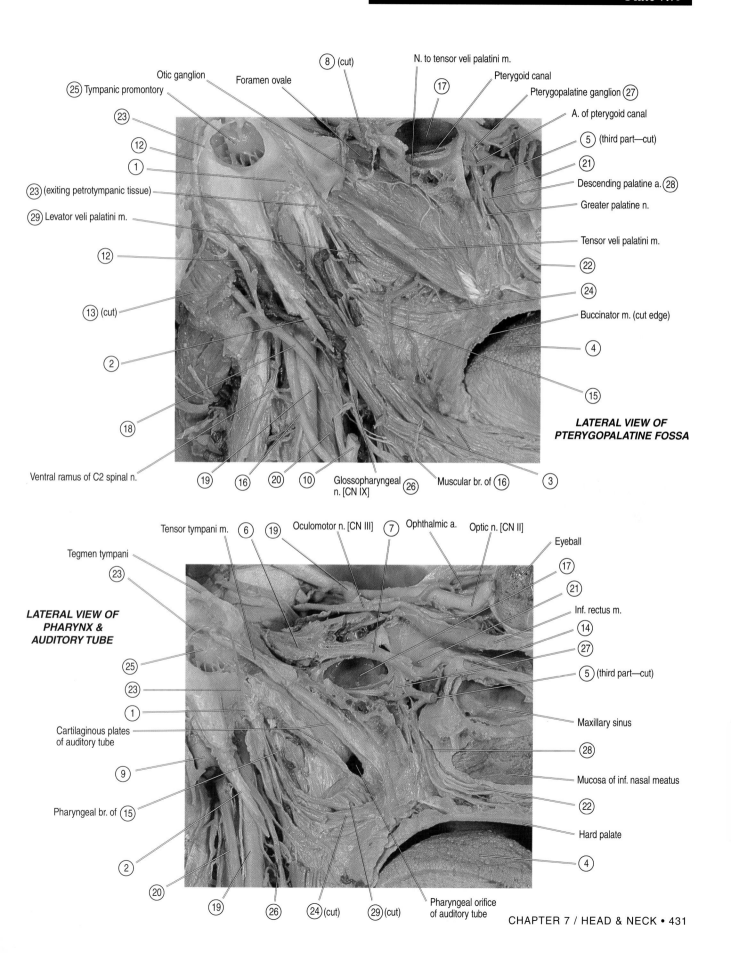

(8) (cut)

N. to tensor veli palatini m.

(25) Tympanic promontory

Otic ganglion

Foramen ovale

(17)

Pterygoid canal

Pterygopalatine ganglion (27)

(23)

(12)

(1)

A. of pterygoid canal

(5) (third part—cut)

(21)

(23) (exiting petrotympanic tissue)

Descending palatine a. (28)

Greater palatine n.

(29) Levator veli palatini m.

(12)

Tensor veli palatini m.

(22)

(24)

(13) (cut)

Buccinator m. (cut edge)

(2)

(4)

(18)

(15)

**LATERAL VIEW OF
PTERYGOPALATINE FOSSA**

Ventral ramus of C2 spinal n.

(19) (16) (20) (10) Glossopharyngeal (26) Muscular br. of (16) (3)
n. [CN IX]

Tensor tympani m. (6) (19) Oculomotor n. [CN III] (7) Ophthalmic a. Optic n. [CN II] Eyeball

Tegmen tympani

(23)

(17)

(21)

**LATERAL VIEW OF
PHARYNX &
AUDITORY TUBE**

Inf. rectus m.

(14)

(27)

(25)

(5) (third part—cut)

(23)

(1)

Maxillary sinus

Cartilaginous plates
of auditory tube

(9)

(28)

Pharyngeal br. of (15)

Mucosa of inf. nasal meatus

(22)

Hard palate

(2)

(4)

(20)

(19) (26) (24) (cut) (29) (cut) Pharyngeal orifice
of auditory tube

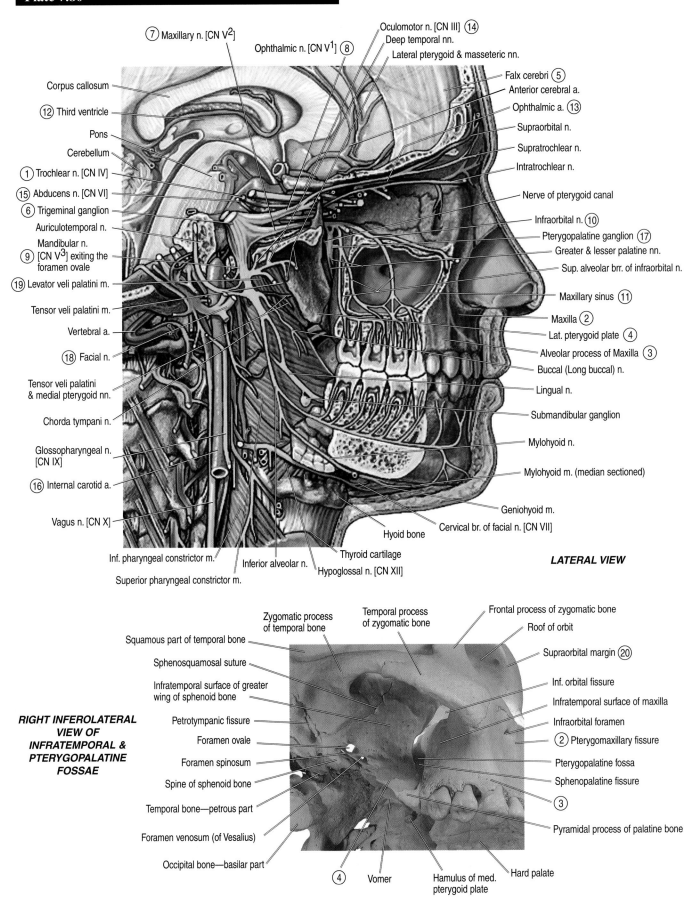

⑦ Maxillary n. [CN V²]

Ophthalmic n. [CN V¹] ⑧

Oculomotor n. [CN III] ⑭
Deep temporal nn.
Lateral pterygoid & masseteric nn.

Corpus callosum

⑫ Third ventricle

Pons

Cerebellum

① Trochlear n. [CN IV]

⑮ Abducens n. [CN VI]

⑥ Trigeminal ganglion

Auriculotemporal n.

Mandibular n.
⑨ [CN V³] exiting the foramen ovale

⑲ Levator veli palatini m.

Tensor veli palatini m.

Vertebral a.

⑱ Facial n.

Tensor veli palatini & medial pterygoid nn.

Chorda tympani n.

Glossopharyngeal n. [CN IX]

⑯ Internal carotid a.

Vagus n. [CN X]

Inf. pharyngeal constrictor m.

Superior pharyngeal constrictor m.

Inferior alveolar n.

Hypoglossal n. [CN XII]

Thyroid cartilage

Hyoid bone

Cervical br. of facial n. [CN VII]

Falx cerebri ⑤
Anterior cerebral a.
Ophthalmic a. ⑬
Supraorbital n.
Supratrochlear n.
Intratrochlear n.
Nerve of pterygoid canal
Infraorbital n. ⑩
Pterygopalatine ganglion ⑰
Greater & lesser palatine nn.
Sup. alveolar brr. of infraorbital n.
Maxillary sinus ⑪
Maxilla ②
Lat. pterygoid plate ④
Alveolar process of Maxilla ③
Buccal (Long buccal) n.
Lingual n.
Submandibular ganglion
Mylohyoid n.
Mylohyoid m. (median sectioned)
Geniohyoid m.

LATERAL VIEW

Zygomatic process of temporal bone

Temporal process of zygomatic bone

Frontal process of zygomatic bone
Roof of orbit
Supraorbital margin ⑳

Squamous part of temporal bone

Sphenosquamosal suture

Infratemporal surface of greater wing of sphenoid bone

RIGHT INFEROLATERAL VIEW OF INFRATEMPORAL & PTERYGOPALATINE FOSSAE

Petrotympanic fissure

Foramen ovale

Foramen spinosum

Spine of sphenoid bone

Temporal bone—petrous part

Foramen venosum (of Vesalius)

Occipital bone—basilar part

④ Vomer

Hamulus of med. pterygoid plate

Inf. orbital fissure
Infratemporal surface of maxilla
Infraorbital foramen
② Pterygomaxillary fissure
Pterygopalatine fossa
Sphenopalatine fissure
③
Pyramidal process of palatine bone
Hard palate

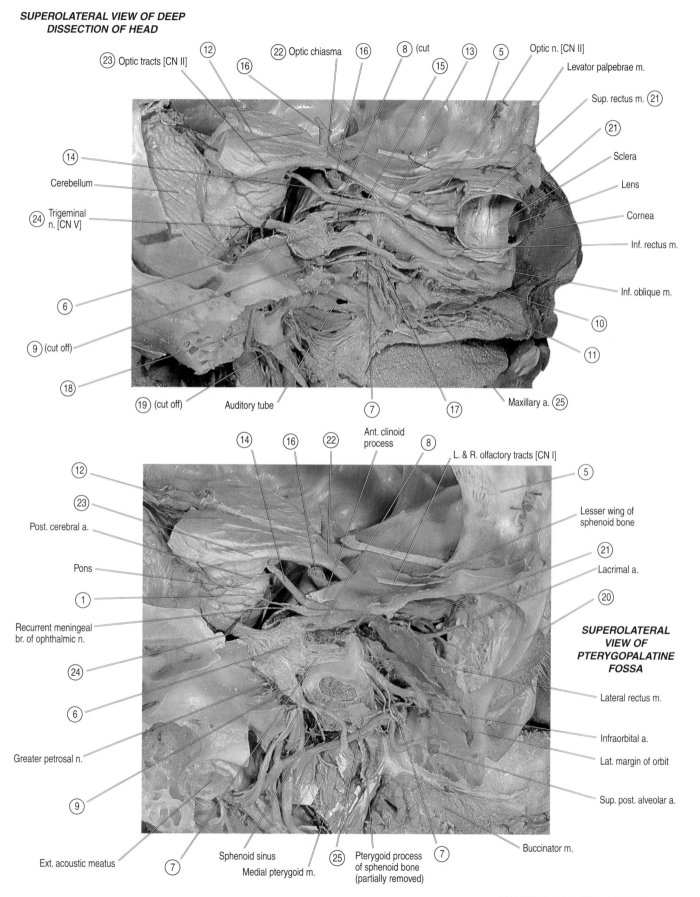

SUPEROLATERAL VIEW OF DEEP DISSECTION OF HEAD

23 Optic tracts [CN II]
12
22 Optic chiasma
16
8 (cut
13
5
Optic n. [CN II]
16
15
Levator palpebrae m.
Sup. rectus m. 21
21
14
Sclera
Cerebellum
Lens
24 Trigeminal n. [CN V]
Cornea
Inf. rectus m.
6
Inf. oblique m.
9 (cut off)
10
11
18
Maxillary a. 25
19 (cut off)
Auditory tube
7
17

14
16
22
Ant. clinoid process
8
L. & R. olfactory tracts [CN I]
12
5
23
Lesser wing of sphenoid bone
Post. cerebral a.
21
Pons
Lacrimal a.
1
20
Recurrent meningeal br. of ophthalmic n.
SUPEROLATERAL VIEW OF PTERYGOPALATINE FOSSA
24
6
Lateral rectus m.
Greater petrosal n.
Infraorbital a.
Lat. margin of orbit
9
Sup. post. alveolar a.
Ext. acoustic meatus
Buccinator m.
7
Sphenoid sinus
25
Pterygoid process of sphenoid bone (partially removed)
7
Medial pterygoid m.

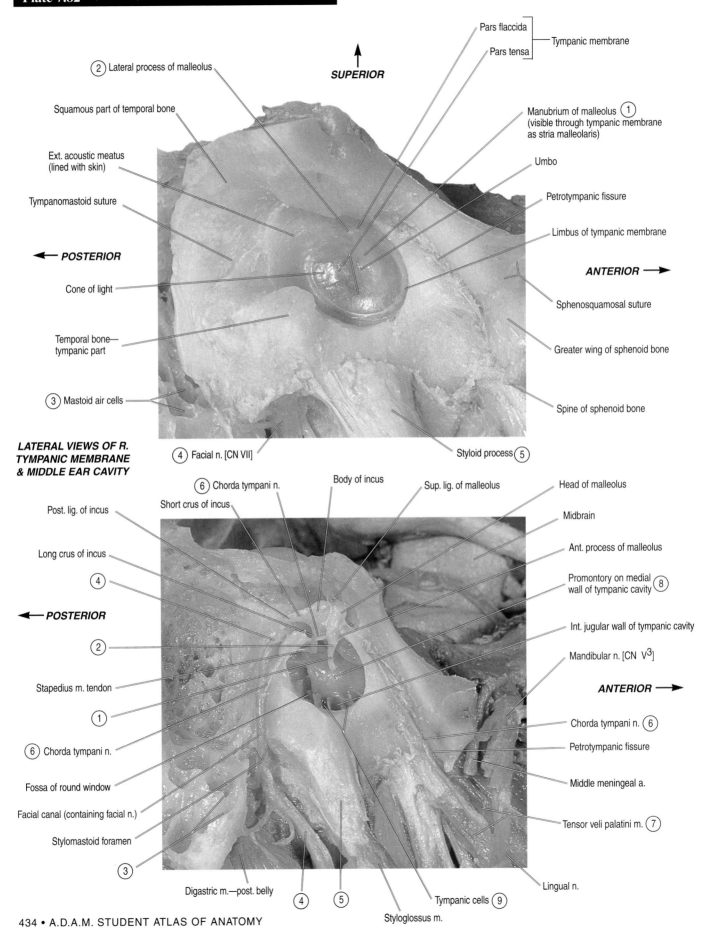

Pars flaccida ⎤
⎥ Tympanic membrane
Pars tensa ⎦

② Lateral process of malleolus

Squamous part of temporal bone

Ext. acoustic meatus (lined with skin)

Tympanomastoid suture

◀ POSTERIOR

Cone of light

Temporal bone—tympanic part

③ Mastoid air cells

SUPERIOR

Manubrium of malleolus ①
(visible through tympanic membrane as stria malleolaris)

Umbo

Petrotympanic fissure

Limbus of tympanic membrane

ANTERIOR ▶

Sphenosquamosal suture

Greater wing of sphenoid bone

Spine of sphenoid bone

LATERAL VIEWS OF R. TYMPANIC MEMBRANE & MIDDLE EAR CAVITY

④ Facial n. [CN VII]

Styloid process ⑤

⑥ Chorda tympani n.

Body of incus

Sup. lig. of malleolus

Head of malleolus

Post. lig. of incus

Short crus of incus

Midbrain

Long crus of incus

Ant. process of malleolus

④

Promontory on medial wall of tympanic cavity ⑧

◀ POSTERIOR

②

Int. jugular wall of tympanic cavity

Mandibular n. [CN V³]

Stapedius m. tendon

ANTERIOR ▶

①

⑥ Chorda tympani n.

Chorda tympani n. ⑥

Petrotympanic fissure

Fossa of round window

Middle meningeal a.

Facial canal (containing facial n.)

Stylomastoid foramen

Tensor veli palatini m. ⑦

③

Digastric m.—post. belly

④

⑤

Tympanic cells ⑨

Lingual n.

Styloglossus m.

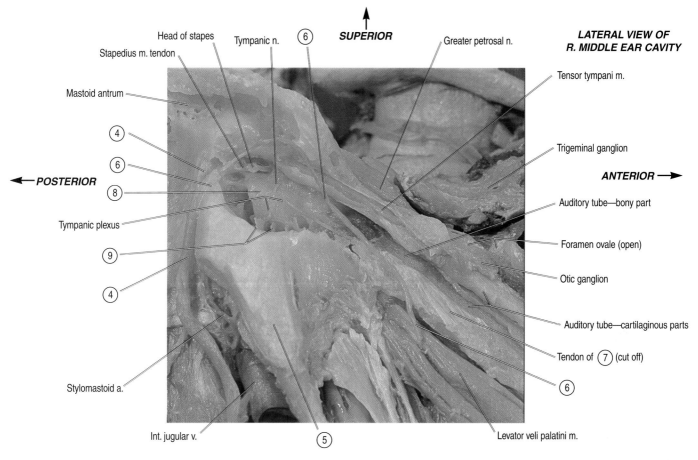

LATERAL VIEW OF R. MIDDLE EAR CAVITY

Head of stapes
Stapedius m. tendon
Tympanic n.
⑥
SUPERIOR
Greater petrosal n.
Tensor tympani m.
Mastoid antrum
Trigeminal ganglion
④
⑥
⑧
POSTERIOR
ANTERIOR
Tympanic plexus
Auditory tube—bony part
Foramen ovale (open)
⑨
Otic ganglion
④
Auditory tube—cartilaginous parts
Tendon of ⑦ (cut off)
Stylomastoid a.
⑥
Int. jugular v.
⑤
Levator veli palatini m.

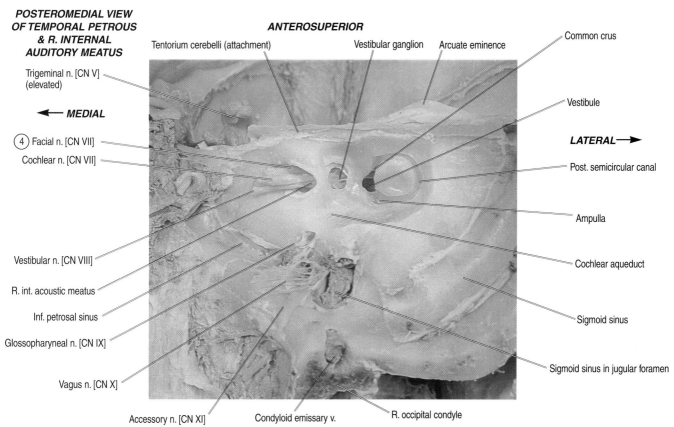

POSTEROMEDIAL VIEW OF TEMPORAL PETROUS & R. INTERNAL AUDITORY MEATUS

ANTEROSUPERIOR
Tentorium cerebelli (attachment)
Vestibular ganglion
Arcuate eminence
Common crus
Trigeminal n. [CN V] (elevated)
Vestibule
MEDIAL
④ Facial n. [CN VII]
LATERAL
Cochlear n. [CN VII]
Post. semicircular canal
Ampulla
Vestibular n. [CN VIII]
R. int. acoustic meatus
Cochlear aqueduct
Inf. petrosal sinus
Glossopharyneal n. [CN IX]
Sigmoid sinus
Vagus n. [CN X]
Sigmoid sinus in jugular foramen
Accessory n. [CN XI]
Condyloid emissary v.
R. occipital condyle

Cranial and Autonomic Nerves

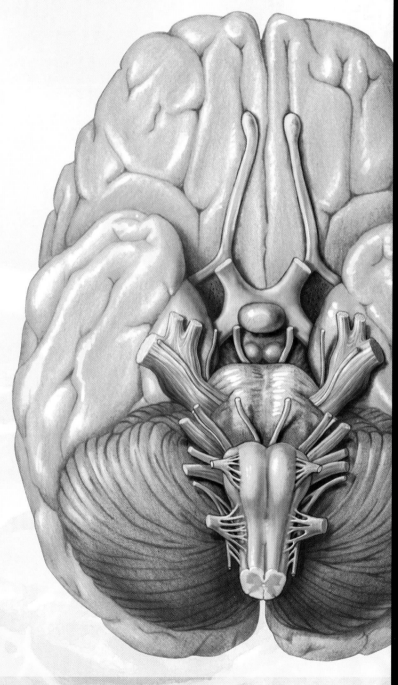

Chapter 8

Overview of Cranial Nerves

Cranial Nerve Functions
Table 8.1

Nerve	Efferent or Motor		Afferent or Sensory		
	Striated Muscles	Smooth & Cardiac Muscles & Glands	Skin	Mucous Membranes & Organs	Special Senses
CN I					Olfaction or sensation of smell
CN II					Vision or sight
CN III	Supplies all muscles of eyeball except lateral rectus	Parasympathetic to ciliary m. (lens) & sphincter m. of iris of eye		Proprioceptive fibers from eye m.	
CN IV	Supplies superior oblique mm. of eyeball			Proprioceptive fibers from eye m.	
CN V	Supplies muscles of mastication & tensors of tympanic membrane & palate & mylohyoid m. ant. belly of digastric m.	Carries parasympathetic preganglionic nerve fibers of CN, III, VII & IX	Face & ant. part of scalp	Teeth, mucous membrane of mouth, nose & eye, general sensory from anterior two-thirds of tongue	Taste (fibers from chorda tympani) from ant. two-thirds of tongue
CN VI	Supplies lateral rectus m. of eyeball			Proprioceptive fibers from lateral rectus m.	
CN VII	Supplies muscles of facial expression, stapedius m., stylohyoid m., & post. belly of digastric m.	Parasympathetic nervus intermedius; glands of mouth, nose & palate; lacrimal gland; submandibular & sublingual glands	Ext. ear	Proprioceptive fibers from muscles of facial expression	Nervus intermedius, taste, ant. two-thirds of tongue
CN VIII					Hearing & equilibrium
CN IX	Supplies stylopharyngeus m.	Parasympathetic to parotid gland		Internal surface of tympanic membrane, middle ear, pharynx & general sensory from tongue (post. one-third)	Taste from post. one-third of tongue
CN X	Supplies muscles of pharynx & larynx	Parasympathetic to organs in neck, thorax & abdomen	Ext. acoustic meatus & tympanic membrane	Organs in neck, thorax & abdomen, general sensory from root of tongue	Taste, epiglottis
CN XI	Supplies muscles of soft palate, pharynx, larynx (from cranial root & distributed in vagus n.) & sternocleidomastoid & trapezius m.				
CN XII	Supplies extrinsic & intrinsic mm. of tongue except palatoglossus m. (from cranial root distributed in vagus n.)				

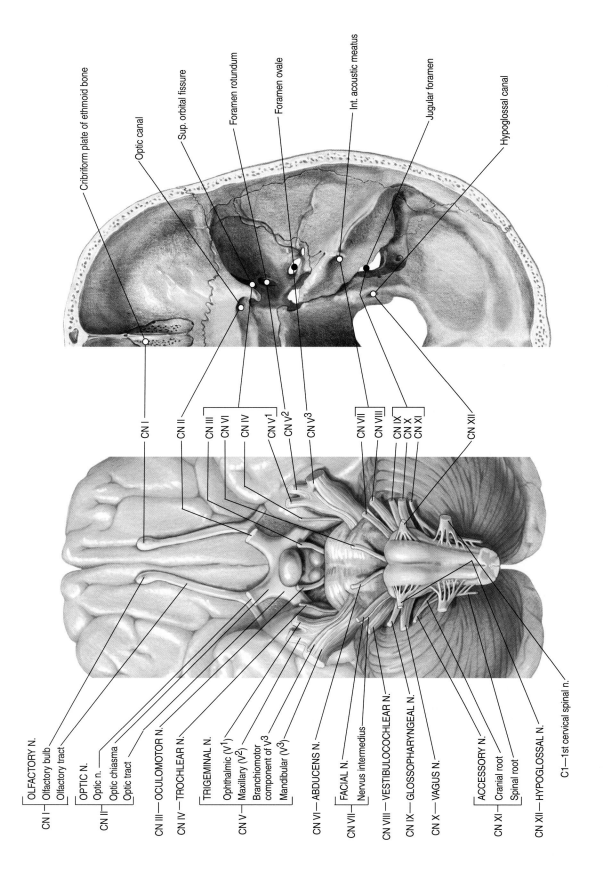

Cribriform plate of ethmoid bone
Optic canal
Sup. orbital fissure
Foramen rotundum
Foramen ovale
Int. acoustic meatus
Jugular foramen
Hypoglossal canal

CN I
CN II
CN III
CN VI
CN IV
CN V¹
CN V²
CN V³
CN VII
CN VIII
CN IX
CN X
CN XI
CN XII

OLFACTORY N.
CN I — Olfactory bulb
— Olfactory tract
OPTIC N.
CN II — Optic n.
— Optic chiasma
— Optic tract
CN III — OCULOMOTOR N.
CN IV — TROCHLEAR N.
TRIGEMINAL N.
Ophthalmic (V¹)
CN V — Maxillary (V²)
Branchiomotor component of V³
Mandibular (V³)
CN VI — ABDUCENS N.
FACIAL N.
CN VII — Nervus intermedius
CN VIII — VESTIBULOCOCHLEAR N.
CN IX — GLOSSOPHARYNGEAL N.
CN X — VAGUS N.
ACCESSORY N.
CN XI — Cranial root
— Spinal root
CN XII — HYPOGLOSSAL N.
C1 — 1st cervical spinal n.

Olfactory Nerve—CN I
Plate 8.2

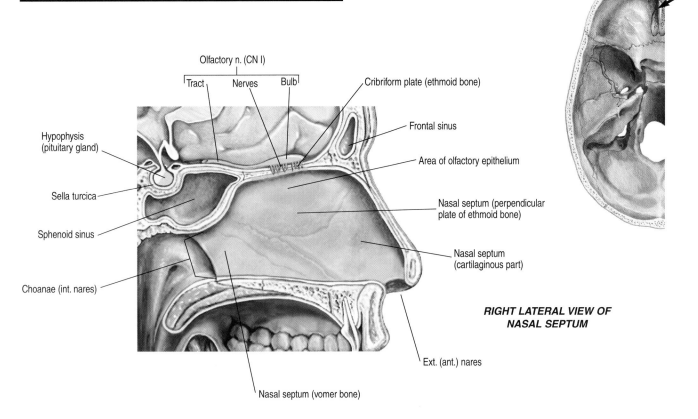

Olfactory n. (CN I)

Tract | Nerves | Bulb

Cribriform plate (ethmoid bone)

Frontal sinus

Hypophysis (pituitary gland)

Area of olfactory epithelium

Sella turcica

Nasal septum (perpendicular plate of ethmoid bone)

Sphenoid sinus

Nasal septum (cartilaginous part)

Choanae (int. nares)

RIGHT LATERAL VIEW OF NASAL SEPTUM

Ext. (ant.) nares

Nasal septum (vomer bone)

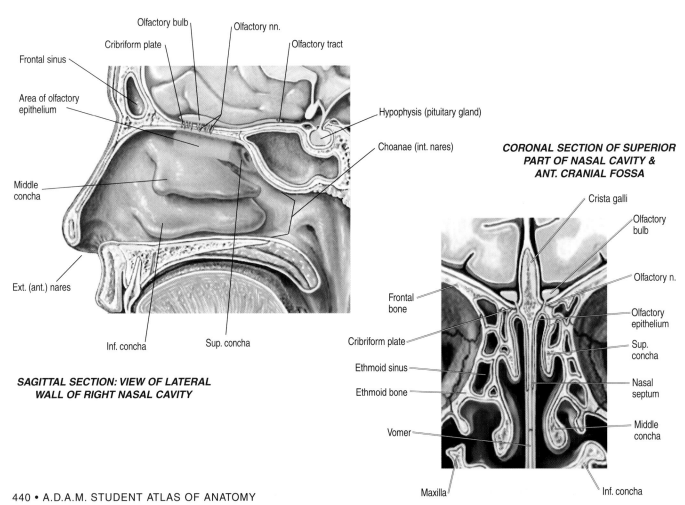

Olfactory bulb

Olfactory nn.

Cribriform plate

Olfactory tract

Frontal sinus

Area of olfactory epithelium

Hypophysis (pituitary gland)

Choanae (int. nares)

CORONAL SECTION OF SUPERIOR PART OF NASAL CAVITY & ANT. CRANIAL FOSSA

Middle concha

Crista galli

Olfactory bulb

Ext. (ant.) nares

Olfactory n.

Frontal bone

Olfactory epithelium

Cribriform plate

Sup. concha

Ethmoid sinus

Inf. concha

Sup. concha

Nasal septum

Ethmoid bone

SAGITTAL SECTION: VIEW OF LATERAL WALL OF RIGHT NASAL CAVITY

Vomer

Middle concha

Maxilla

Inf. concha

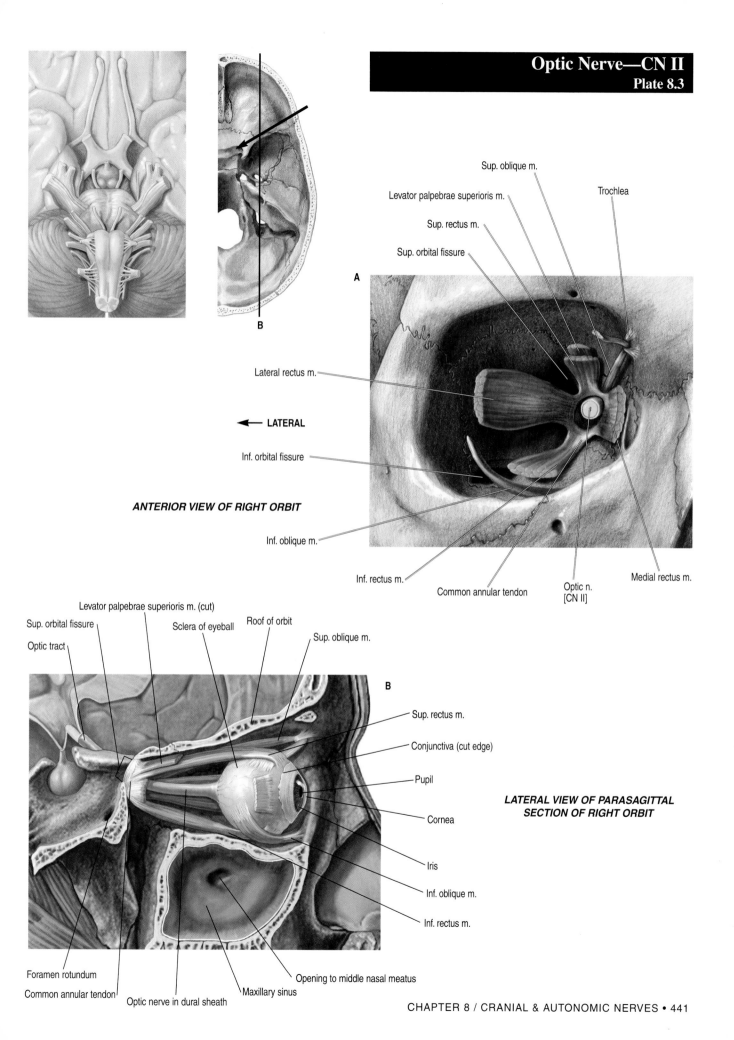

Sup. oblique m.

Levator palpebrae superioris m.

Sup. rectus m.

Sup. orbital fissure

Trochlea

A

Lateral rectus m.

← **LATERAL**

Inf. orbital fissure

ANTERIOR VIEW OF RIGHT ORBIT

Inf. oblique m.

Inf. rectus m.

Common annular tendon

Optic n. [CN II]

Medial rectus m.

Levator palpebrae superioris m. (cut)

Sup. orbital fissure

Optic tract

Sclera of eyeball

Roof of orbit

Sup. oblique m.

B

Sup. rectus m.

Conjunctiva (cut edge)

Pupil

**LATERAL VIEW OF PARASAGITTAL
SECTION OF RIGHT ORBIT**

Cornea

Iris

Inf. oblique m.

Inf. rectus m.

Foramen rotundum

Common annular tendon

Optic nerve in dural sheath

Maxillary sinus

Opening to middle nasal meatus

Oculomotor Nerve—CN III
Plate 8.4

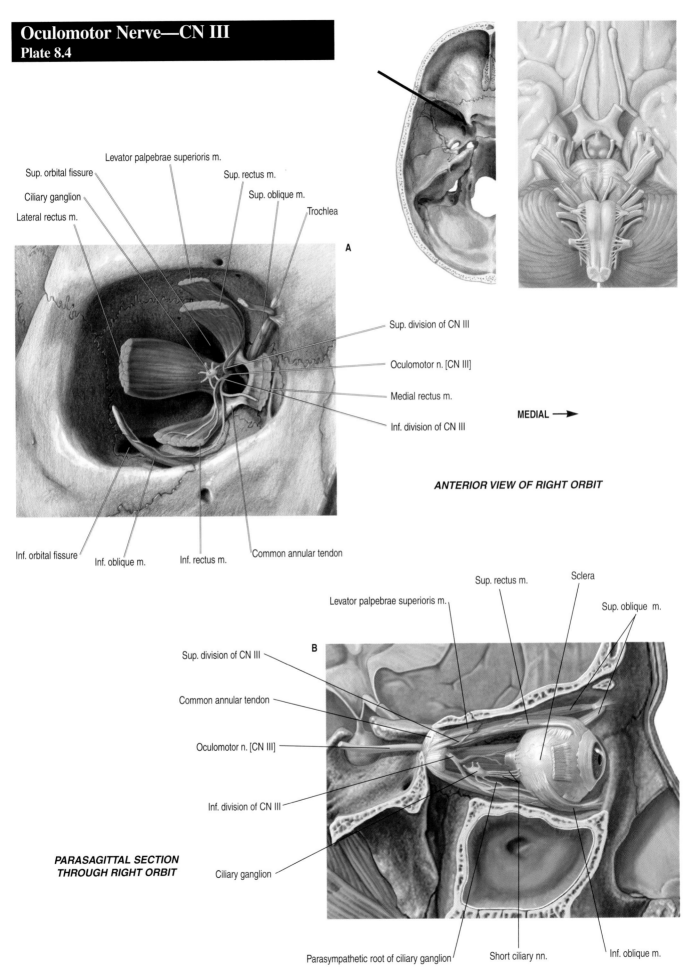

Levator palpebrae superioris m.

Sup. orbital fissure

Ciliary ganglion

Lateral rectus m.

Sup. rectus m.

Sup. oblique m.

Trochlea

A

Sup. division of CN III

Oculomotor n. [CN III]

Medial rectus m.

Inf. division of CN III

MEDIAL ➝

ANTERIOR VIEW OF RIGHT ORBIT

Inf. orbital fissure

Inf. oblique m.

Inf. rectus m.

Common annular tendon

Levator palpebrae superioris m.

Sup. rectus m.

Sclera

Sup. oblique m.

Sup. division of CN III

B

Common annular tendon

Oculomotor n. [CN III]

Inf. division of CN III

*PARASAGITTAL SECTION
THROUGH RIGHT ORBIT*

Ciliary ganglion

Parasympathetic root of ciliary ganglion

Short ciliary nn.

Inf. oblique m.

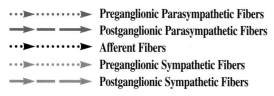

- ···▷·······► Preganglionic Parasympathetic Fibers
- ——▷— —— Postganglionic Parasympathetic Fibers
- ···▶·······► Afferent Fibers
- ···▷·········► Preganglionic Sympathetic Fibers
- ——▷— —— Postganglionic Sympathetic Fibers

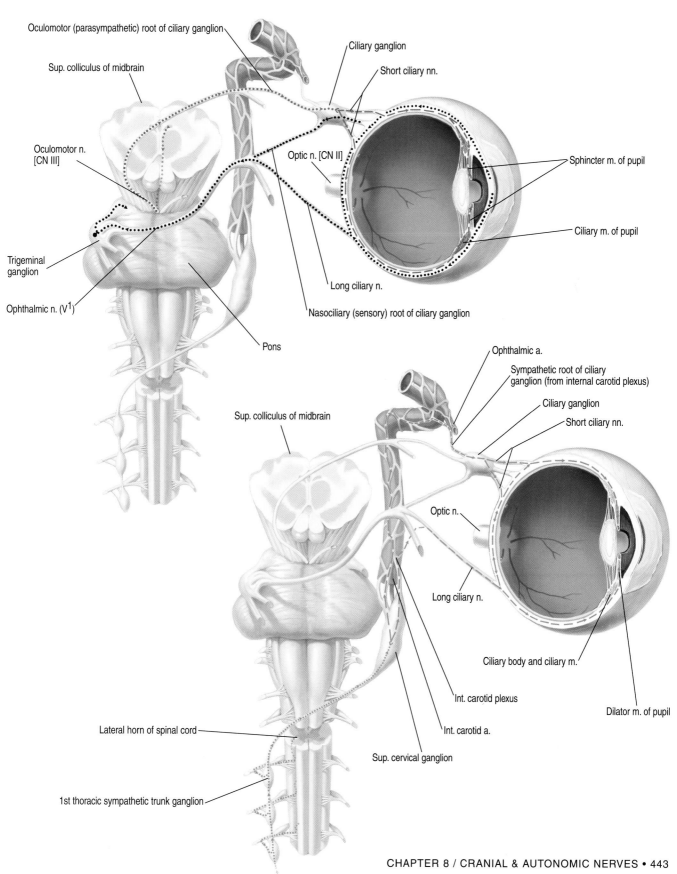

Oculomotor (parasympathetic) root of ciliary ganglion

Ciliary ganglion

Short ciliary nn.

Sup. colliculus of midbrain

Optic n. [CN II]

Sphincter m. of pupil

Oculomotor n. [CN III]

Ciliary m. of pupil

Trigeminal ganglion

Long ciliary n.

Ophthalmic n. (V¹)

Nasociliary (sensory) root of ciliary ganglion

Pons

Sup. colliculus of midbrain

Ophthalmic a.

Sympathetic root of ciliary ganglion (from internal carotid plexus)

Ciliary ganglion

Short ciliary nn.

Optic n.

Long ciliary n.

Ciliary body and ciliary m.

Int. carotid plexus

Dilator m. of pupil

Lateral horn of spinal cord

Int. carotid a.

Sup. cervical ganglion

1st thoracic sympathetic trunk ganglion

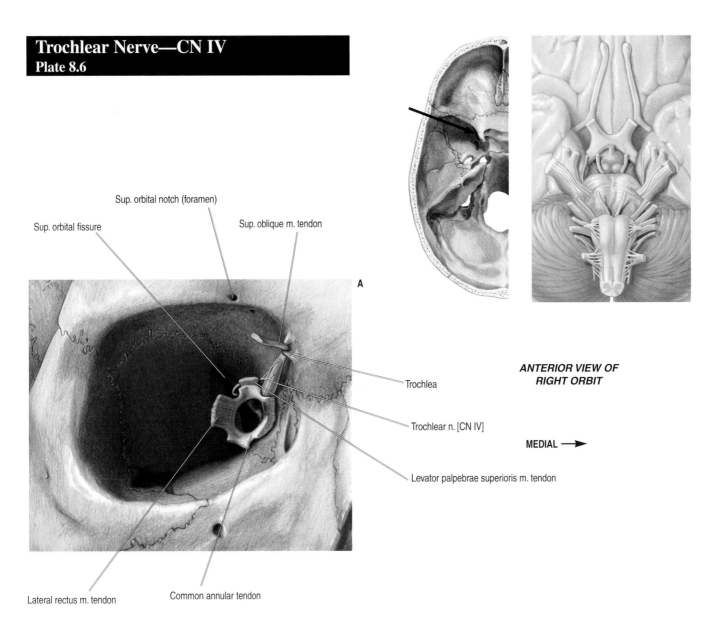

Sup. orbital notch (foramen)

Sup. orbital fissure

Sup. oblique m. tendon

A

Trochlea

**ANTERIOR VIEW OF
RIGHT ORBIT**

Trochlear n. [CN IV]

MEDIAL ➔

Levator palpebrae superioris m. tendon

Lateral rectus m. tendon

Common annular tendon

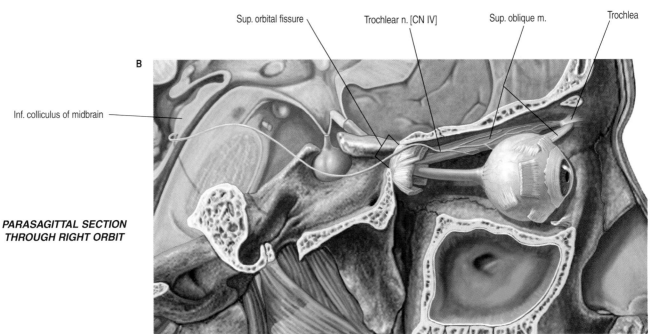

Sup. orbital fissure

Trochlear n. [CN IV]

Sup. oblique m.

Trochlea

Inf. colliculus of midbrain

B

**PARASAGITTAL SECTION
THROUGH RIGHT ORBIT**

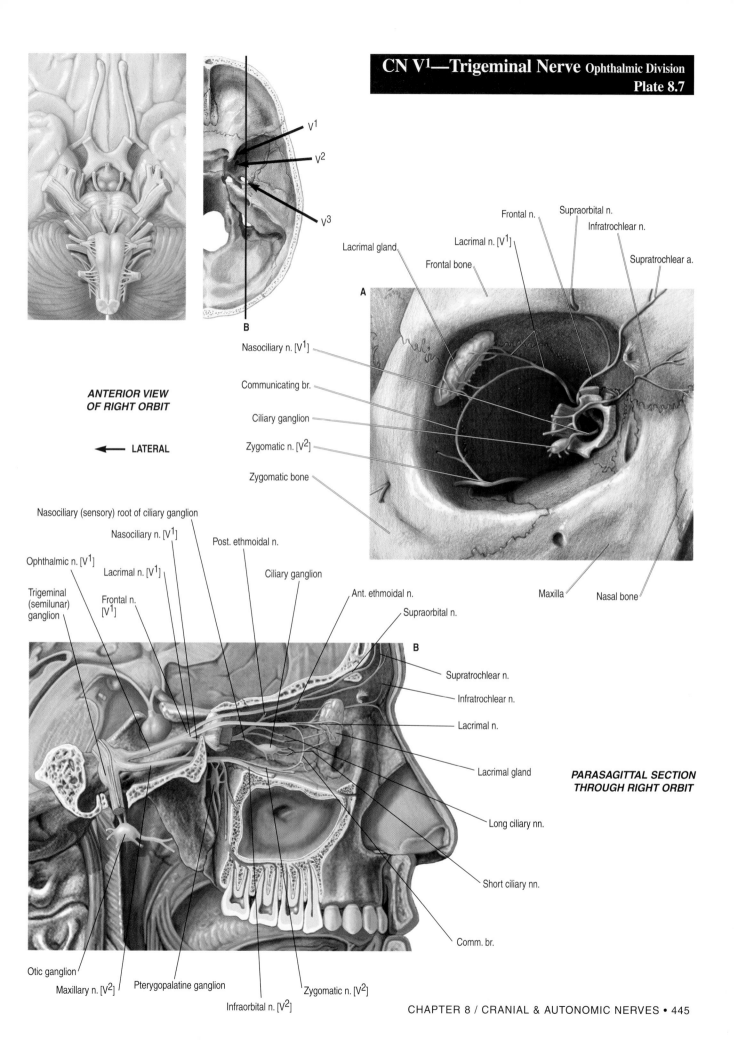

V¹
V²
V³

B

*ANTERIOR VIEW
OF RIGHT ORBIT*

← LATERAL

A

Lacrimal gland

Frontal bone

Frontal n.

Lacrimal n. [V¹]

Supraorbital n.

Infratrochlear n.

Supratrochlear a.

Nasociliary n. [V¹]

Communicating br.

Ciliary ganglion

Zygomatic n. [V²]

Zygomatic bone

Maxilla

Nasal bone

Nasociliary (sensory) root of ciliary ganglion

Nasociliary n. [V¹]

Post. ethmoidal n.

Ophthalmic n. [V¹]

Lacrimal n. [V¹]

Ciliary ganglion

Trigeminal
(semilunar)
ganglion

Frontal n.
[V¹]

Ant. ethmoidal n.

Supraorbital n.

B

Supratrochlear n.

Infratrochlear n.

Lacrimal n.

Lacrimal gland

*PARASAGITTAL SECTION
THROUGH RIGHT ORBIT*

Long ciliary nn.

Short ciliary nn.

Comm. br.

Otic ganglion

Maxillary n. [V²]

Pterygopalatine ganglion

Zygomatic n. [V²]

Infraorbital n. [V²]

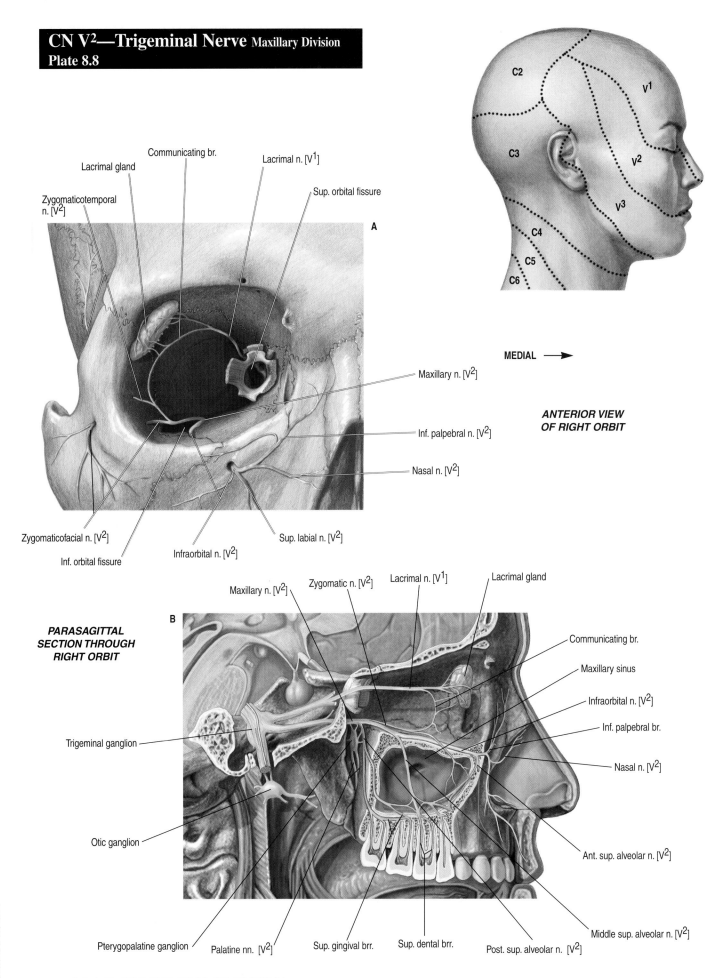

C2

C3

V¹

V²

V³

C4

C5

C6

MEDIAL ⟶

**ANTERIOR VIEW
OF RIGHT ORBIT**

Communicating br.

Lacrimal gland

Lacrimal n. [V¹]

Sup. orbital fissure

Zygomaticotemporal n. [V²]

A

Maxillary n. [V²]

Inf. palpebral n. [V²]

Nasal n. [V²]

Zygomaticofacial n. [V²]

Inf. orbital fissure

Infraorbital n. [V²]

Sup. labial n. [V²]

*PARASAGITTAL
SECTION THROUGH
RIGHT ORBIT*

B

Maxillary n. [V²]

Zygomatic n. [V²]

Lacrimal n. [V¹]

Lacrimal gland

Communicating br.

Maxillary sinus

Infraorbital n. [V²]

Inf. palpebral br.

Nasal n. [V²]

Trigeminal ganglion

Otic ganglion

Ant. sup. alveolar n. [V²]

Middle sup. alveolar n. [V²]

Pterygopalatine ganglion

Palatine nn. [V²]

Sup. gingival brr.

Sup. dental brr.

Post. sup. alveolar n. [V²]

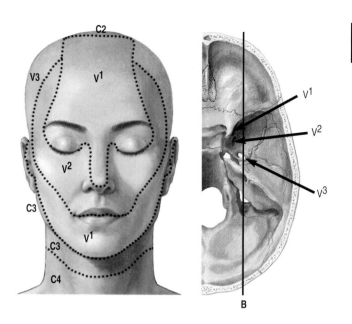

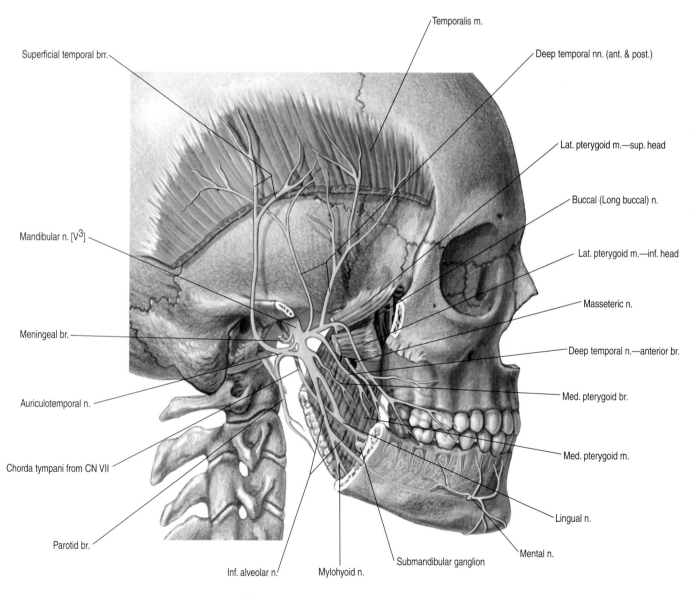

Temporalis m.

Deep temporal nn. (ant. & post.)

Superficial temporal brr.

Lat. pterygoid m.—sup. head

Buccal (Long buccal) n.

Mandibular n. [V³]

Lat. pterygoid m.—inf. head

Masseteric n.

Meningeal br.

Deep temporal n.—anterior br.

Auriculotemporal n.

Med. pterygoid br.

Chorda tympani from CN VII

Med. pterygoid m.

Lingual n.

Parotid br.

Mental n.

Inf. alveolar n.

Mylohyoid n.

Submandibular ganglion

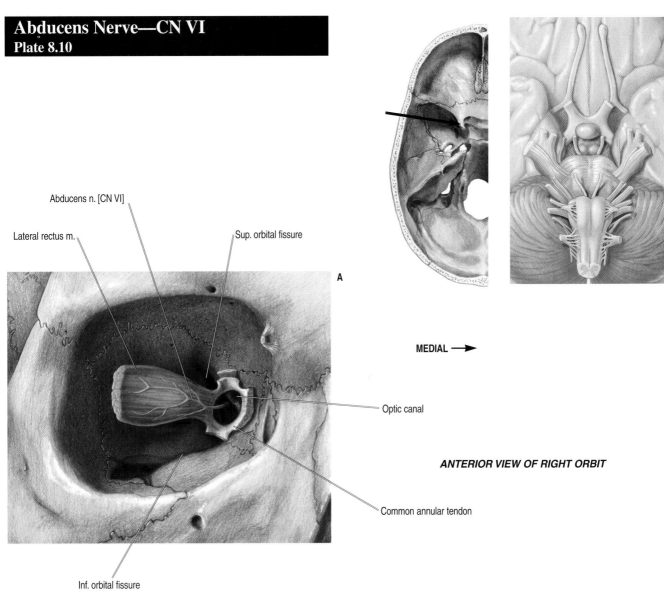

Abducens n. [CN VI]

Lateral rectus m.

Sup. orbital fissure

A

MEDIAL ⟶

Optic canal

ANTERIOR VIEW OF RIGHT ORBIT

Common annular tendon

Inf. orbital fissure

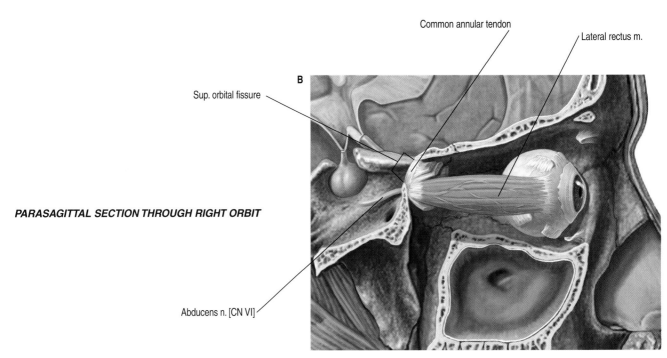

Common annular tendon

Lateral rectus m.

Sup. orbital fissure

B

PARASAGITTAL SECTION THROUGH RIGHT ORBIT

Abducens n. [CN VI]

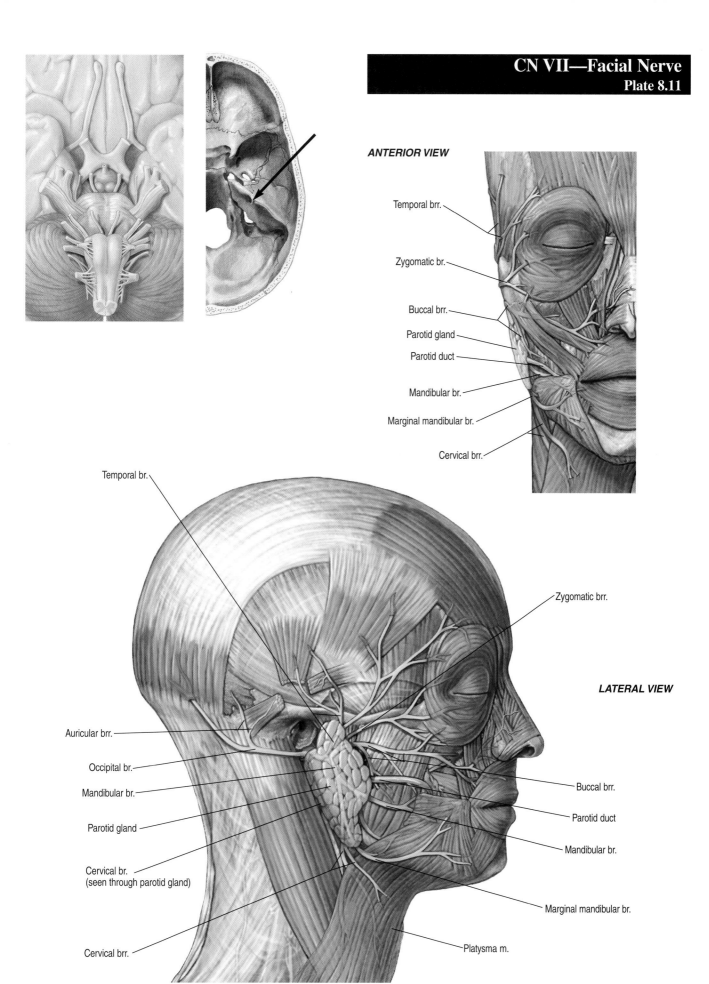

ANTERIOR VIEW

Temporal brr.

Zygomatic br.

Buccal brr.

Parotid gland

Parotid duct

Mandibular br.

Marginal mandibular br.

Cervical brr.

Temporal br.

Zygomatic brr.

LATERAL VIEW

Auricular brr.

Occipital br.

Mandibular br.

Parotid gland

Cervical br.
(seen through parotid gland)

Cervical brr.

Buccal brr.

Parotid duct

Mandibular br.

Marginal mandibular br.

Platysma m.

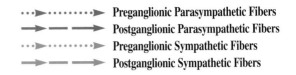

- **····▷········▶** Preganglionic Parasympathetic Fibers
- **————▶ —— — —▶** Postganglionic Parasympathetic Fibers
- **····▷········▶** Preganglionic Sympathetic Fibers
- **————▶ —— — —▶** Postganglionic Sympathetic Fibers

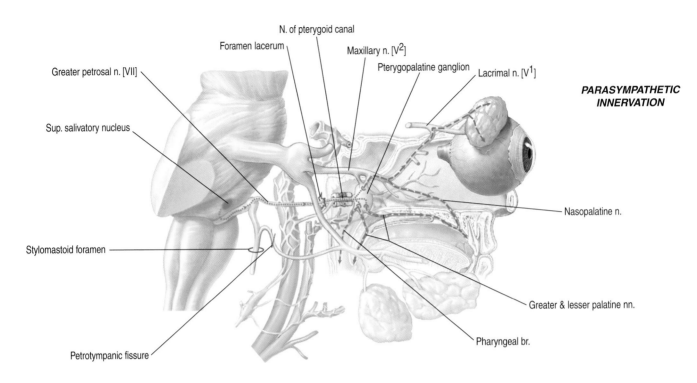

PARASYMPATHETIC INNERVATION

N. of pterygoid canal

Foramen lacerum

Maxillary n. [V²]

Pterygopalatine ganglion

Greater petrosal n. [VII]

Lacrimal n. [V¹]

Sup. salivatory nucleus

Nasopalatine n.

Stylomastoid foramen

Greater & lesser palatine nn.

Pharyngeal br.

Petrotympanic fissure

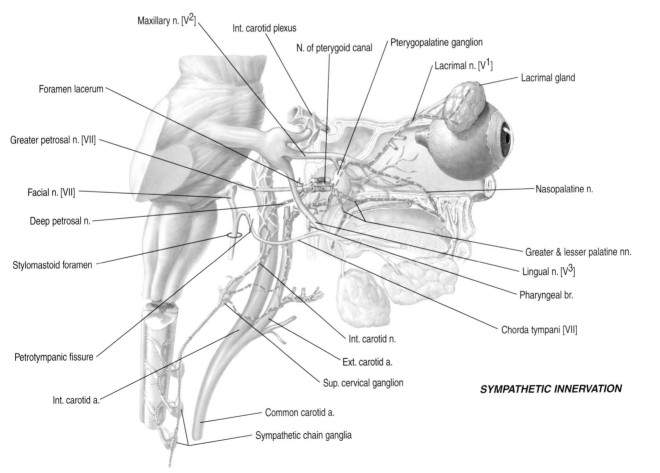

Maxillary n. [V²]

Int. carotid plexus

N. of pterygoid canal

Pterygopalatine ganglion

Lacrimal n. [V¹]

Lacrimal gland

Foramen lacerum

Greater petrosal n. [VII]

Nasopalatine n.

Facial n. [VII]

Deep petrosal n.

Greater & lesser palatine nn.

Lingual n. [V³]

Stylomastoid foramen

Pharyngeal br.

Chorda tympani [VII]

Petrotympanic fissure

Int. carotid n.

Ext. carotid a.

Sup. cervical ganglion

SYMPATHETIC INNERVATION

Int. carotid a.

Common carotid a.

Sympathetic chain ganglia

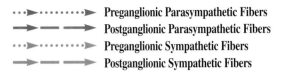

Preganglionic Parasympathetic Fibers
Postganglionic Parasympathetic Fibers
Preganglionic Sympathetic Fibers
Postganglionic Sympathetic Fibers

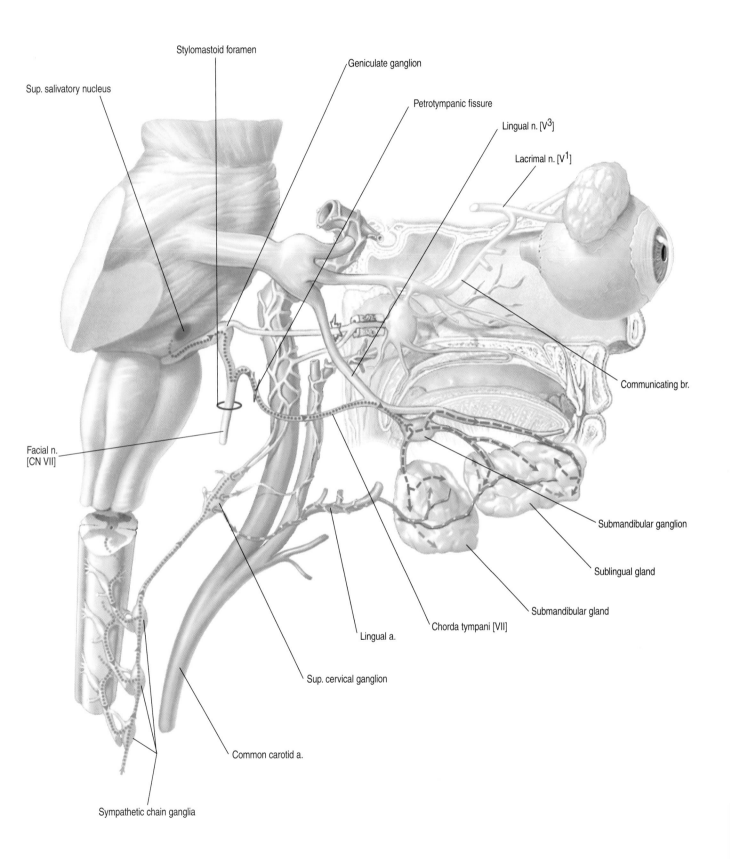

Stylomastoid foramen

Geniculate ganglion

Sup. salivatory nucleus

Petrotympanic fissure

Lingual n. [V³]

Lacrimal n. [V¹]

Communicating br.

Facial n.
[CN VII]

Submandibular ganglion

Sublingual gland

Submandibular gland

Chorda tympani [VII]

Lingual a.

Sup. cervical ganglion

Common carotid a.

Sympathetic chain ganglia

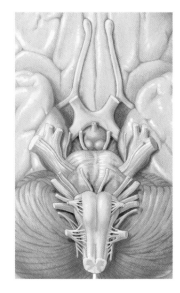

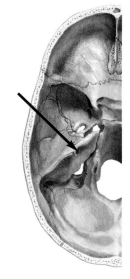

*HORIZONTAL SECTION THROUGH TEMPORAL BONE
AND CHAMBERS OF THE EAR*

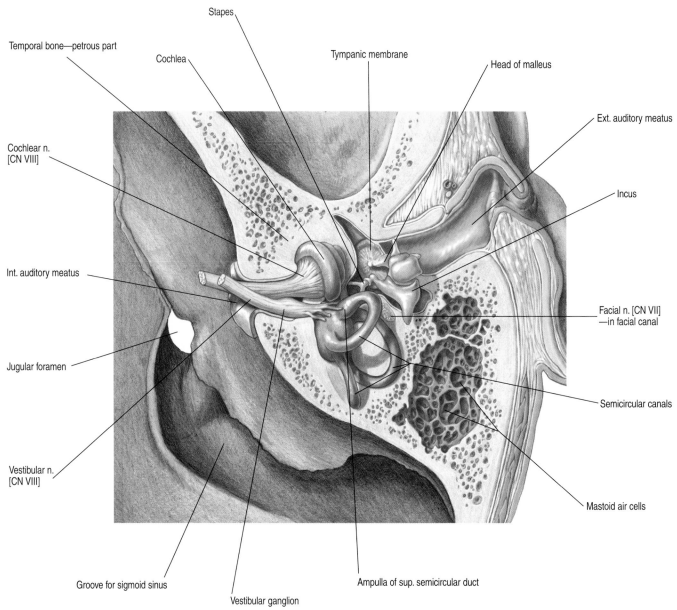

Stapes

Temporal bone—petrous part

Cochlea

Tympanic membrane

Head of malleus

Ext. auditory meatus

Cochlear n.
[CN VIII]

Incus

Int. auditory meatus

Facial n. [CN VII]
—in facial canal

Jugular foramen

Semicircular canals

Vestibular n.
[CN VIII]

Mastoid air cells

Groove for sigmoid sinus

Vestibular ganglion

Ampulla of sup. semicircular duct

Preganglionic Parasympathetic Fibers
Postganglionic Parasympathetic Fibers
Afferent Fibers
Preganglionic Sympathetic Fibers
Postganglionic Sympathetic Fibers

Mandibular n. [V³]

Geniculate ganglion of facial n. [VII]

Tympanic n. [IX]

Sup. ganglion of glossopharyngeal n. [IX]

Greater petrosal n. [VII]

Tympanic plexus

Inf. (petrosal) ganglion of glossopharyngeal n. [IX]

Lesser petrosal n. [IX]

Pterygopalatine ganglion

Foramen ovale

Parotid gland

Otic ganglion

Sup. ganglion of vagus n. [X]

Inf. (nodose) ganglion of vagus n. [X]

Chorda tympani [VII]

Vagus n. [X]

Glossopharyngeal n. [IX]

Lingual n. [V³]

Sup. cervical sympathetic ganglion

Foramen cecum of tongue

Posferior 1/3rd of tongue

Int. carotid a.

Sympathetic chain

Sulcus terminalis

Chorda tympani (br. of CN VII)

Ext. carotid a.

Vallate papillae

Anterior 2/3rds of tongue

Filiform papillae

Common carotid a.

Fungiform papillae

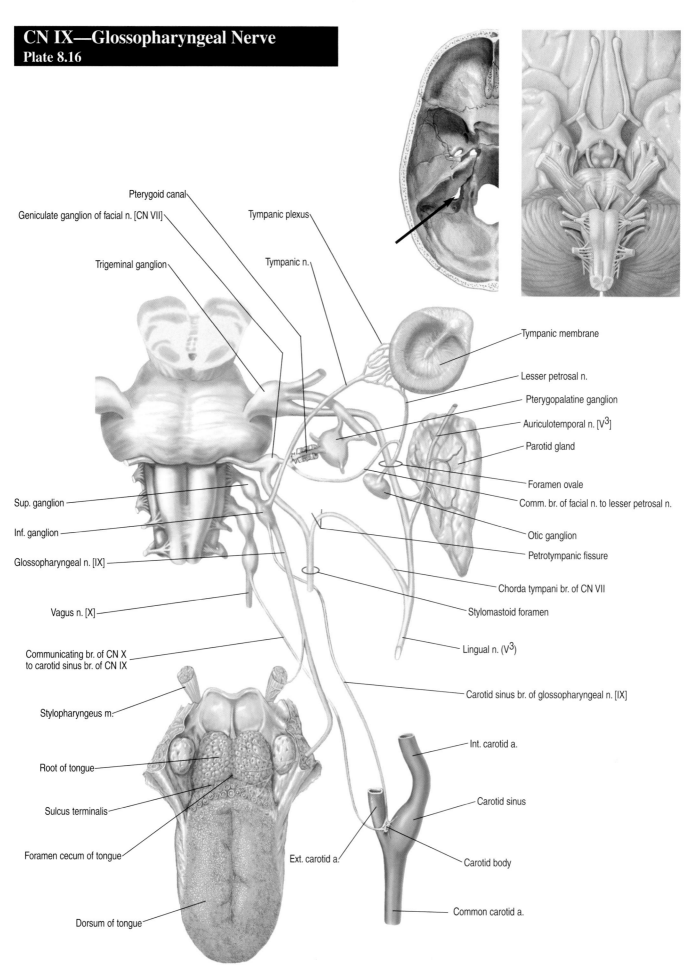

Pterygoid canal

Geniculate ganglion of facial n. [CN VII]

Tympanic plexus

Tympanic n.

Trigeminal ganglion

Tympanic membrane

Lesser petrosal n.

Pterygopalatine ganglion

Auriculotemporal n. [V³]

Parotid gland

Foramen ovale

Comm. br. of facial n. to lesser petrosal n.

Sup. ganglion

Inf. ganglion

Otic ganglion

Glossopharyngeal n. [IX]

Petrotympanic fissure

Chorda tympani br. of CN VII

Vagus n. [X]

Stylomastoid foramen

Lingual n. (V³)

Communicating br. of CN X
to carotid sinus br. of CN IX

Carotid sinus br. of glossopharyngeal n. [IX]

Stylopharyngeus m.

Int. carotid a.

Root of tongue

Sulcus terminalis

Carotid sinus

Foramen cecum of tongue

Ext. carotid a.

Carotid body

Common carotid a.

Dorsum of tongue

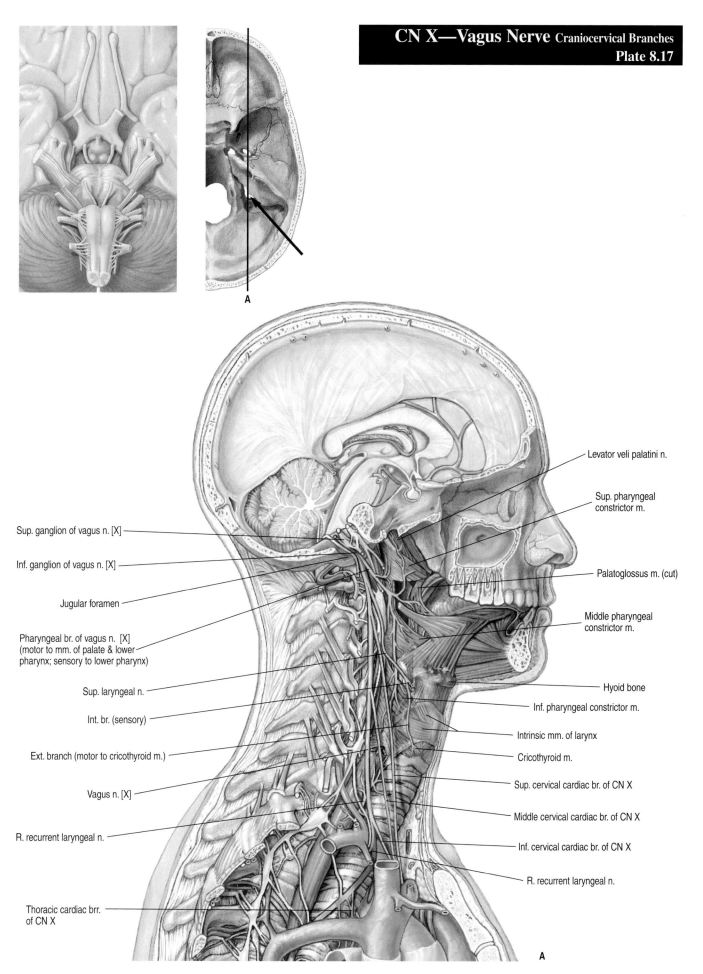

Levator veli palatini n.

Sup. pharyngeal constrictor m.

Sup. ganglion of vagus n. [X]

Inf. ganglion of vagus n. [X]

Palatoglossus m. (cut)

Jugular foramen

Pharyngeal br. of vagus n. [X] (motor to mm. of palate & lower pharynx; sensory to lower pharynx)

Middle pharyngeal constrictor m.

Sup. laryngeal n.

Hyoid bone

Int. br. (sensory)

Inf. pharyngeal constrictor m.

Intrinsic mm. of larynx

Ext. branch (motor to cricothyroid m.)

Cricothyroid m.

Sup. cervical cardiac br. of CN X

Vagus n. [X]

Middle cervical cardiac br. of CN X

Inf. cervical cardiac br. of CN X

R. recurrent laryngeal n.

R. recurrent laryngeal n.

Thoracic cardiac brr. of CN X

A

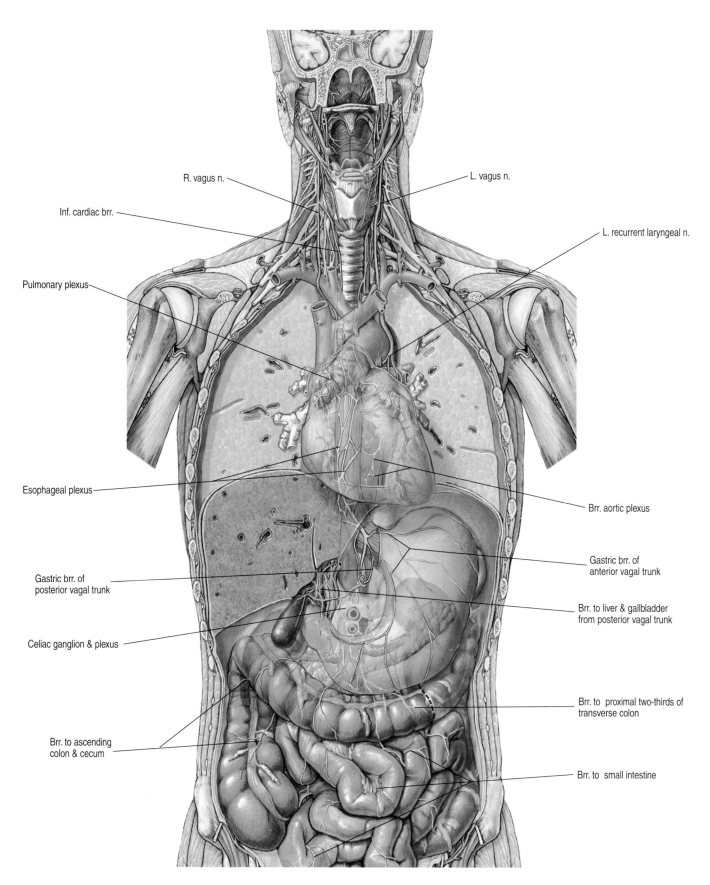

R. vagus n.

L. vagus n.

Inf. cardiac brr.

L. recurrent laryngeal n.

Pulmonary plexus

Esophageal plexus

Brr. aortic plexus

Gastric brr. of anterior vagal trunk

Gastric brr. of posterior vagal trunk

Brr. to liver & gallbladder from posterior vagal trunk

Celiac ganglion & plexus

Brr. to proximal two-thirds of transverse colon

Brr. to ascending colon & cecum

Brr. to small intestine

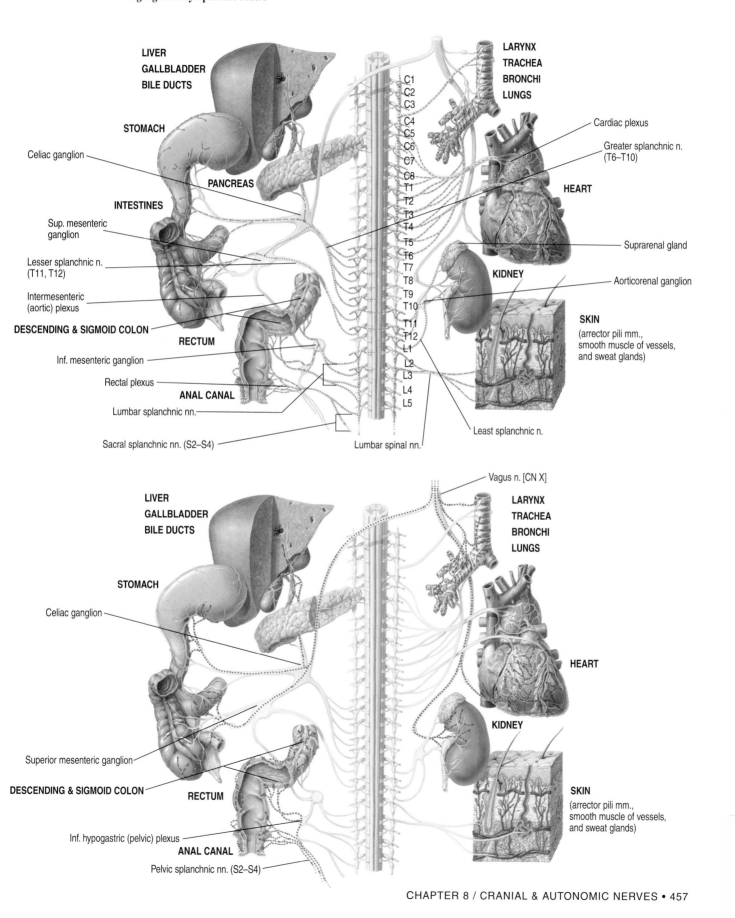

Preganglionic Parasympathetic Fibers
Postganglionic Parasympathetic Fibers
Preganglionic Sympathetic Fibers
Postganglionic Sympathetic Fibers

LIVER
GALLBLADDER
BILE DUCTS

LARYNX
TRACHEA
BRONCHI
LUNGS

STOMACH

Cardiac plexus

Celiac ganglion

Greater splanchnic n.
(T6–T10)

PANCREAS

HEART

INTESTINES

Sup. mesenteric
ganglion

Lesser splanchnic n.
(T11, T12)

Suprarenal gland

KIDNEY

Intermesenteric
(aortic) plexus

Aorticorenal ganglion

DESCENDING & SIGMOID COLON

SKIN
(arrector pili mm.,
smooth muscle of vessels,
and sweat glands)

RECTUM

Inf. mesenteric ganglion

Rectal plexus

ANAL CANAL

Lumbar splanchnic nn.

Least splanchnic n.

Sacral splanchnic nn. (S2–S4)

Lumbar spinal nn.

C1 C2 C3 C4 C5 C6 C7 C8 T1 T2 T3 T4 T5 T6 T7 T8 T9 T10 T11 T12 L1 L2 L3 L4 L5

Vagus n. [CN X]

LIVER
GALLBLADDER
BILE DUCTS

LARYNX
TRACHEA
BRONCHI
LUNGS

STOMACH

Celiac ganglion

HEART

KIDNEY

Superior mesenteric ganglion

DESCENDING & SIGMOID COLON

SKIN
(arrector pili mm.,
smooth muscle of vessels,
and sweat glands)

RECTUM

Inf. hypogastric (pelvic) plexus

ANAL CANAL

Pelvic splanchnic nn. (S2–S4)

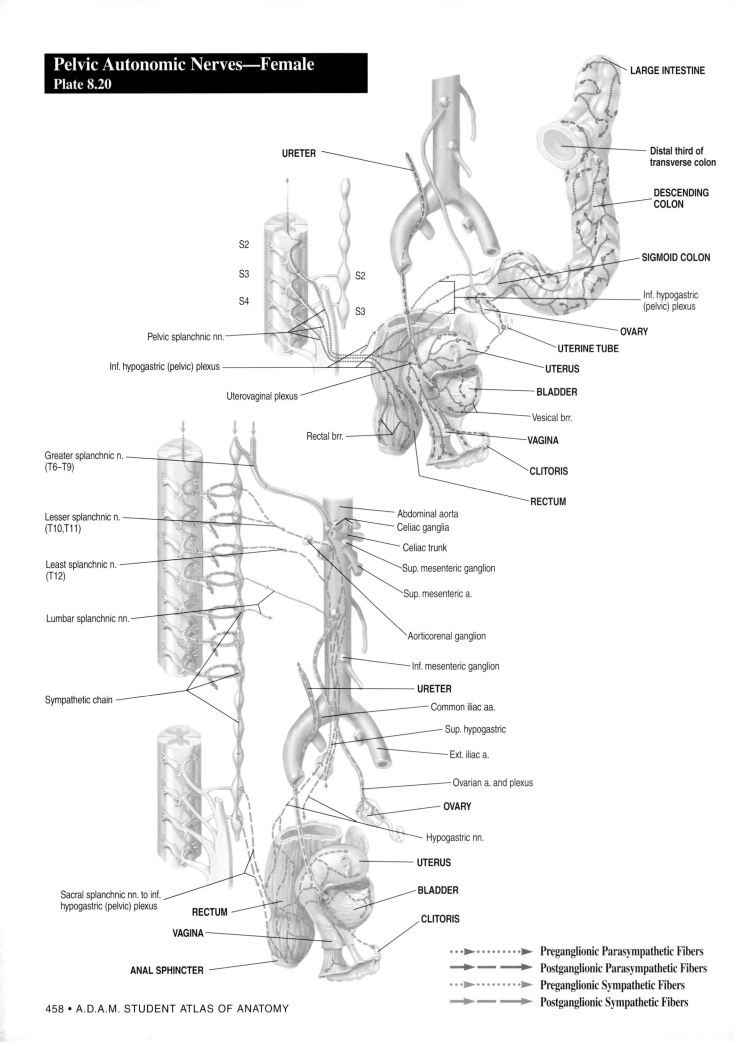

LARGE INTESTINE

Distal third of transverse colon

DESCENDING COLON

URETER

SIGMOID COLON

Inf. hypogastric (pelvic) plexus

OVARY

UTERINE TUBE

UTERUS

BLADDER

Vesical brr.

VAGINA

CLITORIS

RECTUM

S2
S3
S4

S2
S3

Pelvic splanchnic nn.

Inf. hypogastric (pelvic) plexus

Uterovaginal plexus

Rectal brr.

Greater splanchnic n. (T6–T9)

Lesser splanchnic n. (T10,T11)

Least splanchnic n. (T12)

Lumbar splanchnic nn.

Sympathetic chain

Abdominal aorta
Celiac ganglia
Celiac trunk
Sup. mesenteric ganglion
Sup. mesenteric a.

Aorticorenal ganglion

Inf. mesenteric ganglion

URETER

Common iliac aa.

Sup. hypogastric

Ext. iliac a.

Ovarian a. and plexus

OVARY

Hypogastric nn.

UTERUS

BLADDER

Sacral splanchnic nn. to inf. hypogastric (pelvic) plexus

RECTUM

VAGINA

CLITORIS

ANAL SPHINCTER

········▶ Preganglionic Parasympathetic Fibers
——— ▶ Postganglionic Parasympathetic Fibers
········▶ Preganglionic Sympathetic Fibers
——— ▶ Postganglionic Sympathetic Fibers

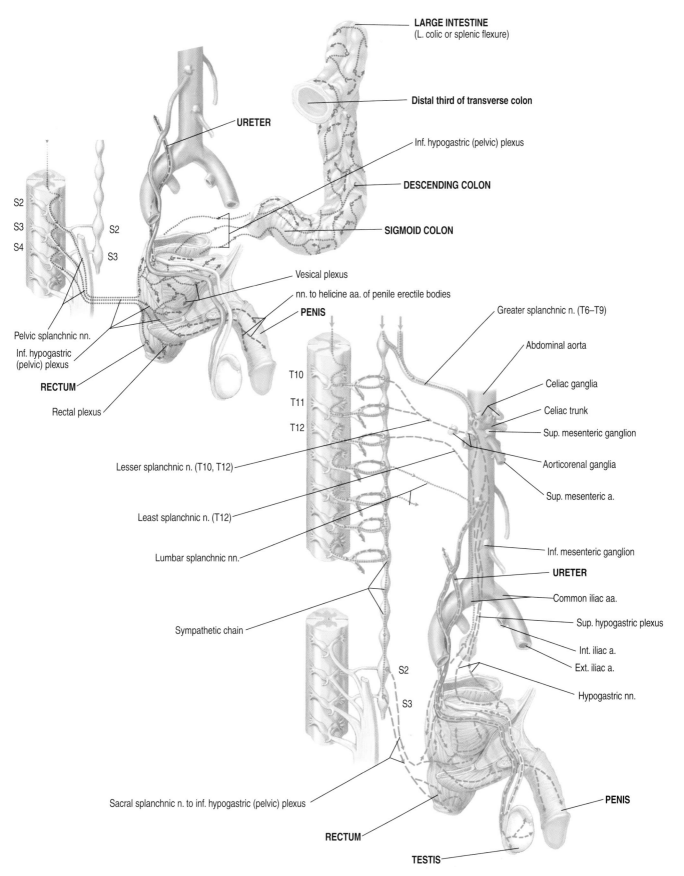

···▷········► Preganglionic Parasympathetic Fibers
━━▷━ ━ ━► Postganglionic Parasympathetic Fibers
···▷········► Preganglionic Sympathetic Fibers
━━▷━ ━ ━► Postganglionic Sympathetic Fibers

LARGE INTESTINE
(L. colic or splenic flexure)

Distal third of transverse colon

URETER

Inf. hypogastric (pelvic) plexus

DESCENDING COLON

SIGMOID COLON

S2
S3
S4

S2

S3

Vesical plexus

nn. to helicine aa. of penile erectile bodies

PENIS

Greater splanchnic n. (T6–T9)

Abdominal aorta

Celiac ganglia

Celiac trunk

Sup. mesenteric ganglion

Aorticorenal ganglia

Sup. mesenteric a.

Pelvic splanchnic nn.

Inf. hypogastric
(pelvic) plexus

RECTUM

Rectal plexus

T10

T11

T12

Lesser splanchnic n. (T10, T12)

Least splanchnic n. (T12)

Lumbar splanchnic nn.

Inf. mesenteric ganglion

URETER

Common iliac aa.

Sup. hypogastric plexus

Int. iliac a.

Ext. iliac a.

Hypogastric nn.

Sympathetic chain

S2

S3

Sacral splanchnic n. to inf. hypogastric (pelvic) plexus

PENIS

RECTUM

TESTIS

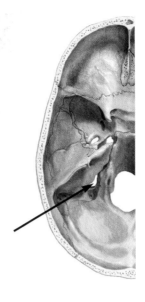

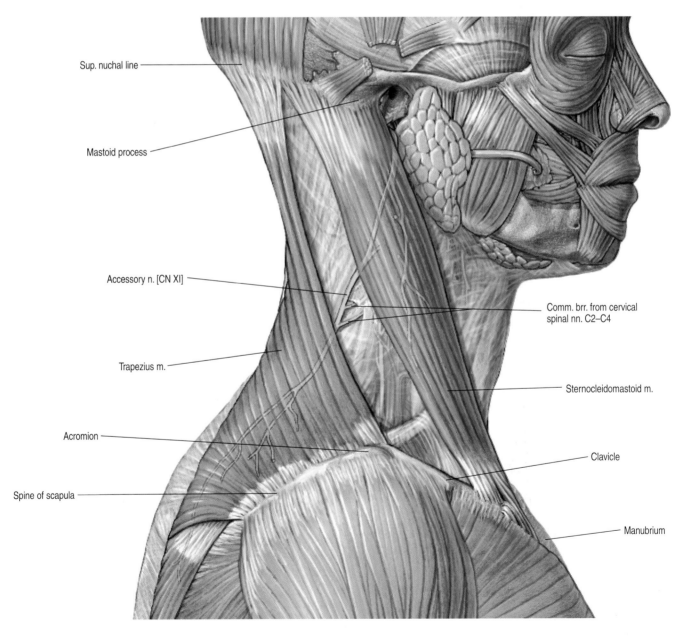

Sup. nuchal line

Mastoid process

Accessory n. [CN XI]

Trapezius m.

Acromion

Spine of scapula

Comm. brr. from cervical spinal nn. C2–C4

Sternocleidomastoid m.

Clavicle

Manubrium

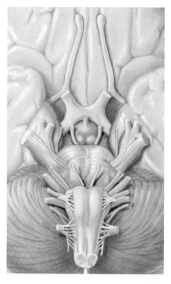

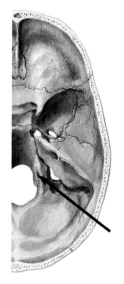

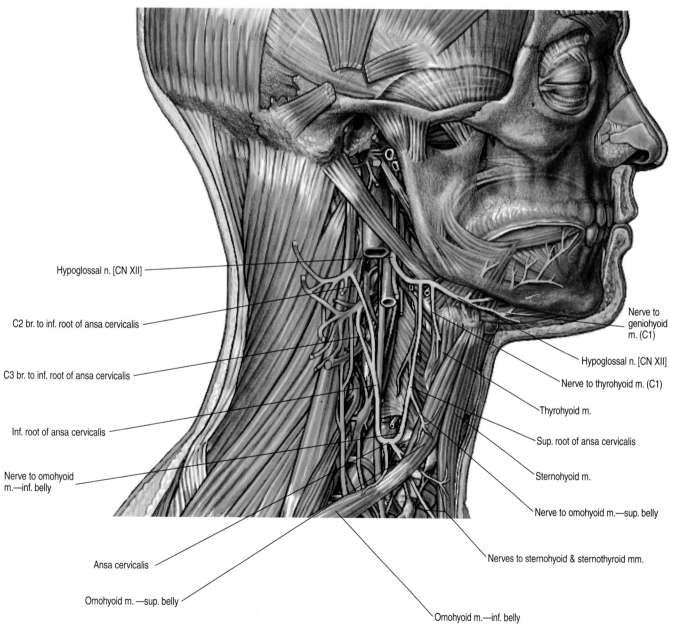

Hypoglossal n. [CN XII]

C2 br. to inf. root of ansa cervicalis

C3 br. to inf. root of ansa cervicalis

Inf. root of ansa cervicalis

Nerve to omohyoid m.—inf. belly

Ansa cervicalis

Omohyoid m. —sup. belly

Nerve to geniohyoid m. (C1)

Hypoglossal n. [CN XII]

Nerve to thyrohyoid m. (C1)

Thyrohyoid m.

Sup. root of ansa cervicalis

Sternohyoid m.

Nerve to omohyoid m.—sup. belly

Nerves to sternohyoid & sternothyroid mm.

Omohyoid m.—inf. belly

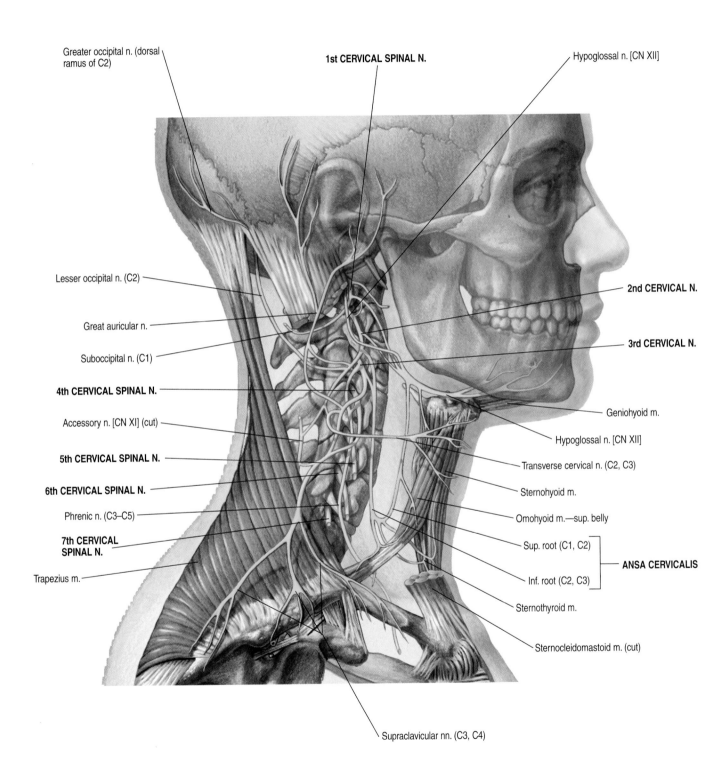

Greater occipital n. (dorsal ramus of C2)

1st CERVICAL SPINAL N.

Hypoglossal n. [CN XII]

Lesser occipital n. (C2)

Great auricular n.

Suboccipital n. (C1)

4th CERVICAL SPINAL N.

Accessory n. [CN XI] (cut)

5th CERVICAL SPINAL N.

6th CERVICAL SPINAL N.

Phrenic n. (C3–C5)

7th CERVICAL SPINAL N.

Trapezius m.

2nd CERVICAL N.

3rd CERVICAL N.

Geniohyoid m.

Hypoglossal n. [CN XII]

Transverse cervical n. (C2, C3)

Sternohyoid m.

Omohyoid m.—sup. belly

Sup. root (C1, C2)

Inf. root (C2, C3)

ANSA CERVICALIS

Sternothyroid m.

Sternocleidomastoid m. (cut)

Supraclavicular nn. (C3, C4)

Overview of Cranial Nerves

Nerve	Efferent or Motor			Afferent or Sensory	
	Striated Muscles	Smooth & Cardiac Muscles & Glands	Skin	Mucous Membranes & Organs	Special Senses
CN I					Olfaction or sensation of smell
CN II					Vision or sight
CN III	Supplies all muscles of eyeball except lateral rectus & superior oblique mm.	Parasympathetic to ciliary m. (lens) & sphincter m. of iris of eye		Proprioceptive fibers from eye m.	
CN IV	Supplies superior oblique m. of eyeball			Proprioceptive fibers from eye m.	
CN V	Supplies muscles of mastication, tensors of tympanic membrane, palate, mylohyoid m. & ant. belly of digastric m.	Carries parasympathetic preganglionic nerve fibers of CN, III, VII & IX	Face & ant. part of scalp	Teeth, mucous membrane of mouth, nose & eye, general sensory from ant. two-thirds of tongue	Taste (fibers from chorda tympani) from ant. two-thirds of tongue
CN VI	Supplies lateral rectus m. of eyeball			Proprioceptive fibers from lateral rectus m.	
CN VII	Supplies muscles of facial expression, stapedius m., stylohyoid m. & post. belly of digastric m.	Parasympathetic nervus intermedius; glands of mouth, nose & palate; lacrimal gland; submandibular & sublingual glands	Ext. ear	Proprioceptive fibers from muscles of facial expression	Nervus intermedius, taste, ant. two-thirds of tongue
CN VIII					Hearing & equilibrium
CN IX	Supplies stylopharyngeus m.	Parasympathetic to parotid gland		Internal surface of tympanic membrane, middle ear, pharynx & general sensory from tongue (post. third)	Taste, from post. third of tongue
CN X	Supplies muscles of pharynx and larynx	Parasympathetic to organs in neck, thorax & abdomen	Ext. acoustic meatus & tympanic membrane	Organs in neck, thorax & abdomen, general sensory from root of tongue	Taste, epiglottis
CN XI	Supplies muscles of soft palate, pharynx, larynx (from cranial root & distributed in vagus n.)& sternocleidomastoid & trapezius m.				
CN XII	Supplies extrinsic & intrinsic mm. of tongue except palatoglossus m.				

Index

rectus abdominis, 22–23, 43–45, 51, 56, 73, 176
  tendinous inscription in, 2
rectus capitis
  anterior, 355, 413
  lateral, 355, 413
  posterior major, 27, 62–63, 355
  posterior minor, 27, 62–63, 355
rectus femoris, 208, 210–211, 214–215, 242, 244–245, 250–253, 261, 264
  tendon of, 152–153, 215, 254
rhomboid
  major, 40, 60, 277, 280–281, 306
  minor, 60, 277, 280–281, 306, 400, 404
risorius, 366–367
rotator cuff, 312–313
rotatores, 24–25, 61
salpingopharyngeus, 374, 416
  left, 374
sartorius, 42–43, 50, 208–212, 214–215, 242, 244–245, 250–253, 260–263
  tendons of, 208, 242, 250, 261
scalene
  anterior, 72–73, 98, 100, 102–103, 308–311, 372, 378–379, 381, 402–406, 413, 429
  middle, 62, 81, 301, 310, 312–313, 378–379, 381, 393, 400–401, 404–405, 413
  posterior, 50, 61–62, 378–379, 381, 413
scapular, 280–283
semimembranosus, 191, 211, 213, 216–217, 246–248, 250–253, 258, 260–261, 263
  tendon of, 258, 261–262
semispinalis, 7, 25
semispinalis capitis, 24, 58, 60–63, 306, 355, 400, 404
semispinalis cervicis, 24, 62–63
semispinalis thoracis, 24, 61
semitendinosus, 191, 198, 209–212, 216–217, 246–248, 250–253, 258, 260–261
  tendon of, 250, 262–263
serratus
  anterior, 33, 42–44, 50, 60, 274, 276, 280, 306–308, 310–313, 317–319, 328–329
  posterior
    inferior, 7, 20, 50, 60, 306
    superior, 7, 20, 50, 306, 328–329
      aponeurosis of, 313
soleus, 208–209, 213, 222, 256–261, 264
sphincter. See also Sphincter
  anal, 163
    external, 156, 163, 180, 184, 190, 192–201, 204, 206
    internal, 163
  urethrae, 157, 159, 159t, 160–161, 190–191, 194, 197, 199
spinalis, 7, 60–61, 306, 328–329
spinalis capitis, 24, 26
spinalis cervicis, 24, 26, 60–62, 410
  communicating branches from, 460
spinalis thoracis, 24, 26, 313
splenius, anterior, 366
splenius capitis, 24–25, 51, 58–60, 62, 306, 313, 328–329, 355, 366, 378–379, 381, 397, 400, 404–405, 410–411
splenius cervicis, 24–25, 60, 328–329, 378–379
stapedius, 365
  tendon of, 434
sternocleidomastoid, 2–3, 42, 58–59, 62, 98, 274, 306–307, 344–345, 348, 352–353, 355, 366–367, 372, 379, 381, 392, 396–399, 401–403, 410–411, 460, 462
  clavicular head of, 378–379
  sternal head of, 378–379, 401
sternohyoid, 307, 364, 372–373, 381, 398–403, 406, 461–462

nerve to, 461
sternothyroid, 103, 364, 373, 381, 402–403, 462
  nerve to, 461
styloglossus, 370–371, 373, 375, 415, 430–431, 434
stylohyoid, 364, 372–373, 411, 430
stylopharyngeus, 374–375, 411, 454
subclavius, 43, 95, 97, 280–281, 307, 401
  nerve to, 301
subcostal, 20–21
suboccipital, 27
subscapularis, 60–61, 276, 282, 308–311, 316–317
  tendon of, 314
superior pharyngeal constrictor, 455
supinator, 278–279, 288, 317, 319–324, 333
suprahyoid, 372
supraspinatus, 60, 276–277, 282–283, 306, 308–310, 312–317, 328–329, 405
tarsal, superior, 421
temporalis, 348, 350, 352–353, 355, 362, 366–369, 396–397, 404, 447
  tendon of, 400
temporoparietalis, 366, 396
tensor fasciae latae, 50–51, 202, 208, 211, 214–215, 242–245, 249–250, 253
tensor tympani, 362, 365, 431, 435
tensor veli palatini, 355, 362, 370–371, 415, 417, 431–432, 434
  left, 374
  nerve to, 431
teres major, 58–61, 274–277, 282–283, 306, 311–314, 316, 328–329
teres minor, 50, 58, 277, 282–283, 306, 313–316, 328, 405
thenar, 274–275, 337
of thigh, posterior compartment of, 209
thoracic, long, 318–319
thyroarytenoid, 365, 376, 407, 409, 412
thyroepiglottic, 407
thyrohyoid, 364, 372–373, 400, 402–403, 405–406, 414, 461
  nerve to, 461
thyroid, 372
tibialis anterior, 208, 212–213, 220, 242, 250, 256–257, 259–261
  tendons of, 208–209, 260, 268
    sheath of, 268
tibialis posterior, 213, 222–223, 258–259, 262
  groove for, 213
  tendon of, 260, 269
trachealis, 377
transverse perineal
  deep, 157, 159, 159t, 196–197, 199
  superficial, 156, 159, 159t, 192–195
transversus abdominis, 22–23, 43–45, 48, 51, 61, 72, 182–185
  aponeurosis of, 23, 44, 56–57
  deep inguinal ring in, 57
transversus thoracis, 20–21, 40, 44, 48–49, 72, 104
trapezius, 3, 33, 40, 42–44, 58–60, 62, 274, 277, 280–281, 306–307, 310, 312–313, 317–319, 328–329, 344–345, 352–353, 355, 366, 381, 398–399, 401, 410–411, 460, 462
triceps brachii, 274–275, 277, 282, 307
  lateral head of, 274–275, 277, 283, 306, 317, 319–320, 322, 328
    tendon of, 329
  long head of, 50, 58–59, 274–277, 283, 306, 313–322, 328–329
  medial head of, 277, 279, 283, 316–322, 329
    tendon of, 279
  ulnar, 318–319
vastus intermedius, 210–211, 214–215, 242, 251–252

tendon of, 264
vastus lateralis, 208–211, 214–215, 242–248, 250–253, 256–257, 261–262
  coronal section of, 243
vastus medialis, 208–211, 214–215, 242–243, 250–253, 256, 260–262
  coronal section of, 243
  tendon of, 215
vocalis, 365, 376
  location of, 412
zygomaticus, 420
  major, 348, 352–353, 366–367, 396
  minor, 348, 352–353, 366–367, 396
Muscles, general
  of abdominal wall, 22–23
  of arm
    anterior, 284–285
    posterior, 282–283
  attachments of, 4–7, 210–213, 276–279
  of back, intrinsic, 24–25
  of foot, intrinsic, 224–225
  of forearm, 284–289
    flexor, 274–275
    posterior, 288–289
  of hand, intrinsic, 290–291
  of head
    lateral, 378–379
    prevertebral, 378–379
    superficial, 366–367
  laryngeal, 376–377
  of leg
    anterior, 220–221
    attachments, 210–213
    lateral, 220–221
    posterior, 222–223
  masticatory, 368–369
  ocular, 368–369
  pectoral, 280–281
  of pelvis, 157, 159–160, 162
    pelvic diaphragm, 158
    superficial perineal, 156
  of perineum, superficial, 159t
  of shoulder
    anterior, 307
    posterior, 306
  of soft palate, 370–371, 374
  of thigh
    anterior, 214–215
    medial, 218–219
    posterior, 216–217
  of thoracic wall, 20–21
  of tongue, 370–371
    intrinsic, 412

Nares
  external (anterior), 346, 440
  internal. See Choana(e)
Nasopharynx, 393
  region of, 410–411, 413, 416–417
Neck
  of femur, 210–211, 255
  of fibula, 210, 212
  of humerus
    anatomical, 276–277, 315
    surgical, 276–277, 312, 315
  of mandible, 362–363
  of radius, 276–279, 324–325
  of rib, 17, 104
  of scapula, 277
  of stapes, 365
  of talus, 270
NECK, THE
  anterior, deep, 402
  anterolateral, 401
  lateral, 400
    deep, 403–405